Microbial Enzymes

Microbial Enzymes

Production, Purification, and Industrial Applications

Volume 2

Edited by Dinesh Yadav, Pankaj Chowdhary, Gautam Anand, and Rajarshi Kumar Gaur

WILEY-VCH

Editors

Dr. Dinesh Yadav
Deen Dayal Upadhyaya Gorakhpur University
Department of Biotechnology
Civil Lines
Gorakhpur, Uttar Pradesh 273009
India

Dr. Pankaj Chowdhary
Society for Green Environment
New Delhi 110067
India

Dr. Gautam Anand
Agricultural Research Organization
Volcani Institute
Department of Plant Pathology and Weed Research
Rishon LeZion 7505101
Israel

Dr. Rajarshi Kumar Gaur
Deen Dayal Upadhyaya Gorakhpur University
Department of Biotechnology
Gorakhpur, Uttar Pradesh 273009
India

Cover Image: © Christoph Burgstedt/Shutterstock

Library of Congress Card No.: applied for

British Library Cataloguing-in-Publication Data
A catalogue record for this book is available from the British Library.

Bibliographic information published by the Deutsche Nationalbibliothek The Deutsche Nationalbibliothek lists this publication in the Deutsche Nationalbibliografie; detailed bibliographic data are available on the Internet at <http://dnb.d-nb.de>.

Print ISBN: 978-3-527-35292-0
ePDF ISBN: 978-3-527-84435-7
ePub ISBN: 978-3-527-84436-4
oBook ISBN: 978-3-527-84434-0

Typesetting Straive, Chennai, India
Printing and Binding CPI Group (UK) Ltd, Croydon, CR0 4YY

C9783527352920_021024

Contents

About the Editors

Dr. Dinesh Yadav is Professor of the Department of Biotechnology and currently the Director of the Research and Development Cell at DDU Gorakhpur University. He has served as the Dean of the Faculty of Rural Sciences, Head of the Department of Biotechnology, Nodal Officer of the IPR Cell and Coordinator of Centre for Genomics and Bioinformatics at D.D.U. Gorakhpur University. He has also served as Associate Professor of the Department of Molecular Biology and Genetic Engineering at G.B. Pant University of Agriculture and Technology, Pantnagar, from 2006 to 2009. He completed his master's degree in biotechnology from Devi Ahilya University, Indore, in 1996 and PhD from G.B. Pant University of Agriculture and Technology, Pantnagar, in 2002. He has more than 23 years of teaching and research experience.

He has availed the DST-BOYSCAST Fellowship at the Australian Centre for Plant Functional Genomics (ACPFG), University of Adelaide, South Australia, from 3 May 2012 to 12 April 2013. He was awarded for Excellence in Teaching and Research in Higher Education by the University on Teacher's Day, 5 September 2021. He received Dr. Pushpendra Kumar Gupta Vishisht Krishi Vaigyanik Puraskar (2015) in the field of agricultural sciences by Uttar Pradesh Academy of Agricultural Sciences (UPAAS), Lucknow, and the Young Scientist Award (2008) by the Uttarakhand State Council of Science & Technology in the discipline of biotechnology, biochemistry, and microbiology.

His areas of specialization include molecular biology, bioinformatics, plant biotechnology, and enzyme technology. He has published more than 150 research papers, including reviews, books, book chapters, and conference proceedings, and has more than 300 GenBank accession numbers. A total of 48 indigenously isolated microbial strains (fungal and bacterial) have been deposited in several culture collection centers in India. He has carried out nine projects with support from funding agencies such as DBT, UGC, UP Council of Agricultural Research, Lucknow, and DST as PI/Co-PI and Mentor. Presently, he is involved in three projects funded by CST (UP) and UPCAR (Lucknow).

He has guided 12 students to PhD in biotechnology, and four students have submitted PhD thesis. He has also supervised more than 114 students for MSc dissertations and short project works in biotechnology. He has been a mentor for five postdoctoral fellowships, namely UGC-Dr. D.S. Kothari (twice), DST-Women Scientist-A, DST-Women Scientist-B, and SERB National PDF.

He is a life member of various scientific societies such as BRSI, Trivandrum; SBC(I), Bangalore; Indian Science Congress Association, Calcutta; Society of Plant Biochemistry and Biotechnology, IARI, New Delhi, Association of Microbiologists of India (AMI), New Delhi; and UPAAS, Lucknow.

He has delivered more than 100 invited talks and lectures at conferences and symposiums and served as Mentor for the DST-INSPIRE Science Internship Camp and Inspire Awards. Currently, he is working on plant-specific transcription factor-DOF (DNA binding with one finger) and nuclear factor-Y (NF-Y) for developing biotic and abiotic stress tolerance crops and pectinases group of enzymes with potential applications in different industries.

His research works have been published in journals of national and international repute, including *Journal of Experimental Botany, Cellulose, World Journal of Microbiology and Biotechnology, Environmental Science and Pollution Research, Theoretical and Applied Genetics, Cellulose, Frontiers in Microbiology, Planta, World Journal of Microbiology and Biotechnology, Process Biochemistry, Molecular Biology Reports, Plant Systematics and Evolution, Molecular Biotechnology, Applied Biochemistry and Biotechnology, Annals of Microbiology, Journal of Basic Microbiology, 3 Biotech, Biologia, Journal of Cereal Sciences, Physiology and Molecular Biology of Plants, Biochemistry (Moscow), Current Proteomics, Interdisciplinary Sciences: Computational Life Sciences, Biocatalysis and Agricultural Biotechnology, Cell Biochemistry and Biophysics, Online Journal of Bioinformatics, Chemistry and Ecology, African Journal of Biotechnology, Applied Biochemistry and Microbiology, Sugar Tech,* and *Enzyme Research*.

Dr. Pankaj Chowdhary is President of the Society for Green Environment (SGE), New Delhi, India. He completed his PhD in 2018 in the area of microbiology from the Department of Environmental Microbiology at Babasaheb Bhimrao Ambedkar University, Lucknow, Uttar Pradesh, India. His doctorate work was mainly focused on the role of ligninolytic-enzyme-producing bacterial strains in the decolorization and degradation of coloring compounds from distillery wastewater. His main research areas include microbial biotechnology, biodegradation and bioremediation of environmental contaminants in industrial wastewaters, metagenomics, and lignocellulosic waste valorization. He has edited eight international books and authored two books. He has published more than 60 research and review papers in national and international peer-reviewed journals with a high impact factor, published by Springer, Elsevier, Royal Society of Chemistry (RSC), Taylor & Francis Group, and Frontiers. He has also published many national and international book chapters and magazine articles on the biodegradation and bioremediation of environmental pollutants. He has presented many posters and papers relevant to research areas in national and international conferences. He has actively worked as a potential reviewer for various SCI journals published by reputed international publishers (Springer, Elsevier, RSC, Taylor & Francis Group, Wiley, and Frontiers). He is a life member of the Association of Microbiologists of India (AMI) and the Indian Science Congress Association (ISCA), Kolkata, India".

Dr. Gautam Anand is a postdoctoral fellow at the Department of Plant Pathology and Weed Research, Agricultural Research Organization (ARO) – Volcani Institute, Israel. He obtained his MSc and PhD degrees in biotechnology from Deen Dayal Upadhyaya Gorakhpur University, India. During his PhD, he worked on an industrially important microbial enzyme of the pectinases group, namely polygalacturonase. He was selected for the Agricultural Research Organization – Postdoctoral Fellowship, Israel, for the year 2020–2021 and the Valazzy Pikovsky Fellowship for postdoctoral research at the Hebrew University of Jerusalem, Israel, for the year 2018–2019. He has also worked as a postdoctoral fellow at the Robert H. Smith Faculty of Agriculture, Food and Environment, Hebrew University of Jerusalem, Israel. He has worked extensively on plant–fungus interactions. His main area of research is characterizing the importance of trafficking pathways in fungal virulence using deletion mutagenesis and cell biology techniques. Dr. Anand has also worked on fungal pectinases, particularly polygalacturonases and pectin lyases. He has published more than 30 papers in reputable international journals and 14 book chapters.

Dr. Rajarshi Kumar Gaur earned his PhD in 2005. Currently, he is Professor at the Department of Biotechnology, Deen Dayal Upadhyaya Gorakhpur University, Gorakhpur, Uttar Pradesh, India. His PhD focused on the molecular characterization of sugarcane viruses, namely, mosaic, streak mosaic, and yellow luteovirus. He received the MA SHAV Fellowship from the Israel government for his postdoctoral studies and joined the Volcani Centre, Israel, and Ben-Gurion University, Negev, Israel. In 2007, he received a Visiting Scientist Fellowship from the Swedish Institute Fellowship, Sweden, to work at Umeå University, Umeå, Sweden. He received a Postdoctoral Fellowship from ICGEB, Italy, in 2008. He has made significant contributions to the study on sugarcane viruses and has published 135 national and international papers, authored 27 edited books, and presented about 50 papers in national and international conferences. He is an honored Fellow of Linnean Society, Royal Society of Biology, Society of Plant Research, Society of Applied Biology (FSAB), International Society of Biotechnology (FISBT), and Indian Virological Society (FIVS). He has received awards such as Prof. B.M. Johri Memorial Award, Society of Plant Research (SPR); Excellent Teaching Award by Astha Foundation, Meerut; UGC-Research Teacher Award; Young Scientist Award-2012 in Biotechnology by Society of Plant Research

(SPR), Meerut; and Scientific & Applied Research Centre Gold Medal Award (2011) for outstanding contribution in the field of biotechnology. He has visited several laboratories in the United States, Canada, New Zealand, the United Kingdom, Thailand, Sweden, and Italy. Currently, he is handling national and international grants and international collaborative projects on plant viruses and disease management.

Preface

The book *Microbial Enzymes: Production, Purification, and Industrial Applications* provides an insight into diverse aspects of microbial enzymes, highlighting strategies for their production, purification, manipulation, and elucidating multifarious industrial applications. Microbial enzymes have played a pivotal role in several industries, and over the years, substantial efforts have been made to reveal the hidden potential of untapped microbial diversity in search of a repertoire of enzymes. A plethora of microbial enzymes have been reported so far, and efforts have been made to incorporate many of these enzymes in this book authored by experts. An emphasis has also been placed on discussing the recent technological interventions in microbial enzyme technology, such as metagenomics, system biology, molecular biology, genomics, directed evolution, and bioinformatics, in this book. The important microbial enzymes highlighted in this book include xylanases, ureases, methane monooxygenase, polyhydroxyalkanoates, pectinases, peroxidases, α-L-rhamnosidase, alkane hydroxylases, laccases, proteases, gallic acid decarboxylase, chitinases, beta-glucosidase, lipases, inulinases, tannase, mycozyme, ACC deaminase, and ligninolytic enzymes, among others. Few chapters are exclusively focused on microbial enzyme intervention as an eco-friendly approach in diverse industrial applications.

From an environmental point of view, all the recent and classic microbial treatment technologies should be amplified to make them more viable and feasible. Contaminate mitigation or removal using enzyme technology has become an attractive and potential alternative in recent days. Further, recent developments in the fields of biotechnology, molecular biology, ecology, and microbiology have been applied to develop different novel treatment methods involving novel strains of microorganisms with desirable properties that would be applicable in the process of bioremediation. Various types of beneficial microbes are present in the ecosystem, and they can play a key role in mitigating climate concern, improving green production technology, enhancing agriculture productivity, and providing a means of earning a livelihood. A few chapters have highlighted the omics-driven research in microbial enzyme technology.

This book is a good collection of chapters reflecting multidimensional aspects of microbial enzyme technology, and it will be of immense importance for students, scientists, biotechnologists, microbiologists, and policymakers working in environmental microbiology, biotechnology, and environmental sciences with the basics and advanced enzyme technology. Moreover, readers can also get state-of-the-art or background information on existing technologies, their challenges, and future prospects.

The editors express sincere thanks to the contributors for submitting their work in a timely and proper manner. The editors are also thankful to national and international reviewers for their evaluation and valuable suggestions and comments to heighten the book's quality for readers. Further, editors also acknowledge the cooperation received from the Wiley team for their guidance in finalizing this book.

2024, Gorakhpur

Dinesh Yadav, PhD
Deen Dayal Upadhyaya Gorakhpur University
Department of Biotechnology, Civil Lines
Gorakhpur, Uttar Pradesh 273009, India

Pankaj Chowdhary, PhD
Society for Green Environment
New Delhi 110067, India

Gautam Anand, PhD
Agricultural Research Organization
Volcani Institute
Department of Plant Pathology and Weed Research
Rishon LeZion 7505101, Israel

Rajarshi Kumar Gaur, PhD
Deen Dayal Upadhyaya Gorakhpur University
Department of Biotechnology
Gorakhpur, Uttar Pradesh 273009, India

21

β-Glucosidase Production and Its Applications

Vaibhav Badoni, Gaurav S. Rana, Ashutosh Dubey, and Ashok K. Verma

G. B. Pant University of Agriculture and Technology, College of Basic Sciences and Humanities, Department of Biochemistry, Pantnagar, Uttarakhand 246145, India

21.1 Introduction

Lignocellulosic biomasses are present in a plentiful amount in the environment due to their presence in plant cell walls and structure. Forest and agricultural residues, municipal and industrial activities are the examples of waste lignocellulosic biomass materials that can be utilized to produce glucose by enzymatic hydrolysis [1, 2]. The biomass-hydrolyzing enzymes of fungi and bacteria have long been used for biomass hydrolysis. There are several enzymes, such as cellulase, xylanase, ligninase, pectinase, etc., that are needed for complete hydrolysis of biomass. Cellulose is a major component of plant biomass and is the most abundant biopolymer in the biosphere; thus, cellulase is very important among biomass-degrading enzymes. Cellulose is a straight chain homopolysaccharide comprising of an anhydro-β-D-glucose unit joined by a β-(1→4) O-glycosidic bonds with units varying from 800 to 10,000 that shape a linear chain with an average molecular weight of 1,00,000 Da [3, 4]. The stability of the cellulose chains is due to the intra and intermolecular hydrogen bonds and van der Waals forces; hence, it is required that cellulose must be first broken down to simple fermentable sugar such as glucose for its usage in various industrial applications like bioethanol production [5]. Cellulase is an enzymatic system constituting a group of three enzymes that are necessary for the production of glucose monomers by efficient hydrolysis of cellulose polymer. Endoglucanase, exoglucanase, and β-glucosidase are the three individual enzymes in this enzymatic system that collectively act to break cellulose molecules into glucose (Figure 21.1). Endoglucanases (1,4-β-D-glucan hydrolase) EC 3.2.1.4, perform the internal hydrolysis of cellulose strands, thus rapidly resulting in a decrease in the level of polymerization. Exoglucanases (1,4-β-D-glucan glucohydrolase) EC 3.2.1.91 hydrolyze glycosidic bonds at the ends of the cellulose chains and release cellobiose. These two enzymes act collectively and are generally inhibited by cellobiose, the end product. β-Glucosidases (β-D-glucoside glucohydrolase) EC 3.2.1.21 finalize hydrolysis, converting cellobiose to glucose

Microbial Enzymes: Production, Purification, and Industrial Applications, First Edition.
Edited by Dinesh Yadav, Pankaj Chowdhary, Gautam Anand, and Rajarshi Kumar Gaur.

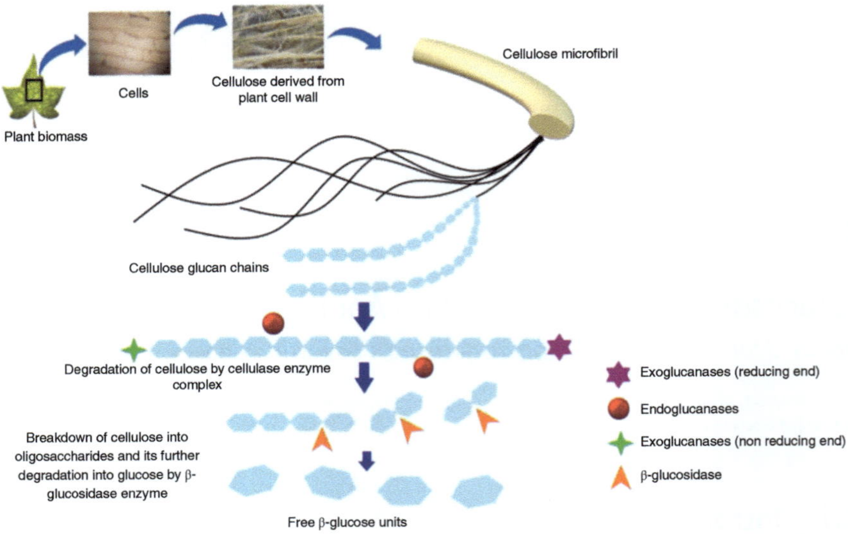

Figure 21.1 Summary of the cellulose degradation by cellulase enzyme complex. Cellulase enzyme complex with the help of the exo- and endoglucanases carries out the hydrolysis process by acting upoun the cellulose fibers and releasing smaller oligosaccharide fragments by hydrolysis. Finally, glucose units are liberated after the overall hydrolysis of the cellulosic substrate by the β-glucosidase enzyme.

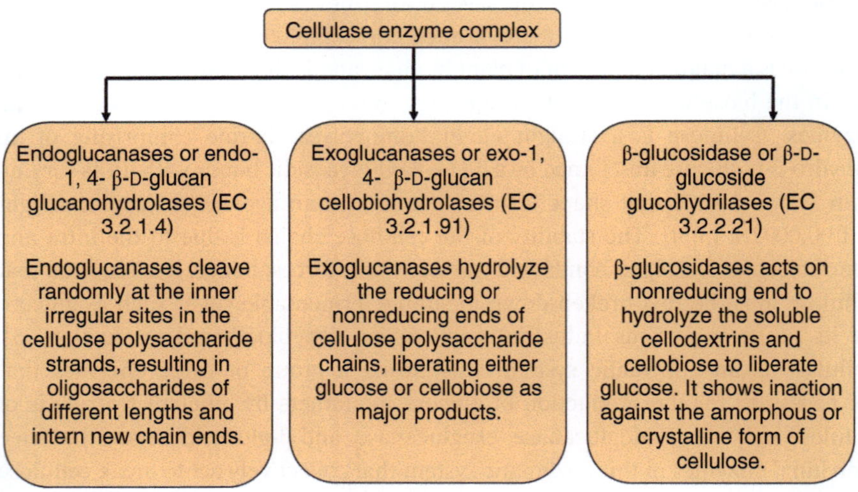

Figure 21.2 Classification of cellulase enzyme.

(Figure 21.2) [6–9]. β-Glucosidase hydrolyzes various β-D-glucosidic bonds of alkyl and aryl β-D-glucosides, cyanogenic glucosides, as well as disaccharides and short-chain oligosaccharides at the nonreducing end, releasing the glucose moiety. β-Glucosidases are well-described enzymes of biological importance that catalyze the reaction by transferring the glycosyl groups amidst the oxygen nucleophiles [10, 11]. Some novel β-glucosidases with the additional β-galactosidase and β-xylosidase activity are also reported [12]. Under certain definite conditions, by means of the reverse hydrolysis process, β-glucosidase (glycosynthase) also carries out the synthesis reactions of oligosaccharides, glycosides, or transglycosylation from an inverted donor without hydrolysis of the product [11, 13].

The aforementioned three enzymes are altogether categorized within the cellulase enzymes and are produced throughout various life forms, such as plants, animals, bacteria, fungi, and protozoa [14–16]. These enzymes can be extracellular, intracellular, or membrane-bound that are produced by a wide array of microbes as they play an important role in the end-point hydrolysis of polymers with a complex structure. Therefore, microorganisms are the preferred choice for the industrial production of these enzymes [17]. Many prime physiological processes among various organisms are β-glucosidase enzyme-dependent. For example, in plants, it has a role in β-glucan chain synthesis, cell wall metabolism and lignification, defense, secondary metabolism, phytohormone activation, and fruit ripening [18–20]. Key functions such as cellulose hydrolysis, cellulase gene activation, and carbon recycling are carried out by the β-glucosidase enzyme in microorganisms [21, 22]. Similarly, β-glucosidase enzyme has a role in the hydrolysis of glucosyl ceramides in mammals, and its malfunction is associated with Gaucher's disease [23]. β-Glucosidase is also known to affect human health positively as it hydrolyzes isoflavone glycosides, thus improving their absorption and uptake from the small intestine. It is well known that isoflavones have a role in averting the risk of specific cancer; they lower cardiovascular diseases and improve bone health [24, 25]. Various biotechnological processes widely use β-glucosidases in several industries, such as ethanol and biofuel industries that utilize cellulose-rich agricultural wastes [26]. Cellulase enzymes are also inclusively applicable in a variety of industries, such as textile industry, laundry and detergents industry, pulp and paper industry, animal feed, and food industry [27, 28]. Industries such as food processing utilize these enzymes for the breakdown of bitter and foul-tasting compounds in juice preparation and the release of aroma from grapes during wine production [29]. Glycosylated compounds having β-glucoside conjugates are in major proportion in fruits and other tissues of plants where β-glucosidase enzyme plays a significant role in the liberation of flavor from these precursors. β-Glucosidase can also be termed as flavor enzyme because of its immense application in the flavor industry for the enhancement of flavor in wine, tea, fruit juices, and beverages. In the food-processing industry, it is a key enzyme that is utilized for the liberation of aromatic compounds from the fruits and fermenting products that comprise glucosidic precursors as major constituents [30–32]. Besides improving the flavor of food and animal feeds, their nutritional quality can also be enhanced by the release of essential amino acids, vitamins, antioxidants, and other valuable components from their glycosides [33].

21.2 Structure and Specificity of β-Glucosidase

β-Glucosidases are often classified according to their amino acid sequence similarities, facilitating useful insights and information regarding the structure and function of these enzymes. The basis for this classification was the idea that proteins in the same family would have structural similarities to allow homology modeling. Thus, in this classification, enzymes having different substrate specificities are often found in the same families due to similar structural similarities, indicating the divergent evolution toward the varying substrate specificities. Contrary to this, some enzymes hydrolyzing similar substrates are often grouped into distant families. Cellulasesare classified across 11 different families, indicating that classification based on sequence and structural similarities differs significantly from the usual system, primarily based on substrate specificity [34].

β-Glucosidases, despite having a diverse structure, have a similarity in the overall fold of the catalytic domain that remains the same in all glucosyl hydrolase (GH) families. The $(\beta/\alpha)_8$ barrel domain, also known as the TIM barrel (triose-phosphate isomerase), is a conserved protein fold consisting of eight alpha (α) helices and eight parallel beta (β) strands alternating along the peptide backbone. It comprises the active site and is similar in the GH1, GH5, and GH30 families that are classified into the GH-A clan [35]. The $(\beta/\alpha)_8$ barrel domains are the conserved structures in the glucosyl hydrolase of clan A (GH-A) and the active site comprises two conserved residues of carboxylic acids on the β-strands 4 and 7 that act as catalytic acid/base and nucleophile respectively [36]. Crystallization and preliminary crystallographic work described for many enzymes have thrown light on the three-dimensional structure of the enzyme β-glucosidases (Figure 21.3). The three-dimensional structure tends to be more conserved than sequences, and some of the enzyme families are grouped on the basis of sequence-based similarities that show related structures. Thus, the enzymes displaying similar structures are grouped into clans. Eighteen such clans have been described in the CAZY database as of March 2022. The largest of these clans is the GH-A, which is also described as the 4/7 superfamily because of the structural uniqueness of a proton donor and nucleophile found on strands 4 and 7 of the $(\beta/\alpha)_8$ barrel. The GH-A clan comprises about 26 enzyme families on the basis of structural similarities, among which families 1, 2, 5, 17, 30, 39, and 128 consist of the β-glucosidase enzymes. Thus, the $(\beta/\alpha)_8$ barrel is a unique structural feature of the β-glucosidase enzymes that are used in the characterization of the enzyme on the basis of structural similarities [37, 38]. β-Glucosidases differing in the substrate specificity also differ in their

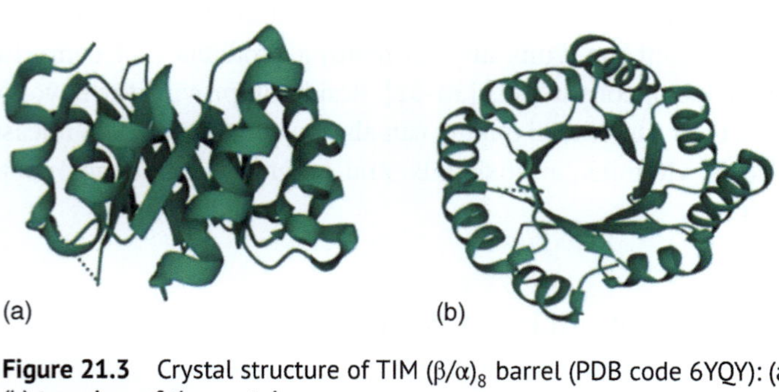

(a) (b)

Figure 21.3 Crystal structure of TIM $(\beta/\alpha)_8$ barrel (PDB code 6YQY): (a) Side view and (b) top view of the protein.

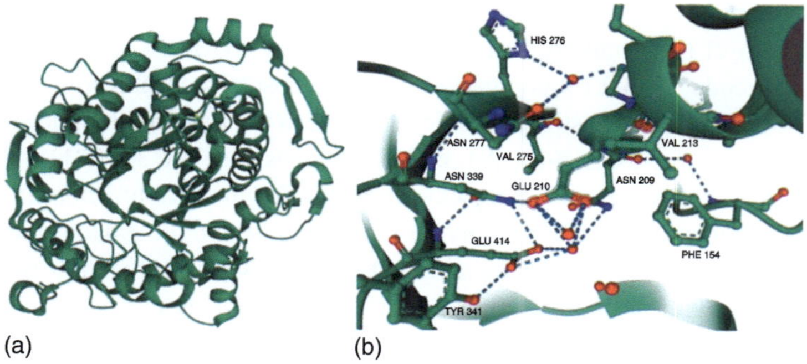

Figure 21.4 Structure of the active site of β-glucosidase (TsBGL) from *Thermofilum* species ex4484_79 (PDB code 7F1N). (a) Overview of the structure of TsBGL displaying the usual $(\beta/\alpha)_8$TIM-barrel fold. (b) The active site regions of the TsBGL.

residues except for the tryptophan residue (W 378), indicating that these sites and the active site morphology are the basis of aglycon recognition, specificity, and binding in these enzymes (Figure 21.4) [39]. Nam et al., studied soil uncultured metagenome and described the X-ray crystal structure of β-glucosidase with glucose and cellobiose fragments as substrates. Different states of the active site pocket, such as the prereactive (original), intermediate (disaccharide cleavage), and postreaction (glucose binding), were derived from various crystal structures, indicating the dependence of the kinetics of β-glucosidase on the configuration of its substrate. Thus, the idea about the substrate specificity of the β-glucosidase enzyme can be taken from the intermediate state of the crystal intermediate of the enzyme [40].

Broad substrate specificity was reported in a widely known, well purified and characterized enzyme identified as GH3 β-glucosidase, BglA. The enzyme degraded (hydrolyzed) cellobiose and *p*-nitrophenyl β-D-glucopyranoside (pNPG) as well as it could effectively degrade cellodextrins and *p*-nitrophenyl β-D-cellobioside (pNPC). Further, the enzyme was functionally expressed in *Escherichia coli* JM109 for the purification and characterization of the recombinant protein [41]. A homodimer enzyme with monomers of 60-kDa having a variety of substrates was identified in maize as β-glucosidase (β-glu). The major natural substrate of the enzyme was found to be 2,4-dihydroxy-7-methoxy-2*H*-1,4-benzoxazin-3(4*H*)-one (DIMBOA-glc), a glucoside hydrolyzed to its products glucose and DIMBOA. Among the various inhibitors of the enzyme, D-gluconic acid lactone, dhurrin, and DIMBOA were found to be the best competitive inhibitors with monosaccharides as the poor inhibitor. Aglycone analogs and other glucosides inhibit the enzyme competitively [42].

21.3 Classes of β-Glucosidase Enzyme

Substrate specificity is one of the simplest criteria for the classification of glycoside hydrolases. Such classification of the enzymes is expressed in terms of the EC number that is unique for a given enzyme and it is based on the guidelines of the International Union of Biochemistry and Molecular Biology (IUBMB). As per the recommendations, code EC 3.2.1.x is given to the O-glycoside hydrolases, where the symbol "x" represents the substrate specificity (and also the type of the molecular mechanism or attachment, e.g., β-1,4; β-1,3; etc.). β-Glucosidase (EC 3.2.1.21) and β-galactosidase (EC 3.2.1.23) are two examples of enzymes that are simply differentiated on the basis of their substrate specificity for β-D-glucoside and β-D-galactoside. The prime advantage of this system is its simplicity, paired with the fact that the system has been widely used, making it a standard medium for describing glycoside hydrolases. The inherent drawback with this system of classification based on substrate or product specificity is the accommodation of enzymes acting on several substrates. Thus, glycoside hydrolases that act on highly complex polysaccharides found in nature frequently display wide overlapping specificities that are particularly difficult to classify under this system of classification. In general, two methods of classification have been utilized for classifying the β-glucosidase enzymes. The two methods include the classification based on the specificity of the substrate and nucleotide sequence identity, respectively [43, 44].

Based on the substrate specificity, β-glucosidases are further divided into three classes: aryl β-glucosidases (class 1), that specifically cleaves aryl-glucosides; true cellobioses (class 2), that catalyze the reactions of conversion of cellobiose, a disaccharide into glucose, and glucosidases (enzymes with broad substrate specificity, class 3). Most commonly found β-glucosidase enzymes belong to class 3, having a variety of substrates with an extensive substrate-specific activity for the cleavage of a broad range of bonds such as β 1,2; β 1,4; β 1,6 and α 1,4; α 1,6; α 1,3 glycosidic bonds [45–47].

The more widely accepted second system of classification is based on both, the identity of nucleotide sequence, as well as the structural similarity of the enzyme that is further based on the similarities in sequences and folding of the structure (hydrophobic cluster analysis, HCA) of these enzymes. Moreover, the active sites also comprise a number of highly conserved amino acids. On the basis of this method of classification, out of the 88 glucosyl hydrolase (GH) families, β-glucosidases are primarily grouped into the family 1 and 3. The β-glucosidases from archaebacteria, animals, and plants have been grouped into the GH family 1, with these enzymes usually displaying additional β-galactosidase activity. Family 3 comprises β-glucosidases having a unique two-domain globular structure that has been identified in bacteria, fungi, and plants [48]. Under this system of classification, the enzymes with similarity in sequences and conserved sequence motifs are kept in a single enzyme family [26, 49]. The presence of the highly conserved amino acids around the catalytic site of the enzymes enabled the study of the structural features, evolutionary relationship, and mechanism of catalysis of these enzymes [50].

Identical structure and sequences are key features of the hydrolytic β-glucosidase enzymes that are widespread and commonly present in fungi, bacteria, and plants from which these enzymes are isolated. According to the sequence and structure-based system of classification, presently (as of March 5, 2022), 173 families of

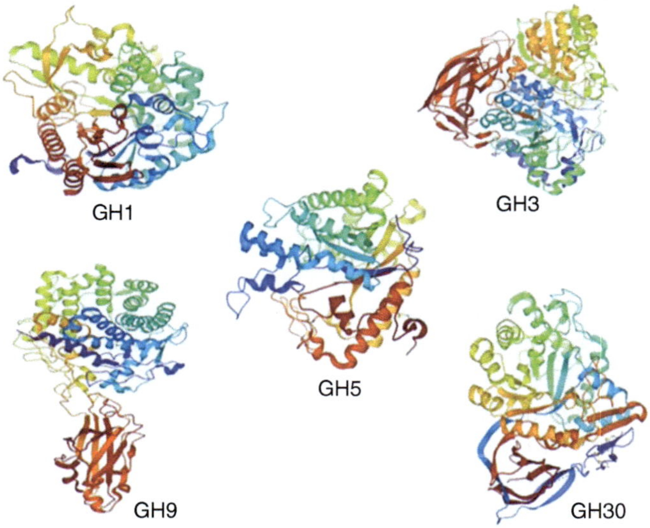

Figure 21.5 Structure β-glucosidase enzymes from various glucosyl hydrolase families. These include β-glucosidase and related enzymes (Maize *Glu*1 β-glucosidase, PDB code 1V08), GH3 (*Trichoderma reesei*, *bgl*1 β-D-glucoside glucohydrolase, PDB code 4I8D), GH5 (*Saccharomyces cerevisiae* exo-1,3-beta glucanse, PDB code 1H4P), GH9 (*Ruminiclostridium cellulolyticum* endoglucanase, PDB code 1G87), GH30 (*Homo sapiens*, GBA1, acid-beta-glucosidase/glucocerebrosidase, PDB code 2V3D). The cartoon structures of the enzymes are colored in a blue-to-red spectrum from their N- to C-termini.

glucosyl hydrolases (GH) along with 18 clans have been classified that can be accessed by means of an online database of carbohydrate-active enzyme (CAZY) (http://www.cazy.org). β-Glucosidase is mainly kept in GH1 and GH3 families. The GH1 family contains about 62 β-glucosidases, derived primarily from archaea, plants, and mammals, while the GH3 family contains about 44 β-glucosidases, primarily derived from mold, yeast, and bacteria [15, 51]. The glucosyl hydrolase enzymes share similar ancestry and mechanism of catalysis; thus, on the basis of the conserved amino acid sequences and similar catalytic domains, the glucosyl hydrolase families are grouped into various clans, e.g., the β-glucosidase families GH1, GH5, and GH30 are grouped into clan GH-A (Figure 21.5) [44, 52]. The GH1 family hydrolases are also grouped under the 4/7 superfamily as they have a common eightfold β/α-barrel motif structure. In these enzymes, the active site is located in a broad cavity marked along the axis of the barrel, with a presumed nucleophile near the end of the β-strand 7 and the acid–base catalyst at the end of β-strand 4. Various enzymes such as the β-galactosidases, xylanases, cellulases, and barley glucanases from the families 2, 10, 5, and 17, respectively, are also included in the 4/7 superfamily of enzymes [36].

The sequence similarity does not necessarily indicate shared functions of the enzymes, thus highlighting the major disadvantage of this system of classifying enzymes of the GH family. According to this method of classification, the number of potential cellulases is overestimated as the GH families contain multiple functions.

21.4 Mechanism of Reaction Catalysis of β-Glucosidase

Several techniques such as inhibition due to pH, effect of isotopes, and studies of structure–reactivity, fluorosugar labeling of crucial amino acids, site-directed mutagenesis, and reactions utilizing deoxy substrate analogs are used to determine the mode of enzyme catalysis and their active site topology. The products of the reaction catalyzed by the β-glucosidases enzyme retain the same anomeric configuration as the substrate; therefore, these enzymes are termed as retaining enzymes [53]. The glycoside hydrolase families and clans have highly conserved catalytic residues. In the GH 3 enzyme family of β-glucosidase, the highly conserved nucleophile is identified as Asp residue, while in different members, different motifs appear to represent the general acid/base catalytic residue. Mostly, it is the histidine side chain present in the His-Asp dyad motif that is involved in catalysis [54–56]. The β-glycosidic bonds between two or more carbohydrate moieties or that between a carbohydrate and a non-carbohydrate molecule are primarily cleaved by the β-glucosidase enzymes. The mechanism of catalysis by glycoside hydrolases is performed in two ways, one through inversion and another by retention mechanism where the configuration (chirality) is maintained at the anomeric carbon of the released glucose molecule.

In both the mechanisms, general acid/base catalyst and nucleophile, play an important role in catalyzing the inverting and retaining enzymatic reactions. These two reaction mechanisms involve the use of a pair of acidic and nucleophilic residue, generally carboxylic acids, incorporating a molecule of water between the substrate and the catalytic base [35]. In the retaining enzymes, hydrolysis reaction is catalyzed in two steps: glycosylation and deglycosylation, or the double displacement reactions. In glycosylation, an oxocarbenium ion is formed, followed by the formation of an enzyme–glycosyl intermediate by nucleophilic attack at the anomeric carbon. The nucleophilic attack on the anomeric carbon is performed by one –COOH group (nucleophile) of the active site, forming an intermediate of the substrate (glucose)–enzyme. The reaction is further facilitated by the transfer of a proton to the substrate by a catalytic acid/base donor. The glycosidic bond is cleaved by donating H^+ to the oxygen of the O-glycosidic bond from other carboxylic groups acting as a proton donor (acid) and leading to the glycosyl enzyme intermediate formation liberating the aglycone [26, 43]. In the deglycosylation or double displacement step, a water molecule displaces the catalytic nucleophile from the glucose molecule at the enzyme–glycosyl intermediate facilitated by a base from the catalytic acid/base [8, 57]. This mechanism can be further understood as such that the carboxylic acid group, previously acting as a proton donor, now acts as a proton acceptor from the nucleophile molecules, such as the water, monosaccharides, and disaccharides. This step completes the catalytic mechanism by liberating the enzyme and product-free by breaking the glucose–enzyme intermediate [58, 59].

Unlike the GH1 and the GH3, the GH9 enzyme family of the β-glucosidases involves a single-step catalytic mechanism known as the invert mechanism [60]. The reaction proceeds by a nucleophilic attack of the activated water molecule on the anomeric carbon, displacing the aglycone moiety in a single-step displacement

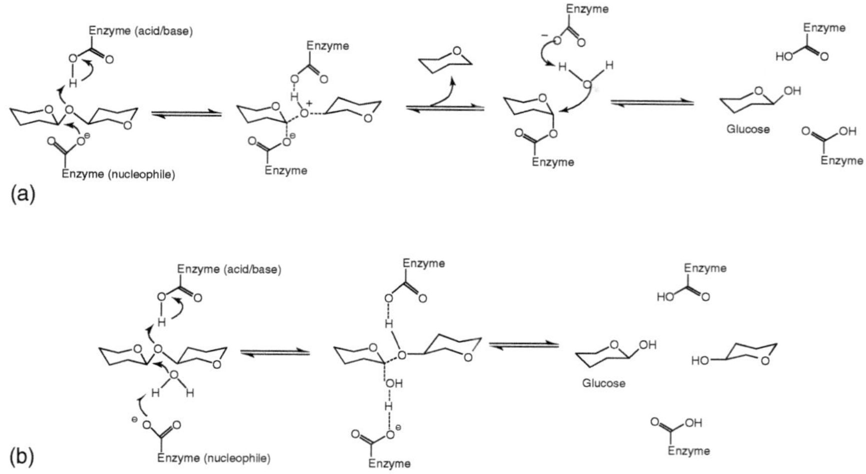

Figure 21.6 Diagrammatic depiction of the retaining and inverting catalytic mechanism of β-glucosidases. (a) Retaining mechanism: here the anomeric configuration is retained in this commonly accepted mechanism of hydrolysis. In the first step of glycosylation, the catalytic nucleophile attacks from the opposite end, whereas the catalytic acid forms an acid-linked intermediate by donating the proton to the leaving group. In the second deglycosylation step, the enzyme is displaced from the anomeric carbon by the attack of the catalytic base (the same carboxylate as the catalytic acid). The catalytic base extracts a proton from the water molecule that improves its nucleophilic power. (b) Inverting mechanism: here in this reaction, an aglycone moiety is replaced in a single-step displacement reaction by a water molecule, leading to the inverted chirality at the anomeric carbon.

reaction. The proton donor (catalytic acid) and proton acceptor (catalytic base) play an important role in this reaction mechanism by protonating the displaced aglycone and extracting the proton from the water molecule respectively (Figure 21.6) [57, 61].

21.5 Source of β-Glucosidase

β-Glucosidase is found in all living things, including bacteria, fungi, plants, and mammals. Although it has been purified from plants and animals [62, 63] microorganisms are thought to be the ideal option for enzyme synthesis in the industrial context due to their rapid growth, easier handling, easy manipulation using genetic engineering, and presence of special characteristics like thermostability and alkalophilicity in some microbes [64, 65]. β-Glucosidase may be found in fungus and bacteria; however, fungi are the most common sources of cellulase enzymes (Table 21.1).

21.5.1 Bacterial β-Glucosidase

The unique and robust properties along with the high multiplication rate of the bacteria have drawn the attention of researchers toward their use for the production

Table 21.1 Some bacterial and fungal sources of β-glucosidase.

Source	Species	References
Bacteria	*Clostridium thermocellum*	[66]
	Pyrococcus furiosus	[67]
	Bacillus circulans subsp. *Alkalophilus*	[68]
	Flavobacterium johnsoniae	[69]
	Actinomycete thermobifidafusca	[70]
	Paenibacillus sp. Strain C5	[71]
	Lactobacillus brevis	[72]
	Caldicellulosiruptor saccharolyticus	[73]
	Terrabacter ginsenosidimutans sp.	[74]
	Thermoanaerobacterium thermosaccharolyticum	[75]
	Pseudonocardia sp. Gsoil 1536	[76]
Fungal	*Trichoderma reesei*	[77]
	Acremonium persicinum	[78]
	Aspergillus oryzae	[79]
	Thermomyces lanuginosus – SSBP	[80]
	Thermoascus aurantiacus	[81]
	Chaetomium thermophilum var. *coprophilum*	[82]
	Penicillium purpurogenum	[83]
	Daldinia eschscholzii	[84]
	Melanocarpus sp. MTCC 3922	[85]
	Neocallimastix patriciarum W5	[86]
	Monascus purpureus	[87]
	Fomitopsis palustris	[88]
	Penicillium purpurogenum KJS506	[89]
	Phoma sp. KCTC11825BP	[90]
	Aspergillus fumigatus Z5	[91]
	Penicillium italicum	[92]
	Fusarium proliferatum NBRC109045	[93]
	Aspergillus saccharolyticus	[94, 95]
	Aspergillus niger A20	[96]
	Fusarium solani	[97]
	Flammulina velutipes	[98]
	Monascus sanguineus	[99]
	Sporothrix schenckii	[100]
	Gongronella butleri	[101]
	Fusarium oxysporum	[102]

of cellulases and β-glucosidase enzymes despite the low secretion of these enzymes [8, 103]. *Fibrobacter succinogenes*, *Ruminococcus flavefaciens*, and *Ruminococcus albus* are predominant cellulosic biomass-degrading bacterial species of herbivore rumen that produce enzymes capable of degrading crystalline cellulose [104]. Other additional fibrolytic bacteria of the rumen include *Butyrivibrio fibrosolvens*, *Prevotella ruminicola*, *Clostridium lochheadii*, *Clostridium longisporum*, *Eubacterium cellulosolvens*, and *Eubacterium ruminantium* that can be isolated from the gut of herbivores as a rich source of the biomass-degrading enzymes such as β-glucosidase [105]. In light of recent studies *Bacillus* (*B. cereus*, *B. licheniformis*, and *B. subtilis*), *Serratia* and *Pseudomonas* are prominent soil microbial genera that are known for their biomass degrading property and cellulose activity [106]. Several *Cellulomonas* spp., such as *C. terrae*, *C. biazotea*, *C. persica*, *C. iranensis*, *C. fimi*, *C. aurantiaca*, *C. uda*, and *C. pachnodae* and of *Streptomyces* including *S. flavogriseus*, *S. olivochromogenes*, and *S. lividans*, *Micromonospora* are some other soil bacteria known to produce a vast array of cellulases [107–109]. Extremophiles inhabiting extreme temperatures, pH, and salt conditions are known to produce β-glucosidases and cellulose that can act under these extreme environmental conditions [110]. Other species of thermophilic *Clostridium* such as *C. stercorarium*, *C. thermohydrosulfuricum*, *C. cellulolyticum*, and thermophilic *Bacilli* including *B. subtilis*, *B. licheniformis*, *B. coagulans*, *Geobacillus thermoleovorans*, and *Paenibacillus* can produce cellulase at extreme temperatures which have shown their cellulolytic activity at temperatures 50 °C or above [111–113]. Most archaea inhabit in extreme temperature conditions and are thus considered a good source of enzymes that can maintain their functional stability at higher temperatures. As a result, archaea are considered to be a good source of industrially suitable enzymes for their utilization in industrial operations [114, 115].

21.5.2 Fungal β-Glucosidase

Most of the fugal β-glucosidase produced, purified, and characterized belongs to the GH3 enzyme family and are secreted extracellularly. *Trichoderma reesei* is one of the most documented species of the genus *Trichoderma*. The diverse type of cellulases and β-glucosidases secreted by the fungus has varied applications in many industries [116]. Currently, fungal enzymes such as β-glucosidase and cellulases are being used in several industries and have great applications in biomass hydrolysis and biofuel production. *Fusarium*, *Colletotrichum*, *Penicillium*, *Trichoderma*, and *Aspergillus* are among the cellulase-producing fungal genera that have important industrial use [117]. Some thermophilic fungi such as *Sporotrichum pulverulentum*, *Aspergillus* (*A. wentii*, *A. versicolor*, and *A. terreus*), *Malbranchea cinnamomea*, *Melanocarpus albomyces*, *Myceliophthora thermophila*, *Humicola insolens*, and *Chaetomium thermophile* have also been reported for their biomass degrading properties in the temperature range of 60–65 °C [118, 119]. Another thermophilic fungus *Thermoascus crustaceus* having considerable potential for β-glucosidase production, was cultivated on agro-industrial residue at low pH and high temperature conditions [120]. Some other important fungal species that produce industrially important β-glucosidase enzymes include *Aspergillus protuberus*, *Pichia pastoris*, *Penicillium piceum*, and *Aspergillus flavus* [121–124]. Thus, a wide variety of fungal species are known to be major sources of β-glucosidase enzymes that have a wide range of applications in various industries.

Microorganisms generate a limited quantity of β-glucosidase in general; for example, the cellulase hyperproducer *T. reesei* lacks significant β-glucosidase activity [125, 126]. As a result, researchers are looking for microorganisms with high β-glucosidase productivity.

21.6 β-Glucosidase Production

β-Glucosidases have been produced using either solid-state fermentation (SSF) or submerged fermentation (SMF) from a variety of fungi, yeast, and bacteria [127–129]. The microorganism is produced in SSF alone or in combination on solid substrates such as castor bean cake, sugarcane bagasse, cassava cake, wheat bran, rice straw, or maize husk. SSF may be done for a long time since the substrate is utilized gradually. It is more suited to the culture of microorganisms that require less moisture. High productivity, inexpensive substrate use, low energy need, little water output, and lack of foam up are the benefits of SSF; however, heat generation and a lack of automation knowledge are the drawbacks [130–132]. Microorganisms are grown in SMF using free-flowing liquids such as molasses and broths containing various nutrients. Since bioactives, enzymes, and metabolic wastes are released into the fermentation medium and the substrates are quickly depleted, nutritional replenishment is required on a regular basis. This fermentation method is great for bacteria and other microorganisms that demand a lot of moisture. The ease of sterility, heat and mass transfer, process monitoring and automation, and extraction and recovery of enzymes and bioactives are the key benefits of SMF [53, 131, 133–136].

For economic enzyme production and commercialization, optimizing fermentation conditions is a critical step. During the fermentation process for enzyme manufacturing, numerous factors must be properly tuned. Carbon supply and concentration, nitrogen source and concentration, salts, pH, temperature, oxygen availability, fermentation duration, inoculum size, and other factors are among them [137, 138]. Fermentation conditions vary based on microbial species, desired end product (e.g., enzymes), and manufacturing processes, among other considerations. The major factors that affect the conditions for β-glucosidases are mentioned as follows.

21.6.1 Carbon Source

β-Glucosidase, like other cellulases, is an inducible enzyme that microbial cells produce in response to different carbon sources in the fermentation medium. Complex carbon sources include cellulose, wheat bran, rice straw, rice husk, sugar cane bagasse, and pectin, as well as simple sugars like glucose, lactose, cellobiose, and sophorose. Because complex sugars cannot pass through the cell membrane, some constitutively expressed enzymes are thought to degrade them to simple sugars like cellobiose and lactose, which can then be transported through the cell membrane via specific transporters to the cytosol, where they induce the expression of these enzymes in a poorly understood mechanism [21, 139–141]. Catabolite suppression is a condition in which metabolizable sugar, such as glucose, inhibits the synthesis of β-glucosidase and other cellulases [142, 143]. The best carbon source for β-glucosidase synthesis varies based on the species, fermentation technique, and other fermentation parameters, as well as the interplay between these factors. When sugarcane bagasse and aviculare were utilized as carbon sources, optimal synthesis of extracellular and intracellular β-glucosidase from *Chaetomium thermophilum* var. *coprophilum* was attained [82]. When quercetin is employed as a carbon source, *Aspergillus oryzae* generates β-glucosidase with high glucose tolerance (HGT-BGL) [79]. When pectin is employed as a carbon source in SSF, *Aspergillus* strain SA 58 produces two extracellular β-glucosidase [144]. Two or more microbial groups are referred to as a microbial consortium. When wheat bran was employed as a carbon source, optimal synthesis of β-glucosidase from the microbial consortia of *Aspergillus niger* and *A. oryzae* was attained [145]. Similarly, when *Fusarium proliferatum* NBRC109045 was cultivated on media containing maize stover and wheat bran, it produced the most β-glucosidase [93]. When *Aspergillus saccharolyticus* was grown on a medium containing xylose, xylan, wheat bran, and pretreated maize stover, it generated the highest levels of β-glucosidase activity [94].

21.6.2 Nitrogen Source

To produce amino acids, proteins, nitrogenous chemicals, vitamins, nucleic acids, and bioactives, bacteria require a nitrogen source in the fermentation medium [65]. Organic or inorganic nitrogen sources are also acceptable. Peptone, yeast extract, beef extract, tryptone, and soybean meal are all examples of organic nitrogen sources. Ammonium sulfate, ammonium chloride, ammonium hydrogen phosphate, and other inorganic nitrogen sources exist. Various species require different nitrogen sources for optimal β-glucosidase synthesis and there is not much information regarding the nitrogen supply optimization for β-glucosidase production. *Penicillium simplicissimum* H-11 generated the most β-glucosidase when grown on a medium using bean cake powder as a nitrogen source [129]. When cultivated on peptone and yeast extract as a nitrogen source, *C. thermophilum* var. *coprophilum* generated the highest levels of β-glucosidase [82]. *Aspergillus* strain SA 58 cultivated on medium containing beef extract as a nitrogen source generated a high level of extracellular β-glucosidase; however, when ammonium salts were employed as a nitrogen source, it produced the least amount [144]. Similarly, when L-asparagine was used as a nitrogen source, *Flammulina velutipes* produced the highest level of extracellular β-glucosidase activity, while other ammonium salts produced negligible to low activity [98].

21.6.3 Temperature

The temperature at which β-glucosidase is produced varies for different species. The ideal temperature required for microorganism development usually corresponds with the temperature at which β-glucosidase is produced, e.g., *Monascus purpureus* at 30 °C [87], *Penicillium italicum* at 28 °C [92], *C. thermophilum* var. *coprophilum* at 45 °C [82], *Penicillium simplicissium* H-11 at 30 °C [129], *Daldinia eschscholzii* at 25 °C [84], *Thermoascus aurantiacus* at 50 °C [81], and *A. oryzae* at 28 °C [79]. *Aspergillus* strain SA 58 produced most β-glucosidase at 35 °C, despite the fact that the organism thrives best at 30 °C. The ideal temperature for β-glucosidase synthesis from *Penicillium purpurogenum* KJS506, which grows best at 28 °C, was 32 °C [89]. When tested in a temperature range of 25–45 and 25–40 °C, optimal synthesis of β-glucosidase from *Lichtheimia ramosa* and *A. protuberus* was achieved at 35 and 30 °C, respectively [121, 146]. *Clostridium thermocellum* at 60 °C [66], archaeon *Pyrococcus furiosus* at 90 °C [67], *Lactobacillus brevis* at 25 °C [72], *Flavobacterium Johnsoniae* at 28 °C [69], and psychrotolerant *Shewanella* sp. G5 at 15 °C have all generated β-glucosidase [71]. The examples and various findings suggest that the temperature optimization for β-glucosidase production should be with respect to the temperature range obtained for diverse microbial species.

21.6.4 pH

For optimum β-glucosidase synthesis, various species required varied beginning pH. Similar to temperature, it is not suggested to optimize the pH for β-glucosidase synthesis; instead, an arbitrary pH at which these species grow optimum can be utilized. For examplethe β-glucosidase production was found to be optimum for *Fusarium oxysporum* at pH 6 [147], *P. italicum* at pH 4.5 [92], *A. oryzae* at pH 6.0 [79], *Fusarium proiferatum* NBRC109045 at pH 5.0 [93], *Candida peltata* at pH 5.0 [148], *D. eschscholzii* at pH 5.5 [84], and *Phoma* sp. KCTC11825BP at pH 4.5, respectively. When *Aspergillus* strain SA 58 was tested from a pH range of 3.0–9.0, it generated optimum β-glucosidase at pH 5.0 [144]. *P. pastoris* produced the most β-glucosidase at pH 7.5 when tested from pH 4 to 8 [147]. Similarly, when the microbial consortium of *A. niger* and *A. oryzae* was screened between pH 4.5 and 7, it was shown that pH 5.5 produced the best β-glucosidase [127].

21.6.5 Incubation Time/Fermentation Period

Another important factor regulating enzyme production is the fermentation duration. The fermentation process must be carried out for an ideal amount of time, or else optimal synthesis of a certain value-added product, such as an enzyme, would not be possible. Usually, when the incubation period is prolonged, the enzyme production increases until it reaches an ideal maximum peak, after which it begins to fall in production and activity. The decrease in enzyme production might be ascribed to a decrease in nutritional availability, the buildup and/or toxicity of waste products, and a decrease in the enzyme's stability. Following four to five days of culture, optimal β-glucosidase production from *A. niger* and *Trichoderma* sp. was obtained, after which production was gradually reduced [137]. *P. purpurogenum* and *C. thermophilum* var. *coprophilum* produced the most extracellular β-glucosidase after 96 and 140 hours of growth period, respectively [82]. On SSF, *Fusarium solani*, *L. ramosa*, and *Thermomucor indicae-seudaticae* produced the most extracellular β-glucosidase at 72, 96, and 196 hours, respectively [127, 146, 149].

Keeping in mind the various factors affecting the culture conditions, different culture methods are used for the production of microbial enzymes at commercial, industrial, and experimental scales. The two prominent methods utilized are the batch and continuous bioprocess culturing methods for enzyme production. In batch fermentation, a fermentor is used for microbial growth, where a fixed volume of the media is inoculated with the desired microorganism. The nutrients from the medium are gradually consumed and depleted with accumulation of byproducts as the microbes tend to grow in the medium, leading to a continuously changing culture environment. Ease of operation and low contamination risk are the major advantages of the batch culture [150]. In a continuous culture method, there is a simultaneous entry and exit of equal amounts of sterile nutrient broth and cultured broth, respectively, keeping the culture volume constant in an open bioreactor. The cultured broth, along with the products, is taken out for purification of products. In this method the fresh medium is continuously added to the reactor to replace the consumed nutrients and toxic metabolites and byproducts [151].

21.7 Methods of Bacterial β-Glucosidase Production

21.7.1 Batch Culture Method

Batch fermentation method is mostly used to optimize reaction conditions in the early stages of experimental design for its utilization in the later large-scale production of the substrate. This is often a convenient initial method for beginners in the field of enzyme production. Comparatively low cell densities and the relatively long breaks between batches due to cleaning, vessel setup, and sterilization are the few disadvantages of the batch culture method that discourage its use for large-scale production. An anaerobic cellulolytic *Clostridium* strain RT9 having the ability to hydrolyze cellulose, carboxymethyl-cellulose (CMC), and cellobiose isolated from bovine rumen fluid exhibited endoglucanase, exoglucanase, and β-glucosidase activities and the reaction were performed in a batch culture with cellulose as the sole carbon source [152]. Soymilk was utilized as a substrate for the production of β-glucosidase enzyme by fermenting it under the action of five strains of *Bifidobacterium (B. pseudolongum, B. longum, B. longum, and B. animalis)*. By the batch culture method, about 500 ml of sterile soymilk was inoculated with an active culture of *Bifidobacterium* sp. in glass bottles for the production of the β-glucosidase enzyme [153]. Successful microbial production of 1,5-diaminopentane (DAP) from a renewable feedstock comprising cellulose as the sole carbon source was performed in a fed-batch fermentor. For this purpose, a genetically engineered β-glucosidase-secreting *Corynebacterium glutamicum* was used to obtain a yield of 0.43 (g/g glucose) of DAP [154].

21.7.2 Continuous Culture Method

The prime advantage of using the continuous culture is that in this method the optimum conditions can be fixed for the maximum and long-term product synthesis. A steady state can be achieved with a constant biomass, homogenous inoculum, and metabolite concentration, thus resulting in a higher productivity per unit volume. Utilizing the continuous culture method, biomass degradation was carried out by a bacterial consortium (*cellulomonas cartae, pseudomonas fluorescens, Pseudomonas putida*, and *Bacillus megaterium*). SSF was utilized for the production of cellulase enzymes from the biomass residual waste [155]. Similarly, cellulase enzyme complex was produced by the action of *Anoxybacillus* sp. 527 on crystalline cellulose as the sole carbon source using the continuous culture method [156]. The cost of production of ethanol from sugarcane biomass was also reduced by using a β-glucosidase enzyme from a recombinant *E. coli* strain. The enzyme was produced by continuous culture method wherein the enzyme production was utilized for the ethanol production by combining both the production units [157].

21.8 Methods of Fungal β-Glucosidase Production

21.8.1 Batch Culture Method

A mutant strain of *Trichoderma citrinoviride* was developed by mutagenesis and the SMF process for enzyme production and assays for the screening of the mutant strain was initially performed in a batch culture system [158]. Production of enzymes of the cellulase complex by the fungus *Neurospora crassa* and the effect of various parameters, such as biomass concentration temperature and initial pH, were studied on milled and sieved wheat straw biomass. The study for various parameters was conducted using the batch culture method in 250-ml Erlenmeyer flasks [159]. Similarly, a 50-l stirred fermenter was used for the production of cellulose enzyme complex from the mutant thermostable *Streptomyces* sp. T3-1 [160]. Similarly, the batch culture method was carried out in 250-ml Erlenmeyer flask with 70 ml of production medium for enzyme production utilizing *Penicillium janthinellum* NCIM 1171 and *Trichoderma viride* NCIM 1051 with sugarcane bagasse as the substrate [161, 162]. *A. niger* NRRL 3112 was cultured by batch culture method in a stirred-tank bioreactor for the production of β-glucosidase on wheat bran medium as a carbon source [146]. *Aspergillus versicolor*, a novel β-glucosidase-producing endophytic fungal strain, was utilized for the production of the β-glucosidase enzyme by a laboratory-scale batch culture method [163].

21.8.2 Continuous Culture Method

In contrast to the batch culture method the amount of the fresh medium or feed solution is not limited by the maximum working volume of the vessel in the course of the production process. A steady state can be maintained by optimizing the rate of medium to be exchanged. The continuous culture method proves to be more economical as the cultures in steady-state can last for days, greatly reducing the downtime [164]. Using the continuous culture method *Thermomyces lanuginosus* was grown for the production of carbohydrate hydrolyzing enzymes at a constant dilution rate of 0.08/h in steady-state conditions [165]. A continuous culture of *Trichoderma reesei* RUT C30 was made in a 1-l Pyrex Erlenmeyer flask to study the cellulase-inducing property of the waste paper hydrolysate. The holding volume of the reactor was maintained at 400 ml with the dilution rate of 0.122/h of the hydrolysate to attain a sixfold higher maximum productivity [166]. *Penicillium* cellulase being rich in β-glucosidase was utilized in a continuous culture method in SSF and SMF for the efficient saccharification of the substrate [167]. Cellulose-rich waste water and activated sludge are used as induction mediums for β-glucosidase production in an optimized continuous culture method by utilizing *Hypocrea* species [168].

21.9 Genetic Engineering of β-Glucosidase

Genetic modification is an important tool to combine multiple desirable characters in a single organism. The process is applied for the production of simple to highly specific therapeutic proteins and metabolites from engineered organisms. Utilizing this approach, several β-glucosidases have been cloned and expressed in various organisms such as bacteria, yeast, fungi, plant, and animal sources for the bulk production of the enzyme on a large scale for various biotechnological, industrial applications, and to engineer β-glucosidases with glucose tolerant properties along with the search of glucose tolerant native β-glucosidases sources [169, 170]. In general, several approaches like heterogeneous expression of β-glucosidase genes from different sources, characterization of immobilized enzymes in several agents, and site-directed mutagenesis to enhance the efficacy of enzymes have been one of the major focuses of the current research on the β-glucosidase enzymes. Various kinds of host organisms, from bacteria to fungi such as *P. pastoris*, *T. reesei*, and *E. coli* species, have been used for the expression of β-glucosidase genes (*bgl* genes) [157, 171]. Thus, for the gene cloning studies of the β-glucosidases enzyme, three prime methods have been used: (i) establishing a genomic DNA library and selection of the clones by screening for β-glucosidase production; (ii) beginning with a cDNA library (or a genomic library) followed by the screening of recombinant clones through specific nucleotide probes derived from the regarding the polypeptide sequence; and (iii) primer designing of existing gene sequences for the PCR based cloning of the genes [11, 26]. The methods can be utilized toward improving the strain in order to achieve higher β-glucosidase titers as well as desired traits through mutation or genetic manipulation. Random mutations are a widely used popular method, but the site-specific mutation for gene manipulation is more promising as it alters specific sequences and proves to be more precise. However, the methods require prerequisite knowledge regarding the primary structure of the protein to incorporate a change in a particular amino acid sequence [52]. Moreover, genetic engineering can be utilized for cloning and over-expression of β-glucosidase, leading to a β-glucosidase-rich cellulase production and thus resulting in improved efficiencies when acted upon the biomass [172]. The desired gene for β-glucosidases proves to be much more beneficial when cloned and expressed in a heterologous system than mixing the enzyme outside to generate a cocktail. Similarly, β-glucosidases having the desired properties with a low expression level in their native parent strain, if cloned and expressed strongly in a different host, can be of great advantage [52]. Considering the cellulolytic activities of the microbes, most of the bacterial enzymes are produced intracellularly, unlike fungi, which produce extracellular proteins. Reports on the cloning of β-glucosidase from fungi are relatively low despite fungi being good producers of the enzyme. Many complexities, such as the presence of introns in their genes and the process of glycosylation, are associated with the cloning of the β-glucosidase gene from fungi. Filamentous fungi can perform post translational modifications such as glycosylation and disulfidation apart from the secretion of the proteins [173]. The transformations are generally carried out using the plasmids that incorporate into the genome thereby generating stable fungal transformants. Thus, these filamentous fungi, along with the bacteria, have proven to be the potential host for these recombinant DNAs, wherein several genes have been cloned and expressed in eukaryotic systems of *T. reesei*, *Aspergillus* sp., *Saccharomyces cerevisiae*, and *P. pastoris* [174–176].

A petri-dish-based double layer high throughput screening method is utilized to improve Glucose tolerance of β-glucosidase Bgl15. Two prominent beneficial mutants 2R1 and 5R1 are identified with attributes of glucose tolerance and increased half-life at high temperatures, respectively. Increased glucose production from pretreated sugar cane bagasse is observed in the 5R1 mutant-supplemented enzyme cocktail [177]. A GH1 family glucose tolerant recombinant thermostable β-glucosidase isolated from *B. subtilis* and cloned and overexpressed in *E. coli* exhibited thermotolerant properties as it retained more than 85% of maximum activity after one hour preincubation at 60 °C and exhibited high tolerance against detergents and organic solvents [178]. Other methods utilized site-directed mutagenesis to engineer seven mutant β-glucosidases from hyperthermophilic *Thermotoga naphthophila* RKU-10. The hydrolysis property of enzyme is seen to strongly suppress in the mutants, leading to enhanced galactooligosaccharide production [179]. A similar site-directed mutagenesis is attempted to genetically modify the β-galactosidase (BgaQ) from *Streptococcus thermophilus*. The active site residues of the enzyme are engineered to obtain an enzyme with an enhanced transgalactosylation activity that leads to a reduced lactose concentration in fermented yogurt [180]. Engineered β-glucosidase (ThBgl) enzyme from *Trichoderma harzianum* displayed improved glucose tolerance. The enzyme is highly expressed in the fungi and the structural analyses of the enzyme combined with site-directed mutagenesis efficiently improved the functional properties of this GH1 β-glucosidase. The product inhibition of the enzyme is prevented by modifying the key active site amino acids, leading to reduced active-site accessibility by the product and thus resulting in glucose tolerance [181]. Yield of enzyme produced by the mutant *Penicillium pinophilum* was found to be much higher than that of *T. reesei*, which is usually utilized for β-glucosidase production [173]. A novel cellulase recycling method has been developed using a combination of cellulosomes of *C. thermocellum* and *Thermoanaerobacter brockii* β-glucosidase (CglT). In this approach, the chimeric carbohydrate-binding module (CBM3)–β-glucosidase (CglT) is designed to recover the CglT enzyme [182].

Yeasts, being a good source of β-glucosidase genes, are well exploited as host organisms to express the fungal β-glucosidase. To achieve the process of simultaneous saccharification of biomass *S. cerevisiae* is sought as the first choice to clone the gene for β-glucosidase as well as other components of the cellulases enzyme complex [183]. A novel β-glucosidase (Bgl3A) from thermophilic *Talaromyces leycettanus* JCM12802 with thermophilic, acidic, thermostable properties is identified and expressed in *P. pastoris* at a high level. The mutant is pH stable with performance and activity similar to commercial enzymes in the saccharification of cellulosic material [184]. Strong inducible promoters such as P*cbh1* are being genetically engineered through the replacement of transcriptional repressors (*cre1*, *ace1*) with transcriptional activators (*xyr1*, *ace2*, *ace3*, *hap2/3/5*), resulting in elevated production of endoglucanases, β-glucosidases, and cellobiohydrolases in *T. reesei*. Synthetic expression systems have made the genetic engineering of such innovative strains easy by extending and making the molecular toolbox accessible [185]. The various genetic modifications carried out in microorganisms for the enhanced β-glucosidase production have been given in Table 21.2.

21.10 Applications

21.10.1 β-Glucosidase in Biofuel Production

Many enzymes work together to breakdown lignocellulosic material to pentose and hexose sugar, which are then fermented to ethanol in the production of biofuels, such as bioethanol, from plant biomass. The main components of these enzymes are cellulases and xylanases [189]. Endoglucanase and cellobiohydrolyase degrade the cellulose chain to cellobiose and short oligosaccharide, respectively, and both are inhibited by cellobiose. β-Glucosidases, which are part of the cellulase enzyme complex, hydrolyze cellobiose and cello-oligosaccharides to yield glucose, which yeasts ferment into fuel ethanol. The breakdown of cellulose to cello-oligosaccharides and glucose, followed by the conversion of glucose to ethanol by microbes, is how ethanol is made from cellulose [190]. Endoglucanases and exoglucanases breakdown cellulose, resulting in cellobiose and some cello-oligosaccharides, which are then converted to glucose by β-glucosidase. Because it restricts the effectiveness of hydrolysis and may alleviate the cellobiose-mediated inhibition of exoglucanase and endoglucanase, the reaction catalyzed by β-glucosidase is the most crucial step in the breakdown of cellulose [191]. However, the most extensively utilized cellulase from *T. viride* has low β-glucosidase activity, resulting in product inhibition when cellobiose accumulates. This is another key barrier in the biomass conversion and biofuel manufacturing process [192]. As a result, the vast majority of β-glucosidase

Table 21.2 β-glucosidase production improvement through genetic engineering approaches in microorganisms.

Microorganism	Modification	Recombinant properties	References
Pencillium oxalicum	Functional mutation	Enhanced cellulose production (150 U/ml)	[172]
Escherichia coli	Site-directed mutagenesis	Enhanced glucose tolerance and thermostability	[177]
Bacillus subtilis	Recombinant gene expression	Increased catalytic efficiency and increased thermostability	[178]
Thermotoga naphthophila	Site-directed mutagenesis	Enhanced galactooligosaccharide	[179]
Streptococcus thermophilus	Site-directed mutagenesis	enhanced transgalactosylation activity	[180]
Trichoderma harzianum	Gene expression and site-directed mutagenesis	Enhanced glucose tolerance	[181]
Penicillium pinophilum	Recombinant gene expression	Enhanced biomass saccharification and hydrolysis and efficient enzyme recovery	[182]
Saccharomycopsis fibuligera	Genetic recombination	Enhanced cellulose hydrolysis during simultaneous saccharification process	[183]
Talaromyces leycettanus	Recombinant gene expression	Enhanced production of acid tolerant β-glucosidase (112.2 IU/ml)	[184]
Trichoderma reesei	Genetic modification	Enhanced cellulase production	[185]
Thermoascus aurantiacus	Recombinant gene expression	Expression of β-glucosidase in osmotolerant and temperature-tolerant yeast strain	[186]
Aspergillus terreus	Random mutation	Enhanced alkaline cellulase production	[187]
Penicillium decumbens	Random mutation	Enhanced cellulase and hemicellulase production	[188]

that have been found and described for their biochemical and kinetic features are intended to be used in biomass hydrolysis and to solve difficulties associated with β-glucosidase, such as low productivity and glucose sensitivity [95].

21.10.2 Isoflavones Glycoside Hydrolysis

Plant secondary metabolites such as phenolic compounds (flavonoid, flavonone, flavones, and isoflavone) have chemical structures and biological roles that differ from one another. Because of their biological activity as antioxidants, anticancer, antiallergic, anti-inflammatory agents, and antihypertensive agents, these compounds have lately drawn the attention of many researchers, particularly in the fields of health and food technology [193–195]. The bulk of these chemicals are found in the form of glycosides, which improve their water solubility and stability while limiting their absorption from the human gastrointestinal tract [196]. Monoglucose units are usually conjugated to other sugars like galactose, arabinose, or xylose in these glycosides. Specific enzymes, such as arabinosidase and β-glucosidase, are required for the release of the aglycone moiety. The biological efficacy of the released aglycone is increased since it is quickly absorbed [197]. The hydrolysis of isoflavone or flavonoid compounds has been observed to need large amounts of β-glucosidase. For example, the hydrolysis of Delphinidin-3-glucoside and Malvidin-3-glucoside by *Lactobacillus acidophilus* LA-5 generates gallic, syringe homogentisic acid [198].

21.10.3 Cassava Detoxification

β-Glucosidase has the potential to facilitate cassava detoxification. Cassava is a carbohydrate-rich plant that grows in a variety of locations across the world and is a staple diet for 500 million people. However, owing to the presence of cyanogenic glycosides such as linamarin and lotaustralin, raw cassava ingestion is hazardous to human health [199]. Furthermore, a link has been shown between the human central nervous system condition, "Konzo" and long-term intake of cassava products. Endogenous β-glucosidase and linamarase found in the roots naturally detoxify cassava during processing and grating. However, these enzymes are underexpressed, resulting in cyanogenic glycosides in processed foods. It is therefore proposed that exogenous linamarase and β-glucosidase from microbial sources be used to improve the hydrolysis of cyanogenic glycoside present in this key food product [199–203].

21.10.4 Dinking of Waste Paper

The paper and pulp sector is one of the most wood-consuming sectors, and it is predicted to grow more as the global economy and population grow. Waste paper is one of the most significant environmental pollutants in order to alleviate this two-dimensional challenge of forest wood consumption and landfill pollution, waste paper recycling is gaining great attention in recent years. Chemical or enzymatic methods can be used to recycle waste paper. The removal of ink is a key barrier to waste paper recycling. Traditional techniques of removing ink from waste paper use a number of chemicals that are both ecologically harmful and reduce the brightness of the paper. It is well established that the enzymatic approach for waste paper recycling is effective in resolving these issues. Cellulase, β-glucosidase, and hemicellulose are all included in enzyme preparations for waste paper recycling [204–208].

21.10.5 β-Glucosidase in Winemaking, Tea, and Other Beverages

β-glucosidases are involved in the enzymatic release of aromatic chemicals from glycosidic precursors found in fruit juices, musts, and fermenting products for winemaking [30, 209], tea [210], and fruit juice [211]. The natural process involving endogenous plant-glucosidases takes a long time. Aroma release is improved by supplementing with effective exogenous enzymes [200]. In grapes, monoterpenols (such as linalol, geraniol, nerol, citronclol, α-terpineol, and linalol oxide) are attached to diglucosides, which add to the taste of wine [212]. Enzymatic hydrolysis of these molecules necessitates a series of reactions that result in monoglucosides, followed by hydrolysis of monoglucosides by the activity of β-glucosidases. Exogenous glucose-tolerant β-glucosidase obtained from fungus (e.g., *A. oryzae*) is found to promote glucoconjugated aromatic component hydrolysis and improve wine quality [79]. β-Glucosidase from a wine strain of *Lactobacillus plantarum* that also ferments lactic acid, demonstrated the necessity for additional enzymes required to release flavorful chemicals [209]. Isolated and characterized an extracellular β-glucosidase from *Issatchenkia terricola* in order to explore the efficacy of immobilized enzyme in enhancing the aroma taste of white Muscat wine [213]. The β-glucosidase in the tea beverage industry is used to increase the quantity of essential oils [44]; it can also be immobilized and utilized to boost the essential oil content by a significant amount [210]. Similarly, the hydrolysis of naringenin by β-glucosidase is a useful application of the enzyme to reduce the bitterness of citrus fruit juices [211].

21.10.6 β-Glucosidase in Soy-based Foods

Various foods and beverages contain soy, which comprises many glucosidic isoflavones such as daidzin, genistin, and glycitin. However, in soy-based diets, isoflavones are mostly found in the inactive form of glycosides, which may be converted into aglycones by using an extracellular β-glucosidase enzyme (daidzein, genistein, and glycitein) [214]. Isoflavones in the aglycone form have stronger biological activity than those in the glucosidic form, and they are also absorbed faster and in greater amounts after digestion [215]. Soybean isoflavones have phytoestrogenic properties, making them useful in the treatment and prevention of diseases like cardiovascular disease and osteoporosis [216], prostate cancer and breast cancer [217], menopause symptoms relief [218], and estrogenic and antioxidant activity. Treatment with β-glucosidase or fermentation with a β-glucosidase-producing

Lactobacillus strain greatly raised the aglycon content of soy milk [219]. Gellan, an exopolysaccharide generated by *Sphingomonaspaucimobilis*, has limited applicability in the food sector due to its high viscosity and low solubility. As a result, the hydrolytic activity of β-glucosidases is advantageous in the manufacture of low-viscosity gellan meals. β-Glucosidases are also involved in the bitterness reduction process in citrus fruit juices [220].

21.10.7 β-Glucosidase in Flavor Industry

The majority of chemicals responsible for taste in plants and fruit tissue are present as glycoconjugates, leaving them flavorless and nonvolatile [221]. Glycoside flavor compounds and are found in a variety of fruits, including grapes [222, 223], yellow plums [224], mangoes [225], and strawberries [226]. The structures of these glycosides, notably the aglycone molecule, are complicated and varied. The glucose unit is commonly conjugated to different glycosides, such as 6-O-α-L-arabinofuranosyl-β-D-glucopyranosides and 6-O-α-L-arabinopyranosyl-β-D-glucopyranosides. To make the aglycone component of these flavorless molecules accessible to flavor content, they must be hydrolyzed. Acids or, more importantly, enzymes are used to carry out this hydrolysis process [227]. Enzymes such as α-L-rhamnosidase and α-L-arabinosidase cleave the terminal sugars arabinose and rhamnose, and then β-glucosidase works on the corresponding β-D-glucoside, releasing glucose and aglycone moiety such as monoterpenol [228].

β-Glucosidases are enzymes that help produce aromatic chemicals from glucosidic precursors found in fruits and fermented foods [229]. β-Glucosidases are employed to enhance the organoleptic qualities of citrus fruit juices, reducing the bitterness caused by naringin, a glucosidic molecule (4,5,7-trihydroxyflavanone-7-rhamnoglucoside) [30, 220]. Reduction of fruit bitterness is observed after treatment with β-glucosidases and hydrolysis of gellan by these enzymes leads to a reduction in fruit juice viscosity [229]. Furthermore, thermostable β-glucosidases like one isolated from *B. subtilis* can be identified and characterized to improve juice quality after immobilizing it on surfaces such as alginate beads [30].

21.10.8 Synthesis of Oligosaccharides and Alkyl-glycosides

The production of oligosaccharides and alkyl-glycosides is also carried out by β-glucosidases. Therapeutic medicines, diagnostic tools, and growth promoters are all possible uses for oligosaccharides. Fertilization, embryogenesis, and cell proliferation are all key activities in biological systems. Nonionic surfactants with strong biodegradability and antibacterial characteristics are known as alkyl-glycosides. As a result of their ability to be hydrolyzed by β-glucosidase, they have prospective applications in the pharmaceutical, chemical, cosmetic, food, and detergent sectors [230]. To improve the food quality, enzymes from source plants or other sources can be added to meals and drinks before, during, or after processing. As a result, β-glucosidases with desirable properties are targeted for plant breeding programs, tissue culture, and recombinant technologies in order to increase their overproduction in transgenic microbial or plant hosts, as well as their catalytic properties for flavor enhancement and stability.

21.10.9 Nutritional Improvement

Aside from flavor improvement, the release of vitamins, antioxidants, and other useful substances from glycosides can improve the nutritional value of meals, feeds, and drinks. β-Glucosidase in rice can liberate vitamin B6 (pyridoxine) from pyridoxine glucoside [231]. Other vitamins are present as glucosides in many plants, and the release of their aglycones can boost nutritional availability. Anthocyanins can also be hydrolyzed by this enzyme, resulting in anthocyanidins and sugars. The aglycones, having fewer colors and less soluble than anthocyanins, tend to precipitate and are easier to remove. It is extremely beneficial to the orange market since it assists in color change during pasteurization and preserving the overall quality [232].

21.11 Conclusion

β-Glucosidase is an important component of the cellulase system produced by all life domains playing fundamental roles in many life processes. The wide range of industrial applications and functions of β-glucosidases make it an important enzyme for the targeted study in the field of novel enzyme production, better stability, etc. Despite having tremendous industrial demand, a suitable industrial β-glucosidase fulfilling all the desired properties and functions is still lacking, and studies continue in search of a novel enzyme with such properties. An understanding of the *in vivo* functional roles of these enzymes, biochemical properties, existing applications, and well-characterized heterogeneous expression technology is helping in the improvement of these enzymes using enzyme engineering and opening up opportunities to explore more applications of the enzyme in the near future. In the process of enzymatic hydrolysis, the high cost of enzymes and the absence of potential microorganisms for β-glucosidase production, as well as the slow enzymatic degradation, are the main obstacles that need to be overcome. The catalytic mechanism is well understood for the major β-glucosidase, but the means by which their exact substrate specificity is established has proven to be divergent among even closely related β-glucosidases and thus remains an area of large proportion to be explored.

References

1 Koupaie, E.H., Dahadha, S., Lakeh, A.B. et al. (2019). Enzymatic pretreatment of lignocellulosic biomass for enhanced biomethane production– a review. *J. Environ. Manage.* 233: 774–784.

2 Pandey, V.C., Bajpai, O., and Singh, N. (2016). Energy crops in sustainable phytoremediation. *Renewable Sustainable Energy Rev.* 54: 58–73.

3 Shahzadi, T., Mehmood, S., Irshad, M. et al. (2014). Advances in lignocellulosic biotechnology: a brief review on lignocellulosic biomass and cellulases. *Adv. Biosci. Biotechnol.* 05 (03): 246–251.

4 Peter, Z. (2021). Order in cellulosics: Historical review of crystal structure research on cellulose. *Carbohydr. Polym.* 254: 117417.

5 Agbor, V.B., Cicek, N., Sparling, R. et al. (2011). Biomass pretreatment: fundamentals toward application. *Biotechnol. Adv.* 29 (6): 675–685.

6 Dashtban, M., Maki, M., Leung, K.T. et al. (2010). Cellulase activities in biomass conversion: measurement methods and comparison. *Crit. Rev. Biotechnol.* 30 (4): 302–309.

7 Tiwari, P., Misra, B.N., and Sangwan, N.S. (2013). β-Glucosidases from the fungus *Trichoderma*: an efficient cellulase machinery in biotechnological applications. *Biomed Res. Int.* 2013: 203735.

8 Ahmed, A., Batool, K., and Bibi, A. (2017). Microbial β-glucosidase: sources, production and applications. *J. Appl. Environ. Microbiol.* 5 (1): 31–46.

9 Liu, L., Huang, W.C., Liu, Y., and Li, M. (2021). Diversity of cellulolytic microorganisms and microbial cellulases. *Int. Biodeterior. Biodegrad.* 163: 105277.

10 Yeoman, C.J., Han, Y., Dodd, D. et al. (2010). Thermostable enzymes as biocatalysts in the biofuel industry. *Adv. Appl. Microbiol.* 70: 1–55.

11 Bhatia, Y., Mishra, S., and Bisaria, V.S. (2002). Microbial β-glucosidases: cloning, properties, and applications. *Crit. Rev. Biotechnol.* 22 (4): 375–407.

12 Zhou, J., Bao, L., Chang, L. et al. (2012). Beta-xylosidase activity of a GH3 glucosidase/xylosidase from yak rumen metagenome promotes the enzymatic degradation of hemicellulosic xylans. *Lett. Appl. Microbiol.* 54 (2): 79–87.

13 Pengthaisong, S., Hua, Y., and Cairns, J.R. (2021). Structural basis for transglycosylation in glycoside hydrolase family GH116 glycosynthases. *Arch. Biochem. Biophys.* 706: 108924.

14 Sangrila, S. and Maiti, T.K. (2013). Cellulase production by bacteria: a review. *Br. Microbiol. Res. J.* 3 (3): 235–258.

15 Srivastava, N., Rathour, R., Jha, S. et al. (2019). Microbial beta glucosidase enzymes: recent advances in biomass conversation for biofuels application. *Biomolecules* 9 (6): 220.

16 Singh, A., Bajar, S., Devi, A., and Pant, D. (2021). An overview on the recent developments in fungal cellulase production and their industrial applications. *Bioresour. Technol. Rep.* 14: 100652.

17 Sukumaran, R.K., Singhania, R.R., and Pandey, A. (2005). Microbial cellulases-production, applications and challenges. *JSIR* 64 (11): 832–844.

18 Minic, Z. (2008). Physiological roles of plant glycoside hydrolases. *Planta* 227 (4): 723–740.

19 Morant, A.V., Jørgensen, K., Jørgensen, C. et al. (2008). β-Glucosidases as detonators of plant chemical defense. *Phytochemistry* 69 (9): 1795–1813.

20 Wang, Y., Chantreau, M., Sibout, R., and Hawkins, S. (2013). Plant cell wall lignification and monolignol metabolism. *Front. Plant Sci.* 4: 220.

21 Fowler, T. and Brown, R.D. Jr., (1992). The bgI1 gene encoding extracellular β-glucosidase from *Trichoderma reesei* is required for rapid induction of the cellulase complex. *Mol. Microbiol.* 6 (21): 3225–3235.
22 Zhang, X., Chen, X., Li, S. et al. (2022). Mechanism of differential expression of β-glucosidase genes in functional microbial communities in response to carbon catabolite repression. *Biotechnol. Biofuels Bioprod.* 15 (1): 1–6.
23 Dvir, H., Harel, M., McCarthy, A.A. et al. (2003). X-ray structure of human acid-β-glucosidase, the defective enzyme in Gaucher disease. *EMBO Rep.* 4 (7): 704–709.
24 Pham, T.T. and Shah, N.P. (2009). Hydrolysis of isoflavone glycosides in soy milk by β-galactosidase and β-glucosidase. *J. Food Biochem.* 33 (1): 38–60.
25 Michlmayr, H. and Kneifel, W. (2014). β-Glucosidase activities of lactic acid bacteria: mechanisms, impact on fermented food and human health. *FEMS Microbiol. Lett.* 352 (1): 1–10.
26 Singh, G., Verma, A.K., and Kumar, V. (2016). Catalytic properties, functional attributes and industrial applications of β-glucosidases. *3 Biotech* 6 (1): 1–4.
27 Kuhad, R.C., Gupta, R., and Singh, A. (2011). Microbial cellulases and their industrial applications. *Enzyme Res.* 2: 280696.
28 Sarwan, J. and Bose, J.C. (2021). Importance of microbial cellulases and their industrial applications. *Ann. Rom. Soc. Cell Biol.* 25 (1): 3568–3575.
29 Yang, H., Cai, G., Lu, J., and Gómez, P.E. (2021). The production and application of enzymes related to the quality of fruit wine. *Crit. Rev. Food Sci. Nutr.* 61 (10): 1605–1615.
30 Gupta, A., Kumar, V., Dubey, A., and Verma, A.K. (2014). Kinetic characterization and effect of immobilized thermostable β-glucosidase in alginate gel beads on sugarcane juice. *Int. Scholar. Res. Not.* 2014: 178498.
31 Liang, Z., Fang, Z., Pai, A. et al. (2022). Glycosidically bound aroma precursors in fruits: a comprehensive review. *Crit. Rev. Food Sci. Nutr.* 62 (1): 215–243.
32 Espejo, F. (2021). Role of commercial enzymes in wine production: a critical review of recent research. *J. Food Sci. Technol.* 58 (1): 9–21.
33 Tharifkhan, S.A., Perumal, A.B., Elumalai, A. et al. (2021). Improvement of nutrient bioavailability in millets: emphasis on the application of enzymes. *J. Sci. Food Agric.* 101 (12): 4869–4878.
34 Davies, G. and Henrissat, B. (1995). Structures and mechanisms of glycosyl hydrolases. *Structure* 3 (9): 853–859.
35 Ketudat Cairns, J.R. and Esen, A. (2010). β-Glucosidases. *Cell. Mol. Life Sci.* 67 (20): 3389–3405.
36 Jenkins, J., Leggio, L.L., Harris, G., and Pickersgill, R. (1995). β-Glucosidase, β-galactosidase, family A cellulases, family F xylanases and two barley glycanases form a superfamily of enzymes wit 8-fold β/α architecture and with two conserved glutamates near the carboxy-terminal ends of β-strands four and seven. *FEBS Lett.* 362 (3): 281–285.
37 Carbohydrate active enzymes database (2023) Available online: www.cazy.org.
38 Henrissat, B. and Davies, G. (1997). Structural and sequence-based classification of glycoside hydrolases. *Curr. Opin. Struct. Biol.* 7 (5): 637–644.

39 Czjzek, M., Cicek, M., Zamboni, V. et al. (2000). The mechanism of substrate (aglycone) specificity in β-glucosidases is revealed by crystal structures of mutant maize β-glucosidase-DIMBOA,-DIMBOAGlc, and-dhurrin complexes. *Proc. Natl. Acad. Sci.* 97 (25): 13555–13560.

40 Nam, K.H., Sung, M.W., and Hwang, K.Y. (2010). Structural insights into the substrate recognition properties of β-glucosidase. *Biochem. Biophys. Res. Commun.* 391 (1): 1131–1135.

41 Zhang, C., Wang, X., Zhang, W. et al. (2017). Expression and characterization of a glucose-tolerant β-1,4-glucosidase with wide substrate specificity from *Cytophaga hutchinsonii. Appl. Microbiol. Biotechnol.* 101 (5): 1919–1926.

42 Babcock, G.D. and Esen, A. (1994). Substrate specificity of maize β-glucosidase. *Plant Sci.* 101 (1): 31–39.

43 Salgado, J.C., Meleiro, L.P., Carli, S., and Ward, R.J. (2018). Glucose tolerant and glucose stimulated β-glucosidases–a review. *Bioresour. Technol.* 267: 704–713.

44 Krisch, J., Takó, M., Papp, T., and Vágvölgyi, C. (2010). *Characteristics and Potential Use of* β*-Glucosidases From Zygomycetes*, vol. 2, 891–896. Formatex Research Center.

45 Hrmova, M., De Gori, R., Smith, B.J. et al. (2002). Structural basis for broad substrate specificity in higher plant β-D-glucan glucohydrolases. *Plant Cell* 14 (5): 1033–1052.

46 Verdoucq, L., Morinière, J., Bevan, D.R. et al. (2004). Structural determinants of substrate specificity in family 1 β-glucosidases: novel insights from the crystal structure of sorghum dhurrinase-1, a plant β-glucosidase with strict specificity, in complex with its natural substrate. *J. Biol. Chem.* 279 (30): 31796–31803.

47 Langston, J., Sheehy, N., and Xu, F. (2006). Substrate specificity of *Aspergillus oryzae* family 3 β-glucosidase. *Biochim. Biophys. Acta* 1764 (5): 972–978.

48 Henrissat, B. and Bairoch, A. (1996). Updating the sequence-based classification of glycosyl hydrolases. *Biochem. J.* 316 (Pt 2): 695.

49 Li, S., Yang, X., Yang, S. et al. (2012). Technology prospecting on enzymes: application, marketing and engineering. *Comput. Struct. Biotechnol. J.* 2 (3): e201209017.

50 Zang, X., Liu, M., Wang, H. et al. (2017). The distribution of active β-glucosidase-producing microbial communities in composting. *Can. J. Microbiol.* 63 (12): 998–1008.

51 Chakraborty, D., Sarkar, N., Biswas, I., and Jacob, S. (2020). Molecular aspects of prokaryotic and eukaryotic cellulases and their modulation for potential application in biofuel production. In: *Genetic and Metabolic Engineering for Improved Biofuel Production from Lignocellulosic Biomass* (ed. A. Kuila and V. Sharma), 81–95. Elsevier.

52 Singhania, R.R., Patel, A.K., Pandey, A., and Gnansounou, E. (2017). Genetic modification: a tool for enhancing beta-glucosidase production for biofuel application. *Bioresour. Technol.* 245: 1352–1361.

53 Singhania, R.R., Patel, A.K., Sukumaran, R.K. et al. (2013). Role and significance of beta-glucosidases in the hydrolysis of cellulose for bioethanol production. *Bioresour. Technol.* 127: 500–507.

54 Li, Y.K., Chir, J., and Chen, F.Y. (2001). Catalytic mechanism of a family 3 β-glucosidase and mutagenesis study on residue Asp-247. *Biochem. J.* 355 (3): 835–840.

55 Paal, K., Ito, M., and Withers, S.G. (2004). *Paenibacillus* sp. TS12 glucosylceramidase: kinetic studies of a novel sub-family of family 3 glycosidases and identification of the catalytic residues. *Biochem. J.* 378 (1): 141–149.

56 Litzinger, S., Fischer, S., Polzer, P. et al. (2010). Structural and kinetic analysis of *Bacillus subtilis N*-acetylglucosaminidase reveals a unique Asp-His dyad mechanism. *J. Biol. Chem.* 285 (46): 35675–35684.

57 Qi, M., Jun, H.S., and Forsberg, C.W. (2008). Cel9D, an atypical 1, 4-β-D-glucan glucohydrolase from *Fibrobacter succinogenes*: characteristics, catalytic residues, and synergistic interactions with other cellulases. *J. Bacteriol.* 190 (6): 1976–1984.

58 Meleiro, L.P., Salgado, J.C., Maldonado, R.F. et al. (2017). Engineering the GH1 β-glucosidase from *Humicola insolens*: insights on the stimulation of activity by glucose and xylose. *PLoS One* 12 (11): e0188254.

59 Coines, J., Raich, L., and Rovira, C. (2019). Modeling catalytic reaction mechanisms in glycoside hydrolases. *Curr. Opin. Chem. Biol.* 53: 183–191.

60 Sandhu, S.K., Mathur, A., Gupta, R. et al. (2018). Cellulosic biomass-hydrolyzing enzymes. In: *Waste to Wealth* (ed. R.R. Singhania, R.A. Agarwal, R.P. Kumar, and R.K. Sukumaran), 441–456. Singapore: Springer.

61 Sawant, S., Birhade, S., Anil, A. et al. (2016). Two-way dynamics in β-glucosidase catalysis. *J. Mol. Catal. B: Enzym.* 133: 161–166.

62 Li, Y.Y., Jiang, C.J., Wan, X.C. et al. (2005). Purification and partial characterization of β-glucosidase from fresh leaves of tea plants (*Camellia sinensis* (L.) O. Kuntze). *Acta Biochim. Biophys. Sin.* 37 (6): 363–370.

63 Pontoh, J. and Low, N.H. (2002). Purification and characterization of β-glucosidase from honey bees (*Apis mellifera*). *Insect Biochem. Mol. Biol.* 32 (6): 679–690.

64 Nigam, P.S. (2013). Microbial enzymes with special characteristics for biotechnological applications. *Biomolecules* 3 (3): 597–611.

65 Sundarram, A. and Murthy, T.P. (2014). α-amylase production and applications: a review. *J. Appl. Environ. Microbiol.* 2 (4): 166–175.

66 Aït, N., Creuzet, N., and Cattaneo, J. (1982). Properties of β-glucosidase purified from *Clostridium thermocellum*. *Microbiology* 128 (3): 569–577.

67 Kengen, S.W., Luesink, E.J., Stams, A.J., and Zehnder, A.J. (1993). Purification and characterization of an extremely thermostable β-glucosidase from the hyperthermophilic archaeon *Pyrococcus furiosus*. *Eur. J. Biochem.* 213 (1): 305–312.

68 Paavilainen, S., Hellman, J., and Korpela, T. (1993). Purification, characterization, gene cloning, and sequencing of a new beta-glucosidase from *Bacillus circulans* subsp. alkalophilus. *Appl. Environ. Microbiol.* 59 (3): 927–932.

69 Okamoto, K., Nakano, H., Yatake, T. et al. (2000). Purification and some properties of a β-glucosidase from *Flavobacterium johnsonae*. *Biosci., Biotechnol., Biochem.* 64 (2): 333–340.

70 Spiridonov, N.A. and Wilson, D.B. (2001). Cloning and biochemical characterization of BglC, a β-glucosidase from the cellulolytic actinomycete *Thermobifida fusca*. *Curr. Microbiol.* 42 (4): 295–301.

71 Cristóbal, H.A., Schmidt, A., Kothe, E. et al. (2009). Characterization of inducible cold-active β-glucosidases from the psychrotolerant bacterium *Shewanella* sp. G5 isolated from a sub-Antarctic ecosystem. *Enzyme Microb. Technol.* 45 (6–7): 498–506.

72 Michlmayr, H., Schümann, C., Barreira Braz Da Silva, N.M. et al. (2010). Isolation and basic characterization of a β-glucosidase from a strain of *Lactobacillus brevis* isolated from a malolactic starter culture. *J. Appl. Microbiol.* 108 (2): 550–559.

73 Hong, M.R., Kim, Y.S., Park, C.S. et al. (2009). Characterization of a recombinant β-glucosidase from the thermophilic bacterium *Caldicellulosiruptor saccharolyticus*. *J. Biosci. Bioeng.* 108 (1): 36–40.

74 An, D.S., Cui, C.H., Lee, H.G. et al. (2010). Identification and characterization of a novel *Terrabacterginsenosidimutans* sp. nov. β-glucosidase that transforms ginsenoside Rb1 into the rare gypenosides XVII and LXXV. *Appl. Environ. Microbiol.* 76 (17): 5827–5836.

75 Pei, J., Pang, Q., Zhao, L. et al. (2012). *Thermoanaerobacterium thermosaccharolyticum* β-glucosidase: a glucose-tolerant enzyme with high specific activity for cellobiose. *Biotechnol. Biofuels* 5 (1): 1–10.

76 Du, J., Cui, C.H., Park, S.C. et al. (2014). Identification and characterization of a ginsenoside-transforming β-glucosidase from *Pseudonocardia* sp. Gsoil 1536 and its application for enhanced production of minor ginsenoside Rg2 (S). *PLoS One* 9 (6): e96914.

77 Chen, H., Hayn, M., and Esterbauer, H. (1992). Purification and characterization of two extracellular β-glucosidases from *Trichoderma reesei*. *Biochim. Biophys. Acta* 1121 (1–2): 54–60.

78 Pitson, S.M., Seviour, R.J., and McDougall, B.M. (1997). Purification and characterization of an extracellular β-glucosidase from the filamentous fungus *Acremonium persicinum* and its probable role in β-glucan degradation. *Enzyme Microb. Technol.* 21 (3): 182–190.

79 Riou, C., Salmon, J.M., Vallier, M.J. et al. (1998). Purification, characterization, and substrate specificity of a novel highly glucose-tolerant β-glucosidase from *Aspergillus oryzae*. *Appl. Environ. Microbiol.* 64 (10): 3607–3614.

80 Lin, J., Pillay, B., and Singh, S. (1999). Purification and biochemical characteristics of β-D-glucosidase from a thermophilic fungus, *Thermomyces lanuginosus*–SSBP. *Biotechnol. Appl. Biochem.* 30 (1): 81–87.

81 Parry, N.J., Beever, D.E., Owen, E. et al. (2001). Biochemical characterization and mechanism of action of a thermostable β-glucosidase purified from *Thermoascus aurantiacus*. *Biochem. J.* 353 (1): 117–127.

82 Venturi, L.L., de Lourdes, P.M., Terenzi, H.F. et al. (2002). Extracellular β-D-glucosidase from *Chaetomium thermophilum* var. *coprophilum*: production, purification and some biochemical properties. *J. Basic Microbiol.* 42 (1): 55–66.

83 Dhake, A.B. and Patil, M.B. (2005). Production of β-glucosidase by *Penicillium purpurogenum*. *Braz. J. Microbiol.* 36: 170–176.

84 Karnchanatat, A., Petsom, A., Sangvanich, P. et al. (2007). Purification and biochemical characterization of an extracellular β-glucosidase from the wood-decaying fungus *Daldinia eschscholzii* (Ehrenb.: Fr.) Rehm. *FEMS Microbiol. Lett.* 270 (1): 162–170.

85 Kaur, J., Chadha, B.S., Kumar, B.A. et al. (2007). Purification and characterization of β-glucosidase from *Melanocarpus* sp. MTCC 3922. *Electron. J. Biotechnol.* 10 (2): 260–270.

86 Chen, H.L., Chen, Y.C., Lu, M.Y. et al. (2012). A highly efficient β-glucosidase from the buffalo rumen fungus *Neocallimastix patriciarum* W5. *Biotechnol. Biofuels* 5 (1): 1–10.

87 Daroit, D.J., Simonetti, A., Hertz, P.F., and Brandelli, A. (2008). Purification and characterization of an extracellular β-glucosidase from *Monascus purpureus*. *J. Microbiol. Biotechnol.* 18 (5): 933–941.

88 Yoon, J.J., Kim, K.Y., and Cha, C.J. (2008). Purification and characterization of thermostable β-glucosidase from the brown-rot basidiomycete *Fomitopsis palustris* grown on microcrystalline cellulose. *J. Microbiol.* 46 (1): 51–55.

89 Jeya, M., Joo, A.R., Lee, K.M. et al. (2010). Characterization of β-glucosidase from a strain of *Penicillium purpurogenum* KJS506. *Appl. Microbiol. Biotechnol.* 86 (5): 1473–1484.

90 Choi, J.Y., Park, A.R., Kim, Y.J. et al. (2011). Purification and characterization of an extracellular β-glucosidase produced by *Phoma* sp. KCTC11825BP isolated from rotten mandarin peel. *J. Microbiol. Biotechnol.* 21 (5): 503–508.

91 Liu, D., Zhang, R., Yang, X. et al. (2012). Characterization of a thermostable β-glucosidase from *Aspergillus fumigatus* Z5, and its functional expression in *Pichia pastoris* X33. *Microb. Cell Fact.* 11 (1): 1–5.

92 Park, A.R., Hong, J.H., Kim, J.J., and Yoon, J.J. (2012). Biochemical characterization of an extracellular β-glucosidase from the fungus, *Penicillium italicum*, isolated from rotten citrus peel. *Mycobiology* 40 (3): 173–180.

93 Gao, Z., Van Hop, D., Yen, L.T. et al. (2012). The production of β-glucosidases by *Fusarium proliferatum* NBRC109045 isolated from *Vietnamese forest*. *AMB Express* 2 (1): 1–3.

94 Sørensen, A., Andersen, J.J., Ahring, B.K. et al. (2014). Screening of carbon sources for beta-glucosidase production by *Aspergillus saccharolyticus*. *Int. Biodeterior. Biodegrad.* 93: 78–83.

95 Sørensen, A., Lübeck, M., Lübeck, P.S., and Ahring, B.K. (2013). Fungal beta-glucosidases: a bottleneck in industrial use of lignocellulosic materials. *Biomolecules* 3 (3): 612–631.

96 Abdel-Naby, M.A., Osman, M.Y., and Abdel-Fattah, A.F. (1999). Purification and properties of three cellobiases from *Aspergillus niger* A20. *Appl. Biochem. Biotechnol.* 76 (1): 33–44.

97 Bhatti, H.N., Batool, S., and Afzal, N. (2013). Production and characterization of a novel β-glucosidase from *Fusarium solani*. *Int. J. Agric. Biol.* 15 (1): 140–144.

98 Mallerman, J., Papinutti, V.L., Levin, L.N. et al. (2014). *J. Microbiol. Biotechnol.* 25 (1): 57–65.

99 Dikshit, R. and Tallapragada, P. (2014). Partial purification and characterization of β-glucosidase from *Monascus sanguineus*. *Braz. Arch. Biol. Technol.* 58: 185–191.

100 Hernández-Guzmán, A., Flores-Martínez, A., Ponce-Noyola, P., and Villagómez-Castro, J.C. (2016). Purification and characterization of an extracellular β-glucosidase from *Sporothrix schenckii*. *FEBS Open Bio* 6 (11): 1067–1077.

101 Santos, F.R., Garcia, N.F., da Paz, M.F. et al. (2016). Production and characterization of β-glucosidase from *Gongronella butleri* by solid-state fermentation. *Afr. J. Biotechnol.* 15 (16): 633–641.

102 Olajuyigbe, F.M., Nlekerem, C.M., and Ogunyewo, O.A. (2016). Production and characterization of highly thermostable β-glucosidase during the biodegradation of methyl cellulose by *Fusarium oxysporum*. *Biochem. Res. Int.* 2016: 3978124.

103 Sethi, S., Datta, A., Gupta, B.L., and Gupta, S. (2013). Optimization of cellulase production from bacteria isolated from soil. *Int. Scholar. Res. Not.* 2013: 1–7.

104 Koike, S. and Kobayashi, Y. (2001). Development and use of competitive PCR assays for the rumen cellulolytic bacteria: *Fibrobacter succinogenes*, *Ruminococcus albus* and *Ruminococcus flavefaciens*. *FEMS Microbiol. Lett.* 204 (2): 361–366.

105 Flint, H.J. (1997). The rumen microbial ecosystem—some recent developments. *Trends Microbiol.* 5 (12): 483–488.

106 Wilhelm, R.C., Singh, R., Eltis, L.D., and Mohn, W.W. (2019). Bacterial contributions to delignification and lignocellulose degradation in forest soils with metagenomic and quantitative stable isotope probing. *ISME J.* 13 (2): 413–429.

107 Poulsen, H.V., Willink, F.W., and Ingvorsen, K. (2016). Aerobic and anaerobic cellulase production by *Cellulomonas uda*. *Arch. Microbiol.* 198 (8): 725–735.

108 Kane, S.D. and French, C.E. (2018). Characterisation of novel biomass degradation enzymes from the genome of *Cellulomonas fimi*. *Enzyme Microb. Technol.* 113: 9–17.

109 Thapa, S., Mishra, J., Arora, N. et al. (2020). Microbial cellulolytic enzymes: diversity and biotechnology with reference to lignocellulosic biomass degradation. *Rev. Environ. Sci. Bio/Technol.* 19 (3): 621–648.

110 Kour, D., Rana, K.L., Kaur, T. et al. (2019). Extremophiles for hydrolytic enzymes productions: biodiversity and potential biotechnological applications. *Bioprocess. Biomol. Prod.* 18: 321–372.

111 Ng, T.K., Ben-Bassat, A., and Zeikus, J.G. (1981). Ethanol production by thermophilic bacteria: fermentation of cellulosic substrates by cocultures of *Clostridium thermocellum* and *Clostridium thermohydrosulfuricum*. *Appl. Environ. Microbiol.* 41 (6): 1337–1343.

112 Wang, C.M., Shyu, C.L., Ho, S.P., and Chiou, S.H. (2008). Characterization of a novel thermophilic, cellulose-degrading bacterium *Paenibacillus* sp. strain B39. *Lett. Appl. Microbiol.* 47 (1): 46–53.

113 Juturu, V. and Wu, J.C. (2018). Production of high concentration of L-lactic acid from oil palm empty fruit bunch by thermophilic *Bacillus coagulans* JI12. *Biotechnol. Appl. Biochem.* 65 (2): 145–149.

114 Li, D., Li, X., Dang, W. et al. (2013). Characterization and application of an acidophilic and thermostable β-glucosidase from *Thermofilum pendens. J. Biosci. Bioeng.* 115 (5): 490–496.

115 Chen, A., Wang, D., Ji, R. et al. (2021). Structural and catalytic characterization of TsBGL, a β-glucosidase from *Thermofilum* sp. ex4484_79. *Front. Microbiol.* 12: 723678.

116 Bischof, R.H., Ramoni, J., and Seiboth, B. (2016). Cellulases and beyond: the first 70 years of the enzyme producer *Trichoderma reesei. Microb. Cell Fact.* 15 (1): 1–3.

117 Srivastava, N., Srivastava, M., Mishra, P.K. et al. (2018). Applications of fungal cellulases in biofuel production: advances and limitations. *Renewable Sustainable Energy Rev.* 82: 2379–2386.

118 Mahajan, C., Basotra, N., Singh, S. et al. (2016). *Malbranchea cinnamomea*: a thermophilic fungal source of catalytically efficient lignocellulolytic glycosyl hydrolases and metal dependent enzymes. *Bioresour. Technol.* 200: 55–63.

119 Ahirwar, S., Soni, H., Prajapati, B.P., and Kango, N. (2017). Isolation and screening of thermophilic and thermotolerant fungi for production of hemicellulases from heated environments. *Mycology* 8 (3): 125–134.

120 Garbin, A.P., Garcia, N.F., Cavalheiro, G.F. et al. (2021). β-Glucosidase from thermophilic fungus *Thermoascus crustaceus*: production and industrial potential. *An. Acad. Bras. Ciênc.* 93.

121 Yadav, P.S., Shruthi, K., Prasad, B.S., and Chandra, M.S. (2016). Enhanced production of β-glucosidase by new strain *Aspergillus protuberus* on solid state fermentation in rice husk. *Int. J. Curr. Microbiol. App. Sci.* 5 (12): 551–564.

122 Gao, L., He, R., Zong, Z., and Zhang, D. (2018). A β-glucosidase hyperproducing strain, *Pencillium piceum*: novel characterization of lignocellulolytic enzyme systems and its application in biomass bioconversion. In: *Fungal Cellulolytic Enzymes* (ed. X. Fang and Y. Qu), 81–106. Singapore: Springer.

123 Chen, Z., Liu, Y., Liu, L. et al. (2019). Purification and characterization of a novel β-glucosidase from *Aspergillus flavus* and its application in saccharification of soybean meal. *Prep. Biochem. Biotechnol.* 49 (7): 671–678.

124 Kao, M.R., Yu, S.M., and Ho, T.H. (2021). Improvements of the productivity and saccharification efficiency of the cellulolytic β-glucosidase D2-BGL in *Pichia pastoris* via directed evolution. *Biotechnol. Biofuels* 14 (1): 1–4.

125 Martinez, D., Berka, R.M., Henrissat, B. et al. (2008). Genome sequencing and analysis of the biomass-degrading fungus *Trichoderma reesei* (syn. *Hypocreajecorina*). *Nat. Biotechnol.* 26 (5): 553–560.

126 Stutzenberger, F. (1990). Thermostable fungal β-glucosidases. *Lett. Appl. Microbiol.* 11 (4): 173–178.

127 Raza, F., Raza, N.A., Hameed, U. et al. (2011). Solid state fermentation for the production of β-glucosidase by co-culture of *Aspergillus niger* and *A. oryzae. Pak. J. Bot.* 43 (1): 75–83.

128 Baraldo Junior, A., Borges, D.G., Tardioli, P.W., and Farinas, C.S. (2014). Characterization of β-glucosidase produced by *Aspergillus niger* under solid-state fermentation and partially purified using MANAE-Agarose. *Biotechnol. Res. Int.* 2014 (9): 317092.

129 Pandey, A., Selvakumar, P., Soccol, C.R., and Nigam, P. (1999). Solid state fermentation for the production of industrial enzymes. *Curr. Sci.* 149–162.

130 Coradi, G.V., da Visitação, V.L., de Lima, E.A. et al. (2013). Comparing submerged and solid-state fermentation of agro-industrial residues for the production and characterization of lipase by *Trichoderma harzianum*. *Ann. Microbiol.* 63 (2): 533–540.

131 Brijwani, K. and Vadlani, P.V. (2011). Cellulolytic enzymes production via solid-state fermentation: effect of pretreatment methods on physicochemical characteristics of substrate. *Enzyme Res.* 2011 (5): 860134.

132 Kovács, K., Megyeri, L., Szakacs, G. et al. (2008). *Trichoderma atroviride* mutants with enhanced production of cellulase and β-glucosidase on pretreated willow. *Enzyme Microb. Technol.* 43 (1): 48–55.

133 Hölker, U. and Lenz, J. (2005). Solid-state fermentation—are there any biotechnological advantages? *Curr. Opin. Microbiol.* 8 (3): 301–306.

134 Viniegra-González, G., Favela-Torres, E., Aguilar, C.N. et al. (2003). Advantages of fungal enzyme production in solid state over liquid fermentation systems. *Biochem. Eng. J.* 13 (2–3): 157–167.

135 Subramaniyam, R. and Vimala, R. (2012). Solid state and submerged fermentation for the production of bioactive substances: a comparative study. *Int. J. Sci. Nat.* 3 (3): 480–486.

136 Acuña-Argüelles, M.E., Gutierrez-Rojas, M., Viniegra-González, G., and Favela-Torres, E. (1995). Production and properties of three pectinolytic activities produced by *Aspergillus niger* in submerged and solid-state fermentation. *Appl. Microbiol. Biotechnol.* 43 (5): 808–814.

137 Melikoglu, M., Lin, C.S., and Webb, C. (2013). Stepwise optimisation of enzyme production in solid state fermentation of waste bread pieces. *Food Bioprod. Process.* 91 (4): 638–646.

138 Herr, D. (1979). Secretion of cellulase and β-glucosidase by *Trichoderma viride* ITCC-1433 in submerged culture on different substrates. *Biotechnol. Bioeng.* 21 (8): 1361–1371.

139 Zhou, Q., Xu, J., Kou, Y. et al. (2012). Differential involvement of β-glucosidases from *Hypocrea jecorina* in rapid induction of cellulase genes by cellulose and cellobiose. *Eukaryotic Cell* 11 (11): 1371–1381.

140 Karaffa, L., Fekete, E., Gamauf, C. et al. (2006). D-Galactose induces cellulase gene expression in *Hypocrea jecorina* at low growth rates. *Microbiology* 152 (5): 1507–1514.

141 Roy, S.K., Raha, S.K., Dey, S.K., and Chakrabarty, S.L. (1988). Induction and catabolite repression of β-glucosidase synthesis in *Myceliophthora thermophila* D-14 (= ATCC 48104). *Appl. Environ. Microbiol.* 54 (8): 2152–2153.

142 Sirilun, S., Chaiyasut, C., Pengkumsri, N. et al. (2016). Screening and characterization of β-glucosidase production by *Saccharomyces cerevisiae*. *J. Appl. Pharm. Sci.* 6 (5): 029–035.

143 Gautam, S.P., Bundela, P.S., Pandey, A.K. et al. (2010). Optimization of the medium for the production of cellulase by the *Trichoderma viride* using submerged fermentation. *Int. J. Environ. Sci.* 1 (4): 656.

144 Ng, I.S., Li, C.W., Chan, S.P. et al. (2010). High-level production of a thermoacidophilic β-glucosidase from *Penicillium citrinum* YS40-5 by solid-state fermentation with rice bran. *Bioresour. Technol.* 101 (4): 1310–1317.

145 Vaithanomsat, P., Songpim, M., Malapant, T. et al. (2011). Production of β-glucosidase from a newly isolated *Aspergillus species* using response surface methodology. *Int. J. Microbiol.* 2011: 949252.

146 Abdella, A., Mazeed, T.E., El-Baz, A.F., and Yang, S.T. (2016). Production of β-glucosidase from wheat bran and glycerol by *Aspergillus niger* in stirred tank and rotating fibrous bed bioreactors. *Process Biochem.* 51 (10): 1331–1337.

147 Christakopoulos, P., Goodenough, P.W., Kekos, D. et al. (1994). Purification and characterisation of an extracellular β-glucosidase with transglycosylation and exo-glucosidase activities from *Fusarium oxysporum*. *Eur. J. Biochem.* 224 (2): 379–385.

148 Rajoka, M.I., Khan, S., Latif, F., and Shahid, R. (2004). Influence of carbon and nitrogen sources and temperature on hyperproduction of a thermotolerant β-glucosidase from synthetic medium by *Kluyveromyces marxianus*. *Appl. Biochem. Biotechnol.* 117 (2): 75–92.

149 Ling, H., Ge, J., Ping, W., and Xu, X. (2011). Fermentation optimization by response surface methodology for enhanced production of beta-glucosidase of *Aspergillus niger* HDF05. *Chin. J. Biotechnol.* 27 (3): 419–426.

150 Yang, Y. and Sha, M. (2019). *A Beginner's Guide to Bioprocess Modes–Batch, Fed-Batch, and Continuous Fermentation*. Enfield, CT: Eppendorf Inc.

151 Ghosh, B., Bhattacharya, D., and Mukhopadhyay, M. (2018). Use of fermentation technology for value added industrial research. *Princ. Appl. Ferment. Technol.* 1: 141–162.

152 Tabassum, R., Rajoka, M.I., and Malik, K.A. (1992). Use of chemostat for enhanced production of β-glucosidase by newly isolated anaerobic cellulolytic *Clostridium* strain RT9. *Appl. Biochem. Biotechnol.* 34 (1): 317–329.

153 Tsangalis, D., Ashton, J.F., McGill, A.E.J., and Shah, N.P. (2002). Enzymic transformation of isoflavone phytoestrogens in soymilk by β-glucosidase-producing bifidobacteria. *J. Food Sci.* 67 (8): 3104–3113.

154 Matsuura, R., Kishida, M., Konishi, R. et al. (2019). Metabolic engineering to improve 1, 5-diaminopentane production from cellobiose using β-glucosidase-secreting *Corynebacterium glutamicum*. *Biotechnol. Bioeng.* 116 (10): 2640–2651.

155 Dabhi, B.K., Vyas, R.V., and Shelat, H.N. (2014). Use of banana waste for the production of cellulolytic enzymes under solid substrate fermentation using bacterial consortium. *Int. J. Curr. Microbiol. App. Sci.* 3 (1): 337–346.

156 Liang, Y., Feng, Z., Yesuf, J., and Blackburn, J.W. (2010). Optimization of growth medium and enzyme assay conditions for crude cellulases produced by a novel thermophilic and cellulolytic bacterium, *Anoxybacillus* sp. 527. *Appl. Biochem. Biotechnol.* 160 (6): 1841–1852.

157 Ferreira, R.D., Azzoni, A.R., and Freitas, S. (2018). Techno-economic analysis of the industrial production of a low-cost enzyme using *E. coli*: the case of recombinant β-glucosidase. *Biotechnol. Biofuels* 11 (1): 1–3.

158 Chandra, M., Kalra, A., Sangwan, N.S. et al. (2009). Development of a mutant of *Trichoderma citrinoviride* for enhanced production of cellulases. *Bioresour. Technol.* 100 (4): 1659–1662.

159 Romero, M.D., Aguado, J., González, L., and Ladero, M. (1999). Cellulase production by *Neurospora crassa* on wheat straw. *Enzyme Microb. Technol.* 25 (3-5): 244–250.

160 Jang, H.D. and Chang, K.S. (2005). *Thermostable cellulases* from *Streptomyce* ssp.: scale-up production in a 50-l fermenter. *Biotechnol. Lett* 27 (4): 239–242.

161 Adsul, M.G., Ghule, J.E., Singh, R. et al. (2004). Polysaccharides from bagasse: applications in cellulase and xylanase production. *Carbohydr. Polym.* 57 (1): 67–72.

162 Kalogeris, E., Fountoukides, G., Kekos, D., and Macris, B.J. (1999). Design of a solid-state bioreactor for thermophilic microorganisms. *Bioresour. Technol.* 67 (3): 313–315.

163 Huang, C., Feng, Y., Patel, G. et al. (2021). Production, immobilization and characterization of beta-glucosidase for application in cellulose degradation from a novel *Aspergillus versicolor*. *Int. J. Biol. Macromol.* 177: 437–446.

164 Li, T., Chen, X.B., Chen, J.C. et al. (2014). Open and continuous fermentation: products, conditions and bioprocess economy. *Biotechnol. J.* 9 (12): 1503–1511.

165 Jensen, B., Nebelong, P., Olsen, J., and Reeslev, M. (2002). Enzyme production in continuous cultivation by the thermophilic fungus, *Thermomyces lanuginosus*. *Biotechnol. Lett* 24 (1): 41–45.

166 Ju, L.K. and Afolabi, O.A. (1999). Wastepaper hydrolysate as soluble inducing substrate for cellulase production in continuous culture of *Trichoderma reesei*. *Biotechnol. Progr.* 15 (1): 91–97.

167 Vaishnav, N., Singh, A., Adsul, M. et al. (2018). *Penicillium*: the next emerging champion for cellulase production. *Bioresour. Technol. Rep.* 2: 131–140.

168 Liang, C., Xu, Z., Wang, Q. et al. (2020). Improving β-glucosidase and xylanase production in a combination of waste substrate from domestic wastewater treatment system and agriculture residues. *Bioresour. Technol.* 318: 124019.

169 Chan, A.K., Wang, Y.Y., Ng, K.L. et al. (2012). Cloning and characterization of a novel cellobiase gene, cba3, encoding the first known β-glucosidase of glycoside hydrolase family 1 of *Cellulomonas biazotea*. *Gene.* 493 (1): 52–61.

170 Ramani, G., Meera, B., Vanitha, C. et al. (2015). Molecular cloning and expression of thermostable glucose-tolerant β-glucosidase of *Penicillium funiculosum* NCL1 in *Pichia pastoris* and its characterization. *J. Ind. Microbiol. Biotechnol.* 42 (4): 553–565.

171 Chang, J., Park, I.H., Lee, Y.S. et al. (2011). Cloning, expression, and characterization of β-glucosidase from *Exiguobacterium* sp. DAU5 and transglycosylation activity. *Biotechnol. Bioprocess Eng.* 16 (1): 97–106.

172 Yao, G., Wu, R., Kan, Q. et al. (2016). Production of a high-efficiency cellulase complex via β-glucosidase engineering in *Penicillium oxalicum. Biotechnol. Biofuels* 9 (1): 1–1.

173 Wang, L., Ridgway, D., Gu, T., and Moo-Young, M. (2005). Bioprocessing strategies to improve heterologous protein production in filamentous fungal fermentations. *Biotechnol. Adv.* 23 (2): 115–129.

174 Dan, S., Marton, I., Dekel, M. et al. (2008). Cloning, expression, characterization, and nucleophile identification of family 3, *Aspergillus niger* β-glucosidase. *J. Biol. Chem.* 275 (7): 4973–4980.

175 Xia, Y., Yang, L., and Xia, L. (2018). Combined strategy of transcription factor manipulation and β-glucosidase gene overexpression in *Trichoderma reesei* and its application in lignocellulose bioconversion. *J. Ind. Microbiol. Biotechnol.* 45 (9): 803–811.

176 Javanmard, A.S., Matin, M.M., and Bahrami, A.R. (2021). Polycistronic cellulase gene expression in *Pichia pastoris. Biomass Convers. Biorefin.* 13: 7151–7163.

177 Cao, L., Chen, R., Huang, X. et al. (2020). Engineering of β-glucosidase Bgl15 with simultaneously enhanced glucose tolerance and thermostability to improve its performance in high-solid cellulose hydrolysis. *J. Agric. Food. Chem.* 68 (19): 5391–5401.

178 Chamoli, S., Kumar, P., Navani, N.K., and Verma, A.K. (2016). Secretory expression, characterization and docking study of glucose-tolerant β-glucosidase from *B. subtilis. Int. J. Biol. Macromol.* 85: 425–433.

179 Yang, J., Wang, Q., Zhou, Y. et al. (2017). Engineering *T. naphthophila* β-glucosidase for enhanced synthesis of galactooligosaccharides by site-directed mutagenesis. *Biochem. Eng. J.* 127: 1–8.

180 Zhao, J.C., Mu, Y.L., Gu, X.Y. et al. (2022). Site-directed mutation of β-galactosidase from *Streptococcus thermophilus* for galactooligosaccharide-enriched yogurt making. *J. Dairy Sci.* 105 (2): 940–949.

181 Santos, C.A., Morais, M.A., Terrett, O.M. et al. (2019). An engineered GH1 β-glucosidase displays enhanced glucose tolerance and increased sugar release from lignocellulosic materials. *Sci. Rep.* 9 (1): 1–10.

182 Waeonukul, R., Kosugi, A., Prawitwong, P. et al. (2013). Novel cellulase recycling method using a combination of *Clostridium thermocellum cellulosomes* and *Thermoanaerobacter brockii* β-glucosidase. *Bioresour. Technol.* 130: 424–430.

183 Shen, Y., Zhang, Y., Ma, T. et al. (2008). Simultaneous saccharification and fermentation of acid-pretreated corncobs with a recombinant *Saccharomyces cerevisiae* expressing β-glucosidase. *Bioresour. Technol.* 99 (11): 5099–5103.

184 Xia, W., Xu, X., Qian, L. et al. (2016). Engineering a highly active thermophilic β-glucosidase to enhance its pH stability and saccharification performance. *Biotechnol. Biofuels* 9 (1): 1–2.

185 Adnan, M., Ma, X., Olsson, S. et al. (2022). Promoter regulation and genetic engineering strategies for enhanced cellulase expression in *Trichoderma reesei*. *Microbiol. Res.* 259: 127011.

186 Smekenov, I., Bakhtambayeva, M., Bissenbayev, K. et al. (2020). Heterologous secretory expression of β-glucosidase from *Thermoascus aurantiacus* in industrial *Saccharomyces cerevisiae* strains. *Braz. J. Microbiol.* 51 (1): 107–123.

187 Isaac, G.S. and Abu-Tahon, M.A. (2015). Enhanced alkaline cellulases production by the thermohalophilic *Aspergillus terreus* AUMC 10138 mutated by physical and chemical mutagens using corn stover as substrate. *Braz. J. Microbiol.* 46: 1269–1277.

188 Liu, G., Zhang, L., Wei, X. et al. (2013). Genomic and secretomic analyses reveal unique features of the lignocellulolytic enzyme system of *Penicillium decumbens*. *PLoS One* 8 (2): e55185.

189 Hu, J., Arantes, V., and Saddler, J.N. (2011). The enhancement of enzymatic hydrolysis of lignocellulosic substrates by the addition of accessory enzymes such as xylanase: is it an additive or synergistic effect? *Biotechnol. Biofuels* 4 (1): 1–4.

190 Kotaka, A., Bando, H., Kaya, M. et al. (2008). Direct ethanol production from barley β-glucan by sake yeast displaying *Aspergillus oryzae* β-glucosidase and endoglucanase. *J. Biosci. Bioeng.* 105 (6): 622–627.

191 Chi, Z., Chi, Z., Liu, G. et al. (2009). *Saccharomycopsis fibuligera* and its applications in biotechnology. *Biotechnol. Adv.* 27 (4): 423–431.

192 Treebupachatsakul, T., Nakazawa, H., Shinbo, H. et al. (2016). Heterologously expressed Aspergillus aculeatus β-glucosidase in *Saccharomyces cerevisiae* is a cost-effective alternative to commercial supplementation of β-glucosidase in industrial ethanol production using *Trichoderma reesei* cellulases. *J. Biosci. Bioeng.* 121 (1): 27–35.

193 Kabera, J.N., Semana, E., Mussa, A.R., and He, X. (2014). Plant secondary metabolites: biosynthesis, classification, function and pharmacological properties. *J. Pharm. Pharmacol.* 2 (7): 377–392.

194 Karimi, E., Oskoueian, E., Hendra, R. et al. (2012). Phenolic compounds characterization and biological activities of *Citrus aurantium* bloom. *Molecules* 17 (2): 1203–1218.

195 Servili, M., Sordini, B., Esposto, S. et al. (2013). Biological activities of phenolic compounds of extra virgin olive oil. *Antioxidants* 3 (1): 1–23.

196 Setchell, K.D., Brown, N.M., Zimmer-Nechemias, L. et al. (2002). Evidence for lack of absorption of soy isoflavone glycosides in humans, supporting the crucial role of intestinal metabolism for bioavailability. *Am. J. Clin. Nutr.* 76 (2): 447–453.

197 Day, A.J., DuPont, M.S., Ridley, S. et al. (1998). Deglycosylation of flavonoid and isoflavonoid glycosides by human small intestine and liver β-glucosidase activity. *FEBS Lett.* 436 (1): 71–75.

198 Ávila, M., Hidalgo, M., Sánchez-Moreno, C. et al. (2009). Bioconversion of anthocyanin glycosides by *Bifidobacteria* and *Lactobacillus*. *Food Res. Int.* 42 (10): 1453–1461.

199 Vasconcelos, A.T., Twiddy, D.R., Westby, A., and Reilly, P.J. (1990). Detoxification of cassava during gari preparation. *Int. J. Food Sci. Technol.* 25 (2): 198–203.

200 Gueguen, Y., Chemardin, P., Janbon, G. et al. (1998 Jan 1). Investigation of the β-glucosidases potentialities of yeast strains and application to bound aromatic terpenols liberation. In: *Studies in Organic Chemistry*, vol. 53 (ed. K. Kieslich, C.P. van der Beek, J.A.M. de Bont, and W.J.J. van den Tweel), 149–157. Elsevier.

201 Maduagwu, E.N. (1983). Differential effects on the cyanogenic glycoside content of fermenting cassava root pulp by β-glucosidase and microbial activities. *Toxicol. Lett.* 15 (4): 335–339.

202 Ugwuanyi, J.O., Harvey, L.M., and McNeil, B. (2007). Linamarase activities in *Bacillus* spp. responsible for thermophilic aerobic digestion of agricultural wastes for animal nutrition. *Waste Manage. (Oxford)* 27 (11): 1501–1508.

203 Etsuyankpa, M.B., Gimba, C.E., Agbaji, E.B. et al. (2015). Assessment of the effects of microbial fermentation on selected anti-nutrients in the products of four local cassava varieties from Niger state, Nigeria. *Am. J. Food Sci. Technol.* 3 (3): 89–96.

204 Elliston, A., Collins, S.R., Wilson, D.R. et al. (2013). High concentrations of cellulosic ethanol achieved by fed batch semi simultaneous saccharification and fermentation of waste-paper. *Bioresour. Technol.* 134: 117–126.

205 Prasad, D.Y., Heitmann, J.A., and Joyce, T.W. (1992). Enzyme deinking of black and white letterpress printed newsprint waste. *Prog. Pap. Recycl.* 1 (3): 21–30.

206 Pathak, P., Bhardwaj, N.K., and Singh, A.K. (2011). Optimization of chemical and enzymatic deinking of photocopier waste paper. *BioResources* 6 (1): 447–463.

207 Lee, C.K., Ibrahim, D., and Omar, I.C. (2013). Enzymatic deinking of various types of waste paper: efficiency and characteristics. *Process Biochem.* 48 (2): 299–305.

208 Elliston, A., Collins, S.R., Faulds, C.B. et al. (2014). Biorefining of waste paper biomass: increasing the concentration of glucose by optimising enzymatic hydrolysis. *Appl. Biochem. Biotechnol.* 172 (7): 3621–3634.

209 Sestelo, A.B., Poza, M., and Villa, T.G. (2004). β-Glucosidase activity in a *Lactobacillus plantarum* wine strain. *World J. Microbiol. Biotechnol.* 20 (6): 633–637.

210 Su, E., Xia, T., Gao, L. et al. (2010). Immobilization of β-glucosidase and its aroma-increasing effect on tea beverage. *Food Bioprod. Process.* 88 (2–3): 83–89.

211 Fan, G., Xu, Y., Zhang, X. et al. (2011). Characteristics of immobilised β-glucosidase and its effect on bound volatile compounds in orange juice. *Int. J. Food Sci. Technol.* 46 (11): 2312–2320.

212 Gunata, Z., Vallier, M.J., Sapis, J.C. et al. (1994). Enzymatic synthesis of monoterpenyl β-D-glucosides by various β-glucosidases. *Enzyme Microb. Technol.* 16 (12): 1055–1058.

213 González-Pombo, P., Fariña, L., Carrau, F. et al. (2011). A novel extracellular β-glucosidase from *Issatchenkia terricola*: Isolation, immobilization and application for aroma enhancement of white Muscat wine. *Process Biochem.* 46 (1): 385–389.

214 Hati, S., Vij, S., Singh, B.P., and Mandal, S. (2015). β-Glucosidase activity and bioconversion of isoflavones during fermentation of soymilk. *J. Sci. Food Agric.* 95 (1): 216–220.

215 Izumi, T., Piskula, M.K., Osawa, S. et al. (2000). Soy isoflavone aglycones are absorbed faster and in higher amounts than their glucosides in humans. *J. Nutr.* 130 (7): 1695–1699.

216 Rimbach, G., Boesch-Saadatmandi, C., Frank, J. et al. (2008). Dietary isoflavones in the prevention of cardiovascular disease–a molecular perspective. *Food Chem. Toxicol.* 46 (4): 1308–1319.

217 Liggins, J., Bluck, L.J.C., Runswick, S. et al. (2000). Daidzein and genistein contents of vegetables. *Br. J. Nutr.* 84 (5): 717–725.

218 Levis, S., Strickman-Stein, N., Doerge, D.R., and Krischer, J. (2010). Design and baseline characteristics of the soy phytoestrogens as replacement estrogen (SPARE) study—a clinical trial of the effects of soy isoflavones in menopausal women. *Contemp. Clin. Trials* 31 (4): 293–302.

219 Marazza, J.A., Garro, M.S., and de Giori, G.S. (2009). Aglycone production by *Lactobacillus rhamnosus* CRL981 during soymilk fermentation. *Food Microbiol.* 26 (3): 333–339.

220 Roitner, M., Schalkhammer, T., and Pittner, F. (1984). Characterisation of naringinase from *Aspergillusniger*. *Monatsh. Chem.* 115 (10): 1255–1267.

221 Maicas, S. and Mateo, J.J. (2005). Hydrolysis of terphenyl glycosides in grape juice and other fruit juices: a review. *Appl. Microbiol. Biotechnol.* 67 (3): 322–335.

222 Gunata, Y.Z., Bayonove, C.L., Baumes, R.L., and Cordonnier, R.E. (1985). The aroma of grapes I. Extraction and determination of free and glycosidically bound fractions of some grape aroma components. *J. Chromatogr. A* 331: 83–90.

223 Williams, P.J., Strauss, C.R., Wilson, B.W., and Massy-Westropp, R.A. (1982). Use of C18 reversed-phase liquid chromatography for the isolation of monoterpene glycosides and nor-isoprenoid precursors from grape juice and wines. *J. Chromatogr. A* 235 (2): 471–480.

224 Krammer, G., Winterhalter, P., Schwab, M., and Schreier, P. (1991). Glycosidically bound aroma compounds in the fruits of Prunus species: apricot (*P. armeniaca*, L.), peach (*P. persica*, L.), yellow plum (*P. domestica*, L. ssp. Syriaca). *J. Agric. Food. Chem.* 39 (4): 778–781.

225 Sakho, M., Chassagne, D., and Crouzet, J. (1997). African mango glycosidically bound volatile compounds. *J. Agric. Food. Chem.* 45 (3): 883–888.

226 Roscher, R., Herderich, M., Steffen, J.P. et al. (1996). 2,5-Dimethyl-4-hydroxy-3[2*H*]-furanone 6′ O-malonyl-β-D-glucopyranoside in strawberry fruits. *Phytochemistry* 43 (1): 155–159.

227 Mateo, J.J. and Jiménez, M. (2000). Monoterpenes in grape juice and wines. *J. Chromatogr. A* 881 (1–2): 557–567.

228 Gunata, Z., Bitteur, S., Brillouet, J.M. et al. (1988). Sequential enzymic hydrolysis of potentially aromatic glycosides from grape. *Carbohydr. Res.* 184: 139–149.

229 Schröder, C., Elleuche, S., Blank, S., and Antranikian, G. (2014). Characterization of a heat-active archaeal β-glucosidase from a hydrothermal spring metagenome. *Enzyme Microb. Technol.* 57: 48–54.

230 Bankova, E., Bakalova, N., Petrova, S., and Kolev, D. (2006). Enzymatic synthesis of oligosaccharides and alkylglycosides in water-organic media via transglycosylation of lactose. *Biotechnol. Biotechnol. Equip.* 20 (3): 114–119.

231 Opassiri, R., Hua, Y., Wara-Aswapati, O. et al. (2004). Beta-glucosidase, exo-beta-glucanase and pyridoxine transglucosylase activities of rice BGlu1. *Biochem. J.* 379 (1): 125–131.

232 Zhang, Z., Marquardt, R.R., Wang, G. et al. (1996). A simple model for predicting the response of chicks to dietary enzyme supplementation. *J. Anim. Sci.* 74 (2): 394–402.

22

Mining of Enzyme with Novel Activity Through Combination of Genomic Information and Traditional Biochemical Approach

Yutaka Kawarabayasi

National Institute of Advanced Industrial Science and Technology (AIST), Tsukuba, Ibaraki 305-8566, Japan

22.1 Introduction

Following the first determination of the entire genomic sequence of one organism, *Mycoplasma genitalium* [1], a large number of entire genomic sequences of many different organisms, from humans to microorganisms, have been determined. Genomic sequencing was expected to provide complete information for recognizing the entire feature of the target organism. Even though genomic sequencing is a powerful approach to recognize one organism, this approach has two limitations. The first is that only comparison of protein or gene sequence is used for estimation of protein or gene function. Only predicted information on function of each protein is generated through this similarity comparison. Thus, estimation of protein or gene function by sequence similarity predicts incorrect function different from actual function experimentally determined. The second limitation is that experimentally analyzed information is required to estimate function of detected genes and their encoding proteins. Function of protein showing no similarity against data in database is generally impossible to be estimated in this approach. Therefore, some proportion of entire genes detected on genomic sequence is estimated just as hypothetical proteins.

The entire genomic sequence of a thermophilic Crenarchaeon, *Sulfolobus tokodaii*, isolated from a Japanese hot spring and optimally growing between 75 and 80 °C under aerobic conditions [2], was already determined 20 years ago [3]. It was observed from its entire sequence that this thermophilic Archaeon has approximately 2.7 Mbp long genome with 32.8% GC content, from which total 2826 genes were detected [3]. Among the genomic information of *S. tokodaii* approximately 30% of entire genes were estimated as hypothetical proteins [3]. Sugar metabolic pathway constructed from these detected genes remains many gaps, indicating that it is required to fill these gaps experimentally for recognizing the entire of this microorganism.

Polysaccharides, attached to cells, proteins, or lipids, play important roles for distinguishing oneself from others, changing inactive forms into active forms, and so

Microbial Enzymes: Production, Purification, and Industrial Applications, First Edition.
Edited by Dinesh Yadav, Pankaj Chowdhary, Gautam Anand, and Rajarshi Kumar Gaur.

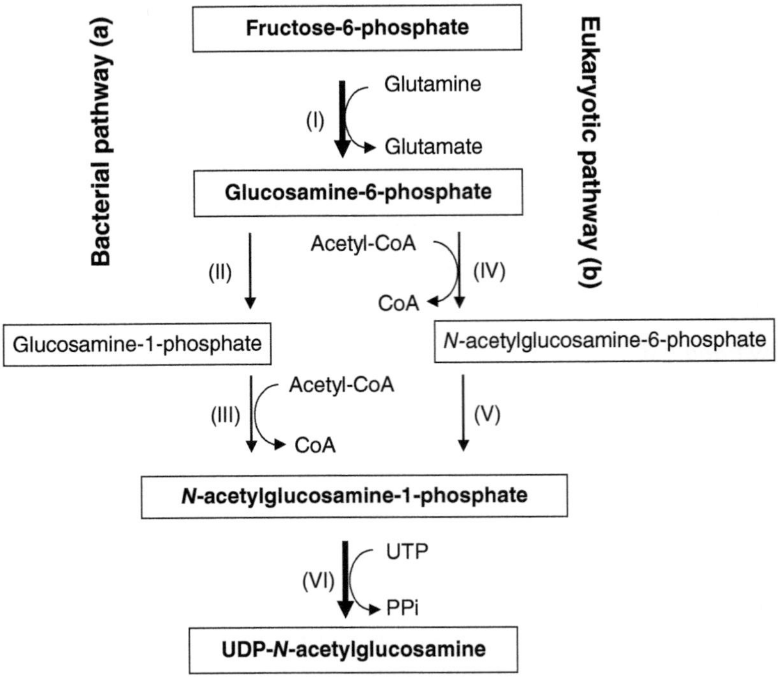

Figure 22.1 The previously identified UDP-*N*-acetylglucosamine biosynthetic pathway from fructose-6-phosphate in bacteria (a) and eukaryotes (b). The common pathway is shown by bold arrows, and the steps specific to bacteria or eukaryotes are shown by normal arrows. The enzymes abbreviated by Roman numerals are as follows: (I) glutamine:fructose-6-phosphate amidotransferase, (II) phosphoglucosamine mutase, (III) glucosamine-1-phosphate acetyltransferase, (IV) glucosamine-6-phosphate acetyltransferase, (V) phosphoacetylglcosamine mutase, and (VI) *N*-acetylglucosamine-1-phosphate uridyltransferase.

on. The most fundamental position of polysaccharide is usually *N*-acetylglucosamine or *N*-acetylgalactosamine in most organisms. For the construction of polymer structure of saccharide molecule, sugar molecules must be combined with nucleotide portion, to provide nucleotide sugar molecules as substrates for sugar transfer enzyme. UDP-*N*-acetylglucosamine, active form of *N*-acetylglucosamine, is well known to be produced from fructose-6-phosphate through a four-step biosynthetic pathway (Figure 22.1). In this biosynthetic pathway, two independent pathways, eukaryotic and bacterial types, are well analyzed. In the eukaryotic type of this biosynthetic pathway, glucosamine-6-phosphate converts to *N*-acetylglucosamine-6-phosphate before the transposition of phosphate portion (Figure 22.1b). Conversely, in the bacterial type of this pathway, phosphate position of glucose-6-phosphate is converted to the first position prior to performing its acetylation (Figure 22.1a).

The 401 amino acid long ST0452 protein was originally detected as glucose-1-phosphate thymidylyltransferase by similarity search [3]. Experimental analyses of the enzymatic activities of the ST0452 protein worked as a trigger for the identification of the actual UDP-*N*-acetylglucosamine and novel UDP-*N*-acetylgalactosamine biosynthetic pathway in *S. tokodaii*. In the following sections, I would like to indicate how to approach to identify biosynthetic pathways for two important nucleotide sugar molecules, UDP-*N*-acetylglucosamine and UDP-*N*-acetylgalactosamine, in an aerobic thermophilic Crenarchaeon, *S. tokodaii*.

22.2 Experimental Identification of UDP-*N*-acetylglucosamine Biosynthetic Pathway in *S. tokodaii*

The ST0452 gene product indicated 26–30% identity with RmlA protein in bacteria, which catalyzes the combining reaction of TTP and glucose-1-phosphate to produce TDP-glucose as the first step of the TDP-rhamnose biosynthetic pathway. The ST0452 protein is the longest protein among proteins estimated as sugar-1-phosphate nucleotidylyltransferase in genomic information of *S. tokodaii* with 170 amino acid long C-terminus region. Therefore, the ST0452 protein was expressed in *Escherichia coli* to produce the recombinant ST0452 protein. Thermostable ST0452 protein was successfully produced and purified ST0452 protein was used for analyses of its enzymatic activities [4].

22.2.1 Enzymatic Activities of the ST0452 Protein

At first, the expected enzymatic activity of the glucose-1-phosphate thymidylyltransferase was analyzed. As expected, glucose-1-phosphate thymidylyltransferase activity was experimentally detected [4]. Next, substrate specificity analyses of the ST0452 protein surprisingly indicated *N*-acetylglucosamine-1-phosphate uridyltransferase activity, which was 4.8 times higher than its glucose-1-phosphate thymidylyltransferase activity of the ST0452 protein. This *N*-acetylglucosamine-1-phosphate uridyltransferase activity is known to catalyze the last reaction, combining UTP and *N*-acetylglucosamine-1-phosphate to produce UDP-*N*-acetylglucosamine [4], of the UDP-*N*-acetylglucosamine biosynthetic pathway from fructose-6-phosphate. It is known that bacterial enzyme with *N*-acetylglucosamine-1-phosphate uridyltransferase activity usually also possesses glucosamine-1-phosphate acetyltransferase activity, which converts glucosamine-1-phosphate to *N*-acetylglucosamine-1-phosphate under the presence of acetyl-CoA (step III in Figure 22.1). Therefore, it was analyzed whether the ST0452 protein possesses this activity. This acetyltransferase activity was measured with a coupling reaction of the ST0452 sugar-1-phosphate nucleotidylyltransferase activity, since it can combine *N*-acetylglucosamine-1-phosphate but cannot catalyze glucosamine-1-phosphate. If glucosamine-1-phosphate and UTP are added as substrates in the reaction mixture and UDP-*N*-acetylglucosamine is detected, this observation indicates that the ST0452 protein possesses glucosamine-1-phosphate acetyltransferase activity. As shown in Figure 22.2, only when acetyl-CoA was added to the reaction mixture was the peak for UDP-*N*-acetylglucosamine detected, revealing that the ST0452 protein possesses this glucosamine-1-phosphate acetyltransferase activity. This observation

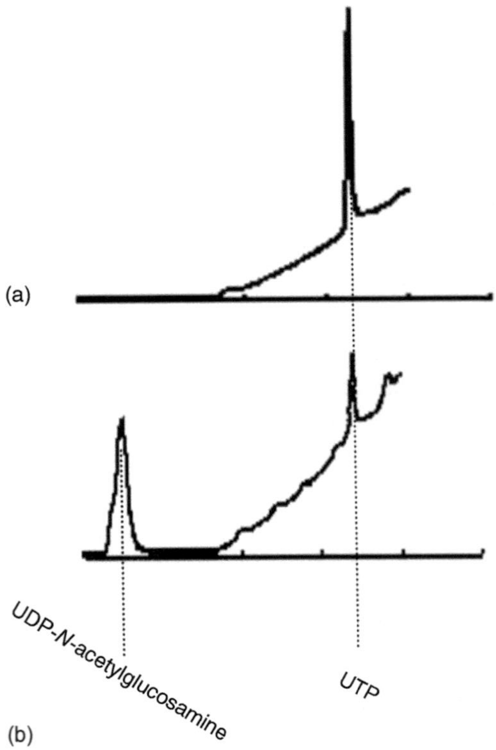

Figure 22.2 HPLC elution profile of the nucleotide sugar. HPLC elution profiles of the substrate UTP and UDP-*N*-acetylglucosamine product. The reaction was progressed at 80 °C for 10 minutes in the acetyltransferase reaction solution with 0.1 mM UTP and 2 mM glucosamine-1-phosphate without acetyl-CoA (a), with 0.1 mM UTP, 2 mM acetyl-CoA, and 2 mM glucosamine-1-phosphate (b). This result indicates that the ST0452 protein possesses glucosamine-1-phosphate acetyltransferase activity.

indicates that the ST0452 protein is actually a dual enzyme with sugar-1-phosphate uridyltransferase and amino-sugar-1-phosphate acetyltransferase activities [5].

22.2.2 Enzymatic Activities of Candidates for Glutamine:Fructose-6-Phosphate Amidotransferase and Phospho-sugar Mutase

To confirm the actual presence of bacterial-type UDP-*N*-acetylglucosamine biosynthetic pathway in *S. tokodaii,* two essential enzymatic activities were experimentally analyzed on candidate protein for each activity.

It is known that the first step of UDP-*N*-acetylglucosamine biosynthetic pathway is the conversion of fructose-6-phosphate to glucosamine-6-phosphate catalyzed with glutamine:fructose-6-phosphate amidotransferase enzyme (step I in Figure 22.1), and the second step of the bacterial-type UDP-*N*-acetylglucosamine biosynthetic pathway is the transfer of phosphate group on the glucosamine moiety from the sixth position to the first position catalyzed with phospho-sugar mutase (step II in Figure 22.1). To obtain evidence that the bacterial type UDP-*N*-acetylglucosamine biosynthetic pathway is actually working in *S. tokodaii*, experimental analyses of these two candidate enzymatic activities were performed.

The ST2186 protein was detected as a candidate for glutamine:fructose-6-phosphate amidotransferase in *S. tokodaii* genomic information. The ST2186 protein from the first ATG codon (ST2186L in Figure 22.5) was easily expressed as

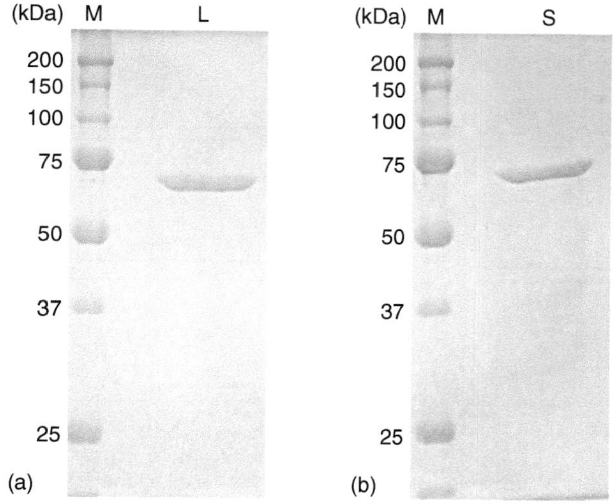

Figure 22.3 SDS-PAGE separation patterns of the purified recombinant ST2186 proteins. SDS-PAGE analyses of the ST2186 protein synthesized from the first ATG codon (ST2186L) and from the third TGT codon (ST2186S). The separated proteins were stained with Coomassie brilliant blue R-250. Lanes L, S, and M indicate the ST2186L protein, the ST2186S protein, and the standard molecular weight proteins.

thermostable protein in *E. coli* (Figure 22.3a). When its activity was analyzed, glutamate, a by-product of this reaction, was not detected, as shown in Figure 22.4a. Thus, amino acid sequence of the N-terminus of the ST2186 protein was carefully again compared with the N-terminus of known glutamine:fructose-6-phosphate amidotransferases. As shown in Figure 22.5, it was observed that the ST2186 protein possesses an additional three amino acid residues at the N-terminus when compared against known enzymes. Then, the ST2186 gene product translated from the fourth residue changed from Val to Met was expressed in *E. coli*. This short form of the ST2186 protein (ST2186S in Figure 22.5) was also clearly expressed as thermostable protein (Figure 22.3b) then it was used for activity analyses. After incubation with fructose-6-phosphate and glutamine, the ST2186S protein can produce glutamate (Figure 22.4b), indicating that the ST2186S protein catalyzes glutamine:fructose-6-phosphate amidotransferase activity [6]. This observation indicates two important information. The first is that the enzyme catalyzing the first step of the bacterial-type UDP-*N*-acetylglucosamine biosynthetic pathway is actually present in *S. tokodaii*. The second is the possibility of the novel type regulation of the enzymatic activity in *S. tokodaii*. It can be expected that the ST2186L protein is produced and stored in inactive form in *S. tokodaii*, and when UDP-*N*-acetylglucosamine molecule is required, the induced unidentified protease cleavages and removes the N-terminus additional three residues from the ST2186L protein for activation of this enzyme. These novel observations are obtained not from the genomic information but only from experimental analyses.

The ST0242 protein was detected as sole phospho-manno/phospho-gluco mutase (PMM/PGM) candidate by similarity search. This ST0242 protein was expressed

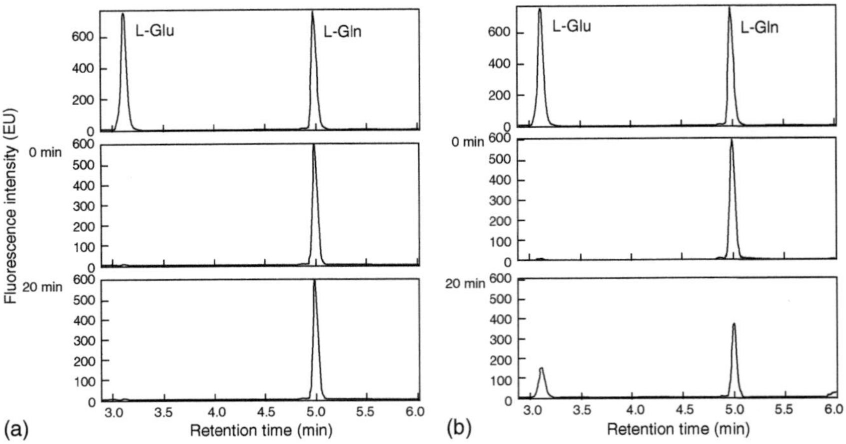

Figure 22.4 UPLC elution profile of glutamine and the products produced by the action of the two ST2186 proteins. The top panel of each figure indicates the elution profile of the glutamine and glutamic acid standard molecules, and the other panels indicate the elution profile of products formed by incubation with the ST2186L (a) and the ST2186S (b) proteins for the indicated periods at 80 °C.

```
ST2186n ATG TCT CTT GTG TGC GGA ATA ATT GGT ATA GTA TCA CTA AGG GAA
ST2186p  M   S   L   V   C   G   I   I   G   I   V   S   L   R   E  SKKLAEMTVSALKR
Ec_p                 M   C   G   I   V   G   A   I   A   Q   R   D  ---VAEILLEGLRR
Ec_n                ATG TGT GGA ATT GTT GGC GCG ATC GCG CAA CGT GAT
```

Figure 22.5 Sequence alignment of the N-terminal regions of the ST2186 protein and homologous *E. coli* protein. ST2186n and Ec_n indicate the nucleotide sequences corresponding to the N-terminal regions of the ST2186 protein and the GF6PAT protein from *E. coli* (locus, AE005174), respectively. ST2186p and Ec_p indicate the amino acid sequences of the N-terminal regions of the ST2186 protein and the glutamine:fructose-6-phosphate amidotransferase proteins from *E. coli* (locus, AE005604_9), respectively. The underlined codon is the start codon (ATG) used for the construction of the expression vector for the ST2186L protein. The double-underlined minor start codon (GTG) was used for the construction of the expression vector for the ST2186S protein after conversion to the ATG codon. Gaps are shown by dashes.

as thermostable protein in *E. coli*, and its expected PMM/PGM activities were observed (data not shown). As this protein was predicted as sole phospho-sugar mutase protein in genomic information of *S. tokoaii*, it was thought that the ST0242 protein can catalyze the phospho-glucosamine mutase reaction. Therefore, the phospho-glucosamine mutase activity was analyzed on this thermostable ST0242 protein. Because there was no equipment detectable of glucosamine-1-phosphate and glucosamine-6-phosphate and only a UV detector was able to be used in my laboratory at that time, for detection of the phospho-glucosamine mutase activity, the coupling reaction with the ST0452 protein was used. When glucosamine-6-phosphate is added as a substrate, even with the presence of acetyl-CoA, the ST0452 protein cannot produce UDP-*N*-acetylglucosamine. However, if phospho-glucosamine mutase activity is present in the same reaction mixture, produced glucosamine-1-phosphate is catalyzed with the ST0452 protein to

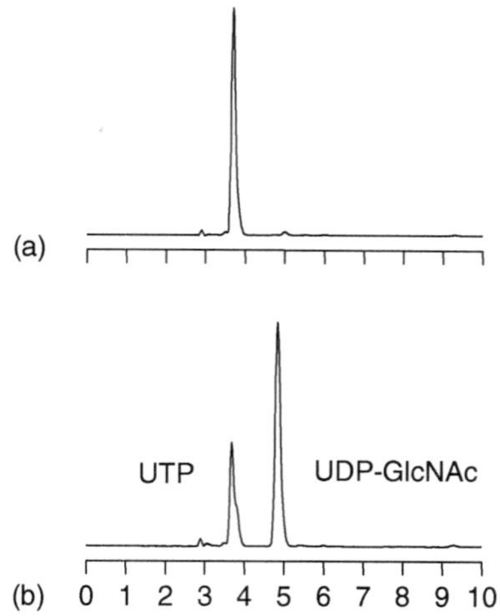

Figure 22.6 HPLC elution profile of the product by the ST0242 protein. HPLC elution profiles of UTP and UDP-*N*-acetlglucosamine molecules, a product of the coupling reaction with the ST0242 and ST0452 activity under the presence of UTP, glucosamine-6-phosphate, and acetyl-CoA. The top and bottom panels indicate the elution profile of the products formed before (a) and after five minutes incubation (b) with the ST0242 and ST0452 proteins at 80 °C. This result indicates that the ST0343 protein possesses phospo-glucosamine mutase activity.

UDP-*N*-acetylglucosamine, which is easily detected by HPLC. When the ST0242 protein was added into this reaction solution, actually UDP-*N*-acetylglucosamine was detected as shown in Figure 22.6. It indicates that the ST0242 protein can catalyze phospho-glucosamine mutase reaction, the third step of the bacterial-type UDP-*N*-acetylglucosamine biosynthetic pathway. The observation that the ST0242 protein can catalyze phospho-glucosamine mutase activity is able to be obtained only from experimental analyses. These observations obtained on the ST2186S and ST0242 proteins indicate the actual presence of the bacterial-type UDP-*N*-acetylglucosamine biosynthetic pathway in *S. tokodaii* and the importance of the experimental analyses combined with the genomic information.

22.2.3 UDP-*N*-acetylglucosamine Biosynthetic Pathway Determined from Experimentally Identified Enzymatic Activities in *S. tokodaii*

The experimental detection of enzymatic activities of the ST0452, ST2186S, and ST0242 proteins indicated that the actual presence of the bacterial-type UDP-*N*-acetylglucosamine biosynthetic pathway in a Crenarchaeon, *S. tokodaii*. This was the first identification of the complete UDP-*N*-acetylglucosamine biosynthetic pathway in one archaeal species [6].

The ST2186S protein, which catalyzes the first reaction in the bacterial-type UDP-*N*-acetylglucosamine biosynthetic pathway, was analyzed for its feedback regulation by midway products of this pathway. The ability of the feedback regulation of the midway products of this pathway, UDP-*N*-acetylglucosamine, *N*-acetylglucosamine-1-phosphate, glucosamine-1-phosphate, and glucosamine-6-phosphate, was investigated. No feedback regulation on the ST2186S protein by any of the three midway products, and the final product was observed [6]. This observation also supports the hypothesis that the UDP-*N*-acetylglucosamine biosynthetic pathway in *S. tokodaii* is regulated by the digestion of the additional three residues at the N-terminus of the ST2186 protein. It is indicated that experimental analyses are essential for the recognition of organisms; even genomic information is available.

22.3 Experimental Identification of UDP-*N*-acetylgalactosamine Biosynthetic Pathway in *S. tokodaii*

Recently, it was generally believed that UDP-*N*-acetylgalactosamine was produced from UDP-*N*-acetylglucosamine by UDP-*N*-acetylglucosamine 4-epimerase (c in Figure 22.7), which was identified from many organisms from microorganisms to Eukarya. There was no exception for this UDP-*N*-acetylgalactosamine biosynthetic pathway at the time of starting our research for the identification of the novel UDP-*N*-acetylgalactosamine biosynthetic pathway in *S. tokodaii*.

The substrate specificity analyses of the ST0452 protein indicate that this protein can catalyze two similar reactions: acetyltransferase activity for galactosamin-1-phosphate and uridyltransferase activity for *N*-acetylgalactosamine-1-phosphate, the last two reactions in the expected UDP-*N*-acetylgalactosamine biosynthetic pathway in *S. tokodaii* (steps VI and VII in Figure 22.7) [5]. In addition to these

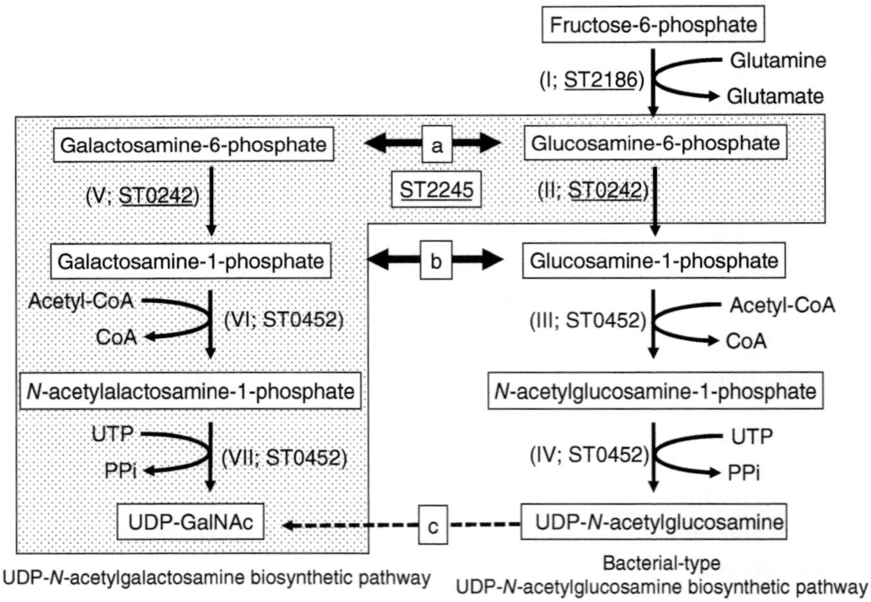

Figure 22.7 Outline of the confirmed UDP-*N*-acetylglucosamine and UDP-*N*-acetylgalactosamine biosynthetic pathways in *S. tokodaii*. The chemical names within boxes are sugar compounds in these metabolic pathways. The enzymatic activity required for each step is shown within parentheses as a roman numeral. Bold arrows labeled a or b are the predicted reactions required for the construction of the distinct UDP-*N*-acetylgalactosamine biosynthetic pathway and are analyzed in this work. The hatched arrow labeled c indicates the known UDP-*N*-acetylgalactosamine biosynthetic pathway. The hatched background indicates the UDP-*N*-acetylgalactosamine biosynthetic pathway present in *S. tokodaii* identified in this study. Each cofactor used for each reaction is shown alongside the reaction. The ST + four-digit number gene ID indicates the protein catalyzing the corresponding reaction identified from *S. tokodaii*; the underlined ID number indicates the proteins characterized in this study.

results, the candidate gene encoding UDP-*N*-acetylglucosamine 4-epimerase was not detected in the genomic information of *S. tokodaii*. These observations strongly suggest the presence of a novel and distinct UDP-*N*-acetylgalactosamine biosynthetic pathway in *S. tokodaii*. To analyze this possibility, experimental approaches were performed.

22.3.1 Identification of the Novel Enzymatic Activities for Phospho-glucosamine Epimerase in *S. tokodaii*

If the UDP-*N*-acetylgalactosamine biosynthetic pathway in *S. tokodaii* is entirely similar to the UDP-*N*-acetylglucosamine biosynthetic pathway, the starting substance as fructose-6-phosphate in UDP-*N*-acetylglucosamine biosynthetic pathway should be rare sugar-6-phosphate. The usage of the rare sugar-6-phosphate molecule as a starting substrate is unusual for producing an abundantly utilized sugar molecule *N*-acetylgalactosamine. Then, it was thought that this UDP-*N*-acetylgalactosamine biosynthetic pathway should not be a completely independent pathway and that some midway compound in the UDP-*N*-acetylglucosamine biosynthetic pathway should provide as substrate for the UDP-*N*-acetylgalactosamine biosynthetic pathway in *S. tokodaii*. Then, this hypothesis was examined.

There were two possibilities: one was converting glucosamine-1-phosphate to galactosamine-1-phosphate and the other was the construction of galactosamine-6-phosphate from glucosamine-6-phosphate. When glucosamine-1-phosphate was incubated with the extract of *S. tokodaii* cells, no new peak was detected on HPLC analysis (data not shown), indicating that glucosamine-1-phosphate was not used as the starting material of the UDP-*N*-acetylgalactosamine biosynthetic pathway in *S. tokodaii*. Then, glucosamine-6-phosphate was added to the reaction mixture as a substrate with an extract of *S. tokodaii* cells, after incubation an unknown peak was detected (line d in Figure 22.8). This observation indicated the presence of a novel protein capable of catalyzing glucosamine-6-phosphate in *S. tokodaii* cells. As the compound present in this unknown peak was directly indicated as galactosamine-6-phosphate, it is evident that galactosamine-6-phosphate was produced from glucosamine-6-phosphate in *S. tokodaii*. However, since galactosamine-6-phosphate is not commercially available, it was not possible to compare the elution position of standard galactosamine-6-phsphate with that of the product produced from glucosamine-6-phosphate by the *S. tokodaii* cell extract.

As shown in Figure 22.7, when galactosamine-6-phosphate is provided from glucosamine-6-phosphate, the mutase activity converting galactosamine-6-phosphate to galactosamine-1-phosphate is required to proceed with this distinct UDP-*N*-acetylgalactosamine biosynthetic pathway. As described in Section 22.2.2, the ST0242 protein was detected as the sole phospho-sugar mutase candidate in *S. tokodaii*. As galactosamine-1-phosphate was commercially available, galactosamine-1-phosphate was interacted with the ST0242 protein. The unknown peak was detected when galactosamine-1-phosphate was incubated with the ST0242

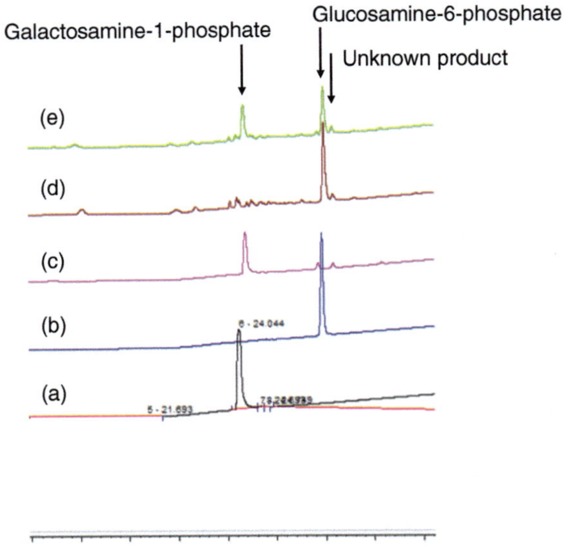

Figure 22.8 Elution profiles of standards and the phosphorylated amino-sugar molecules. Ion chromatography elution patterns of the two standard molecules, galactosamine-1-phosphate (a) and glucosamine-6-phosphate (b). Line (c) indicates the elution profile of the product obtained from galactosamine-1-phosphate following incubation with the ST0242 protein at 80 °C, and line (d) indicates the elution profile of the product obtained from glucosamine-6-phosphate following incubation with the *S. tokodaii* cell-free extract. Line (e) indicates the elution profile of the mixture of the two samples, (c) and (d). The arrows indicate the peaks for galactosamine-1-phosphate, glucosamine-6-phosphate, and unknown product as shown, respectively.

protein (line c in Figure 22.8). If this product peak could migrate to the same position as that of the unknown product peak formed from glucosamine-6-phosphate by the *S. tokodaii* cell extract, it should be evident that the unknown peak was galactosamine-6-phosphate.

As shown in lines c and d in Figure 22.8, two independent unknown peaks produced from glucosamine-6-phosphate and galactosamine-1-phosphate were migrated at almost the same position. To evaluate whether these two unknown products were exactly the same, these two reaction solutions were mixed and analyzed. As shown in line e in Figure 22.8, unknown products in the mixed solution were migrated at exactly the same position, revealing that the unknown product was galactosamine-6-phosphate.

This observation indicated that the uncharacterized novel phosphorylated amino sugar isomerase enzymatic activity converting glucosamine-6-phosphate to galactosamine-6-phosphate was present in the *S. tokodaii* cell extract. Thus, it was attempted to purify this uncharacterized protein (Figure 22.9a). The N-terminal amino acid sequence of the purified protein indicated that the ST2245 protein was the candidate protein with this novel activity. The ST2245 protein expressed in *E. coli* (Figure 22.9b) indicated the clear galactosamine-6-phosphate peak after reaction with glucosamine-6-phosphate (Figure 22.10), revealing that this was

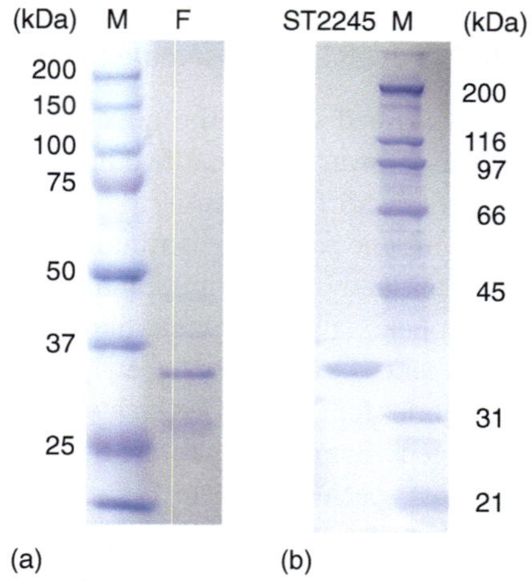

Figure 22.9 SDS-PAGE separation patterns of the purified fraction and the recombinant ST2245 protein. SDS-PAGE patterns of the final fraction (F) of purified *S. tokodaii* cell-free extract and the recombinant ST2245 protein (ST2245) stained with Coomassie brilliant blue R-250. Lane M indicates the standard molecular weight proteins.

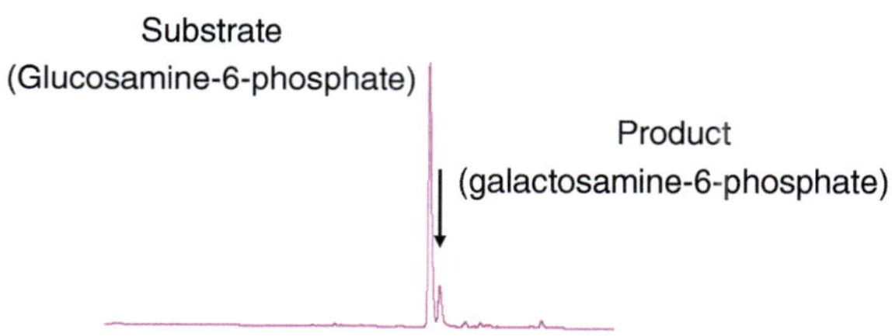

Figure 22.10 Elution profiles of the substrate and the phosphorylated amino-sugar molecules produced by the recombinant ST2245 protein. Ion chromatography elution profiles of the product from glucosamine-6-phosphate by the recombinant ST2245 protein. The arrow indicates the product (galactosamine-6-phosphate) peak produced from substrate (glucosamine-6-phosphate).

the first identification of glucosamine-6-phosphate/galactosamine-6-phosphate 4-epimerase activity [6].

22.3.2 Identification of the Novel Enzymatic Activities for Phospho-galactosamine Mutase in *S. tokodaii*

As shown in Section 22.2.2, it was indicated that the ST0242 possessed the phospho-galactosamine mutase activity (step V in Figure 22.7). The ST0242 protein was the sole phospho-sugar mutase candidate catalyzing all phospho-sugar mutase activities in *S. tokodaii*. To complete novel UDP-*N*-acetylgalactosamine biosynthetic pathway from glucosamine-6-phosphate in *S. tokodaii*, cooperative work of two novel enzymatic activities, glucosamine-6-phosphate/galactosamine-6-phosphate 4-epimerase and phospho-galactosamine mutase activities were essential. For the capability of usage of widely different substrates by the ST0242 protein, it is expected that wide flexibility is present at the reaction center of the ST0242 protein. To understand this flexibility, a three-dimensional structure of the ST0242 protein cocrystal with different substrates is required.

22.3.3 Distribution of the Novel and Distinct UDP-*N*-acetylgalactosamine Biosynthetic Pathway

As described earlier, the novel and distinct UDP-*N*-acetylgalactosamine biosynthetic pathway was identified in *S. tokodaii*. As this identified biosynthetic pathway is strictly different from the previously identified UDP-*N*-acetylgalactosamine biosynthetic pathway, distribution of this novel biosynthetic pathway was analyzed. For this analysis, distribution of the key enzymes in each pathway, glucosamine-6-phosphate/galactosamine-6-phosphate 4-epimerase, UDP-*N*-acetylglucosamine 4-epmerase, and UDP-*N*-acetylglucosamine/UDP-glucose 4-epimerase, were used as queries for similarity search of database. As shown in Table 22.1, it was indicated that gene homologous to the ST2245 gene were detected only within the Crenarchaeota species (Cre-1 in Table 22.1), and this homologous gene was not detected within the Euryarchaeota and bacteria. Euryarchaeota species (Eu in Table 22.1) and a part of bacteria (Bac-1 in Table 22.1) were found to possess a gene homologous to the UDP-*N*-acetylglucosamine 4-epimerase. All other bacterial species (Bac-2 in Table 22.1) possessed gene homologous to the UDP-*N*-acetylglucosamine/UDP-glucose 4-epimerase. This observation reveals that each microorganism species utilizes only one of these three systems, except for a part of Crenarchaeota (Cre-2 in Table 22.1). They were found not to possess any of the three homologous genes, revealing that these species could not form UDP-*N*-acetylgalactosamine via the common or distinct UDP-*N*-acetylgalactosamine biosynthetic pathway. It indicates the possible presence of another distinct UDP-*N*-acetylgalactosamine biosynthetic pathway in these Crenarchaeota species.

22.4 Conclusion and Future Perspectives

As whole genome sequencing of microorganisms now becomes easier than in the past, entire genomic information is easily obtained. However, function of each gene or encoded protein is estimated by a similarity search against a database constructed with functionally identified genes or proteins encoded. Genomic information generally provides important and useful information to every researcher. However, this approach for estimation of function or activity of each gene or gene product contains miss-estimation and impossibility of estimation when homologous information is not present in the database. Moreover, the novel function or activity previously not identified is never predicted by a similarity search.

To compensate this limitation of the present estimation of genomic information, the traditional biochemical approach should be powerful enough to identify novel function or activity of gene products without similarity. In this chapter, examples of identification of novel function or activity by experimental approach are described. A combination of genomic information and experimental approach should provide great success in your research.

Three novel enzymatic activities experimentally identified from *S. tokodaii* are registered under a new EC number: galactosamine-1-phosphate *N*-acetyltransferase as

Table 22.1 Distribution of three genes in each microorganism.

	Typical species detected	ST2245	UDP-GlcNAc 4-Ep[a)]	UDP-Glc 4-Ep[b)]
	Sulfolobus acidocaldarius	+	nd	nd
Cre-1	*Sulfolobus islandicus*	+	nd	nd
	Sulfolobus solfataricus	+	nd	nd
	Metallosphaera sedula	+	nd	nd
	Pyrococcus horikoshii	nd	+	nd
Eu	*Pyrococcus furiosus*	nd	+	nd
	Pyrococcus abyssi	nd	+	nd
	Methanococcus jannaschii	nd	+	nd
Bac-1	*Rhodothermus obamensis*	nd	+	nd
	Hydrogenobaculum sp. Y04AAS1	nd	nd	+
	Desulforudis audaxviator	nd	nd	+
	Chloroherpeton thalassium	nd	nd	+
Bac-2	*Anaerocellum thermophilum*	nd	nd	+
	Caldicellulosiruptor saccharolyticus	nd	nd	+
	Hydrogenivirga sp. 128-5-R1-1	nd	nd	+
	Dictyoglomus turgidum	nd	nd	+
	Desulfurococcus kamchatkensis	nd	nd	nd
Cre-2	*Caldivirga maquilingensis*	nd	nd	nd
	Aeropyrum pernix	nd	nd	nd
	Thermofilum pendens	nd	nd	nd

+ indicates presence, nd indicates not detected.

a) UDP-GlcNAc 4-epimerase.

b) UDP-GlcNAc/Glc 4-epimerase.

Cre-1 and Cre-2, Eu, plus Bac-1 and Bac-2 indicate Crenarchaeota, Euryarchaeota, and bacteria, respectively.

EC 2.3.1.276, D-glucosamine-6-phosphate 4-epimerase as EC 5.1.3.42, and phosphogalactosamine mutase as EC 5.4.2.13. These EC numbers evidence the greatness of the experimental approach.

References

1 Fraser, C.M., Gocayne, J.D., White, O. et al. (1995). The minimal gene complement of *Mycoplasma genitalium*. *Science* 270 (5235): 397–403.

2 Suzuki, T., Iwasaki, T., Uzawa, T. et al. (2002). *Sulfolobus tokodaii* sp. nov. (f. *Sulfolobus* sp. strain 7), a new member of the genus *Sulfolobus* isolated from Beppu Hot Springs, Japan. *Extremophiles* 6 (1): 39–44.

3 Kawarabayasi, Y., Hino, Y., Horikawa, H. et al. (2001). Complete genome sequence of an aerobic thermoacidophilic crenarchaeon, *Sulfolobus tokodaii* strain 7. *DNA Res.* 8 (4): 123–140.

4 Zhang, Z., Tsujimura, M., Akutsu, J. et al. (2005). Identification of an extremely thermostable enzyme with dual sugar-1-phosphate nucleotidylyltransferase activities from an acidothermophilic archaeon, *Sulfolobus tokodaii* strain 7. *J. Biol. Chem.* 280 (10): 9698–9705.

5 Zhang, Z., Akutsu, J., and Kawarabayasi, Y. (2010). Identification of novel acetyltransferase activity on the thermostable protein ST0452 from *Sulfolobus tokodaii* strain 7. *J. Bacteriol.* 192 (13): 3287–3293.

6 Dadashipour, M., Iwamoto, M., Hossain, M.M. et al. (2018). Identification of a direct biosynthetic pathway for UDP-*N*-acetylgalactosamine from glucosamine-6-phosphate in thermophilic crenarchaeon *Sulfolobus tokodaii*. *J. Bacteriol.* 200 (10): e00048–18.

23

Strategies for Discovery and Enhancement of Enzyme Function: Current Developments and Opportunities

Menaka D. Salam, Swati Tripathi, and Simran

Amity Institute of Microbial Technology, Amity University Uttar Pradesh, Sector 125, Noida, Uttar Pradesh 201301, India

23.1 Introduction

Enzymologists already have a wide variety of demands for discovering enzymes that can be used industrially for many different purposes. The usefulness of the enzyme depends on many parameters like the rate of activity of the enzyme, stability of the enzyme in different environmental conditions, specificity, and efficiency of the enzyme. Conventionally, identifying novel enzymes is done by cultivating and screening pure strains of organisms. This has been a standard and a powerful methodology. With the help of this methodology to date, many researchers have found a variety of organisms and enzymes produced by them. And it is done from both regular environments (e.g., soil, lake, and plants nearby) and rare environments (extreme conditions like alkaline lakes, Antarctic ice, and hot springs). But only a tiny portion of organisms can be cultured from the existing genomic diversity from any environment sample and that will limit the possible number of enzymes that can be deduced from the sample. The 16s rRNA gene sequencing showed that there still are many major taxonomic groups that are yet to be studied because they are uncultivable and therefore, remain undiscovered. This raises the need to use a new and more promising approach for the discovery of novel biocatalysts. Metagenomics is one of the emerging trends that has proven to be very effective and efficient for this purpose. Since uncultivable microorganisms can also be sequenced with the help of metagenomics, it broadens the spectrum of the new enzymes found in the bioprocessing industries [1].

Protein engineering procedures and advances in crystallography have permitted the manufacture of protein catalysts for targeted purposes and the development of desirable features since the late 1970s, when molecular biology was first introduced. Two questions must be considered before beginning any protein engineering project: "what template should we start with?" and "what tools from the biocatalyst toolbox should we use?". Engineered proteins are rapidly progressing from its initial stage

Microbial Enzymes: Production, Purification, and Industrial Applications, First Edition.
Edited by Dinesh Yadav, Pankaj Chowdhary, Gautam Anand, and Rajarshi Kumar Gaur.

of balanced design to its second stage of merged designing or guided evolution, then finally to its third stage of data-focused biocatalyst designing. Protein development is now driven by a trivial number of tailored archives with a limited set of options for codons and predictive techniques that optimize the trait in issue, rather than a wide library size [1].

23.2 Bioprospecting of Novel Microbial Extremozymes

There are many sources of living organisms for obtaining novel enzymes, e.g., plants, animals, annelids etc. However, microbial enzymes are greatly on demand in industries because of their advantages such as stability of enzymes, fast growth of microorganisms, easy availability, and easy manipulation of microbial cells through recombinant DNA technology. Microorganisms thriving in extremely harsh environments are the ones that are of interest with regards to their applications in industries. These types of microorganisms can be obtained from extreme environmental conditions such as hot springs, hydrothermal vents, hyperacidic lakes, mud volcanoes, hypersaline lakes, deserts and arid environments, nuclear contaminated sites, and acid mine drainage. In addition, microorganisms isolated from waste-contaminated sites have the ability to secrete enzymes such as laccases, esterases, dehalogenases, etc. which can degrade complex polymers that are natural or synthetic [2]. But the site of sampling should be selected where there is continuous disposal of the contaminant for a significant time period, for example, more than 30 years [3]. Scientists still need to explore microorganisms from these synthetic extreme environments [4]. However, the process is quite challenging as a vast majority of the microorganisms fall under the uncultivable category and it is practically difficult to isolate and cultivate them using conventional microbial growth media. Scientists have estimated that 7.3×10^{29} at genus level fall under the uncultivable group and 81% of these microorganisms inhabit the underground and hot-spring environments, marine sediments, hydrothermal vents, etc. [5]. Nevertheless, culture-based approach is still required to study structure and function of enzymes as it is a cheap and reliable technique [6]. Many extremophiles and extremozymes have been discovered and their possible functions, specifically in biorefinery, detergent, and food manufacturing have been studied [7]. The search for novel enzymes is not an easy task. Therefore, looking in rare and broad environments increases the potential to find novel enzymes.

The earth comprises three-fourth of water and is yet to be explored. So far, only a small portion of the oceans has been mapped, and explored for the microorganisms present in them, explored not just microbiologically but physically as well. Therefore, marine environments, oceans, and any other large water bodies are good sources for the search of novel microbes and/or novel enzymes. The Antarctica which lies at the south pole of the planet earth, for example, is very much unexplored to date. Therefore, there are higher chances of finding novel microbes and enzymes from Antarctica. Also, as it is an extreme environment, some extremophiles like cryophiles can be found in these areas.

Hot springs can be found naturally near hilly and snow-covered areas. They tend to appear near volcanos as well. Since they propose an extreme environment, some extremophiles like thermophiles can be found in these regions.

In wastewaters, such as industrial wastes and contaminated sites, microbes having tolerance to heavy metals and harmful organic pollutants are common [8]. Microbes tend to withstand heavy metals, while some can surprisingly digest them and convert them into another metal as in case of the bacterium *Cupriavidus metallidurans* [9]. This is a novel microbe that tends to digest heavy metals and convert them into gold. Also, some methanogens can be found in industrial samples as well [10]. Since these microbes are not completely studied and sequenced, there are chances of finding novel microbes and enzymes in their functioning.

Desert soil are not fully explored, specifically for their microbial community composition. Therefore, exploring desert soils for novel microbes and enzymes will help in the contribution of bioprospection of extremozymes since they show unique features like heating up to very high temperatures.

The focus at present should be to fill the technological gap between laboratories-based studies and actual development of extremozymes for use in industries. Novel technologies need to be adopted to overcome the challenges against the development of extremozymes and their applications for various industries. Table 23.1 shows some of the robust microbial enzymes studied from highly extreme environments and their potential industrial relevance.

23.2.1 Conventional Isolation Method and Screening

The method used for the isolation of microorganisms producing novel enzymes is the most critical tool for obtaining the desirable type of microorganisms. Screening of microorganisms for enzyme production requires a convenient, sensitive, and easy method to allow a maximum number of microorganisms to be screened. Also, the analytical methods for enzyme activity measurement are critical tools for purification, optimization, and application studies of the enzyme. Two important factors are generally considered in order to isolate microorganisms with a desired biotechnological property. These are (i) selection pressure and (ii) selection criteria. Selection pressure is an external factor that has to be applied in the growth medium to allow the proliferation of microorganisms that can resist the selection pressure. This can be further supported by enrichment culture technique to finally make the desired microorganisms acclimatize to the *in vitro* conditions. For example, addition of xenobiotic compounds as the selection pressure to isolate microorganisms that are able to degrade the compound from contaminated water and soil [19]. The other important factor that should be considered for the isolation of microorganisms with desirable traits is selection criteria. It should be exclusive to the particular biotechnological activity that is being studied, distinguishable result, and compatible with a large number of isolates [20]. The selection criteria comprise the primary and secondary screening methods. The primary method is rather a qualitative approach to check whether the microorganism is positive or negative for the desired biotechnological activity. For example, appearance of halo zone due to hydrolysis

Table 23.1 Microbial enzymes obtained from various extreme environments.

S. no.	Microorganism source	Enzyme	Properties	Applications (potential)	References
1.	*Chryseobacterium polytrichastri* ERMR1:04	Lipase	Active at a broad temperature range of 5–65 °C	Detergent formulations	[11]
2.	*Geobacillus thermoleovorans* DA2	Lipase	Thermophilic and alkalophilic lipase	Degreasing of leather	[12]
3.	*Anoxybacillus* sp. GXS-BL	α-Amylase	Thermophilic	Food industries, pharmaceutical applications, textile industry, detergent manufacturing, and bioenergy production	[13]
4.	*Staphylothermus marinus*	Pullulan- and cyclodextrin-degrading activities	Thermophilic 100 °C	Food industry	[14]
5.	Metagenomic library	Esterase	Thermophilic 60 °C, halotolerant, and resistant to heavy metals	Leather production, flavor improvement in the dairy commerce, oil biodegradation, and the formulations of pharmaceuticals and related chemicals	[15]
6.	*Pyrococcus yayanosii* strain CH1	Not yet reported	Resistant to high hydrostatic pressures 38 MPa	Food processing and antibiotic production	[16]
7.	*Sulfolobus solfataricus*	Transaminase	Thermophilic up to 70 °C	Pharmaceutical industries	[17]
8.	*Pyrococcus* sp.	Nitrilase	Thermophilic up to 90 °C	Pharmaceutical industries and food industries	[18]

of substrate. On the other hand, secondary screening method includes quantitative assays and the result depends on efficiency of the primary screening method. For example, detection of a metabolite by high-performance liquid chromatography (HPLC) and gas chromatography (GC). Development of improved and specific screening methods is a prerequisite for exploring microorganisms that can show novel biotechnological activities.

23.2.2 Metagenomic Approach for Enzyme Discovery

The term "*de novo*" enzyme discovery denotes the characterization of a completely new enzyme. This can be explained as the enzyme discovered should be a member of protein families and folds that are not already characterized functionally. Up to the present time, only culturable bacteria and fungi were used for the discovery of de novo enzymes. It is no news that only 0.1% of the entire population of bacteria and fungi can be cultured; there is a dire need to come up with another approach that broadens the spectrum.

According to Wyman et al. [21], more than 1,18,000 distinct protein families are not properly functionally characterized and 6688 families were classified into two specific and distinct taxonomic classes of microorganisms. Therefore, a bioinformatics pipeline was developed to identify the functionally unknown families through metagenomic profiling and it was also found that the function-unknown families were from the metagenomes of the Tara Oceans Expedition and Human Microbiome Project [21].

Utilizing reference-based enzyme discovery, which is a strategy of metagenomics study wherein the characterization of new functions found in the families is done with reference to previously characterized members, a great number of novel enzymes have been discovered. CreM, for example, is an ATP-dependent enzyme that preferentially installs diazo moieties within cremeomycin. CreM homologs are listed in databases as acyl-CoA ligases; however, CreM from *Streptomyces cremus* was discovered experimentally to use nitrites to catalyze the formation of the Nitrogen—Nitrogen bond [22].

Functional metagenomics based on clone activity screening was one of the first methods developed in the field of metagenomics. Clones are prepared using cosmid, fosmid, or artificial libraries of chromosomes in a manner that they possess preferred phenotypes. Some commonly used methods for the identification of activities of enzymes are colorimetric or fluorimetric readings, zones of clearance or inhibition, antibiotic resistance etc. Because the activity-guided workflow does not depend on sequence homology, it is particularly useful for discovering new enzymes. It has also been widely used in enzyme expansion, typically for industrially important enzyme families such as amylases, lipases, chitinases, and hemicellulases [23]. There have been a few disadvantages of the activity-guided method, e.g., some biosynthetic enzymes need specific substrates and cannot be detected by general assays. Therefore, they are unlikely to show any activity with general assays, which are formulated for primary metabolic enzymes. Other constraints include incompatibilities in codon usage bias, insufficient expression levels, and nutritional requirements in library hosts. Irrespective of all the disadvantages and limitations, activity-guided screenings are very popular and effective methodologies for enzyme discoveries that are sequence independent.

Advantage of activity-guided screening is that it leads to the identification of some novel protein folds or enzymes that can catalyze their reactions. They also tend to have well-established methods that can screen industrially crucial enzymes, e.g., lipases, cellulases, etc. [23]. It also guarantees that enzymes remain active and are expressed well in *Escherichia coli* [23].

The other strategy is PCR-based functional metagenomics which majorly depends on the amplification of the genes by utilizing degenerate primers, from environmental DNA coding for preferred enzyme. The method is highly specific and sensitive. PCR-dependent analysis of commonly found biosynthetic markers has been widely used for the detection of new natural products [23]. An example is an entirely novel class of calcium-dependent antibiotics which were identified by PCR-dependent screening of adenylation activities from metagenomics samples of soil [24].

However, a major disadvantage is that it is dependent on the homology of the sequence to already identified enzymes, in return limiting the identification of novel enzymes. Also, PCR-dependent procedures have integral amplification biased against GC-rich sequences and for low-abundant taxa. Functional amplicons that are short may not offer useful information regarding organism's taxonomy or coexistence with other genes. Some advantages of PCR-based screening are that it is sensitive to sequences that are of low abundance and that have sequence variations. On the other hand, shotgun metagenomic sequencing is an untargeted sequencing method, which includes library preparation, sequencing, assembly, and analysis. With the sequencing cost continuing to drop through the years, shotgun sequencing has the potential to advance as it is less biased and can cover a wide range of new sequence data. Some challenges of this method are that it requires qualitatively and quantitatively good sample of the environmental DNA from complex samples of the environment and depth of sequencing information. For detection purposes of biosynthetic gene clusters from rarely found organisms, some of the latest workflow like Samplix technology is used to provide solutions for handling lesser quantity of genetic material [23]. Also, in order to know the phenotypic characteristics, further cloning, and expression are prerequisite for the identification of novel enzymes.

Genome mining methods using heterologous expression and Mass Spectrometry-based molecular networking are establishing themselves as potent, complementary methods for screening bioactivity in the postgenomic era. The mentioned techniques have proven to be reliable for the quick dereplication of candidate compounds to minimize rediscovery. Even then novel natural products are being regularly identified through regular bioactivity-based screening methods. However, activity-guided and PCR-dependent metagenomics technology is a crucial part of the discovery and expansion of enzymes. Most metagenomics studies in the literature have found a variety of enzymes that trigger pre-resolved reactions. There are not many cases where a novel enzyme gets translated into a processor shown to regenerate or physicochemically very different from those previously reported. For example, the unique ability to hydrolyze C—O bonds and C—C bonds in polyaromatic hydrocarbons and heterocyclic compounds has been demonstrated in α/β hydrolases. They have been isolated from crude oil and industrial effluent-contaminated sites. Additionally, microbes growing at low temperatures have been shown to possess high enzymatic activity at temperatures up to 70 °C [25]. However, there are some challenges in facilitating the transformation from the enzyme acquisition phase with the help of its metagenomic analysis and ultimately to its end-user. Major technical issues include (i) reduced selected enzymes that perform well in industrial settings, (ii) lack of suitable test substrates, (iii) inadequate testing methods for abnormal enzymatic activity, (iv) malfunction of enzymes under nonoptimal environmental conditions, (v) the presence of inactive enzymes after exposure to the widely used host *E. coli*, (vi) lack of fidelity of bioinformatics pipeline analysis, and (vii) lack of reliable predictors of protein synthesis. In addition, the annotation errors (sequence/incompatibility) in the database are among the most challenging problems to be solved. For example, using metagenomics methods, a cold-tolerant esterase was reported, but later found to be annotated in the database as a transcriptional regulator of MarR family [26].

The provided data on the use of high-impact procedures in natural libraries has shown that the production of easily recognizable libraries presents a small challenge when searching for high-performance biotechnology enzyme activities and using simple substrates. In fact, a set of several hundred enzymes can be easily formed within a few months using a simple/single substrate. However, the rate of incidence, or the rate at which a good clone with the desired function occurs in all the clones tested, depends on the enzyme activity in the test and the substrates used. The other important potential drivers, such as metagenome source, DNA extraction method, cloning vector, host cells, test method, and test conditions, are additional factors that influence the success of the enzyme identification process. Common targets in metagenomic research are enzymes widely used in the biocatalysis and industry sectors (i.e., food, laundry, and biofuels), such as amylases, phosphatase, proteases, oxidoreductases, glycosyl hydrolases, and lipases/esterases [26]. Other industrial enzymes, such as nitrilases and transaminases, although industrial-related, have been briefly tested by metagenomic methods [27]. A substrate may cause bias in the screening of enzyme activities and the selection of the right substrate is highly recommended.

The recent evolution of high-density DNA sequencing technology has resulted in a significant reduction in sequencing costs, which has led to an explosion of *in silico* data production and a dramatic increase in information. The sequence of the next generation of enzyme identification in metagenomes is therefore becoming increasingly important to produce enzyme clusters because it provides faster and less costly enzyme detection technology.

23.2.3 Enhancement of Enzyme Function

Biocatalysis has the potential to provide a highly selective and resource-efficient synthesis process and is already being used in industry as a supplement to classical chemical catalysis, particularly in the chemical and pharmaceutical industries [28].

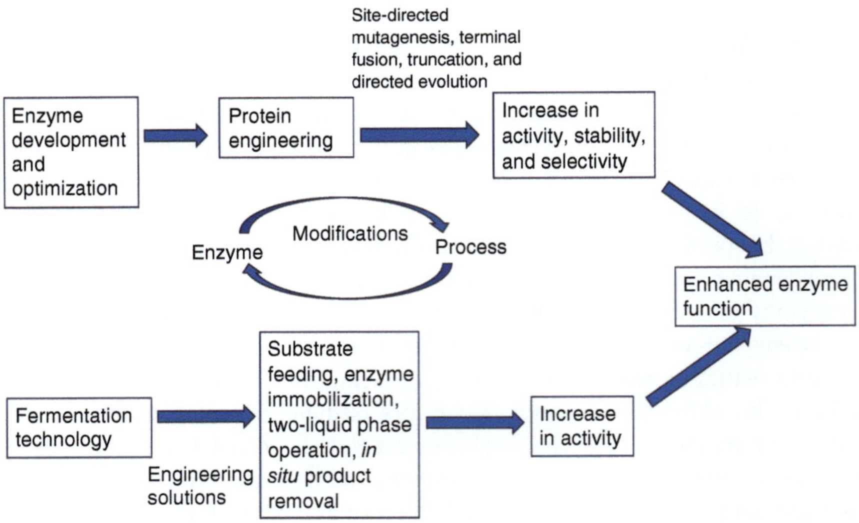

Figure 23.1 Flowchart showing the possible steps used for the enhancement of enzyme function.

The requirements for high catalyst productivity at increasing substrate concentrations are on demand for an economically and environmentally sustainable process. To improve and build a cost-effective biocatalyst, protein engineering and fermentation technology are employed. To enable the process to function successfully, the process component focuses on bringing engineering solutions such as substrate feeding, *in situ* product removal, enzyme immobilization, and two-liquid phase operation. Furthermore, the interplay between the two elements must be recognized, i.e., whether the enzyme should be adapted to fit the process or the process should be modified to fit the enzyme. A flowchart of the possible steps used for the enhancement of enzyme function is given in Figure 23.1. A biocatalytic process entails the creation of various subprocesses or systems, including (i) biocatalyst generation (fermentation and expression), (ii) biocatalyst development and optimization (protein engineering and formulation, e.g., immobilization), and (iii) downstream process (DSP) design. Changes to one part can have a good or negative impact on the others, as well as have an impact on the performance requirements. For instance, changes to the protein that may enhance the reaction can, however, have a negative impact on the ability to create the biocatalyst (e.g., expression or secretion). Opposing goals will almost always necessitate compromises in crucial question of how the various components (such as biocatalyst development or process development) should be addressed.

Protein engineering developments have made it possible to tailor the biocatalyst to the process. Once the enzyme's initial activity for the desired process has been detected, protein engineering can be used to increase desired features such as activity, stability, and selectivity. The commonly used strategies for protein engineering are site-directed mutagenesis, terminal fusion, truncation, and directed evolution. The mutant enzymes often have increased stability and catalytic efficiency. There have been multiple cases where new biocatalytic routes have been discovered by iterative rounds of mutagenesis and screening to significantly improve an existing enzyme [29, 30].

23.2.4 Protein Engineering Tools and Approaches

23.2.4.1 Iterative Saturation Mutagenesis

Iterative saturation mutagenesis (ISM) has been a well-liked method for developing new biocatalyst through directed evolution of functional enzymes. It greatly minimizes the labor and screening time required. The Cartesian representation of the 3D protein structure is employed by ISM. First, the protein is examined in terms of the impact that its constituent parts may have, i.e., by focusing on regions or positions that will be critical for improving a particular catalytic feature. The standards for choosing these locations depend on the catalytic characteristic that has to be improved. Saturation mutagenesis is employed to randomize each of the locations, leading to separate libraries of mutant enzymes that are then screened, with the simplest hit in each library being selected and sequenced. Each new cycle of ISM, on the opposite hand, maximizes the probabilities of recently introduced mutations having additive and/or cooperative effects in an exceedingly specific portion of the fitness landscape in protein sequence space [31].

It is evident that this method of applying evolutionary pressure differs significantly from the various error-prone (epPCR) cycles that are utilized in most directed evolution research. In each cycle, the latter treats the complete enzyme again, which implies that each one of its regions are considered again, whether or not only some places are literally crucial for fast producing favorable reactions. As a result, the higher mutants discovered by ISM are unlikely to be discovered by repeated rounds of epPCR. Because sequences are recombined, DNA shuffling cannot be anticipated to supply identical forms of hits as ISM. Individual residue saturation has been shown to provide unique functionality, enantioselectivity, and thermostability. Therefore, the main advantage of ISM is a superior quality mutant library for each round of evolution [32].

23.2.4.2 Combinatorial Active-site Saturation Testing

CASTing (combinatorial active-site saturation testing) is another useful technique for creating more active, thermostable, or selective mutants. CASTing is helpful because it can assess the synergistic effects of saturating tiny parts of the site of a protein. Random gene mutagenesis, production of mutant enzymes, and high-throughput screening are all a part of the method. The technique is fundamentally different from so-called rational design-supported site-specific mutagenesis since structural and mechanistic information is not required. With the goal of improving ligand binding, increasing catalytic activity, or modifying enantioselectivity, targeted libraries combining rational design and random mutagenesis at specific sites are used [31].

Because the screening requirement grows exponentially with each successive mutation, CASTing libraries can soon overwhelm screening capabilities. CASTing works best when there's already some activity toward the specified substrate; otherwise, betting on the precision of the screening assay, low levels of activity could also be overlooked. Despite their low activity, transitory mutants play a crucial role in the iterative process of developing a good catalyst. The temperature value (B-FIT) technique, which could be a version of CASTing, aims to extend thermostability by targeting organic compound locations with high crystallographic B-factors, which indicate great flexibility related to places within the crystal structure. This strategy improved lipase (lip A) [33].

23.2.4.3 Site-saturated Mutagenesis

Site-saturated mutagenesis targets on catalytically active site of the enzyme or on specific residues which are identified by searching through structural comparison and homology modeling methods for mutational variability. One amino acid at a chosen site will be replaced by all alternative amino acids in order to check the performance of each possible variant with regards to structural or functional features of the resulting variant. The resulting clones comprise a collection in which each one of them has a different codon in the position targeted [34]. This approach is simple and easy to implement and can be applied along with ISM and CAST [33]. Efforts to improve the method by reducing codon redundancy and screening have been done using a mixed set of primers [1]. Furthermore, library design tools have been developed in order to minimize the library size and simplify the downstream screening, e.g., Dynamic Management of Codon Compression (DYNAMCC) approach [35].

23.3 Computational Tools in Protein Engineering for Improved Enzymes

Protein engineering was founded based on the development of methods from molecular biology and genetic engineering. Initially, the dilemma of which residues to target and which replacements to introduce in protein engineering was tackled either through a rational approach or through random search. Expert knowledge is required for rational engineering, which is frequently aided by the increasing availability of protein structures. Directed evolution is a random strategy that introduces mutations mimicking natural evolution and requires high-throughput systems for screening protein variants in large libraries. The rational design requires detailed information on the protein and develop computer simulations in order to design new variants. In order to overcome the limitations of both approaches, a combination of the two methods which is referred to as semirational engineering can be used and the most promising sites can be determined to create mutagenesis and produce new variants with effective property [36].

Structural models and mathematical procedures have made computer tools an integral part of semirational engineering processes. Every year, numerous new tools with various purposes and uses are developed and released as a result of continuous attempts to introduce more advanced computational approaches to semirational engineering. Tools are available for each particular task; furthermore, the ensuing diversity of available tools can be daunting for both novice users and experienced practitioners. Computational approaches have recently made substantial advancements in protein engineering. The need to probe randomized sequence space is considerably reduced by computational design, making the path to novel biocatalysts much more efficient. Over the last few years, several significant methods of rational design have been introduced. SCHEMA, ProSAR, and ROSETTA are the most well-known platforms available [37, 38]. Rosetta suite can perform most of the tasks required in computational protein engineering. FuncLib webserver application can be used for semirational sequence design, molecular docking, and screening of variants, thus, improving the performance of Rosetta-based application [39].

Computational tools in protein engineering are increasingly on demand as these have potential to identify and create highly stable biocatalysts for sustainable application. The development of online tools and easy-to-use software has made researchers use the modern computational protein engineering methods. However, more advanced pipelines for accurate structure modeling and application analysis are required [39].

23.4 Conclusion and Future Prospects

Exploration of novel enzymes as well as producing new variants of existing ones through various techniques have grown tremendously in the last few decades. Yet, the demand for highly stable and effective enzymes, which can be applied in the industry is still continuing. This has driven the need to develop novel isolation techniques and methods to obtain new and improved variants of the enzymes. Exploration of microbes using conventional techniques needs careful selection of the sampling sites and also the cultivation methods. As the majority of the novel microorganisms are unculturable, adopting metagenomics approach is one such strategy to recover enzymes from rare and unculturable microorganisms. However, appropriate vectors that can express the foreign gene and specific high throughput screening methods of the clone libraries are required. Protein engineering is a promising approach, which has yielded an astounding array of genetic engineering and computational tools, as well as various breakthroughs in the modification and improvement of enzyme characteristics over the last three decades. The protein of interest can be efficiently mutated using machine learning to create new protein variants and thereafter screen them and experimentally tested based on their fitness scores. Thus, protein engineering using computational tools has made the process of obtaining efficient biocatalysts much easier and less time-consuming. Several of the technologies mentioned, such as targeted libraries, limited codons, and structure-guided consensus, have helped to develop biocatalysts to the point that they may be used in large-scale applications. Furthermore, redeveloping existing processes, introducing entirely new processes for existing products that utilize new, bio-derived feedstocks, and bringing new products made via new routes will all provide possibilities for biocatalytic process implementation. Protein engineering can be further improved by information from structural biology and biochemistry. Detailed knowledge of the three-dimensional structures of complex proteins and membrane proteins will help in understanding their mode of action and discovering new reaction mechanisms that will help in the precise prediction of active biocatalysts and in the rational design of protein engineering. Furthermore, the algorithms for modeling enzyme–substrate interactions need to be efficient and optimized in order to get improved variants of the enzymes.

References

1 Kille, S., Acevedo-Rocha, C.G., Parra, L.P. et al. (2013). Reducing codon redundancy and screening effort of combinatorial protein libraries created by saturation mutagenesis. *ACS Synth. Biol.* 2 (2): 83–92.

2 Mohanan, N., Montazer, Z., Sharma, P.K., and Levin, D.B. (2020). Microbial and enzymatic degradation of synthetic plastics. *Front. Microbiol.* 11: 580709.

3 Nademo, Z.M., Shibeshi, N.T., and Gemeda, M.T. (2023). Isolation and screening of low-density polyethylene (LDPE) bags degrading bacteria from Addis Ababa municipal solid waste disposal site “Koshe”. *Ann. Microbiol.* 73: 6.

4 Sibanda, T., Selvarajan, R., and Tekere, M. (2017). Synthetic extreme environments: overlooked sources of potential biotechnologically relevant microorganisms. *Microb. Biotechnol.* 10 (3): 570–585.

5 Lloyd, K.G., Steen, A.D., Ladau, J. et al. (2018). Phylogenetically novel uncultured microbial cells dominate Earth microbiomes. *mSystems* 3: e00055–e00018.

6 Sysoev, M., Grötzinger, S.W., Renn, D. et al. (2021). Bioprospecting of novel extremozymes from prokaryotes-the advent of culture-independent methods. *Front. Microbiol.* 12: 630013.

7 Zhu, D., Adebisi, W.A., Ahmad, F. et al. (2020). Recent development of extremophilic bacteria and their application in biorefinery. *Front. Bioeng. Biotechnol.* 8: 483.

8 Tarekegn, M.M., Salilih, F.Z., Ishetu, A.I., and Yildiz, F. (Reviewing editor) (2020). Microbes used as a tool for bioremediation of heavy metal from the environment. *Cogent Food Agric.* 6: 1.

9 Mergeay, M. and Van Houdt, R. (2021). *Cupriavidus metallidurans* CH34, a historical perspective on its discovery, characterization and metal resistance. *FEMS Microbiol. Ecol.* 97 (2): fiaa247.

10 Vítězová, M., Kohoutová, A., Vítěz, T. et al. (2020). Methanogenic microorganisms in industrial wastewater anaerobic treatment. *Processes* 8 (12): 1546.

11 Kumar, A., Mukhia, S., Kumar, N. et al. (2020). A broad temperature active lipase purified from a psychrotrophic bacterium of Sikkim Himalaya with potential application in detergent formulation. *Front. Bioeng. Biotechnol.* 8: 642.

12 Abol Fotouh, D.M., Bayoumi, R.A., and Hassan, M.A. (2016). Production of thermoalkaliphilic lipase from *Geobacillus thermoleovorans* DA2 and application in leather industry. *Enzyme Res.* 2016: 9034364.

13 Liao, S.M., Liang, G., Zhu, J. et al. (2019). Influence of calcium ions on the thermal characteristics of α-amylase from thermophilic *Anoxybacillus* sp. GXS-BL. *Protein Pept. Lett.* 26 (2): 148–157.

14 Li, X., Li, D., and Park, K.-H. (2013). An extremely thermostable amylopullulanase from *Staphylothermus marinus* displays both pullulan- and cyclodextrin-degrading activities. *Appl. Microbiol. Biotechnol.* 97 (12): 5359–5369.

15 Mohamed, Y., Ghazy, M., Sayed, A. et al. (2013). Isolation and characterization of a heavy metal-resistant, thermophilic esterase from a Red Sea Brine Pool. *Sci. Rep.* 3: 3358.

16 Michoud, G. and Jebbar, M. (2016). High hydrostatic pressure adaptive strategies in an obligate piezophile *Pyrococcus yayanosii*. *Sci. Rep.* 6: 27289.

17 Littlechild, J.A. (2015). Enzymes from extreme environments and their industrial applications. *Front. Bioeng. Biotechnol.* 3: 161.

18 Cabrera, M.Á. and Blamey, J.M. (2017). Cloning, overexpression, and characterization of a thermostable nitrilase from an Antarctic *Pyrococcus* sp. *Extremophiles* 21: 861–869.

19 Marchand, C., St-Arnaud, M., Hogland, W. et al. (2017). Petroleum biodegradation capacity of bacteria and fungi isolated from petroleum-contaminated soil. *Int. Biodeterior. Biodegrad.* 116: 48–57.

20 Olicón-Hernández, D.R., Camacho-Morales, R.L., Pozo, C. et al. (2019). Evaluation of diclofenac biodegradation by the ascomycete fungus *Penicillium oxalicum* at flask and bench bioreactor scales. *Sci. Total Environ.* 662: 607–614.

21 Wyman, S.K., Avila-Herrera, A., Nayfach, S., and Pollard, K.S. (2018). A most wanted list of conserved microbial protein families with no known domains. *PLoS One* 13 (10): e0205749.

22 Waldman, A.J. and Balskus, E.P. (2018). Discovery of a diazo-forming enzyme in cremeomycin biosynthesis. *J. Organomet. Chem.* 83 (14): 7539–7546.

23 Robinson, S.L., Piel, J., and Sunagawa, S. (2021). A roadmap for metagenomic enzyme discovery. *Nat. Prod. Rep.* 38 (11): 1994–2023.

24 Hover, B.M., Kim, S.H., Katz, M. et al. (2018). Culture-independent discovery of the malacidins as calcium-dependent antibiotics with activity against multidrug-resistant Gram-positive pathogens. *Nat. Microbiol.* 3 (4): 415–422.

25 Pandey, A., Dhakar, K., Sharma, A. et al. (2015). Thermophilic bacteria that tolerate a wide temperature and pH range colonize the Soldhar (95 °C) and Ringigad (80 °C) hot springs of Uttarakhand, India. *Ann. Microbiol.* 65: 809–816.

26 Ferrer, M., Martínez-Martínez, M., Bargiela, R. et al. (2016). Estimating the success of enzyme bioprospecting through metagenomics: current status and future trends. *Microb. Biotechnol.* 9 (1): 22–34.

27 Gong, J.S., Lu, Z.M., Li, H. et al. (2013). Metagenomic technology and genome mining: emerging areas for exploring novel nitrilases. *Appl. Microbiol. Biotechnol.* 97 (15): 6603–6611.

28 Bell, E.L., Finnigan, W., France, S.P. et al. (2021). Biocatalysis. *Nat. Rev. Methods Primers* 1: 46.

29 Yang, H., Li, J., Shin, H.D. et al. (2014). Molecular engineering of industrial enzymes: recent advances and future prospects. *Appl. Microbiol. Biotechnol.* 98 (1): 23–29.

30 Li, C., Zhang, R., Wang, J. et al. (2020). Protein engineering for improving and diversifying natural product biosynthesis. *Trends Biotechnol.* 38 (7): 729–744.

31 Reetz, M.T. and Carballeira, J.D. (2007). Iterative saturation mutagenesis (ISM) for rapid directed evolution of functional enzymes. *Nat. Protoc.* 2 (4): 891–903.

32 Sun, L., Ma, X., Zhang, B. et al. (2022). From polymerase engineering to semi-synthetic life: artificial expansion of the central dogma. *RSC Chem. Biol.* 3 (10): 1173–1197.

33 Valetti, F. and Gilardi, G. (2013). Improvement of biocatalysts for industrial and environmental purposes by saturation mutagenesis. *Biomolecules* 3 (4): 778–811.

34 Rodrigo, M.P.S. and Randall, J.W. (2012). Site saturation mutagenesis: methods and applications in protein engineering. *Biocatal. Agric. Biotechnol.* 1 (3): 181–189.

35 Pines, G., Pines, A., and Eckert, C.A. (2022). Highly efficient libraries design for saturation mutagenesis. *Synth. Biol.* 7 (1): ysac006.

36 Sequeiros Borja, C., Surpeta, B., and Brezovsky, J. (2021). Recent advances in user-friendly computational tools to engineer protein function. *Briefings Bioinf.* 22: 1–15.

37 Kuhlman, B. (2019). Designing protein structures and complexes with the molecular modeling program Rosetta. *J. Biolumin. Chemilumin.* 294 (50): 19436–19443.

38 Berland, M., Offmann, B., André, I. et al. (2014). A web-based tool for rational screening of mutants libraries using ProSAR. *Protein Eng. Des. Sel.* 27 (10): 375–381.

39 Scherer, M., Fleishman, S.J., Jones, P.R. et al. (2021). Computational enzyme engineering pipelines for optimized production of renewable chemicals. *Front. Bioeng. Biotechnol.* 9: 673005.

24

Promises of Systems Biology to Better Understand the Kinetics of Industrially Important Enzymes

Koel Mukherjee[1], Vinod Kumar Nigam[1], and Santhosh Pillai[2]

[1] *Birla Institute of Technology Mesra, Department of Bioengineering and Biotechnology, Ranchi, Jharkhand 835215, India*
[2] *Durban University of Technology, Faculty of Applied Sciences, Department of Biotechnology and Food Science, Durban 4000, South Africa*

24.1 Introduction

Over the last few decades, techniques have been developed with immense diversity to expand the range and difficulty of handling biological macromolecules relevant to bio-industries. The application of these tools and technologies shows their impacts as advantageous or detrimental to the betterment of life. However, advancements in experimental as well as computational techniques have transformed biological research many folds. The postgenomic period has led to the generation of enormous amounts of data at the genomics, proteomics, and transcriptomic level [1]. After the reveal of new techniques such as next-generation sequencing and microarray analysis [2], insightful investigations and interpretations can easily be made to identify the specific genes and their function-driven expression. Genome sequencing has also enhanced the option of studying proteins, as most of the functional information on the genes resides in the proteome. Proteomics deals with the complete set of proteins in an organism and the proteomics approach [3] includes the study of protein profiling, their expression, posttranslational modifications, and protein–protein interactions using analytical techniques such as MS and MALDI-ToF [4].

Interactions between molecules across cell types and their functional role are important with respect to understanding disease, food, and health issues. For instance, a group of researchers working on genomic region alignment, pathway context, and functionality of a structurally characterized enzyme of seven unidentified proteins from *Pelagibaca bermudensis* using a combination of theoretical and experimental approaches that can led to the screening of different proteins and their role in biochemical pathways [5]. The Enzyme Function Initiative aims to establish enzyme chemistry and catalytic action employing both experimental and computational methods. Moreover, system biology is a systematic, efficient, and interdisciplinary approach to biological science that can focus on a greater diversity of molecules or macromolecular complexes and microbes (Figure 24.1).

Microbial Enzymes: Production, Purification, and Industrial Applications, First Edition.
Edited by Dinesh Yadav, Pankaj Chowdhary, Gautam Anand, and Rajarshi Kumar Gaur.

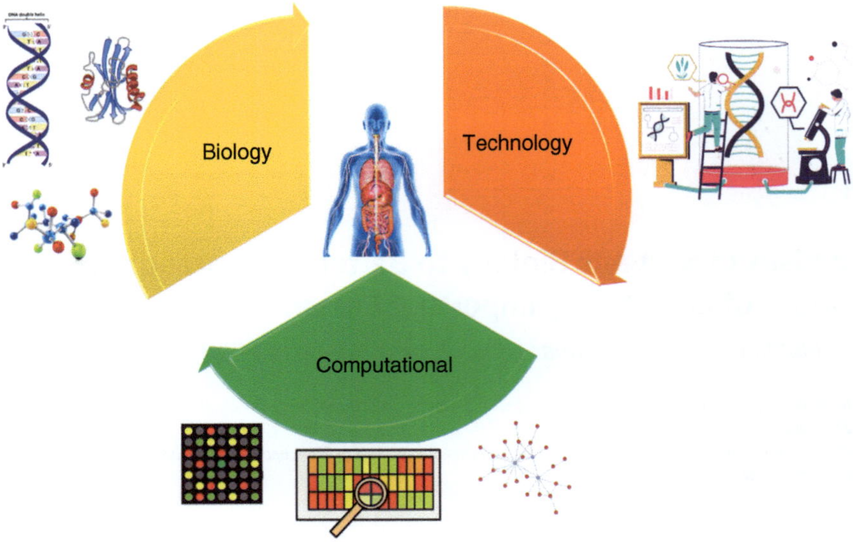

Figure 24.1 Overview of different sections of system biology.

In classical metabolic engineering, pathway enzymes or regulatory proteins are identified as the critical factors for cell metabolism, and then changes are made by recombinant DNA techniques to improve the efficiency and yield of an industrial fermentation product or some novel biochemical intermediates for further use in product development. However, this approach rarely reflects gene regulation, and therefore it is difficult to evaluate the selection of the target genes. Nevertheless, functional genomics with high-end technological applications intends for more effective metabolic engineering design and analysis, but still faces several challenges. Furthermore, our knowledge on the biosynthetic pathways is still limited, and it has been found that these pathway enzymes are primarily dependent on two factors: one is the microbial strain selection and the second is finding the specific genes from the environment through the metagenomics approach [6]. To overcome these challenges, "system biology" is now considered to explain its own hypothesis for every biochemical network in the cell and the cellular responses. In this regard, modern biotechnology industries have begun exploring the advantages of using new or modified enzymes in their production platforms. One such application of the system biology approach was to improve the yield of alcohol-based biofuels in yeast where bacterial xylose isomerase (EC 5.3.1.5), which transforms D-xylose into D-xylulose, was designed by directed evolution [7].

The last 30–40 years of research on biological systems have revealed many untold stories that portray the nature and depth of complex systems, but now, in the twenty-first century, the foremost challenge is to deal with those complexities. But it is clear that only one section or level of biology, that is a gene, protein, or metabolite, cannot expose the complexity of the biological system; rather, a fully integrated knowledge is required. Furthermore, until we have a comprehensive depiction of a cell and its multifaceted metabolic and regulatory networks and signal cascades, functional improvement and its application in bioprocess will not be complete [8].

Overall, systems biology provides a modeling framework that consists of a mathematical equation, graph models, and programming language that can provide insight into a cell system. The growing interest in systems biology is in models' execution and their analysis using the methods of computer science, such as formal analysis, model checking, static analysis, and runtime verification.

24.2 System Biology: An Integration of Interdisciplinary Approaches

The mechanism by which genetic or hereditary information flows from gene to protein within a cell is known as the "central dogma of molecular biology" and came to light only after the elucidation of DNA double helix structure by Watson and Crick. It was clear from the central dogma theory how unidirectional genetic information flows from one step to another: DNA to RNA and RNA to protein. It suggests that DNA conserves all information of protein synthesis, whereas RNA plays the role of messenger. Many decades ago, researchers started addressing individual protein structure, their expression analysis, and DNA mechanisms. But as time flew, it became very prominent that only a part of a cell cannot solve the puzzle, but it should involve everything, starting from DNA structure to gene location on a chromosome, posttranslational modification, slicing mechanism, protein–protein interactions, to expression. Thus, the word "systems biology" came to the fore. As known to everyone, it is an approach to distinguish the working nature of whole biological systems. Foundations of systems biology were achieved at the beginning of the twenty-first century and it requires a diversified range of experimental and computational analysis tools [9].

The main aim of system biology lies in the explanation and interpretation of biological properties that evolve from the normal processes of transcription and translation within a cell as well as their interactions with neighboring cells [10, 11]. For example, a single gene can be expressed for a particular individual, but the system biology approach attempts to address the whole biological properties that emerge from organisms, cells, metabolites, proteins, and genes [12]. Furthermore, system biology is an interdisciplinary approach that involves biology, technology, and computation (Figure 24.1). The aim is to find the explanation of biological systems with the help of tools, software, and assumptions [13]. It is the platform of skill, knowledge, and convention where all blend to understand biology at the system level. System biology also investigates the functionality of cells and dynamics of the organism for processing the consecutive networks and system properties. The mathematical tools help to retrieve, store, interpret, and integrate large data sets produced from genome projects. Due to the influence and usefulness of the World Wide Web nowadays, researchers are dealing with massive databases and data sets, thus lifting system biology experiments to a higher degree of completeness [14]. Overall, the vast knowledge from genomics, proteomics, transcriptomics, metabolomics, and the impact of advanced technologies have proven the existence and requirement of system biology in dissolving the boundaries of a subject or discipline [15].

24.2.1 Different Features of System Biology in Cell Metabolic System

The word "system" encodes the meaning of an assembly of elements comprising all the elements and fundamentals related to each other. In simple terms, every element should be interconnected with each other, and if they are not related, then they are not part of the system. For example, a cell of a living system works correspondingly where DNA, RNA, protein, and metabolites are interconnected. System biology focuses on the problem and defines the network of each element of the system. Cell composition and how individual organelles work do not shed light on the whole system's working principles. Similarly, the study of a single gene or protein cannot focus on all the aspects of system biology; instead, an understanding of their quantitative relationship and interactions can be portrayed.

24.2.2 Top-down and Bottom-up Approaches to System Biology

In system biology, the biological or chemical behavior of a cell can be categorized in two ways: bottom-up and top-down (Figure 24.2). The whole biological system is associated with many pathways, signals, processes, involvement of macromolecules and other components. Therefore, various approaches can be employed to interpret and analyze those data.

In bottom-up, the focus is given to the smallest part of the metabolic process. Mathematical models are designed and developed based on different physiological conditions. Tools and software are used to interpret the results combining specific information from the molecular to the genomic level. The whole model can

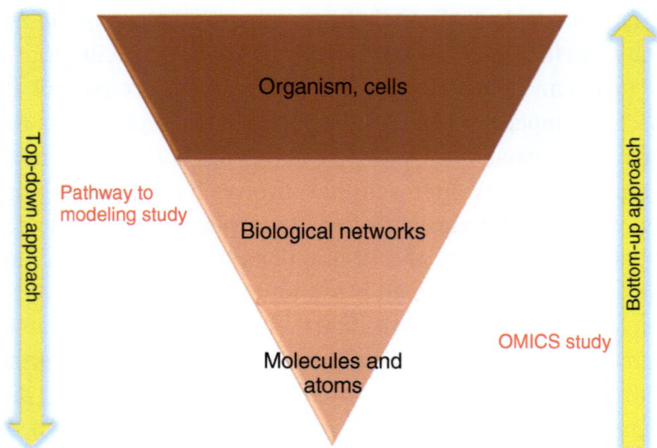

Figure 24.2 Schematic representation of top-down and bottom-up approaches of system biology.

represent the biological interactions happening inside the cell through four steps: (i) draft checking and remodeling, (ii) curation, (iii) develop model with the curated data, and (iv) validation [16].

In the top-down approach, the metabolic model is reconstructed based on the experimental data and methods. A wide range of "Omics" tools and software are used in this approach to reveal the interactions of molecules and their connectivity to others. Here, the genome level is the starting point, which covers the transcriptomics and finally flux-balanced metabolic pathways [17].

24.3 Data Integration and Model Construction in System Biology

In the last few decades, there has been a massive increase in information related to scientific communities in the field of system biology. Increasing evidence of such nature is emerging in the analysis of sequences of proteins, genomes, and gene expression data. As a result, the requirement for operative and competent computational tools to store, analyze, and interpret these data has been directed. System biology [18–21] involves the utilization of various techniques, which include informatics, applied mathematics, computer science, statistics, artificial intelligence, biochemistry as well as chemistry to solve the problems related to biology at the molecular level. The major research focus has been given on the fields like the alignment of sequence, finding the gene, assembly of genome, alignment of protein structure, assessment of protein structure, protein–protein interactions, analysis of gene expressions, and the modeling of evolution [22].

24.3.1 Pathway Databases and Resources

A signaling pathway can be defined as a chain of interactions between two points: the starting point (reception of a signal) and the ending point (response). A signal is reflected by an element against in which the cell reacts, which can be activated after binding to a specific receptor on the cell surface. In the signaling pathway, active molecules relay the signal from one to another by the deactivation–activation state until a target is attained. In a signaling pathway, a transcription factor is considered as a molecule that has significant involvement in the "central dogma." Such control is believed to be the response of the cells to the recognized signal.

A Pathway diagram is a flowchart that represents the steps of a pathway (reaction) in uni-/multidirectional ways and represents a graphical version providing information related to the complicatedness of biological systems. The pathway offers pictorial elucidations of every connection and their interactions among themselves. However, there are drawbacks with the majority of these biomolecule related pathway illustrations as they are generated with no proper format and guidelines to distinguish their composition or metabolites involved. As a result, they provide instructions only in short context on the accompanying legend, text, or abbreviation. Thus, they cannot be used as a collective resource with such limited information.

Process diagrams (flow diagrams) help in understanding the sequence of activities of a particular process. These flow diagrams provide information that is usually common with Petri nets, a biological pathway modeling approach [23, 24]. Petri nets is a rule-based approach and it is established on the hypothesis of modelling events flowing inside a system. In Petri nets, networks are composed of two types of nodes: places and transitions (generally denoted by circles or black rectangles, respectively). A strict prerequisite of Petri nets is that they are made of bipartite graphs, representing entity–process–entity recurrent structure. The Signaling Petri Net (SPN) algorithm first designs the dynamic model flow through an mEPN diagram, and after the refinement, the result can be made available for the network visualization and analysis software BioLayout *Express*^{3D} [25] (www.biolayout.org).

24.3.2 Servers and Tools

In the informatics science context, metabolic or gene networks of biological systems can be depicted as a distributed system. Therefore, they can be designed and modeled within the Timed Automata paradigm. However, software/tools designed to model this type of large distributed system often require a vast knowledge and implementation of informatics, computer science, mathematics, and codes that help biologists with metabolic pathway analysis and functional elucidation.

Moreover, biologists often lack expertise in understanding the input formats and files for analyzing big data. However, a number of software and tools (Table 24.1) are available for modeling complex networks of biochemical interactions [26, 27]. These tools can significantly give insight into the biological process and model the metabolic pathways using computational analysis. The elementary features of Flux Balance Analysis (FBA) software are the installation of operating systems, usability, functionality, and exchange of models and visualization of the network [28].

Analysis of Networks with Interactive Modeling (ANIMO; http://fmt.cs.utwente.nl/tools/animo) was built with the plan to provide biologists with easy access to control modeling with the formalism of timed automation by adding dynamicity to static representations of signaling networks [29, 30]. Here, continuous dynamics are handled by discrete approximations [31]. ANIMO uptakes wet-lab data, compares its model behavior, and analyzes in a user-friendly way; therefore, the complexity of timed automation is hidden under the hood. Generally, ANIMO acts as an application and is linked to **Cytoscape** [32], which is beforehand considered and developed for visualization and insight into biological networks. Additionally, a web interface for ANIMO has also been developed, which can be accessed from any web browser. Thus, the functions are not dependent on any software installation [33]. Many biomedical students follow courses in which ANIMO is taught in order to learn signaling networks, data formats, and to analyze and plan new experiments. From time to time, features of ANIMO have been constantly improved from the feedback of various stakeholders. Moreover, this tool is currently being used in biological studies to increase the understanding of cell differentiation and to provide information to represent the key interactions under investigation.

Table 24.1 Representation and description of pathways, software, and tools involved in system biology data procurement and analysis.

S. no.	Name	Description	URL
Pathway databases			
1.	KEGG Pathway	KEGG is a database resource platform to understand the high-level functions of biological systems and their applications in various sectors. This resource platform collects information from cells, organisms, and their ecosystem. The primary data are collected from genome sequencing and other high-throughput experimental technologies. The platform provides many analysis tools, web services, pathway information related to disease–drugs–biochemical reactions, etc.	KEGG: Kyoto Encyclopedia of Genes and Genomes
2.	PID: the Pathway Interaction Database	Publicly open database, free, and provides information related to human molecular signaling and cellular processes. The database also provides insight into the key proteins involved in the process	http://pid.nci.nih.gov
3.	Roche Biochemical Pathways	Free, user-friendly, and explores both metabolic pathways and cellular and molecular processes	biochemical-pathways.com
4.	Pathway Commons	Consists of 5772 pathways, 2,424,055 interactions, and is linked with 22 more databases. Stores information on molecular interactions, signaling pathways, metabolic pathways, and regulatory networks	Pathway Commons: A Resource for Biological Pathway Analysis
Software			
1.	COPASI: Biochemical system simulator	System software that helps in the simulation and analysis of biochemical networks, their dynamics, and pathways. Various stochastics simulation algorithms are applied and parameter estimation can also be performed. A good graphical user interference is provided in the new versions	COPASI
2.	ANIMO: Analysis of Networks with Interactive Modeling	Free for academic purposes, it runs both in Windows and Linux systems. It requires user interference of Cytoscape for modeling and network visualization	ANIMO—Analysis of Networks with Interactive Modeling (utwente.nl)

(Continued)

Table 24.1 (Continued)

S. no.	Name	Description	URL
Tool Box			
1.	FASIMU	Free; functions and parameters can be customized. It can provide flux minimizations and fitness maximizations based on expression profile new model generation	FASIMU: FBA simulation software for metabolomics (bioinformatics.org)
2.	COBRA toolbox	The COnstraint-Based Reconstruction and Analysis Toolbox. It is a MATLAB-based toolbox that helps in the prediction of biochemical networks and their modelling. It can also regenerate the model depending on biased and unbiased conditions	Home Page – The COBRA Toolbox (opencobra.github.io)
3.	Opt Flux	Open source and can design metabolic processes using *in silico* approaches	Optflux
4.	SurreyFBA	Provides constraint-based simulations and network map visualization	SurreyFBA bio.tools
5.	MetaFlux	Java script processed for modeling and simulation at the basic level	MetaFlux | MetaFlux Documentation
6.	Microbes Flux	Provides a place to build metabolic models for more than 1000 organisms sequenced in the KEGG database	MicrobesFlux: a web platform for drafting metabolic models from the KEGG database
	FAME	Developed for agent-based model simulations, high execution speed, and combined high computational speed. This is a Java-based package, supporting simulations	FAME—Helmholtz—Association of German Research Centres

The assessment of tools used for data analysis in system biology has five basic criteria: operational requirements, model exchange, functionality, network visualization, and usability. In order to evaluate this tool, standards should be based on the flexibility of objectives and constraints, as well as the capabilities of calculations.

24.4 Methods of System Biology

24.4.1 Flux Balance Analysis

The FBA is a recognized method to understand biochemical networks, specifically to reform the metabolic network at the genomic level that has been made up in earlier days [34]. It has application in the computational method to illustrate and engineer intrinsic metabolism. The straightforward flux balance application depends only on the biomass maximization and assumption of a steady state. The FBA software is branded into three forms: standalone form, use of toolbox, and online applications (Figure 24.3).

The metabolic performance can be evaluated by balancing the metabolic fluxes. The basis of flux balancing is the fundamental law of mass conservation. The FBA describes the limitations of flux supplies that are potential and attainable with a

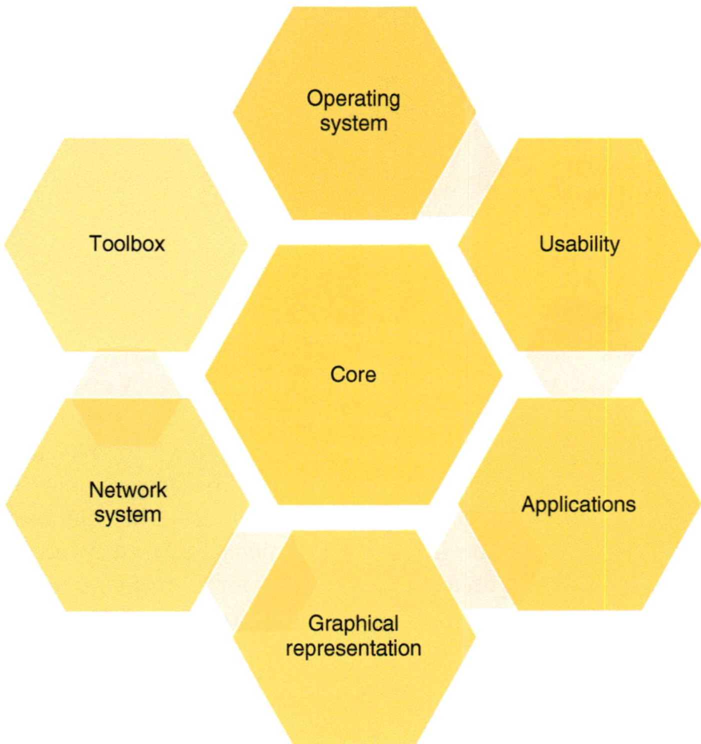

Figure 24.3 Different sectors of the Flux Balance Analysis software model.

defined set of genes. By computing the flow of metabolites, one can predict the growth rate of an organism as well as the rate of metabolite production. This technology has proven to be valuable in bioprocessing, where it can be utilized to detect alterations in the metabolic networks of microbes that are used in fermentation, which can improve the yield of compounds with commercial importance [35].

The mathematical model establishment through FBA requires two important features: metabolic stoichiometry and mass function. The stoichiometry equations help in writing the chemical reactions of the metabolic network and provide evidence concerning the demands in the metabolic system. These demands can be any of the parameters related to the synthesis of biomass or maintenance requirements [35]. All this information helps in organizing a framework and flowchart which leads to metabolic flux distribution. However, this method faces some limitations. At the starting point, FBA begins with a mathematical demonstration of the given metabolic reactions [34], which is in the form of a tabularized matrix that includes the stoichiometric coefficient(s) of the reaction. The stoichiometry executes the restrictions over the network on the metabolites flow [36, 37] and can be expressed in two ways: (i) as an equation to have equilibrium in the reaction and (ii) the variations which wreak the system. The stoichiometric matrix executes the flux balance constraints, confirming the mass balance, i.e., at steady state, the compounds produced must be equal to the quantity of compound utilized. The following step is to describe the biological objective, i.e., the phenotype. The production of biomass can be signified mathematically over a reaction based on the experimental dimension of the associated components of biomass that utilize the precursor metabolites stimulating the production. The reaction of biomass can be ascended in order to align the flux of the reaction at the exponential growth rate of the associated organism. Once the biomass is characterized, the determined rate of growth can be retrieved from the maximum flux. Once composed, steps can be described as an arrangement of linear equations that can be resolved by linear programming.

24.4.2 Molecular Dynamic Simulation and Topological Analysis

The 3D structure of biomolecule is reported from the results of X-ray crystallography or NMR. Both the experimental studies provide coordinates of the atoms of the amino acids of protein molecules. These coordinate results conform to the protein conformation, static nature of proteins, and their stability. However, in real, the atoms of protein molecules are in continual dynamic motion. The conformational changes also play an essential role in protein's function [38]. Thus, molecular dynamics (MD) simulation [39] has become a valuable tool for studying the molecular structure and motional properties of biologically important molecules at the microscopic level [40].

MD is a method of computer simulation where atoms and molecules are allowed to interact for a time period under some force fields (known laws of physics, chemistry, and mathematics) [41] giving a view of the continual motion of the atoms. Indirectly, it can be said that structural changes of biomolecules can be visualized after the simulation run. However, there are some key ingredients to MD simulation, which are boundary condition, force field calculation, and integrator/ensemble. A brief overview of them is given below.

Molecular dynamics is the time-dependent integration of the classical equations of motion [41] for molecular systems. All classical simulation methods depend more or less on empirical approximations, known as "force fields" that help to calculate the interactions and evaluate the energy of the system [42]. Thus, the first step in molecular mechanics is to construct a potential energy surface that is a function of atomic coordinates. The force field is composed of bonding and nonbonding terms representing bond lengths, bond angles and torsional angles, electrostatic, and Van der Waals interaction contribution [43].

Topological data analysis has been considered one of the latest established techniques [44] that focuses on operational features in data. For the analysis purpose, abundantly accepted techniques are readily available in the "Topology ToolKit" [45]. For specific analysis, vortices have been acknowledged as local minima of ρ and their section of effect was given by a merge tree-based segmentation ([46]). The rotational direction of vortices is judged by the depiction of the orthogonal element of the curl of V.

24.5 Challenges and Limitation

Systems biology approaches offer insight into a large amount of genomic, proteomic, and transcriptomic data and try to model the whole complex system. However, the big data set and the enormous time required for *in silico* analysis could be the potential limitations in this process. Moreover, it is technically challenging to construct and implement a living system with all the complexities and possibilities of changes. More than a hundred thousand molecules and interconnected networks are playing a significant role in the human body system. Therefore, an individual mathematical model and/or process diagram cannot visualize the entire process. Moreover, computational approaches are based on the data gathered from experimental parts and algorithms. Both the units are human-based, which are prone to be incorrect. Nowadays, more and more advanced technologies are coming onboard, which can help analyze and interpret big data but at the same time can confuse young researchers about its authenticity and applicability for the same purpose.

24.6 Conclusion

Biological systems especially microbial cells are employed to produce specific compounds for pharmaceuticals, fine chemicals, fuels, biomaterials, food additives, etc. By directed genetic modifications of cell factories (metabolic engineering and protein engineering), it is feasible to improve biotechnological processes to be more effective, environmentally friendly, sustainable, and that may be involved in the synthesis of novel compounds. In this regard, system biology has shed new light on industrial biotechnology and has been successfully applied to create microbial cell factories for the synthesis of numerous products that are derived from different modes of industrial processes. It has been found that system biology has constantly expedited the development of industrial biotechnology for solving resource, energy, and environmental problems in a sustainable manner. Furthermore, applications of "multi-omics" are being optimized for the synthesis of microbial products in terms of quality and quantity in a cost-effective and robust manner.

Acknowledgment

Koel Mukherjee and Vinod Kumar Nigam are thankful to Birla Institute of Technology Mesra, Ranchi, for the infrastructure facility.

References

1 Ge, H., Walhout, A.J., and Vidal, M. (2003). Integrating 'omic' information: a bridge between genomics and systems biology. *Trends Genet.* 19 (10): 551–560.

2 Schena, M., Shalon, D., Davis, R.W., and Brown, P.O. (1995). Quantitative monitoring of gene expression patterns with a complementary DNA microarray. *Science* 270: 467–470.

3 Domon, B. and Aebersold, R. (2006). Challenges and opportunities in proteomics data analysis. *Mol. Cell. Proteomics* 5 (10): 1921–1926.

4 Kearney, P. and Thibault, P. (2003). Bioinformatics meets proteomics—bridging the gap between mass spectrometry data analysis and cell biology. *J. Bioinform. Comput. Biol.* 1 (1): 183–200.

5 Zhao, S., Kumar, R., Sakai, A. et al. (2013). Discovery of new enzymes and metabolic pathways by using structure and genome context. *Nature* 502 (7473): 698–702.

6 Culligan, E.P., Sleator, R.D., Marchesi, J.R., and Hill, C. (2014). Metagenomics and novel gene discovery. *Virulence* 5 (3): 399–412.

7 Van Maris, A.J.A., Winkler, A.A., Kuyper, M. et al. (2007). Development of efficient xylose fermentation in *Saccharomyces cerevisiae*: xylose isomerase as a key component. *Adv. Biochem. Eng./Biotechnol.* 108: 179–204.

8 Christensen, C., Thakar, J., and Albert, R. (2008). Systems-level insights into cellular regulation: inferring, analysing, and modelling intracellular networks. *IET Syst. Biol.* 1 (2): 61–77.

9 Dhar, P.K., Zhu, H., and Mishra, S.K. (2004). Computational approach to systems biology: from fraction to integration and beyond. *IEEE Trans. Nanobiosci.* 3 (3): 144–152.

10 Kitano, H. (2002). Systems biology: a brief overview. *Science* 295: 1662–1664.

11 Snoep, J. and Westerhoff, H. (2005). *Systems Biology: Definitions and Perspectives Topics, Current Genetics*, 13–30. Springer-Verlag.

12 Chuang, H.Y., Hofree, M., and Ideker, T. (2010). A decade of systems biology. *Annu. Rev. Cell Dev. Biol.* 26: 23.1–23.24.

13 Cvijovic, M., Höfer, T., and Hohmann, S. (2016). Strategies for structuring interdisciplinary education in systems biology: an European perspective. *npj Syst. Biol. Appl.* 2 (1): 1–7.

14 Hood, L., Rowen, L., Galas, D.J., and Aitchison, J.D. (2008). Systems biology at the Institute for Systems Biology. *Briefings Funct. Genom. Proteomics* 7 (4): 239–248.

15 Friboulet, A. and Thomas, D. (2005). Systems biology-an interdisciplinary approach. *Biosens. Bioelectron.* 20 (12): 2404–2407.

16 Thiele, I. and Palsson, B.O. (2010). A protocol for generating a high-quality genome-scale metabolic reconstruction. *Nat. Protoc.* 5 (1): 93–121.

17 Shahzad, K. and Loor, J.J. (2012). Application of top-down and bottom-up systems approaches in ruminant physiology and metabolism. *Curr. Genomics* 13 (5): 379–394.

18 Cios, K.J., Mamitsuka, H., Nagashima, T., and Tadeusiewicz, R. (2005). Computational intelligence in solving bioinformatics problems. *Artif. Intell. Med.* 35 (1–2): 1–8.

19 Gusfield, D. (2004). Introduction to the IEEE/ACM transactions on computational biology and bioinformatics. *IEEE/ACM Trans. Comput. Biol. Bioinf.* 1 (1): 2–3.

20 Kelemen, A., Abraham, A., and Chen, Y. (ed.) (2008). *Computational Intelligence in Bioinformatics. Studies in Computational Intelligence.* Berlin, Heidelberg: Springer-Verlag.

21 Valentini, G., Tagliaferri, R., and Masulli, F. (2009). Computational intelligence and machine learning in bioinformatics. *Artif. Intell. Med.* 45 (2–3): 91–96.

22 Smolinski, T.G., Milanova, M.M., and Hassanien, A.E. (2008). Applications of computational intelligence in bioinformatics and biomedicine: current trends and open problems. In: *Studies in Computational Intelligence* (ed. T.G. Smolinski, M.M. Milanova, and A.E. Hassanien), 151. Springer.

23 Balazki, P., Lindauer, K., Einloft, J. et al. (2015). MONALISA for stochastic simulations of Petri net models of biochemical systems. *BMC Bioinf.* 16 (215).

24 Majumdar, A., Scott, S.D., Deogun, J.S., and Harris, S. (2014). Yeast pheromone pathway modeling using Petri nets. *BMC Bioinf.* 15 (7): S13.

25 Ruths, D., Muller, M., Tseng, J.T. et al. (2008). The signaling petri net-based simulator: a non-parametric strategy for characterizing the dynamics of cell-specific signaling networks. *PLoS Comput. Biol.* 4: e1000005.

26 Ciocchetta, F. and Hillston, J. (2009). Bio-PEPA: a framework for the modelling and analysis of biological systems. *Theor. Comput. Sci.* 410: 3065–3084.

27 Mendes, P., Hoops, S., Sahle, S. et al. (2009). Computational modeling of biochemical networks using COPASI systems biology, Chap. 2. In: *Methods in Molecular Biology*, vol. 500, 17–59. Totowa, NJ: Humana Press.

28 Lakshmanan, M., Koh, G., Chung, B.K., and Lee, D.Y. (2012). Software applications for flux balance analysis. *Briefings Bioinf.* 15 (1): 108–122.

29 Schivo, S., Scholma, J., van der Vet, P.E. et al. (2016). Modelling with ANIMO: between fuzzy logic and differential equations. *BMC Syst. Biol.* 10 (1): 56.

30 Schivo, S., Scholma, J., Wanders, B. et al. (2013). Modelling biological pathway dynamics with timed automata. *IEEE J. Biomed. Health. Inf.* 18 (3): 832–839.

31 Langerak, R., van de Pol, J., Post, J.N., and Schivo, S. (2017). Improving the timed automata approach to biological pathway dynamics. In: *Models, Algorithms, Logics and Tools*. Springer International Publishing.

32 Killcoyne, S., Carter, G.W., Smith, J., and Boyle, J. (2009). Cytoscape: a community-based framework for network modeling. *Methods Mol. Biol.* 563: 219–239.

33 Siers, W., Bakker, M., Rubbens, B. et al. (2016). webANIMO: improving the accessibility of ANIMO [version 1]. *F1000Research* 5: 1714.

34 Orth, J.D., Thiele, I., and Palsson, B.Ø. (2010). What is flux balance analysis? *Nat. Biotechnol.* 28 (3): 245.

35 Anand, S., Mukherjee, K., and Padmanabhan, P. (2020). An insight to flux balance analysis for biochemical networks. *Biotechnol. Genet. Eng. Rev.* 36 (1): 32–55.

36 Covert, M.W., Schilling, C.H., Famili, I. et al. (2001). Metabolic modeling of microbial strains in silico. *Trends Biochem. Sci* 26 (3): 179–186.

37 Edwards, J.S., Covert, M., and Palsson, B. (2002). Metabolic modelling of microbes: the flux-balance approach. *Environ. Microbiol.* 4 (3): 133–140.

38 Karplus, M. and Andrew McCammon, J. (2002). Molecular dynamics simulations of biomolecules. *Nat. Struct. Biol.* 9 (9): 646–652.

39 Van Gunsteren, W.F. and Berendsen, H.J.C. (1990). Computer simulation of molecular dynamics: methodology, applications, and perspectives in chemistry. *Angew. Chem.* 29 (9): 992–1023.

40 Schlick, T. (2002). *Molecular Modeling and Simulation: An Interdisciplinary Guide*, Interdisciplinary Applied Mathematics, vol. 21. Springer. ISBN: 978-0-387-22464-0.

41 Allen, P. and Tildesley, D.J. (1987). *Computer Simulation of Liquids*. Oxford: Clarendon Press.

42 Ponder, J.W. and Case, D.A. (2003). Force field for protein simulations. *Adv. Protein Chem.* 66: 27–85.

43 Warshel, A., Sharma, P.K., Kato, M. et al. (2006). Electrostatic basis for enzyme catalysis. *Chem. Rev.* 106 (8): 3210–3235.

44 Tierny, J. (2018). *Topological Data Analysis for Scientific Visualization*. Springer. ISBN: 3319715070.

45 Tierny, J., Favelier, G., Levine, J.A., et al. (2017). The Topology ToolKit. IEEE TVCG. https://topology-tool-kit.github.io/.

46 Gueunet, C., Fortin, P., and Jomier, J. (2016). Contour forests: Fast multi-threaded augmented contour trees. *IEEE 6th Symposium on Large Data Analysis and Visualization (LDAV)*. https://doi.org/10.1109/LDAV.2016.7874333.

25

Metagenomics: New Insight in Microbial Diagnosis

Deepika Chaudhary, Aman Kumar, Kanisht Batra, and Sushila Maan

Lala Lajpat Rai University of Veterinary and Animal Sciences (LUVAS), Department of Animal Biotechnology, Hisar, Haryana 125004, India

25.1 Introduction

Metagenomics, a revolutionary field within microbiology, has emerged as a powerful tool providing unprecedented insights into microbial communities. This chapter deals into the role of metagenomics in microbial diagnosis, shedding light on its transformative impact on understanding and characterizing the vast array of microorganisms that play pivotal roles in human health and the environment. Life on earth relies heavily on microorganisms, serving as its fundamental support. They are necessary for every aspect of human life particularly, food, shelter, and health. Furthermore, they are responsible for providing many essential components of nature like carbon source, nitrogen, oxygen, and sulfur by transforming into another form utilizable by living organisms on earth. Although photosynthesis is typically attributed to plants, the majority of the planet's photosynthetic capability is really provided by bacteria. Numerous beneficial microorganisms are found in human and animal gut. Microorganisms present as abundant moiety survive in all types of environmental conditions, e.g. high temperatures (thermophiles), high pressures (barophiles), high pH levels (alkaliphiles), and high salt (halophiles) conditions. Microorganisms have the ability to develop a number of master plans to survive under extreme conditions. Changes in microorganisms' genomes lead to biochemical transformations, helping them to survive under specific conditions. So, it is very interesting to know about these changes. Microorganisms also play a crucial role in improving life of mankind, e.g. production of antibiotics (penicillin), beverages (wine, beer, etc.), food products like bread, pickles, curd, etc. and biofuels. They also play a very important role in environment cleaning, as pollutant removers in soil, water, and air. They also work in crop enhancement as they provide nutrients, water, and protection against harmful weeds. They show their importance in disease diagnosis and forensic study as standards. In the new era of biotechnology, they play a crucial role in various molecular studies, e.g. polymerase chain reaction (PCR) and cloning.

Microbial Enzymes: Production, Purification, and Industrial Applications, First Edition.
Edited by Dinesh Yadav, Pankaj Chowdhary, Gautam Anand, and Rajarshi Kumar Gaur.

A long history of microorganisms began with the work of Antonae van Leeuwenhoek to Alexander Fleming. At that time, scientists used to focus on pure culture isolation behind any microbiological process to find out which microorganism was responsible for any biological process. After that, an era came which linked microorganisms to biochemical processes. Gradually, advancements in technology enhance scientific interest in community study. Different processes like biofilm formation, waste-water treatment, biogas production, etc., created more interest to study them as a whole and not as an individual. Hence, the study of different genome pools from the same place simultaneously studied is referred as metagenomics. Metagenomics studies include actual scenarios of complex communities as how they actually live, what they are capable of, and how they work. The metagenomics study gives a platform for microbiologists to revamp microbiology for understanding processes in the living world. It takes lesser time than traditional methods. It generates huge data, and this database gives a meaningful base for further studies. There are different microbial interactions that can be deciphered using metagenomics approach and have the potential of improving human health, food security, and in processes involving the production of energy. Metagenomics is a wider science and includes different branches of science, i.e. bioinformatics, genomics, molecular, and system biology. The novelty of this branch of science is that it supports the study of many genomes at the same time. It is well documented that only 1% of microorganisms are culturable under wet conditions. So, a huge number of microorganisms' roles are still unknown. Interestingly, this is possible using metagenomics studies. In this chapter, gives an insight into metagenomics studies. In 1998, for the first time, the term metagenomics came into existence. It includes the study of complete nucleotide sequences obtained from any bulk sample, e.g. water, soil, and rumen gut. It is a technique that comprise many approaches and methods to carry out research in any field. Word "Meta" in Greek means "transcendent" that means to overcome problems related to un-culturability and genomic diversity. *Meta* gives two insights: (i) Collective study of gene pools present in samples. This gives an overview of communities present at a particular place. This also gives cumulative interaction among different populations. (ii) It has identified the need for computational methods development, which has enhanced the capability to understand complex communities. Metagenomics is a developing science, which generates a wealth of knowledge related to unculturable microorganisms. The process in this study includes three steps: (i) extraction of DNA from a sample of all microbes, (ii) preparation of library from purified DNA samples, and (iii) analysis of prepared library using different approaches, e.g. using fragment analyzer and cubit. In the finally prepared library, there are millions of clones having fragments of DNA. The metagenomics is similar to jigsaw puzzles, where many pieces are jumbled into a single box and when we again put puzzles in the box the same challenge appears. This new approach is possible because of the discovery of inexpensive high throughput sequence technology and a higher level of computer-based programs that make sense of millions of reads obtained during sequencing. Metagenomics have a two-way approach: (i) sequence-based and (ii) function-based approach. Sequence-based approach works on millions of sequences for Sargasso sea water using a metagenomic approach [1]. They found 70,000 novel genes with 1.2 million genes by open reading frame. They describe a novel ammonia oxidation pathway uninhibited by UV light. In functional metagenomics, the library generated by random DNA fragments is translated into proteins by bacteria. After this, these are screened for their function, e.g. vitamin producer and antibiotic producer. This gives a very important result to know about characters without knowing their structure.

25.2 Classification

On the basis of approaches, metagenomics is classified into two types: targeted metagenomics and shotgun metagenomics. Targeted metagenomics is becoming less common as sequencing costs are falling and the technology is improving, but it is still used infrequently as each approach has its own pros and cons. Although both can answer the question of what is there in your sample, but only shotgun metagenomics can truly address their function.

25.2.1 Targeted Metagenomics

As the name suggests, it is based on sequencing of some targets like 16s rRNA, 18s rRNA, and internal transcribed spacer (ITS) regions (conserved regions of the genome). These conserved regions are amplified using PCR and sequenced. Within these conserved regions, there are variable regions, which allow the identification of different groups of organisms. However, identifying these organisms down to the species level is nearly impossible. Another limitation is that there is no way to directly assess function from these data.

25.2.2 Shotgun Metagenomics

It is a target-independent method, also called as nondiscriminant method in which the entire population of nucleic acid of a sample is sequenced. This method not only can assign taxonomy and quantify the organisms down to the species level, but it can also assign function as it will sequence many different parts of each organism's genome. Depending upon the depth of the data obtained, it can reconstruct entire genomes, genes, as well as infer different metabolic pathways of the organism. This method provides a way to study unculturable microorganisms that are otherwise difficult or impossible to analyze.

25.3 Methods and Protocols

Culture-based technology gives very little information. Pure culture techniques conducted in soil have revealed that metagenomes are rich sources of anticancer agents [2], therapeutic compounds [3], and immunosuppressants [4]. However, these soil organisms are not culturable in laboratory conditions; hence, alternative approaches need to be developed. Metagenomics is one of the most important technologies, which can be used to investigate the potential of uncultured microorganisms [5–7].

Metagenomics technology includes the extraction of samples for obtaining a complete DNA population, it's cloning or construction of libraries and analysis of the entire data obtained from any sample [8].

25.3.1 DNA Extraction

Extraction of DNA from environmental sample is a very important step for successful functional and sequence-based metagenomic approaches. Three main things should be taken into consideration. First, extracted DNA is representative of the original microbial population in the sample. Second, DNA should be intact. Third, extracted DNA should be free from contaminants. All these three parameters are important for the success of metagenomic approach that the microorganisms may have lysis variation as they are present in starved states in different environments. Thus, the nucleic acid extraction protocols might vary [9]. In market various commercial kits are available for DNA isolation directly from environmental samples. Different research groups also developed their own protocols [10–12]. Some *in situ* extraction methods are also used in which cells are directly lysed in the soil sample and DNA is obtained. Another method is indirect extraction in which first cells are removed from soil and then lysed for DNA purification. After extraction, purification of DNA is a must. Sephadex G-200 spin columns are the best method of choice for removing contaminants from soil DNA. So many approaches can be used for the removal of contaminants, such as pulse field electrophoresis [13] and precultivation step [14].

25.3.2 Library Preparation

Library preparation depends upon the target of the research. The use of small or big library size is totally dependent upon aim of the study. Large size libraries for example study of soil have been used with the help of cosmids [15, 16], bacterial artificial chromosome [17], or fosmids [18, 19].

25.3.3 Library Screening Methodology

Function and sequence-based screening is required to be performed for the analysis of libraries. In the case of function-based screening type, heterologous gene expression is required in metagenomic study. The most common host is *Escherichia coli*. But *Streptomyces lividans* and *Pseudomonas putida* have also been used as alternate for function-based study [20]. Rhizobium group members are very appropriate hosts for environmental metagenomic studies [21].

25.4 Sequencing Platforms

Different generation sequencing platforms are present ranging from Sanger conventional dideoxy chain termination method to next-generation sequencing (NGS). Sanger sequencing is also called the first generation of sequencing technology. This provides an automated DNA sequencer at a large scale [22]. Since the first generation, changes in technology have risen, which resulted in major advancements in technology, ultimately high-throughput technology called as NGS. Different variants of NGS are Roche 454, Illumina, and Ion Torrent [23–25], which are also called as second-generation sequencing. The NGS has very prominent use in metagenomics studies.

The Illumina platforms use sequencing by synthesis chemistry. In this, a chip-like object called flow cells is used. Illumina NGS technology utilizes a fundamentally different approach from the classic Sanger chain-termination method. It leverages sequencing by synthesis technology – tracking the addition of labeled nucleotides as the DNA chain is copied – in a massively parallel fashion. This technique has high throughput, with a low error rate per base of only 0.1–1% [26].

Illumina keeps releasing newer versions of sequencers from time to time so that the latest modern technologies can be adopted. For example, the release of NovaSeq 6000, which generates approximately 6 Tb and 20 billion data and is economically cheaper as compared to early versions. Out of these two sequencers, NovaSeq 6000 and HighSeq X Tenare were used in human genome sequencing [27].

There have been major developments in technologies recently that counted as third-generation sequencing. They can generate long-length sequences, e.g. PacBio and Oxford Nanopore (Minion). The technology in PacBio sequencer used DNA template (250–25,000 bp), which is ligated with adapters having hairpin structure, which results in the formation of a circular template. This circular template settles down in single molecule real time cell. The DNA polymerase adds nucleotides in each well. This process repeats multiple times, i.e. called as circular consensus sequencing. This process generates highly accurate data [28].

The Oxford Nanopore Technology (ONT) uses protein pores those embedded on the flow cell in membrane. These protein pores are called nanopores. When ion current is given, single-stranded DNA moves through the nanopores. There is the generation of characteristic disruption due to the movement of ion current, which is identified by sensors [29]. The main problem in long read platforms is the generation of high raw error rates near to 10–20%. But modern technology tries to minimize these errors [30–32]. Latest release by ONT kit 12 chemistry and R10.4 cells supported 1D2 technology. This Showed 99% sequencing accuracy [33, 34].

25.4.1 Metagenomic Next Generation Sequencing (mNGS)

The discovery of high throughput sequencing technique, i.e. NGS brings a major breakthrough change in fields of metagenomics research in such a way it also called mNGS (Metagenomics NGS). It came in knowledge around mid-2000s. The role of this technology is there in diverse fields, e.g. clinical diagnostics in humans and animals, therapeutics, food industry, agriculture, biofuels, and biotechnology. The research world is giving high importance to this technology because the mNGS can simultaneously sequence billions of nucleic acid fragments independently. So, at one point, many samples can be analyzed in a short time, which is very important in clinical diagnosis. Early diagnosis can help take precautionary measures, e.g. SARS-COV-2 diagnosis during COVID 19 pandemic.

mNGS process all nucleic acids present in single or multi-samples. These samples may have mixed populations from various genera of microorganisms. Here, the reference genome is also kept as a control, which is helpful to understand in which proportions different microbes are present in a sample. This method also gives data regarding unidentified populations present in samples. So this technique has applications in the field of clinics for the development of diagnostics, identification of outbreak, infection control surveillance, novel pathogen discovery, etc. In mNGS, various sample types can be used for study, e.g. respiratory samples, cerebrospinal fluid, gastrointestinal fluid, blood, and ocular fluid.

25.4.2 NGS Workflow Steps

25.4.2.1 Extraction of Genetic Material

mNGS process starts with DNA/RNA as template which is extracted from collected samples. The different types of samples can be used. The extraction method can vary depending on the requirement. The method should give a high yield of nucleic acid with maximum purity, so that it qualifies for the next step of the workflow (Figure 25.1). The quality of extracted nucleic acid must be checked before moving to the next step. Purity and yield are very important.

25.4.2.2 Library Preparation

Library preparation is an important step for a successful run of NGS. In this step, extracted nucleic acid are fragmented in short fragments. Adapters are also attached to sequences so that sequencer machine can read them. Specific sequences are called BARCODES or INDEXES. These barcoded samples are pooled as a single

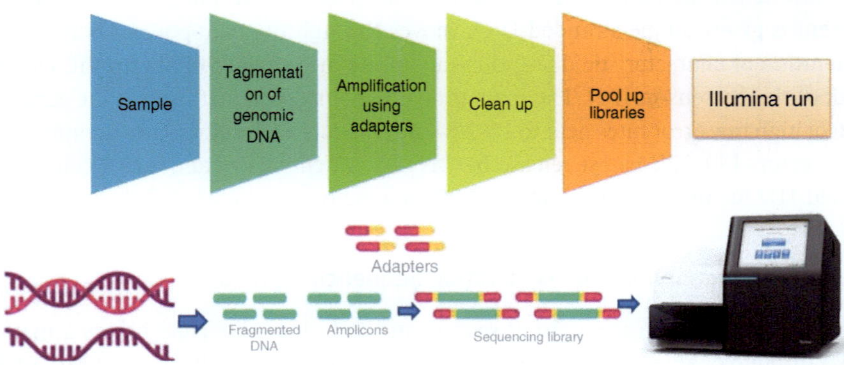

Figure 25.1 An overview presentation of mNGS procedure using Illumina Miseq platform. Source: Illumina, Inc.

sample. These barcodes will provide their identification. This makes it possible to run many samples at the same time. The number of samples can vary according to machine type, running kit, and purpose of analysis.

25.4.2.3 Sequencing

After library preparation in the next step, this library should be sequenced. For this, prepared libraries are pooled to make one sample and loaded onto the machine. The most common platform is provided by Illumina.

25.4.2.4 Data Analysis

At the end of each run, the data will be generated. The data are then subjected to bioinformatic analysis (Figure 25.2). Different types of pipelines for data analysis are constantly being developed by researchers. Nowadays, artificial intelligence (AI) and machine learning tools (ML) are frequently used to analyze the data.

25.4.2.5 Read Processing

It is a series of processes that involve quality control of data. This process involves cleaning the sequences reads by the sequencer itself. This is represented as base calling. In this, a specific nucleotide present at each position in a single sequencing read is identified. A good quality score is mandatory for a successful run. Additional sequences of adapters are also removed in this process and only sample sequences will be kept.

25.4.2.6 Sequence Analysis

In this type of analysis, a reference genome or database will be used. Obtained new sequences will be directly aligned with already present reference data. Then, any

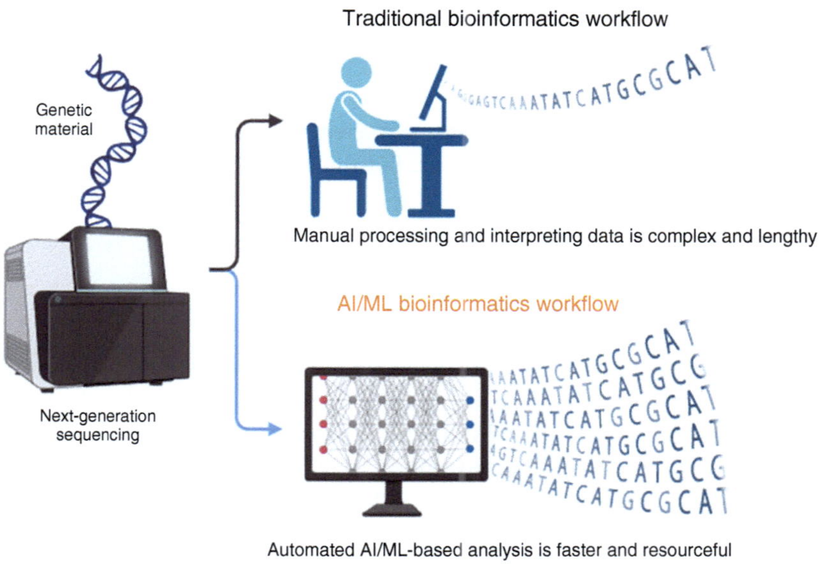

Figure 25.2 mNGS data analysis platform.

number of steps can be performed, including removal of duplicate reads, alignment, and assembly (when performing *de novo* sequencing), genome annotation, variant calling/annotation, determination of gene counts, and more. There are a wide variety of bioinformatics tools and data analysis apps that can be used to analyze the sequences, each with its own differences.

25.4.3 Importance of mNGS

The strength of mNGS in comparison to traditional approaches is that it gives an unbiased analysis. It also doesnot use rediscussed hypothesis during diagnostic studies. In traditional methods like PCR emphasis is on specific primers that work for targeted pathogens for amplification and detection. Even this metagenomic study can be done using universal or broad-range PCR methods. In PCR, we use specific primers against conserved 16S ribosomal RNA (rRNA) gene and ITS sequences. These primers amplified distinctive nucleic acid sequences those classified by bioinformatics in various microbial groups, i.e. bacteria/archaea, or fungi. Problem with using universal primers is that a mixed sequence is obtained with infection-causing agent, so it is interpretation may not be adequate.

25.4.4 Challenges of mNGS

There is an enormous potential of mNGS; however, it is a long way to become a mainstream part of diagnostic laboratories. Main reasons are listed below:

1) Challenges in analysis of bigdata. The results must be able to distinguish contamination and colonization from true pathogens.
2) Authentic validation of assay.
3) Contaminated samples can be problematic.
4) Good bioinformatician is required for the analysis of big data.

The analysis of big data is the most important step in mNGS. A good laboratory that is occupied with an excellent data-storage system, internet facility, and a bioinformatician is mandatory for data analysis. But the availability of all these is not always possible with most of clinical laboratories that's why this technology has not come at general laboratory level.

25.4.5 Application of mNGS

The mNGS also very important for the detection of different diseases like cancer, women's health-related disease, etc. at an early stage. This advanced technology provides an opportunity for early treatment of patients by ensuring the detection of problems at the right time. This technology provides the best platform for the detection of genetic difference-related disease diagnosis. In one test, huge data are obtained, thus reducing per sample cost in mNGS test. The importance of metagenomics has been recognized in different fields, e.g. agriculture, medicine, environment, and ecology [35].

25.4.5.1 Agriculture

Different types of soils is full of microorganisms. The population of microorganisms vary 10^9–10^{10} in one gram of soil. The soil contains both cultured and uncultured types of population of organisms [36, 37]. These microorganisms still have not been discovered completely despite their economic importance due to their complex nature [38]. The microbial population has a wide role in enhancing crop production, improving soil condition, and maintaining sustainability of the soil ecosystem. They play an important role in nitrogen fixation, recycling of nutrients, solubilization of phosphorus, and sequestration of metals [39]. Functional metagenomics provides an opportunity to understand the role of microbes [40, 41]. The success in identifying microbes' role and their mechanism behind the above-said mechanism. This plays a great role in the improvement of agriculture style [35].

25.4.5.2 Production of Renewable Energy Source

Renewable and nonrenewable energy source are two major categories. World population is increasing day by day. For fulfillment of the requirement of increased population, only nonrenewable source is not enough. So, renewable energy source is required. For this, the use of biofuel is required. This is not harmful, and it is easily producible technology. Biofuels are produced from corn stalk, different biomass full of cellulose, which gets converted into ethanol by microbial consortia. Microorganisms also produce methanol, hydrogen, and different types of enzymes. Metagenomics is very helpful to identify microbes with the desired trait, which can be used for industry-scale production of biofuels from consortia of microbes [42]. The manufacturing cost is also low. The synthesis of biomolecules and novel chemicals also uses metagenomics [43]. Different enzymes like cellulases, xylanases, lipases, and amylases, are confined from soil metagenome studies [44]. In biotechnology, different types of enzymes, active chemicals, drug discovery, and manufacturing at a large level from microbes [45, 46]. Metagenomics has resulted in the development of many industries like commodity and fine chemicals, pharmaceuticals and agrochemicals [47]. Metagenomic sequencing has been widely applied in different industry-based application, e.g. microbial-based food industry [48, 49], study plant-based production [50], and the effect of soil fertilizers [51].

25.4.5.3 Ecological Study

The study of metagenomics can be used for the mining of different microbes having potential applications in industry. This can be used for identifying new genomes from unculturable organisms and deciphering the new gene clusters present in environmental gene pool. Microbial communities are very diverse and rich in number in different ecosystems. Extreme ecological niche has a diverse range of microbes [52]. Metagenomic study can be used for providing functional role of microbes present in extreme conditions. One example of metagenomic study is of Australian sea lions fecal matter, which showed its importance in coastal area nutrient enrichment. Because microbial population present converts this fecal into its bioavailable form. This enters into the food chain and gives nutrients at different trophic levels [53]. In different waterbodies, soil, and fecal matter from different ecosystems are also studied by metagenomics [54, 55].

25.4.5.4 Environment Cleaning

In environment so many pollutants contaminate the environment. Metagenomics play a very important role in the diagnosis of pollutants and their impact of pollutant on the environment. Microorganisms that work on pollutants can also be studied by metagenomics [56]. The microbial population can be monitored on wastewater. It has been seen that wastewater from sewage could be used for tracking infectious agents like SARS-CoV-2. Hu et al. [56, 57] reported a read map of *E. coli* using nanopore sequencing. Hence, this metagenome method can be used as an indicator test of fecal contamination in water. Metagenome sequencing by Illumina of wastewater treatment plants gave information on the presence of antibiotic-resistant bacteria [58, 59].

25.4.5.5 Characterization of Microorganisms

Importance of microorganisms in animal and human health is of utmost significance, but its proper characterization still has not been done [60]. So the study of animal and human microbiota from the gut is a milestone study of using metagenomic technique. There are only 31–48.8% reads in a database, which could be aligned with 194 human bacterial genome present in the gut. It indicates that there is still a long way to find out different novel bacterial genomes. In the case of animal health, metagenomics have played a role in the profiling of rumen gut microbiotas [61, 62]. This also has a role in surveillance study, which monitor the spread of disease from wild to domestic animals or humans. Different programs were initiated by different governments either alone or in calibrations.

25.4.5.6 Disease Diagnosis

The diagnosis of disease at the right time is very important for the treatment and control of disease spread. Real-time sequencing will also have a large impact on agro-food industry. Hu et al. [63] utilize the metagenomics for identification of fungal species responsible for causing diseases in wheat plants. The metagenome technology could be used for monitoring viral diseases, providing rapid response in outbreaks [63, 64]. This study has helped in the characterization of the microbiome of a salmon ectoparasite, indicating its role as a reservoir for fish pathogens [65]. In clinical infection, still most of culture-dependent technologies were used. But it does not give complete knowledge. So, the use of high-throughput metagenomic sequencing is very important due to its ability to identify multiple pathogens at strain level in a single test [66].

25.5 Milestones in Metagenomics

The important case studies that reflect the importance of metagenomics in research are also very important. They showed a journey of an era related to this science.

The journey started with Leeuwenhoek, the discoverer of microorganism, and to the Human Genome Project. So here we include a few of them.

25.5.1 Metagenomic of Ocean

The study of ocean microbiome using metagenomic tools is a very ambitious project which started in 2015. This project was financially supported by the European Micro B3 (Marine Microbial Biodiversity and Bioinformatics) agency. It was the mega-scale sequencing drive that generated the microbial data extensively in a single day. There was a high amount of environmental metadata generated by researchers including 150 metagenomes and 18S/16S rRNA amplicon sequence data sets [67]. So this study is a major milestone in the history of metagenomics.

25.5.2 Human Genome Project

The Human Genome Project was funded by the National Institute of Health (NIH), USA. The use of metagenomics in the Human Genome Project is very crucial. This technology is behind the success of this project. This project was the first initiative for understanding the microbiota involved in health and disease of humans. This project was done in two phases. The first phase involves identification and characterization of human microbiota [68]. The second phase includes generation of resources that can be utilized for the characterization of microbiome. In this project, more than 10,000 microbes were identified along with 81% genera.

25.5.3 Host-targeted Drugs Affecting Microbiota Populations

In current lifestyle, we are so much dependent on medication. The effect of these medications on natural flora of our body can also be studied using metagenomics. The effect of commonly used medications on gut microbiota can be studied using this technique. The gene expression analysis can be correlated to the positive or negative effects of drugs on human health. There are various proton pump inhibitors (Xenobiotics) that have been studied and their effect on gut microbiota was seen. They are involved in changing the function and dynamics of human gut microbiota [69].

25.6 Conclusions and Future Perspectives

In conclusion, metagenomics stands at the forefront of microbial diagnosis, offering a paradigm shift in our understanding of microbial communities. Due to its ability to uncover hidden pathogens, decipher microbial diversity, and inform personalized treatment positions, metagenomics acts as a transformative force in the fields of microbiology and healthcare. As technology continues to advance, the integration of metagenomic approaches into routine diagnostic practices holds the promise of more accurate, timely, and tailored interventions, ultimately benefiting both individual patients and public health on a global scale.

References

1 Venter, J.C., Remington, K., Heidelberg, J.F. et al. (2004). Environmental genome shotgun sequencing of the Sargasso Sea. *Science* 304: 66–74.

2 Shen, B., Du la Shen, B., Du, L. et al. (2000). The biosynthetic gene cluster for the anticancer drug bleomycin from *Streptomyces verticillus* ATCC15003 as a model for hybrid peptide–polyketide natural product biosynthesis. *J. Ind. Microbiol. Biotechnol.* 17: 378–385.

3 Raaijmakers, J.M., Weller, D.M., and Thomashow, L.S. (1997). Frequency of antibiotic-producing *Pseudomonas* spp. in natural environments. *Appl. Environ. Microbiol.* 63: 881–887.

4 Skoko, N., Vujovic, J., Savic, M. et al. (2005). Construction of *Saccharomyces cerevisiae* strain FAV20 useful in detection of immunosuppressants produced by soil actinomycetes. *J. Microbiol. Methods* 61: 137–140.

5 Handelsman, J. (2004). Metagenomics: application of genomics to uncultured microorganisms. *Microbiol. Mol. Biol. Rev.* 68: 669–685.

6 Pettit, R.K. (2004). Soil DNA libraries for anticancer drug discovery. *Cancer Chemother. Pharmacol.* 54: 1–6.

7 Streit, W.R. and Schmitz, R.A. (2004). Metagenomics—the key to the uncultured microbes. *Curr. Opin. Microbiol.* 7: 492–498.

8 Handelsman, J., Rondon, M.R., Brady, S.F. et al. (1998). Molecular biological access to the chemistry of unknown soil microbes: a new frontier for natural products. *Chem. Biol.* 5: R245–R249.

9 Bertrand, H., Poly, F., Tran Van, V. et al. (2005). High molecular weight DNA recovery from soils prerequisite for biotechnological metagenomic library construction. *J. Microbiol. Methods* 62: 1–11.

10 Frostegard, A., Courtois, S., Ramisse, V. et al. (1999). Quantification of bias related to the extraction of DNA directly from soils. *Appl. Environ. Microbiol.* 65: 5409–5420.

11 Krsek, M. and Wellington, E.M. (1999). Comparison of different methods for the isolation and purification of total community DNA from soil. *J. Microbiol. Methods* 39: 1–16.

12 Miller, D.N., Bryant, J.E., Madsen, E.L., and Ghiorse, W.C. (1999). Evaluation and optimization of DNA extraction and purification procedures for soil and sediment samples. *Appl. Environ. Microbiol.* 65: 4715–4724.

13 Quaiser, A., Ochsenreiter, T., Klenk, H. et al. (2002). First insight into the genome of an uncultivated crenarchaeote from soil. *Environ. Microbiol.* 4: 603–611.

14 Daniel, R. (2005). The metagenomics of soil. *Nat. Rev. Microbiol.* 3: 470–478.

15 Entcheva, P., Liebl, W., Johann, A. et al. (2001). Direct cloning from enrichment cultures, a reliable strategy for isolation of complete operons and genes from microbial consortia. *Appl. Environ. Microbiol.* 67: 89–99.

16 Courtois, S., Cappellano, C.M., Ball, M. et al. (2003). Recombinant environmental libraries provide access to microbial diversity for drug discovery from natural products. *Appl. Environ. Microbiol.* 69: 49–55.

17 Rondon, M.R., August, P.R., Bettermann, A.D. et al. (2000). Cloning the soil metagenome: a strategy for accessing the genetic and functional diversity of uncultured microorganisms. *Appl. Environ. Microbiol.* 66: 2541–2547.

18 Quaiser, A., Ochsenreiter, T., Klenk, H. et al. (2003). First insight into the genome of an uncultivated crenarchaeote from soil. *Environ. Microbiol.* 4: 603–611.

19 Treusch, A.H., Kletzin, A., Raddatz, G. et al. (2004). Characterization of large-insert DNA libraries from soil for environmental genomic studies of Archaea. *Environ. Microbiol.* 6: 970–980.

20 Martinez, A., Kolvek, S.J., Yip, C. et al. (2004). Genetically modified bacterial strains and novel bacterial artificial chromosome shuttle vectors for constructing environmental libraries and detecting heterologous natural products in multiple expression hosts. *Appl. Environ. Microbiol.* 70: 2452–2463.

21 Wexler, M., Bond, P.L., Richardson, D.J., and Johnston, A.W. (2005). A wide host-range metagenomic library from a waste water treatment plant yields a novel alcohol/aldehyde dehydrogenase. *Environ. Microbiol.* 7: 1917–1926.

22 Heather, J.M. and Chain, B. (2016). The sequence of sequencers: the history of sequencing DNA. *Genomics* 107: 1–8.

23 Allali, I., Arnold, J.W., Roach, J. et al. (2017). A comparison of sequencing platforms and bioinformatics pipelines for compositional analysis of the gut microbiome. *BMC Microbiol.* 17: 194.

24 Gupta, A.K. and Gupta, U. (2020). Next generation sequencing and it applications. In: *Animal Biotechnology*, 2e (ed. A.S. Verma and A. Singh), 395–421. Boston, MA: Academic Press: ISBN 978-0-12-811710-1.

25 Thomas, T., Gilbert, J., and Meyer, F. (2020). Metagenomics—aguide from sampling to data analysis. *Microb. Inf. Exp.* 2: 3.

26 Ma, X., Shao, Y., Tian, L. et al. (2019). Analysis of error profiles in deep next-generation sequencing data. *Genome Biol.* 20: 50.

27 Stoler, N. and Nekrutenko, A. (2021). Sequencing error profiles of Illumina sequencing instruments. *NAR Genome Bioinf.* 3: lqab019.

28 Kanwar, N., Blanco, C., Chen, I.A., and Seelig, B. (2021). PacBio sequencing output increased through uniform and directional fivefold concatenation. *Sci. Rep.* 11: 18065.

29 Hu, T., Chitnis, N., Monos, D., and Dinh, A. (2021). Next-generation sequencing technologies: an overview. *Hum. Immunol.* 82: 801–811.

30 Zhang, H., Jain, C., and Aluru, S. (2020). A comprehensive evaluation of long read error correction methods. *BMC Genomics* 21: 889.

31 Amarasinghe, S.L., Su, S., Dong, X. et al. (2020). Opportunities and challenges in long-read sequencing data analysis. *Genome Biol.* 21: 30.

32 Dohm, J.C., Peters, P., Stralis-Pavese, N., and Himmelbauer, H. (2020). Benchmarking of long-read correction methods. *NAR Genome Bioinf.* 2: lqaa037.

33 Cornelis, S. (2019). Forensic lab-on-a-chip DNA analysis. Ph.D. thesis. Ghent University, Ghent, Belgium.

34 Lin, B., Hui, J., and Mao, H. (2021). Nanopore technology and its applications in gene sequencing. *Biosensors* 11: 214.

35 Committee on Metagenomics: Challenges and Functional Applications, National Research Council (2007). *The New Science of Metagenomics: Revealing the Secrets of Our Microbial Planet*. Washington, D.C.: The National Academies Press https://doi.org/10.17226/11902. ISBN 978-0-309-10676-4. PMID 21678629.

36 Copeland, C.S. (2017). "The World within us" (PDF). *Healthcare J. New Orleans* 6: 21–26.

37 Vogel, T.M., Simonet, P., Jansson, J.K. et al. (2009). TerraGenome: a consortium for the sequencing of a soil metagenome. *Nat. Rev. Microbiol.* 7 (4): 252. https://doi.org/10.1038/nrmicro2119.

38 TerraGenome Homepage. TerraGenome international sequencing consortium. http://www.terragenome.org/ (accessed 30 December 2011).

39 Committee on Metagenomics: Challenges and Functional Applications, National Research Council *Understanding Our Microbial Planet: The New Science of Metagenomics 2007*. The National Academies Press.

40 Charles, T. (2010. ISBN 978-1-904455-54-7). The potential for investigation of plant-microbe interactions using metagenomics methods. In: *Metagenomics: Theory, Methods and Applications* (ed. D. Marco), X+212. Caister Academic Press.

41 Bringel, F. and Couée, I. (2015). Pivotal roles of phyllosphere microorganisms at the interface between plant functioning and atmospheric trace gas dynamics. *Front. Microbiol.* 6: 486.

42 Li, L.L., McCorkle, S.R., Monchy, S. et al. (2009). Bioprospecting metagenomes: glycosyl hydrolases for converting biomass. *Biotechnol. Biofuels* 2: 10. https://doi.org/10.1186/1754-6834-2-10. PMC 2694162. PMID 19450243.

43 Schloss, P.D. and Handelsman, J. (2005). Introducing DOTUR, a computer program for defining operational taxonomic units and estimating species richness. *Appl. Environ. Microbiol.* 71: 1501–1506.

44 Sharma, V., Kumar, R., Sharma, V.K. et al. (2019). Expression, purification, characterization and in silico analysis of newly isolated hydrocarbon degrading bleomycin resistance dioxygenase. *Mol. Biol. Rep.* 47: 533–544. https://doi.org/10.1007/s11033-019-05159-x.

45 Simon, C. and Daniel, R. (2011). Metagenomic analyses: past and future trends. *Appl. Environ. Microbiol.* 77 (4): 1153.

46 Simon, C. and Daniel, R. (2009). Achievements and new knowledge unraveled by metagenomic approaches. *Appl. Microbiol. Biotechnol.* 85 (2): 265–276. https://doi.org/10.1007/s00253-009-2233-z. PMC 2773367. PMID 19760178.

47 Wong, D. (2010. ISBN 978-1-904455-54-7). Applications of metagenomics for industrial bioproducts. In: *Metagenomics: Theory, Methods and Applications* (ed. D. Marco), X+212. Caister Academic Press.

48 Jonnala, B.Y., McSweeney, P., Sheehan, J. et al. (2018). Sequencing of the cheese microbiome and its relevance to industry. *Front. Microbiol.* 9: 1020.

49 Morgan, H., Du Toit, M., and Setati, M. (2017). The grapevine and wine microbiome: insights from high-throughput Amplicon sequencing. *Front. Microbiol.* 8: 820.

50 Jacoby, R., Peukert, M., Succurro, A. et al. (2017). The role of soil microorganisms in plant mineral nutrition—current knowledge and future directions. *Front. Plant Sci.* 8: 1617.

51 Cassman, N., Lourenço, K., do Carmo, J. et al. (2018). Genome-resolved metagenomics of sugarcane vinasse bacteria. *Biotechnol. Biofuels* 11: 270.

52 Raes, J., Letunic, I., Yamada, T. et al. (2011). Toward molecular trait-based ecology through integration of biogeochemical, geographical and metagenomic data. *Mol. Syst. Biol.* 7: 473. https://doi.org/10.1038/msb.2011.6. PMC 3094067. PMID 21407210.

53 Lavery, T.J., Roudnew, B., Seymour, J. et al. (2012). High nutrient transport and cycling potential revealed in the microbial metagenome of Australian sea lion (*Neophoca cinerea*) faeces. *PLoS One* 7 (5): e36478.

54 Chua, P.Y.S., Carøe, C., Crampton-Platt, A. et al. (2022). A two-step metagenomics approach for the identification and mitochondrial DNA contig assembly of vertebrate prey from the blood meals of common vampire bats (Desmodusrotundus). *Metabarcoding Metagenomics* 6: e78756. https://doi.org/10.3897/mbmg.6.78756. ISSN 2534-9708. S2CID 248041252.

55 George, I., Stenuit, B., and Agathos, S.N. (2010). Application of metagenomics to bioremediation. In: *Metagenomics: Theory, Methods and Applications* (ed. D. Marco). Caister Academic Press. ISBN 978-1-904455-54-7.

56 Mallapaty, S. (2020). How sewage could reveal true scale of coronavirus outbreak. *Nature* 580: 176–177.

57 Hu, Y., Ndegwa, N., Alneberg, J. et al. (2018). Stationary and portablesequencing-based approaches for tracing wastewater contamination in urban stormwater systems. *Sci. Rep.* 8: 11907.

58 Che, Y., Xia, Y., Liu, L. et al. (2019). Mobile antibiotic resistome in wastewater treatment plants revealed by nanopore metagenomic sequencing. *Microbiome* 7: 44.

59 Zimmer, C. (2010). How microbes defend and define us. *New York Times* (29 December 2011).

60 Nelson, K.E. and White, B.A. (2010. ISBN 978-1-904455-54-7). Metagenomics and its applications to the study of the human microbiome. In: *Metagenomics: Theory, Methods and Applications* (ed. D. Marco), X+212. Caister Academic Press.

61 Qin, J., Li, R., Raes, J. et al. (2010). A human gut microbial gene catalogue established by metagenomic sequencing. *Nature* 464 (7285): 59–65. https://doi.org/10.1038/nature08821. PMC 3779803. PMID 20203603.

62 Chua, P., Shi, Y., and Rasmussen, J.A. (2022). Taking metagenomics under the wings. *Nat. Rev. Microbiol.* 20 (8): 447. https://doi.org/10.1038/s41579-022-00746-5. ISSN 1740-1534. PMID 35546350. S2CID 248739527.

63 Hu, Y., Green, G., Milgate, A. et al. (2019). Pathogen detection and microbiome analysis of infected wheat using a portable DNA sequencer. *J. Phytobiomes* 3: 92–101.

64 Boykin, L., Ghalab, A., De Marchi, B.R. et al. (2018). Real time portable genome sequencing for global food security. *F1000Res* 7: 1101.

65 Gonçalves, A., Collipal-Matamal, R., Valenzuela-Muñoz, V. et al. (2020). Nanopore sequencing of microbial communities reveals the potential role of sea lice as a reservoir for fish pathogens. *Sci. Rep.* 10: 2895.

66 Wilson, M.R., Naccache, S.N., Samayoa, E. et al. (2014). Actionable diagnosis of neuroleptospirosis by next-generation sequencing. *N. Engl. J. Med.* 370: 2408–2417.

67 Kopf, A., Bicak, M., Kottmann, R. et al. (2015). The ocean sampling day consortium. *Gigascience* 4: 27. https://doi.org/10.1186/s13742-015-0066-5.

68 Krulwich, R. (2011). Cracking the code of life. PBS, 2003 Tripp, S. and Grueber, M. Economic Impact of the human Genome Project Battle.

69 Tsuda, A., Suda, W., Morita, H. et al. (2015). Influence of proton-pump inhibitors on the luminal microbiota in the gastrointestinaltract. *Clin. Transl. Gastroenterol.* 6: e89.

26

Production and Therapeutic Applications of Monoclonal Antibodies in Cancer and Other Diseases

Ambuj Shahi[1], Girijesh K. Patel[1,2], Sushil Kumar[3], Madhuri Singh[1], Anshika Varshney[1], and Uday C. Ghoshal[1]

[1] *Sanjay Gandhi Post Graduate Institute of Medical Sciences, Department of Gastroenterology, Lucknow, Uttar Pradesh 226014, India*
[2] *Motilal Nehru National Institute of Technology Allahabad, Department of Biotechnology, Prayagraj, Uttar Pradesh 211004, India*
[3] *Deen Dayal Upadhyaya Gorakhpur University, Department of Zoology, Gorakhpur, Uttar Pradesh 273009, India*

26.1 Introduction

Antibodies are small proteins, often referred to as immunoglobulins (Igs), which are produced primarily by B-lymphocytes or B-cells and help our body to fight against pathogens and diseases. B-cells recognize target antigens (surface proteins of viruses and bacteria) when they enter our body and produce a large number of specific antibodies against them. These antibodies can help in the destruction of such antigens or prevent them from entering our cells [1, 2]. Additionally, antibodies help in recognizing and combating pathogens that may reenter into our body in the future by developing memory cells [3]. Monoclonal antibodies (mAbs) are laboratory-produced identical clones of a single kind of antibody. However, for clinical use, there is a need for lots of B-lymphocytes to produce mAb on an industrial scale but there is a limitation that B-lymphocytes do not divide quickly. Therefore, to resolve this issue, hybridoma technology has been used where B-cells are fused with rapidly dividing tumor cells (myeloma cells). As a result, a hybridoma cell is created that divides quickly like a tumor cell and produces a large number of identical antibodies like B-lymphocytes [4–6]. Therefore, by selecting the appropriate B-lymphocyte, we may successfully produce mAbs that bind to the desired target/antigen. mAb can be developed to bind to a specific protein, cells in the human body, infectious agents, or chemicals. mAbs can also be attached to the different agents like drugs, fluorescent proteins, or radioactive materials [7], e.g., specific monoclonal antibodies attached to drugs or radioactive material help to locate or destroy the cancer cells with targeted antigens. mAbs are administered either by injection or an infusion to help our bodies fight against a specific germ or disease. The Coronavirus typically attaches to and enters human cells via markers on its surface; however, mAb can bind to these markers to block the virus from

Microbial Enzymes: Production, Purification, and Industrial Applications, First Edition.
Edited by Dinesh Yadav, Pankaj Chowdhary, Gautam Anand, and Rajarshi Kumar Gaur.

attaching to cells and unable to cause infection [8]. Moreover, there is always a chance for some side effects with any type of medication. mAb may also result in allergic reactions with symptoms like rashes, itching, nausea, headaches, chills, fever, and dizziness [9]. There are multifaceted uses of mAbs, including cancer treatment, poisoning, osteoporosis, organ transplant rejection, viral infections, and other diseases [10]. Orthoclone OKT3 (now known as muromonab-CD3) was the first mAb used therapeutically to treat acute organ transplant rejection [11]. Now, there are hundreds of mAbs that have been approved by the United States Food and Drug Administration (FDA) for clinical use [12]. Trastuzumab, pembrolizumab, and rituximab are some common mAbs that are being used for cancer treatment [13]. Besides the hybridoma technology [14], mAbs can also be produced by phage-display technique, plasmid, transgenic animal, and transgenic plants [15].

In this chapter, we discussed the recent advancements in mAb production and their therapeutic applications in different diseases including cancer.

26.2 Background of Monoclonal Antibodies

Antibodies were first described as a magic bullet by Paul Ehrlich, who received the Nobel Prize in 1908 for his work [16]. In 1975, Kohler and Milstein developed the technique allowing large numbers of identical antibodies to be produced using a single cell line or clone obtained from mice; antibodies produced in this way are known as mAbs [17]. Scientists harnessed this method to develop therapeutic antibodies that could be engineered to recognize and target specific antigens present on cell surfaces that are involved in disease development and progression [18]. This was the breakthrough in the development of mAb-based medicines. Orthoclone OKT3 (Muromonab-CD3) was the first therapeutic mAb approved in 1986 for preventing kidney transplant rejection [19]. mAbs were developed in cells derived from mice, but their clinical potential was restricted because the patient's immune cells would recognize that antibodies themselves as foreign and thus inactivate or destroy them. By 1990, chimeric mAbs were developed, which possess around two-thirds of the molecule from human origin, making them less likely to be attacked by the patient's immune system [20]. The first chimeric mAbs were approved in 1994 for the treatment of cardiovascular disease [21]. FDA approved Rituximab (Rituxan) in 1997 for cancer treatment, which was a milestone in mAb-based cancer therapy. Leukemias and lymphomas are among the malignancies that are commonly treated with Rituximab [22]. Further advancement in the field of mAbs led to the development of humanized mAbs exhibiting <10% mouse protein to eventually fully human mAbs. Trastuzumab, a humanized mAb, is used for the treatment of those cancers where epidermal growth factor receptor (EGFR) is overexpressed [23]. Interestingly, the first fully humanized mAb drug, Adalimumab, was launched in 2002 under the trade name Humira [24]. mAbs today are produced from cells of mammals that are grown in a lab under controlled conditions in a long and complex process that requires a high degree of expertise, including standard processes such as viral screening, purification, and decontamination in an effort to ensure high quality [25]. Further advances in mAbs engineering have brought new hope for optimizing their role as potential medicines like antibody–drug conjugates (ADCs). In ADC, a toxin molecule used to attach with mAbs and delivered directly to the target cells [26, 27]. Moreover, the glycoengineered antibodies are also designed, which have been specifically modified to activate the immune system more effectively and at a greater specificity [28].

26.3 Nomenclature of Monoclonal Antibodies

For clinical development as well as simple identification, mAb nomenclature is crucial. In 1991, the World Health Organization (WHO) directed the International Nonproprietary Names (INN) to develop a scheme for mAb nomenclature [29]. Prefix, substem A, substem B, and suffix make up this structure (Table 26.1). The nomenclature used for monoclonal antibodies indicates the "Humanization" level and classifies whether an antibody is a mouse or murine-derived (-omab), chimeric (-ximab), humanized (-zumab), or totally human (-umab) [30]. All mAbs ended with the "mAb" (which means monoclonal antibody), the exception is only with the first monoclonal antibody "Muromonab CD3." "Muro" stands for murine, while monab stands for monoclonal antibody [31].

Recently, in October 2021, the nomenclature scheme of mAbs was revised by WHO INN [32]. According to the new nomenclature scheme, "stem-mAb" is replaced by four new stems (Table 26.2):

a) **-bart:** will be used for monospecific, full-length Igs exhibiting engineered constant domains.
b) **-mig:** will be used for bispecific/multi-specific Igs.
c) **-tug:** will be used for monospecific, full-length, and Fc unmodified Igs.
d) **-ment:** will be used for monospecific fragments derived from the variable domain of Igs.

26.4 Structure of Monoclonal Antibodies

Antibodies are highly specific proteins produced by plasma cells/white blood cells. It recognizes foreign proteins called antigens present on the surface of viruses and bacteria, which helps the immune system target those foreign invaders [33, 34]. Antibodies are also called Igs which consist of four polypeptide subunits (Figure 26.1). These polypeptides are joined together by noncovalent and covalent bonds (disulfide bridges) and form a very specialized Y-shaped structure containing two different regions, namely constant and variable regions. The constant region makes the stem of the antibody and is conserved. Therefore, most of the antibodies have a very similar constant region. The variable region contains a unique sequence of amino acids that recognize and bind specific antigens called antigen-binding sites. Therefore, an antibody consists of two identical light chains (L) and two identical heavy chains (H) [33, 35, 36].

Table 26.1 Classical nomenclature of monoclonal antibody based on International Nonproprietary Name (INN).

Source substem	Meaning	Suffix
-mo-	Mouse	-mab
-xi-	Chimeric (mouse/human)	
-zu-	Humanized	
-mu-	Human	

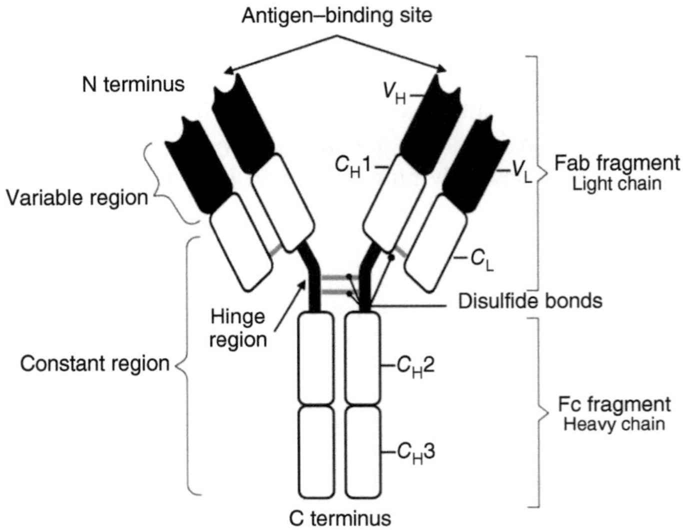

Figure 26.1 Structure of a monoclonal antibody (mAb). The mAb molecule possesses two heavy chains and two light chains joined by disulfide bonds. In mAb, there are two regions namely variable and constant regions. The variable region (*V*) possesses antigen binding sites, while the constant regions (*C*) interact with various cell receptors. The heavy chain consists of one variable (V_H) and three constant regions (C_H1, C_H2, and C_H3), while the light chain consists of one variable region (V_L) and one constant region (C_L).

The majority of antibodies produced during a specific immune response are polyclonal, originating from several plasma cell types that can bind to various antigen epitopes. A single type of plasma cell produces mAbs, which bind to a single epitope on a particular antigen [37]. The monoclonal antibody can be produced in different ways, including:

- **Murine mAb:** This was the first mAb produced on a lab scale and named murine because its origin was from mice, e.g., Muromonab anti-CD3 [38].
- **Chimeric mAb:** This form of mAb, known as chimeric, contains proteins from both mouse and human origins. The human Fc part of the antibody replaces the mouse Fc portion using recombinant DNA technology. As a result, chimeric mAbs have variable portions of antibody from mice and constant portions of

Table 26.2 Updated International Nonproprietary Name (INN) nomenclature for monoclonal antibody.

Target substem	Meaning
-ami-	Serum amyloid protein (SAP)
-ba-	Bacterial
-ci-	Cardiovascular
-de-	Metabolic or endocrine pathways
-eni-	Enzyme inhibition
-fung-	Fungal
-gro-	Skeletal muscle mass-related growth factors and receptors
-ki-	Cytokine and cytokine receptor
-ler-	Allergen
-ne-	Neural
-os-	Bone
-pru-	Immunosuppressive
-sto-	Immunostimulatory
-ta-	Tumor
-toxa-	Toxin
-vet-	Veterinary use (substem)
-vi-	Viral
Target stem suffix	
-bart	Artificial antibody
-mig	Multi-immunoglobulin
-tug	Unmodified immunoglobulin
-ment	Fragment derived from a variable domain

antibody from human origin [39]. Basiliximab (anti-IL-2 receptor) and Tituximab (anti-B-cell CD 20) are some examples of chimeric mAb.

- **Humanized mAb:** Most of the mouse antigenic components are replaced by human components in humanized mAbs. To increase resemblance to human antibodies, protein sequences are altered. The remaining antibody is of the human type, and only the hypervariable regions of the mouse antibodies are retained [40, 41]. For example, bevacizumab (anti-VEGF-A), certolizumab (anti-TNF-alpha), daclizumab (anti-IL-2 receptor), omalizumab (anti-IgE), and trastuzumab (anti-HER2) are the humanized mAbs.
- **Fully human mAb:** These proteins are entirely derived from human cells. However, the amino acid sequences have been changed using genetic engineering [42]. As a result, sequences that are not in the repertoire of humans are acquired, changing the specificity, affinity, or biological functions. Therefore, they do not cause hypersensitive reactions [43], e.g., Adalimumab (anti-TNF-alpha).

26.5 Monoclonal Antibody Production

mAbs are derived from a single clone of B-cell and are highly specific for a single epitope. Different techniques have been established for the development of mAbs which are hybridoma technology, phage display, transgenic technology, and direct screening. Both, hybridoma and transgenic technology are commonly applied approaches for mAb production. In 1975, the first monoclonal antibody was produced, and by 1986, it was approved for clinical use by the FDA. Significant technological advancements throughout this time have speeded up and improved the research and development of mAb production and treatments.

26.5.1 Hybridoma Technology

Hybridoma technology is a powerful technique used in the field of immunology and biotechnology to produce mAbs with high specificity and uniformity. The traditional mouse hybridoma technology was development by Kohler and Milstein in 1975 to produce mAbs for therapy [44]. This ground-breaking work brought them the Nobel Prize in Physiology and Medicine in 1984. The term hybridoma was coined by Leonard Herzenberg in 1976. This innovation revolutionized the field of immunology and had a significant impact on diagnostics and treatment. Hybridoma technology is used to combine innate functions of immune cells and cancer cells to generate hybridoma cells, which continuously produce mAbs specific to desired antigens. In this process, mice are immunized with specific antigens and thereafter antibody-producing B-lymphocytes are isolated and fused with myeloma cells to generate hybrid cells, called hybridoma cells. These hybridoma cells are used to culture at large scale to produce mAb, (Figure 26.2) via *in vivo* or *in vitro* method. Several mammalian cell lines have been developed for mAbs production, particularly, Chinese Hamster Ovary (CHO) cell line, murine myeloma cells (NSO), and SP2/0. Applications of mAbs produced from hybridomas are still growing, opening new opportunities for industries and advancing science and medicine because of their high purity, sensitivity, and specificity [45]. The process of hybridoma technology involves several key steps (Figure 26.2), including immunization, cell fusion, selection, screening, and large-scale production, which are described below.

26.5.1.1 Immunization

The immunization of an animal, typically a mouse with the necessary antigen, is the initial step in hybridoma technology. A protein, peptide, virus, or other molecule of interest that may stimulate an immune response can serve as an antigen against which mAbs should be raised [6]. A sequence of injections is administered over a period of several weeks to enhance the differentiation and maturation of B-lymphocytes. Once enough antibodies are produced in the serum of immunized animals within a few weeks of immunization, animals are sacrificed for B-lymphocyte isolation [46].

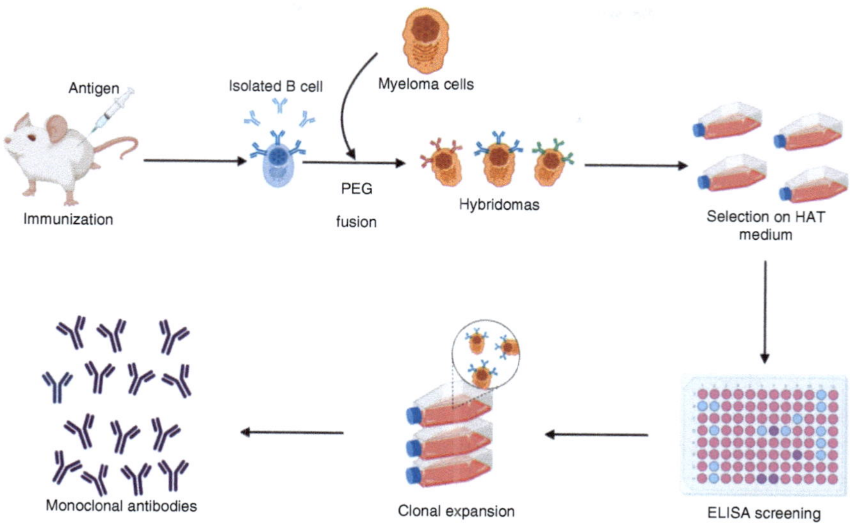

Figure 26.2 Production of monoclonal antibody using hybridoma technology. The first step in producing mAb is to inject an animal with an antigen containing the specific epitope of interest, a process called immunization. Each B-cell produces a single type of antibody. B-cells are isolated from the spleen and then fused with myeloma cells. Cells were selected using Hypoxanthine-aminopterin-thymidine (HAT) medium that allows the growth of only the hybridoma cells. The single hybridoma cells are screened for the ability to produce the desired antibody. Validated hybridoma cells are used for producing the desired mAb.

26.5.1.2 Isolation of B-lymphocytes

To isolate the activated B-cells, spleen or lymph nodes of immunized animals are removed in aseptic conditions. Mechanical disruption, enzymatic digestion, and density gradient centrifugation are used to isolate B cells. The isolated B cells are then used in the subsequent steps of hybridoma technology [47].

26.5.1.3 Cell Fusion

The next step in hybridoma technology is fusion of B-lymphocytes with myeloma cells in the presence of polyethylene glycol (PEG). However, a few weeks before fusion, myeloma cells should be treated with 8-azaguanine to achieve myeloma cells with non-functional Hypoxanthine-guanine phosphoribosyltransferase (HGPRT), a useful selective marker. The fusion of cells may result to B-cells-B-Cell, B-cell-myeloma cells, myeloma cells-myeloma cells and unfused B-cells, and myeloma cells. Therefore, a selective medium, hypoxanthine aminopterin thymidine (HAT) medium, is used to select only the B-cells fused with myeloma cells [48] and other cells died.

26.5.1.4 Hybridoma Selection

The most efficient fusion method generally results ~1–2% of fused hybridoma cells only. Among them, only 1% hybridoma remains viable upon selection (10–14 days) on HAT media [49]. Aminopterin present in HAT media blocks *de novo* nucleotide synthesis [49], thus helpful in hybrid cell selection. The unfused B-cells, due to a limited life span, die within a few days. Unfused malignant neoplastic cells die because of the lack of the HGPRT gene; however, hybrid cells remain viable in the media due to the presence of functional HGPRT [50].

26.5.1.5 Screening of Hybridoma Cells

Hybridoma cells after selection on HAT media are counted and seeded into ELISA plates in a dilution that results in one hybridoma cell per well. Screening is performed to select specific hybridomas clone that produces the desired antibodies which can target specific epitopes of an antigen [51]. After screening, the cells from selected well(s) are further propagated to procure and mAb production.

26.5.1.6 Propagation of Hybridoma Cells

Once hybridoma clones that produce the desired mAbs are screened, hybridoma cells are preserved in the freezing media for future use [52]. For production, hybridoma cells are expanded to produce a large quantity of mAbs under controlled conditions in bioreactors or flasks. The mAbs can then be extracted from the culture medium. The hybridoma cells are cultured using *in vivo* or *in vitro* methods.

In Vivo Method In the *in vivo* method, mice are used to produce monoclonal antibodies inside their body. For this, mice are injected intraperitoneally with 10^6 viable hybridoma cells suspended into phosphate buffer saline. After a few weeks, mice were anesthetized, and ascites fluid was collected for mAb isolation. Ascites fluid also contains mouse immunoglobulins to some extent as a contamination. Therefore, isolation and purification of mAb is essential. If there is stringent purity of the antibody is required, then this method may not be used [53].

In Vitro Method In this method of mAb production, hybridoma cells are cultured in the laboratory and mAb is isolated and purified from the culture media. This method is more reliable for the culturing of hybrid cells, which reduces the risk of contamination and yields highly pure mAb [54].

26.5.2 Phage Display Technique

The phage display system is extensively used in the development and production of mAbs [55]. In phage display, coding gene of the phage's coat protein is fused with a fragment of DNA, which codes for the desired antibody. The resulting fusion polypeptide is expressed on the phage surface [56]. M13 filamentous phage is the most frequently used; however, filamentous T4, T7, and lambda (λ) phage is also used for this purpose [57]. In this technique, the antibody sequence information is obtained from B-cells from spleen, peripheral blood, or bone marrow. Thereafter, mRNA was isolated, and cDNA synthesized. The antigen-recognizing variable heavy chain (VH) and variable light (VL) regions were amplified and joined using synthetic DNA linkers as a single-chain variable fragment (scFv), which is a combination of VH and VL genes [58, 59] as shown in Figure 26.3. This construct is now inserted into a phagemid vector (like a plasmid) containing an

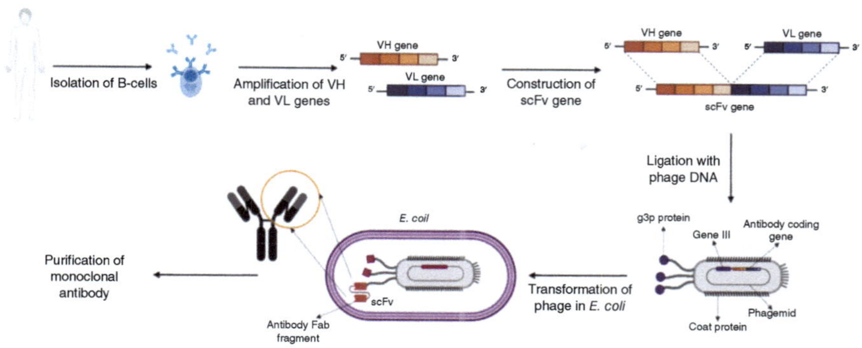

Figure 26.3 Schematic representation of phage display technique to produce monoclonal antibodies. In the first step, B-cells are isolated from humans. Then the genes of variable heavy chain (V_H) and variable light chain (V_L) are isolated and amplified by using polymerase chain reaction (PCR). In the next step, these V_H and V_L genes are connected via DNA linkers. This construct is called a single chain variable fragment (scFv). scFv is ligated with phage DNA and transferred to *E. coli* (expression vector). Lastly, antibodies that are produced on phage are isolated and purified for downstream applications.

antibiotic marker, gene coding the antibody gene-3-protein (g3p) fusion protein and regions required for M13 chromosome replication [60, 61]. The phagemids are typically packaged by an M13 helper phage in *E. coli*. Once a library of phage showing various scFvs, screening can be started. High throughput processes used in screening include developing phage libraries, washing nonbinders, and elution by trypsin/acid/base enzymatic digestion. Once the best clones have been identified after repeating the same steps two or three times, the scFv sequence is cloned into the expression vectors to produce full-length antibodies. This technology also offers the opportunity for modification of mAbs [62, 63].

26.5.3 Transgenic Animal

Transgenic technique is used to introduce one or more foreign genes into the host animal [64]. It can be a choice of human antibody production for therapeutic interventions. For this, mouse immunoglobulin gene has been genetically knocked out (KO) and replaced by human immunoglobulin genes. These KO mice were immunized, and B-cells were harvested to fuse with myeloma cell lines as established hybridoma technology. The hybridomas cells are used to screen for anticipated specificity to produce desired human antibody [65]. Transgenic mice are the most effective platform for the discovery of fully human antibodies. To date, several mAbs are approved for clinical use [66]. Several attempts are also made to produce mAb from transgenic animals. One such example is transgenic silkworms, which express recombinant mouse mAb in their cocoons [67]. In another study, human–mouse chimeric anti-CD20 mAb was produced by transgenic silkworms [67]. In this, enhancer-linked sericin-1 promoter-controlled two transgenic lines, designated L- and H-, were created that encode for L- and H-chains of a mouse IgG mAb, respectively [67]. Similarly, a recombinant anti-CD20 mAb was developed from transgenic cattle. In the bovine milk, the recovery rate was 80% with >99% purity and the yield up to ~6.8 mg/ml [68].

26.5.4 Transgenic Plants

Transgenic plants have been developed to produce valuable proteins, enzymes, and metabolites. They offer a promising biotechnological application in the production of mAbs [69]. Plant cells can be multiplied indefinitely and can produce biomass on a large scale at a lower cost. Lack of mammalian pathogens, and the presence of eukaryotic posttranslational modification system, plants and green alga are emerging as a viable production platform for mAbs [70]. Apart from these, plants also have the inbred capacity to produce antibodies [71]. Among leafy plants, tobacco [72] and alfalfa [73] have been also used to produce antibodies. Moreover, cereal crops (maize, soybean, and rice) have also been used for antibody production in their seeds, where maize is the most common cereal used for antibody production [74]. Successfully developed plant systems mAbs include anti-rabies mAb and anti-colorectal cancer mAb [71].

The stable and transient expression methods are used for mAb production. The stable expression generally includes transformation by *Agrobacterium* or particle bombardment to stably insert fragments of DNA encoding both heavy and light chains to the nucleus or chloroplast. Transient expression includes the *Agrobacterium* infiltration method for the transient introduction of genes. The gene gun method also is used for the direct introduction of the desired gene to get a transgenic plant for mAb production [75, 76].

26.5.5 B-cell Immortalization

As we know, certain B-cells can produce specific antibody to target a specific antigen's epitope. However, these B-cells cannot proliferate in such a way to fulfill the need of antibody production at an industrial scale [77]. Therefore, B-cell immortalization technology adapted to provide a solution for unlimited proliferation of B-cells for antibody production using Epstein–Barr virus (EBV) [78, 79]. EBV can effectively transform B-cells into lymphoblastoid cell lines (LCLs). After infection, the proliferating cells (LCLs) are visualized by a light microscope. Thereafter, cells are screened using immunogenic techniques for antibody specificity [80]. Positive cells are further cultured to produce human mAbs from immortalized B-cells [81].

26.6 Therapeutic Applications of Monoclonal Antibody

From the last four decades from being research tools to effective treatments, significant advancement has been taken place in the field of mAbs. Currently, the FDA has approved about 100s of therapeutic mAbs for the treatment of cancer and other diseases [12, 82].

Through the activation of the antibody-dependent and complement-mediated cytotoxicity, mAb treatment harnesses host defense mechanisms. They also work

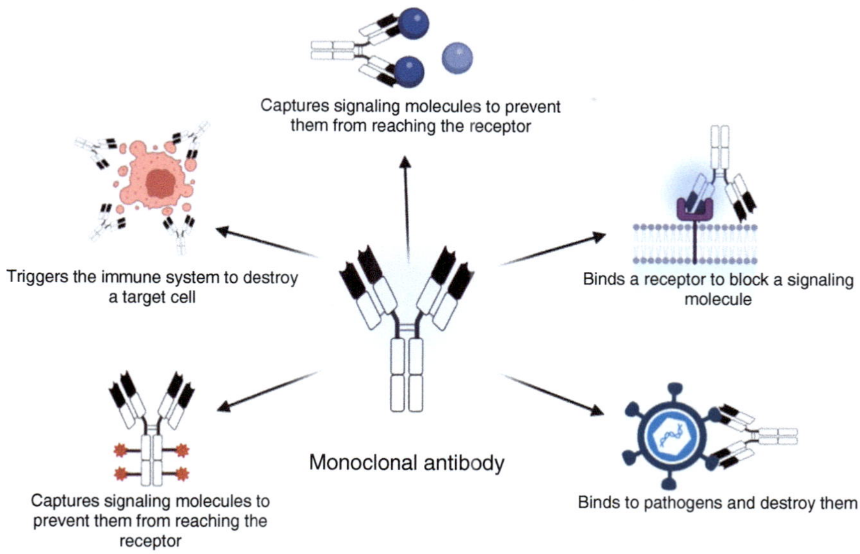

Figure 26.4 Therapeutics application of monoclonal antibody (mAb). The mAbs are used in several applications in the biomedical field. They can be used for disease diagnosis, neutralization, and destruction of the pathogenic antigens, blocking signaling pathways either by binding with ligands or receptors, delivering conjugated drugs to the tumor sites, triggering the immune response, etc.

by inhibiting cell cycle and apoptotic signaling pathways. Combining mAbs therapy with chemotherapeutic drugs or radioactive substances provides additional therapeutic options. Conjugated mAbs circulate throughout the body, bind to the target antigen, and deliver the antigen to immune elimination processes [83–85]. mAbs have a major impact on a variety of disease processes, including solid and hematological malignancies [86, 87].

mAbs play a very significant role in the disease diagnosis as well as treatment (Figure 26.4). mAbs trigger the immune response to destroy a target cell e.g., Herceptin or trastuzumab (for breast cancer), Rituxan (lymphoma, rheumatoid arthritis), etc. mAbs bind a receptor to block a signaling molecule, e.g., Vecitibix or panitumumab (for colorectal cancer), Yervoy, or ipilimumab (for melanoma). mAbs can also capture signaling molecules to prevent them from reaching the receptor, e.g., Avastin (various cancers), Humira adalimumab (Crohn's disease, rheumatoid arthritis). mAbs can bind to pathogens, e.g., Bebtelovimab (COVID-19), and Synagis (respiratory syncytial virus). mAbs also help to deliver toxic drugs to the tumor cells. Antibody–drug conjugate binds to receptor of tumor cells, e.g., Kadcyla or ado-trastuzumab emtansine (for breast cancer), Adcetris, or Brentuximab (for Hodgkin lymphoma).

26.6.1 Current mAbs in Cancer Therapy

Antibodies represent the single largest class of new drug agents under development due to target specificity and efficacy. To date, several mAbs are approved to treat different malignancies (Table 26.3). These mAbs work via several mechanisms,

Table 26.3 FDA-approved monoclonal antibodies (mAbs) for cancer treatment.

mAbs	Format	Target	Technology	Indication	FDA approval	References
Rituximab	Chimeric IgG1	CD20	Hybridoma	Non-Hodgkin lymphoma	1997	[88]
Trastuzumab	Humanized IgG1	HER2	Hybridoma	Breast cancer	1998	[89]
Gemtuzumab ozogamicin	Humanized IgG4, conjugated	CD33	Hybridoma	Acute myeloid leukemia	2000	[90]
Alemtuzumab	Humanized IgG1	CD52	Hybridoma	Chronic myeloid leukemia	2001	[91]
Ibritumomab tiuxetan	Murine IgG1	CD20	Hybridoma	Non-Hodgkin lymphoma	2002	[92]
Cetuximab	Chimeric IgG1	EGFR	Hybridoma	Colorectal cancer	2004	[93]
Bevacizumab	Humanized IgG1	VEGF-A	Hybridoma	Colorectal cancer	2004	[94]
Panitumumab	Humanized IgG2	EGFR	Transgenic mice	Colorectal cancer	2006	[95]
Ofatumumab	Human IgG1	CD20	Transgenic mice	Chronic lymphocytic leukemia	2009	[96]
Ipilimumab	Human IgG1	CTLA-4	Transgenic mice	Metastatic melanoma	2011	[97]
Brentuximab vedotin	Chimeric IgG1, conjugated	CD30	Hybridoma	Hodgkin lymphoma, systemic anaplastic large cell lymphoma	2011	[98]
Pertuzumab	Humanized IgG1	HER2	Hybridoma	Breast cancer	2012	[99]
Trastuzumab emtansine	Humanized IgG1, conjugated	HER2	Hybridoma	Breast cancer	2012	[100]
Obinutuzumab	Humanized IgG1 glycoengineered	CD20	Hybridoma	Chronic lymphocytic leukemia	2013	[101]
Ramucirumab	Human IgG1	VEGFR2	Phage display	Gastric cancer, colorectal cancer, non-small cell lung cancer	2014	[102]
Blinatumomab	Murine bispecific	CD19, CD3	Hybridoma	Acute lymphoblastic leukemia	2014	[103]
Nivolumab	Human IgG4	PD-1	Transgenic mice	Melanoma, non-small cell lung cancer	2014	[104]
Pembrolizumab	Humanized IgG4	PD-1	Hybridoma	Melanoma	2014	[105]
Necitumumab	Human IgG1	EGFR	Phage display	Non-small cell lung cancer	2015	[106]
Dinutuximab	Chimeric IgG1	GD2	Hybridoma	Neuroblastoma	2015	[107]
Daratumumab	Human IgG1	CD38	Transgenic mice	Multiple myeloma	2015	[108]

Elotuzumab	Humanized IgG1	SLAMF7	Hybridoma	Multiple myeloma	2015	[109]
Olaratumab	Human IgG1	PDGFRα	Transgenic mice	Soft tissue sarcoma	2016	[110]
Atezolizumab	Humanized IgG1	PD-L1	Hybridoma	Bladder cancer, triple negative breast cancer	2016	[111]
Inotuzumab Ozogamicin	Humanized IgG4, conjugated	CD22	Hybridoma	Acute lymphoblastic leukemia	2017	[112]
Avelumab	Human IgG1	PD-L1	Phage display	Merkel cell carcinoma	2017	[113]
Gemtuzumab ozogamicin	Humanized IgG4, conjugated	CD33	Hybridoma	Acute myeloid leukemia	2017	[114]
Durvalumab	Human IgG1	PD-L1	Transgenic mice	Bladder cancer, lung cancer	2017	[115]
Cemiplimab	Human MAb	PD-1	Transgenic mice	Cutaneous squamous cell carcinoma	2018	[116]
Moxetumomab pasudodox	Murine IgG1, conjugated	CD22	Phage display	Hairy cell leukemia	2018	[117]
Polatuzumab vedotin	Humanized IgG1, conjugated	CD79β	Hybridoma	Diffuse large B-cell lymphoma	2019	[118]
Enfortumab vedotin	Human IgG1	Nectin-4	Transgenic mice	Urothelial cancer	2019	[119]
Trastuzumab deruxtecan	Humanized IgG1, conjugated	HER2	Hybridoma	Breast cancer	2019	[120]
Isatuximab	Chimeric IgG1	CD38	Hybridoma	Multiple myeloma	2020	[121]
Sacituzumab govitecan	Humanized IgG1, conjugated	TROP-2	Hybridoma	Triple-neg. breast cancer	2020	[122]
Tafasitamab	Humanized IgG1	CD19	Hybridoma	Diffuse large B-cell lymphoma	2020	[123]
Belantamab mafodotin	Humanized IgG1, conjugated	B-cell maturation antigen	Hybridoma	Multiple myeloma	2020	[124]
Margetuximab	Chimeric IgG1	HER2	Hybridoma	Breast cancer	2020	[125]
Dostarlimab	Humanized IgG4	PD-1	Hybridoma	Endometrial cancer	2021	[126]
Loncastuximab tesirine	Humanized IgG1	CD19	Hybridoma	Diffuse large B-cell lymphoma	2021	[127]
Amivantamab	Human bispecific IgG1	EGFR	Hybridoma	metastatic non-small cell lung cancer (NSCLC)	2021	[128]
Tisotumab vedotin	Human IgG1, conjugated	Tissue factor	Hybridoma	Cervical cancer	2021	[129]
Relatlimab	Human IgG4	LAG-3	Hybridoma	Melanoma	2022	[130]
Teclistamab	Humanized IgG4	BCMA, CD3	Hybridoma	Multiple myeloma	2022	[131]
Tremelimumab	Human IgG2A	CTLA-4	Murine cell line	Antineoplastic; liver cancer	2022	[132]
Mirvetuximab soravtansine	Humanized IgG1, conjugated	Folate receptor alpha	Hybridoma	Ovarian cancer	2022	[133]

including direct targeting of malignant cells, altering the host response, transferring cytotoxic moieties, and retargeting cellular immunity toward cancer cells [134]. In addition, mAbs help to combat cancerous growth through many functions that include opsonization [135], initiating apoptosis [136], blocking growth signals [137], preventing angiogenesis [138], and they also deliver radiation and drugs to specific locations. Abs aid in the immune system's ability to recognize cancer cells. Rituximab (Rituxan) is a mAb that has received FDA approval for the treatment of non-Hodgkin lymphoma and chronic lymphocytic leukemia [139]. Rituximab functions by closely attaching to and targeting a particular protein called CD20 that is expressed on both mature and malignant B-cells but not on immature B-cells [140]. When Rituximab attaches to CD20 on the B-cells, it makes the cells more visible to an immune cell to attack [141]. This mechanism is called antibody-dependent cell-mediated cytotoxicity (ADCC) [140, 142]. Similarly, the binding of the antibody leads to the classical pathway of complement activation, which recruits complement proteins to make holes in the plasma membrane via membrane attack complex leading to cell lysis. This mechanism is also known as complement-dependent cytotoxicity (CDC) [143]. Binding of this antibody signals cells to self-destruction or apoptosis. The primary function of Rituximab is to lower the number of B-cells. However, the body will produce new healthy B-cells to replace malignant B-cells. So, ultimately, the malignant B-cells are less likely to reoccur [144].

Another example is cetuximab, a chimeric mAb with the commercial name Erbitux used to treat head and neck cancer as well as colon cancer [145]. EGFRs, which are overexpressed in malignant cells responsible for oncogenic signaling are inhibited by cetuximab [146]. Necitumumab and panitumumab both target the extracellular domain of the EGFR to prevent ligand binding and intracellular signaling, which in ultimately inhibit the growth of tumor cells [147, 148]. The human epidermal growth factor receptor 2 (HER2) is another receptor that promotes rapid cell proliferation in gastric and breast cancer [149]. Herceptin or trastuzumab, is used to treat cancerous cells that overexpress HER2 receptors [150]. It inhibits the proliferation of tumor cells by binding HER2 receptor [151]. Pertuzumab, which is combined with trastuzumab, was another mAb approved by the FDA in the year 2012 [152]. Moreover, margetuximab and pertuzumab are used to treat metastatic breast cancer that is HER2 positive [125, 153]. Pertuzumab is a humanized mAb, whereas margetuximab is an Fc-optimized chimeric mAb. Bevacizumab, also known as Avastin, a humanized mAb that has received FDA approval for the treatment of several malignancies, including colon, kidney, glioblastoma, ovarian, hepatic, and lung cancers [154–156].

Angiogenesis plays an important role in cancer progression and metastasis. Blood vessels are the only source of oxygen and nutrient supply required for the growth and proliferation of tumor cells. The requirement for nutrients and oxygen grows along with tumor's size [157]. In order to achieve this, cancer cells secrete vascular endothelial growth factor A (VEGF-A), which promotes angiogenesis [158]. Several mAb has been developed to prevent angiogenesis. Bevacizumab functions by attaching to all VEGF-A protein isoforms and preventing VEGF-A from interacting with VEGF receptors. Hence, preventing angiogenesis inside the tumor [159]. Similarly, ramucirumab is another important antiangiogenic mAb that has shown an encouraging inhibitory effect on solid tumor growth by interfering with VEGF-A and its receptor [160].

The transport of radioactive agents to cancer cells by mAb became a promising treatment strategy [161, 162]. Ibritumomab tiuxetan, also known as Zevalin, is a conjugated mAb approved for the treatment of B-cell follicular non-Hodgkin lymphoma, a kind of white blood cell malignancy [163]. It is a radioactive medication that possesses a radioactive isotope (yttrium-90 or indium-111) with the chelator tiuxetan [164, 165]. This combination kills B-cells by attaching to the CD20 antigen present on cancerous B-cells, which enables radiation from the attached isotopes to do so. Some mAbs are used to treat cancer cells by delivering medication to the intended site [166]. For example, brentuximab vedotin is connected to a chemotherapeutic medication that delivers antimicrotubule agents into CD30-expressing cells [167]. By this way, the antibody delivers the chemotherapeutic agent to bind and subsequently kill cancer cells. Another example is Ado-trastuzumab emtansine (Kadcyla), used in the treatment of early as well as metastatic $HER2^+$ breast cancer [168].

Immune checkpoint inhibitors are thought to be next-generation cancer therapy and are emerging as a frontline cancer therapy [169]. This type of therapy is one of the innovative therapeutic approaches that is used to treat several malignancies by modulating a patient's immune system. Within the immune system, T-cell play a central role to fight cancer [170]. T-cells can infiltrate the tumor microenvironment where activated tumor antigen-specific T-cells recognize tumor cells through the interaction between T-cell receptors and major histocompatibility complex. After recognition, T-cells release cytokines to eliminate the tumor cells [171]. Programmed death ligand-1 (PD-L1) is one of the inhibitory ligands that under normal conditions help to maintain immune homeostasis [172]. However, in many cancer, PD-L1 can help tumor cells to evade the immune system, particularly when it is overexpressed. PD-L1 deactivates the activity of T-cells by binding with the programmed cell death protein 1 (PD-1) expressed on T-cells [173, 174]. However, cancer cells take advantage of these checkpoints to switch the T-cells off and thereby evade immune surveillance. Some anticancer mAbs are used to block PD-1 or PD-L1 [175]. When these proteins are blocked, the ability of T-cells is increased to eliminate cancer cells. mAbs are promising candidates to target immune checkpoint inhibitors. Dostarlimab, brand name Jemperli, is one of the most recent examples of PD-1 blocker [126, 175]. It is a humanized IgG4 mAb. It blocks the PD-1 receptor, allowing the immune system to recognize, attack, and destroy the tumor cells. Recently, it is also being used to treat colorectal cancer [176]. Similarly, pembrolizumab, nivolumab, and durvalumab are several FDA-approved mAb drugs that are used as immune checkpoint inhibitors by targeting PD-1 and PD-L1 [177–179]. Cancer researchers are continuing to investigate new ways to use the precision of mAb to treat cancer patients.

Table 26.4 FDA-approved monoclonal antibodies (mAbs) for microbial diseases.

mAbs	Format	Target	Technology	Indication	FDA approval	References
Palivizumab	Humanized IgG1	RSV	Hybridoma	Prevention of respiratory syncytial virus	1998	[180]
Raxibacumab	Human IgG1	*B. anthrasis* PA	Transgenic mice	Anthrax infection	2012	[181]
Bezlotoxumab	Human IgG1	*Clostridium difficile* enterotoxin B	Transgenic mice	Treatment of *Clostridium difficile* infection	2016	[182]
Obiltoxaximab	Chimeric IgG1	*B. anthrasis* PA	Hybridoma	Anthrax infection	2016	[183]
Ibalizumab	Humanized IgG4	CD4	Hybridoma	HIV infection	2018	[184]
Atoltivimab, maftivimab, and odesivimab-ebgn	Mixture of 3 human IgG1	Ebola virus	Hybridoma	Ebola virus infection	2020	[185]
Ansuvimab	Human IgG1	Ebola virus glycoprotein-1,2	Hybridoma	Ebola virus infection	2020	[186]

26.6.2 Monoclonal Antibodies Used in Microbial Diseases

Antibodies are also utilized in the diagnosis and treatment of diseases caused by different microbes and heir toxins. Unfortunately, there are only a few mAbs (Table 26.4) that have been approved for the treatment of these diseases, even though the mAb revolution has provided numerous new options to clinicians for treating malignancies and inflammatory disorders. Palivizumab was the first FDA-approved mAb, which works against an epitope in the A antigenic site of the fusion (F) protein of respiratory syncytial virus (RSV). Palivizumab inhibits viral entry into the human cell and thereby prevents infection. Raxibacumab and obiltoxaximab are designed to treat *Bacillus anthrax* exposure. The protective antigen (PA) a component of the anthrax toxin is the target of these mAbs. Three primary toxins are produced by anthrax bacteria: edoema toxin, lethal toxin, and a capsule consisting of protein called PA. PA plays a crucial role in allowing the other toxins to enter cells. mAbs binds to PA, preventing it from attaching to receptors on cells and thereby blocking the entry of the other toxins into cells. mAbs neutralize PA, which enables the body's immune system to eradicate the bacteria and inhibits the progression of anthrax infection [187, 188]. Ibalizumab is a recombinant humanized mAb approved by the FDA in 2018 for adults in combination with other antiretroviral drugs. It blocks human immunodeficiency viruses (HIV) from infecting CD4 cells and acts as an inhibitor of postattachment steps that allow HIV particles to enter the host cell. Thus, preventing the viral transmission [189]. Ansuvimab is fully human mAb prescribed for treating Ebola virus infection. It targets glycoprotein-1,2 surface protein and blocks its entry into host cell [190]. Similarly, atoltivimab, maftivimab, and odesivimab-ebgn (Inmazeb) are effective treatments against Ebola virus. This is the fixed-dose combination of three mAb [191].

26.6.3 Monoclonal Antibodies Used in Other Diseases

Besides the uses of mAbs in cancer and other infectious diseases, it is broadly used in other diseases as well. The first chimeric mAb, abciximab (ReoPro), was approved in 1994 and used as a blood thinner. It prevents coagulation by attaching to functional platelet receptors that are involved in platelet aggregation and is commonly used to prevent thrombosis and myocardial ischemia [192–194]. Omalizumab (Xolair) is an example of a humanized monoclonal antibody used to stop an asthmatic cascade. Surfaces of mast cells, basophils, and eosinophils exhibit Fc epsilon receptor, and Omalizumab prevents IgE binding to Fc epsilon receptor. When an antigen binds to the IgE Fc epsilon receptor, it stimulates granulocyte degranulation and releases inflammatory mediators, including histamine [195–197]. In addition, omalizumab has also showed promising effects for bullous pemphigoid and a component of chronic idiopathic urticaria, which are both autoimmune disorders [198, 199].

Adalimumab, a mAb commonly used against rheumatoid arthritis, targets tumor necrosis factor (TNF), a cytokine secreted mainly by macrophages to induce local inflammation. The TNF-induced inflammation causes dilation of blood vessels and facilitates the recruitment of natural killer cells [200]. When there is an infection, it is beneficial; however, excessive amounts of TNF, especially when there is no infection, may cause autoimmune diseases like rheumatoid arthritis [201]. Adalimumab (Humira) works by preventing or neutralizing the excess TNF proteins from adhering to healthy cells, hence lowering the harmful consequences of the excess TNF [202]. The anti-TNF-alpha mAbs, certolizumab [203], golimumab [204], and infliximab [205] are also used to reduce inflammation (Table 26.5). Inflammatory bowel disease (IBD) [260, 261], psoriasis [262], and severe instances of rheumatoid arthritis [263] are all being treated with this mAb. Natalizumab, is a humanized mAb against α-4 Integrin (α4β1). Natalizumab is frequently used to treat Crohn's disease. It is a multifactorial disease and the activation of specific pathways of the immune system is important. Specially, integrins (α4-integrin or α4β7-integrin) mediate the specific binding between the leukocytes and the endothelial cells. This binding regulates the migration of leukocytes into the normal and inflamed intestine. Natalizumab inhibits both α4β7-integrin/mucosal addressing-cell adhesion molecule-1 interaction and α4β1/vascular-cell adhesion molecule-1 (VCAM-1) binding. Thus, it is beneficial for the patients with active inflammation or chronically active disease [264].

Altogether, mAb has great importance to be utilized for a variety of purposes from diagnosis and treatment of different diseases.

Table 26.5 FDA approved monoclonal antibodies (mAbs) for other diseases.

mAbs	Format	Target	Technology	Indication	FDA approval	References
Muromonab-CD3	Murine IgG2a	CD3	Hybridoma	Kidney transplant rejection	1986	[11]
Abciximab	Chimeric IgG1	GPIIb/IIa	Hybridoma	Prevention of blood clot	1994	[192]
Basiliximab	Chimeric IgG1	IL-2R	Hybridoma	Prevention of kidney transplant rejection	1998	[206]
Infliximab	Chimeric IgG1	TNF-α	Hybridoma	Crohn's disease	1998	[207]
Adalimumab	Human IgG1	TNF-α	Phage display	Rheumatoid arthritis	2002	[208]
Omalizumab	Humanized IgG1	IgE	Hybridoma	Asthma	2003	[209]
Natalizumab	Humanized IgG1	ITGA4	Hybridoma	Multiple sclerosis, Crohn's disease	2004	[210]
Ranibizumab	Humanized IgG1	VEGF-A	Hybridoma	Macular degeneration	2006	[211]
Eculizumab	Humanized IgG2	C5	Hybridoma	Paroxysmal nocturnal hemoglobinuria	2007	[212]
Certolizumab pegol	Humanized, pegylated, conjugated	TNF-α	Hybridoma	Crohn's disease	2008	[213]
Ustekinumab	Human IgG1	IL-12/23	Transgenic mice	Psoriasis	2009	[214]
Canakinumab	Human IgG1	IL-1 β	Transgenic mice	Muckle–Wells syndrome	2009	[215]
Golimumab	Human IgG1	TNF-α	Transgenic mice	Rheumatoid and psoriatic arthritis, IBD	2009	[216]
Tocilizumab	Humanized IgG1	IL-6R	Hybridoma	Rheumatoid arthritis	2010	[217]
Denosumab	Human IgG2	RANKL	Transgenic mice	Bone loss	2010	[218]
Belimumab	Human IgG1	BLyS	Phage display	Systemic lupus erythematosus	2011	[219]
Siltuximab	Chimeric IgG1	IL-6	Hybridoma	Castleman disease	2014	[220]
Vedolizumab	Humanized IgG1	α4β7 integrin	Hybridoma	Ulcerative colitis, Crohn's disease	2014	[221]
Idarucizumab	Humanized Fab	Dabigatran	Hybridoma	Reversal of dabigatran-induced anticoagulation	2015	[222]
Secukinumab	Human IgG1	IL-17α	Transgenic mice	Psoriasis	2015	[223]
Mepolizumab	Humanized IgG1	IL-5	Hybridoma	Severe eosinophilic asthma	2015	[224]

Alirocumab	Human IgG1	PCSK9	Transgenic mice	Hypercholesterolemia	2015	[225]
Evolocumab	Human IgG2	PCSK9	Transgenic mice	Hypercholesterolemia	2015	[226]
Ixekizumab	Humanized IgG4	IL-17α	Hybridoma	Psoriasis	2016	[226]
Reslizumab	Humanized IgG4	IL-5	Hybridoma	Asthma	2016	[227]
Brodalumab	Human IgG2	IL-17R	Transgenic mice	Plaque psoriasis	2017	[228]
Guselkumab	Human IgG1	IL-23 p19	Phage display	Plaque psoriasis	2017	[229]
Dupilumab	Human IgG4	IL-4Rα	Transgenic mice	Atopic dermatitis	2017	[230]
Sarilumab	Human IgG1	IL-6R	Transgenic mice	Rheumatoid arthritis	2017	[231]
Ocrelizumab	Humanized IgG1	CD20	Hybridoma	Multiple sclerosis	2017	[232]
Emicizumab	Humanized IgG4	Factor IX and X	Hybridoma	Hemophilia A	2017	[233]
Benralizumab	Humanized IgG1	IL-5Rα	Hybridoma	Asthma	2017	[234]
Burosumab	Human IgG1	FGF23	Transgenic mice	X-linked hypophosphatemia	2018	[235]
Lanadelumab	Human IgG1	Plasma kallikrein	Phage display	Hereditary angioedema attacks	2018	[236]
Erenumab	Human IgG2	CGRPR	Transgenic mice	Migraine prevention	2018	[237]
Galcanezumab	Humanized IgG4	CGRP	Hybridoma	Migraine prevention	2018	[238]
Tildrakizumab	Humanized IgG1	IL-23 p19	Hybridoma	Plaque psoriasis	2018	[239]
Emapalumab	Human IgG1	IFNγ	Phage display	Primary hemophagocytic lymph histiocytosis	2018	[240]
Fremanezumab	Humanized IgG2	CGRP	Hybridoma	Migraine prevention	2018	[241]
Ravulizumab	humanized IgG2/4	C5	Hybridoma	Paroxysmal nocturnal hemoglobinuria	2018	[242]
Caplacizumab	Humanized Nanobody	von Willebrand factor	Hybridoma	Acquired thrombotic thrombocytopenic purpura	2019	[243]
Romosozumab	Sclerostin	Humanized IgG2	Hybridoma	Osteoporosis	2019	[244]
Risankizumab	Humanized IgG1	IL-23 p19	Hybridoma	Plaque psoriasis	2019	[245]
Brolucizumab	Humanized scFv	VEGF-A	Hybridoma	Macular degeneration	2019	[246]
Crizanlizumab	Humanized IgG2	P-selectin	Hybridoma	Sickle cell disease	2019	[247]

(Continued)

Table 26.5 (Continued)

mAbs	Format	Target	Technology	Indication	FDA approval	References
Eptinezumab	Humanized IgG1	CGRP	Yeast display	Migraine prevention	2020	[248]
Teprotumumab	Human IgG1	IGF-1R	Transgenic mice	Thyroid eye disease	2020	[249]
Inebilizumab	Humanized IgG1	CD19	Hybridoma	Neuromyelitis optica and neuromyelitis optica spectrum disorders	2020	[250]
Satralizumab	Humanized IgG2	IL-6R	Hybridoma	Neuromyelitis optica and neuromyelitis optica spectrum disorders	2020	[251]
Naxitamab	Humanized IgG1	GD2	Hybridoma	High-risk neuroblastoma and refractory osteomedullary disease	2020	[252]
Aducanumab	Human IgG1	Amyloid beta	Hybridoma	Alzheimer's disease	2021	[252]
Evinacumab	Human IgG4	Angiopoietin-like 3	Hybridoma	Homozygous familial hypercholesterolemia	2021	[253]
Tralokinumab	Human IgG4	IL-13	Murine cell line	Atopic dermatitis	2021	[254]
Anifrolumab	Human IgG1	IFNAR1	Murine cell line	Systemic lupus erythematosus	2021	[255]
Tezepelumab	Human IgG2	Thymic stromal lymphopoietin	Hybridoma	Severe asthma	2021	[256]
Sutimlimab	SutimlimAb	C1s	Hybridoma	Cold agglutinin disease	2022	[257]
Faricimab	Human/humanized IgG1 kappa/lambda	VEGF-A, Ang-2	Hybridoma	neovascular age-related macular degeneration (nAMD) and diabetic macular edema (DME)	2022	[258]
Spesolimab	Humanized IgG1	IL-36 receptor	Hybridoma	Pustular psoriasis	2022	[259]

26.7 Challenges and Future Prospects

The monoclonal antibodies (mAbs) have enormous potential from diagnosis to treatment of several malignancies and infectious diseases. Although several mAbs have been approved to date, there is a huge access gap of the population at most risk of infectious diseases living in low- and middle- income countries. Therefore, there is an unmet need for planning to reduce the cost of these products for the people who need them most. In addition, major challenges also occur at the level of mAb production such as low yield, maintenance of cell viability for the production of antibody, contamination, which lead to an increase in the cost of development. This can be reduced by optimizing cell line, culture process, and mAb production system. In addition, the mutation(s) in the target genes (e.g. EGFR) and reduced expression (e.g. triple negative breast cancer) level also leads to resistance or ineffectiveness to mAb-based therapy. Therefore, next-generation drugs are being developed to manage such issues in the clinics.

Treating cancer requires aggressive but specific and effective therapy. Some therapeutic drugs are highly toxic that adversely affect healthy cells along with fast-proliferating tumor cells. So, researchers are trying to develop drug agents that specifically target cancer cells. One possible way of this might be linking drug with an antibody specific to the protein expressed on tumor cells. There are some antibody–drug conjugates in clinics; however, it is important to titrate the right amount of conjugated drugs administered to patients to effectively target cancer cells. Moreover, therapeutic efficacy should also be improved by their stability to sustain their nontoxic concentration levels within the blood circulation for a longer duration.

Acknowledgments

The authors Ambuj Shahi, Madhuri Singh (UGC-CSIR), and Girijesh K. Patel (DBT-RRF) acknowledge the fellowship support from CSIR and DBT, Government of India, respectively. The authors also acknowledge the Department of Gastroenterology (Medicine), SGPGIMS, and MNNIT Allahabad for the necessary space and facilities.

References

1 Alam, R. (1998). A brief review of the immune system. *Prim Care* 25 (4): 727–738.

2 Sundberg, E.J. (2009). Structural basis of antibody-antigen interactions. *Methods Mol. Biol.* 524: 23–36.

3 Sela-Culang, I., Kunik, V., and Ofran, Y. (2013). The structural basis of antibody-antigen recognition. *Front. Immunol.* 4: 302.

4 Rita Costa, A., Elisa Rodrigues, M., Henriques, M. et al. (2010). Guidelines to cell engineering for monoclonal antibody production. *Eur. J. Pharm. Biopharm.* 74 (2): 127–138.

5 Buss, N.A., Henderson, S.J., McFarlane, M. et al. (2012). Monoclonal antibody therapeutics: history and future. *Curr. Opin. Pharmacol.* 12 (5): 615–622.

6 Tomita, M. and Tsumoto, K. (2011). Hybridoma technologies for antibody production. *Immunotherapy* 3 (3): 371–380.

7 O'Mahony, D. and Bishop, M.R. (2006). Monoclonal antibody therapy. *Front. Biosci.* 11: 1620–1635.

8 Conti, P., Pregliasco, F.E., Calvisi, V. et al. (2021). Monoclonal antibody therapy in COVID-19. *J. Biol. Regul. Homeost. Agents* 35 (2): 423–427.

9 Hansel, T.T., Kropshofer, H., Singer, T. et al. (2010). The safety and side effects of monoclonal antibodies. *Nat. Rev. Drug Discovery* 9 (4): 325–338.

10 Shepard, H.M., Phillips, G.L., Thanos, C.D., and Feldmann, M. (2017). Developments in therapy with monoclonal antibodies and related proteins. *Clin. Med. (Lond)* 17 (3): 220–232.

11 Canafax, D.M. and Draxler, C.A. (1987). Monoclonal antilymphocyte antibody (OKT3) treatment of acute renal allograft rejection. *Pharmacotherapy* 7 (4): 121–124.

12 Mullard, A. (2021). FDA approves 100th monoclonal antibody product. *Nat. Rev. Drug Discovery* 20 (7): 491–495.

13 Christofi, T., Baritaki, S., Falzone, L. et al. (2019). Current perspectives in cancer immunotherapy. *Cancers (Basel)* 11 (10): 1472.

14 Zhang, C. (2012). Hybridoma technology for the generation of monoclonal antibodies. *Methods Mol. Biol.* 901: 117–135.

15 Rodrigues, M.E., Costa, A.R., Henriques, M. et al. (2010). Technological progresses in monoclonal antibody production systems. *Biotechnol. Progr.* 26 (2): 332–351.

16 Bosch, F. and Rosich, L. (2008). The contributions of Paul Ehrlich to pharmacology: a tribute on the occasion of the centenary of his Nobel Prize. *Pharmacology* 82 (3): 171–179.

17 Doevendans, E. and Schellekens, H. (2019). Immunogenicity of innovative and biosimilar monoclonal antibodies. *Antibodies (Basel)* 8 (1).

18 Adams, G.P. and Weiner, L.M. (2005). Monoclonal antibody therapy of cancer. *Nat. Biotechnol.* 23 (9): 1147–1157.

19 Leavy, O. (2010). Therapeutic antibodies: past, present and future. *Nat. Rev. Immunol.* 10 (5): 297.

20 Alters, S.E., Sakai, K., Steinman, L., and Oi, V.T. (1990). Mechanisms of anti-CD4-mediated depletion and immunotherapy. A study using a set of chimeric anti-CD4 antibodies. *J. Immunol.* 144 (12): 4587–4592.

21 Guan, M., Zhou, Y.P., Sun, J.L., and Chen, S.C. (2015, https://doi.org/10.1155/2015/428169). Adverse events of monoclonal antibodies used for cancer therapy. *Biomed Res. Int.* 428169.

22 Smith, M.R. (2003). Rituximab (monoclonal anti-CD20 antibody): mechanisms of action and resistance. *Oncogene.* 22 (47): 7359–7368.

23 Goldenberg, M.M. (1999). Trastuzumab, a recombinant DNA-derived humanized monoclonal antibody, a novel agent for the treatment of metastatic breast cancer. *Clin. Ther.* 21 (2): 309–318.

24 Weinblatt, M.E., Keystone, E.C., Furst, D.E. et al. (2003). Adalimumab, a fully human anti-tumor necrosis factor alpha monoclonal antibody, for the treatment of rheumatoid arthritis in patients taking concomitant methotrexate: the ARMADA trial. *Arthritis Rheum.* 48 (1): 35–45.

25 Li, F., Vijayasankaran, N., Shen, A.Y. et al. (2010). Cell culture processes for monoclonal antibody production. *MAbs* 2 (5): 466–479.

26 Panowski, S., Bhakta, S., Raab, H. et al. (2014). Site-specific antibody drug conjugates for cancer therapy. *MAbs* 6 (1): 34–45.

27 Wang, Z., Zhu, J., and Lu, H. (2020). Antibody glycosylation: impact on antibody drug characteristics and quality control. *Appl. Microbiol. Biotechnol.* 104 (5): 1905–1914.

28 Fox, E., Lovett-Racke, A.E., Gormley, M. et al. (2021). A phase 2 multicenter study of ublituximab, a novel glycoengineered anti-CD20 monoclonal antibody, in patients with relapsing forms of multiple sclerosis. *Mult. Scler.* 27 (3): 420–429.

29 Kopp-Kubel, S. (1995). International Nonproprietary Names (INN) for pharmaceutical substances. *Bull. World Health Organ.* 73 (3): 275–279.

30 Scheen, A.J. (2009). International classification of various types of monoclonal antibodies. *Rev. Med. Liege* 64 (5–6): 244–247.

31 Akioka, Y., Hattori, M., and Ito, K. (2005). Muromonab CD3. *Nihon Rinsho.* 63 (Suppl 5): 747–750.

32 Balocco, R., Koch, S.D.S.G., Thorpe, R. et al. (2022). New INN nomenclature for monoclonal antibodies. *Lancet* 399 (10319): 24.

33 Chiu, M.L., Goulet, D.R., Teplyakov, A., and Gilliland, G.L. (2019). Antibody structure and function: the basis for engineering therapeutics. *Antibodies (Basel)* 8 (4): 55.

34 Kapingidza, A.B., Kowal, K., and Chruszcz, M. (2020). Antigen-antibody complexes. *Subcell. Biochem.* 94: 465–497.

35 Goulet, D.R. and Atkins, W.M. (2020). Considerations for the design of antibody-based therapeutics. *J. Pharm. Sci.* 109 (1): 74–103.

36 Cymer, F., Beck, H., Rohde, A., and Reusch, D. (2018). Therapeutic monoclonal antibody N-glycosylation – structure, function and therapeutic potential. *Biologicals* 52: 1–11.

37 Newcombe, C. and Newcombe, A.R. (2007). Antibody production: polyclonal-derived biotherapeutics. *J. Chromatogr. B* 848 (1): 2–7.

38 Peterson, N.C. (1996). Recombinant antibodies: alternative strategies for developing and manipulating murine-derived monoclonal antibodies. *Lab Anim. Sci.* 46 (1): 8–14.

39 Chakhtoura, M. and Abdelnoor, A.M. (2010). Monoclonal antibodies used as prophylactic, therapeutic and diagnostic agents. *Immunopharmacol. Immunotoxicol.* 32 (4): 533–542.

40 Klingbeil, C. and Hsu, D.H. (1999). Pharmacology and safety assessment of humanized monoclonal antibodies for therapeutic use. *Toxicol. Pathol.* 27 (1): 1–3.

41 Jarboe, J., Gupta, A., and Saif, M.W. (2014). Therapeutic human monoclonal antibodies against cancer. *Methods Mol. Biol.* 1060: 61–77.

42 Weiner, L.M. (2006). Fully human therapeutic monoclonal antibodies. *J. Immunother.* 29 (1): 1–9.

43 Hirohata, S. (2007). Fully human anti TNF-alpha monoclonal antibodies (adalimumab, golimumab). *Nihon Rinsho.* 65 (7): 1202–1208.

44 Petrosian, M.N., Mats, A.N., Ibragimov, A.R. et al. (1982). Isolation and properties of monoclonal antibodies to human erythrocytes. *Dokl Akad Nauk SSSR* 267 (4): 1002–1005.

45 Mitra, S. and Tomar, P.C. (2021). Hybridoma technology; advancements, clinical significance, and future aspects. *J. Genet. Eng. Biotechnol.* 19 (1): 159.

46 Kim, H.Y., Stojadinovic, A., and Izadjoo, M.J. (2014). Immunization, hybridoma generation, and selection for monoclonal antibody production. *Methods Mol. Biol.* 1131: 33–45.

47 Huang, J., Doria-Rose, N.A., Longo, N.S. et al. (2013). Isolation of human monoclonal antibodies from peripheral blood B cells. *Nat. Protoc.* 8 (10): 1907–1915.

48 Greenfield, E.A. (2018). Polyethylene glycol fusion for hybridoma production. *Cold Spring Harb Protoc.* 2018 (3): 191–196.

49 Köhler, G. and Milstein, C. (1975). Continuous cultures of fused cells secreting antibody of predefined specificity. *Nature* 256 (5517): 495–497.

50 Greenfield, E.A. (2021). Selecting for and checking cells with HGPRT deficiency for hybridoma production. *Cold Spring Harb Protoc.* 2021 (9): pdb-prot103325.

51 Hanack, K., Messerschmidt, K., and Listek, M. (2016). Antibodies and selection of monoclonal antibodies. *Adv. Exp. Med. Biol.* 917: 11–22.

52 Jayme, D.W. and Blackman, K.E. (1985). Culture media for propagation of mammalian cells, viruses, and other biologicals. *Adv. Biotechnol. Processes* 5: 1–30.

53 Zaroff, S. and Tan, G. (2019). Hybridoma technology: the preferred method for monoclonal antibody generation for in vivo applications. *Biotechniques* 67 (3): 90–92.

54 Bodeus, M., Burtonboy, G., and Bazin, H. (1985). Rat monoclonal antibodies. IV. Easy method for in vitro production. *J. Immunol. Methods* 79 (1): 1–6.

55 Ronca, R., Benzoni, P., De Luca, A. et al. (2012). Phage displayed peptides/antibodies recognizing growth factors and their tyrosine kinase receptors as tools for anti-cancer therapeutics. *Int. J. Mol. Sci.* 13 (4): 5254–5277.

56 Johns, M. (2000). Phage display technology. *Methods Mol. Med.* 40: 53–62.

57 Deng, X., Wang, L., You, X. et al. (2018). Advances in the T7 phage display system (review). *Mol. Med. Rep.* 17 (1): 714–720.

58 Kiguchi, Y., Oyama, H., Morita, I. et al. (2018). Antibodies and engineered antibody fragments against M13 filamentous phage to facilitate phage-display-based molecular breeding. *Biol. Pharm. Bull.* 41 (7): 1062–1070.

59 Dasch, J.R. and Dasch, A.L. (2017). Using phage display to create recombinant antibodies. *Cold Spring Harbor Protoc.* 2017 (9): pdb.prot093864.

60 Zhang, L., Cong, Y., Li, H. et al. (2021). Construction of a full-length antibody phage display vector. *J. Immunol. Methods* 494: 113052.

61 Kumar, R., Parray, H.A., Shrivastava, T. et al. (2019). Phage display antibody libraries: a robust approach for generation of recombinant human monoclonal antibodies. *Int. J. Biol. Macromol.* 135: 907–918.

62 Dal Ferro, M., Rizzo, S., Rizzo, E. et al. (2019). Phage display technology for human monoclonal antibodies. *Methods Mol. Biol.* 1904: 319–338.

63 Nagano, K. and Tsutsumi, Y. (2021). Phage display technology as a powerful platform for antibody drug discovery. *Viruses* 13 (2): 178.

64 Houdebine, L.M. (2007). Transgenic animal models in biomedical research. *Methods Mol. Biol.* 360: 163–202.

65 Lonberg, N. and Huszar, D. (1995). Human antibodies from transgenic mice. *Int. Rev. Immunol.* 13 (1): 65–93.

66 Mompó, S.M. and González-Fernández, Á. (2019). Antigen-specific human monoclonal antibodies from transgenic mice. *Methods Mol. Biol.* 1904: 253–291.

67 Iizuka, M., Ogawa, S., Takeuchi, A. et al. (2009). Production of a recombinant mouse monoclonal antibody in transgenic silkworm cocoons. *FEBS J.* 276 (20): 5806–5820.

68 Zhang, R., Tang, C., Guo, H. et al. (2018). A novel glycosylated anti-CD20 monoclonal antibody from transgenic cattle. *Sci. Rep.* 8 (1): 13208.

69 Hood, E.E., Woodard, S.L., and Horn, M.E. (2002). Monoclonal antibody manufacturing in transgenic plants – myths and realities. *Curr. Opin. Biotechnol.* 13 (6): 630–635.

70 Yusibov, V., Kushnir, N., and Streatfield, S.J. (2016). Antibody production in plants and green algae. *Annu. Rev. Plant Biol.* 67: 669–701.

71 Ko, K., Brodzik, R., and Steplewski, Z. (2009). Production of antibodies in plants: approaches and perspectives. *Curr. Top. Microbiol. Immunol.* 332: 55–78.

72 Hiatt, A., Cafferkey, R., and Bowdish, K. (1989). Production of antibodies in transgenic plants. *Nature* 342 (6245): 76–78.

73 Bardor, M., Loutelier-Bourhis, C., Paccalet, T. et al. (2003). Monoclonal C5-1 antibody produced in transgenic alfalfa plants exhibits a N-glycosylation that is homogenous and suitable for glyco-engineering into human-compatible structures. *Plant Biotechnol. J.* 1 (6): 451–462.

74 Nessa, M.U., Rahman, M.A., and Kabir, Y. (2020). Plant-produced monoclonal antibody as immunotherapy for cancer. *Biomed Res. Int.* 2020: 3038564.

75 Garabagi, F., McLean, M.D., and Hall, J.C. (2012). Transient and stable expression of antibodies in Nicotiana species. *Methods Mol. Biol.* 907: 389–408.

76 Ueki, S., Magori, S., Lacroix, B., and Citovsky, V. (2013). Transient gene expression in epidermal cells of plant leaves by biolistic DNA delivery. *Methods Mol. Biol.* 940: 17–26.

77 Rudin, C.M. and Thompson, C.B. (1998). B-cell development and maturation. *Semin. Oncol.* 25 (4): 435–446.

78 Sugimoto, M., Tahara, H., Ide, T., and Furuichi, Y. (2004). Steps involved in immortalization and tumorigenesis in human B-lymphoblastoid cell lines transformed by Epstein-Barr virus. *Cancer Res.* 64 (10): 3361–3364.

79 Steinitz, M. (2014). Production of human monoclonal antibodies by the Epstein-Barr virus method. *Methods Mol. Biol.* 1060: 111–122.

80 Hui-Yuen, J., Koganti, S., and Bhaduri-McIntosh, S. (2014). Human B cell immortalization for monoclonal antibody production. *Methods Mol. Biol.* 1131: 183–189.

81 Tosato, G. and Cohen, J.I. (2007). Generation of Epstein-Barr virus (EBV)-immortalized B cell lines. *Curr. Protoc. Immunol.* 76: 7–22.

82 Kaplon, H., Chenoweth, A., Crescioli, S., and Reichert, J.M. (2022). Antibodies to watch in 2022. *MAbs* 14 (1): 2014296.

83 von Mehren, M. and Weiner, L.M. (1996). Monoclonal antibody-based therapy. *Curr. Opin. Oncol.* 8 (6): 493–498.

84 Lu, R.M., Hwang, Y.C., Liu, I.J. et al. (2020). Development of therapeutic antibodies for the treatment of diseases. *J. Biomed. Sci.* 27 (1): 1.

85 Fu, Z., Li, S., Han, S. et al. (2022). Antibody drug conjugate: the "biological missile" for targeted cancer therapy. *Signal Transduction Targeted Ther.* 7 (1): 93.

86 Kimiz-Gebologlu, I., Gulce-Iz, S., and Biray-Avci, C. (2018). Monoclonal antibodies in cancer immunotherapy. *Mol. Biol. Rep.* 45 (6): 2935–2940.

87 Weiner, G.J. (2015). Building better monoclonal antibody-based therapeutics. *Nat. Rev. Cancer* 15 (6): 361–370.

88 Anderson, D.R., Grillo-López, A., Varns, C. et al. (1997). Targeted anti-cancer therapy using rituximab, a chimaeric anti-CD20 antibody (IDEC-C2B8) in the treatment of non-Hodgkin's B-cell lymphoma. *Biochem. Soc. Trans.* 25 (2): 705–708.

89 Perry, C.M. and Wiseman, L.R. (1999). Trastuzumab. *BioDrugs* 12 (2): 129–135.

90 de Vetten, M.P., Jansen, J.H., van der Reijden, B.A. et al. (2000). Molecular remission of Philadelphia/bcr-abl-positive acute myeloid leukaemia after treatment with anti-CD33 calicheamicin conjugate (gemtuzumab ozogamicin, CMA-676). *Br. J. Haematol.* 111 (1): 277–279.

91 Ferrajoli, A., O'Brien, S., and Keating, M.J. (2001). Alemtuzumab: a novel monoclonal antibody. *Expert Opin. Biol. Ther.* 1 (6): 1059–1065.

92 Gordon, L.I., Witzig, T.E., Wiseman, G.A. et al. (2002). Yttrium 90 ibritumomab tiuxetan radioimmunotherapy for relapsed or refractory low-grade non-Hodgkin's lymphoma. *Semin. Oncol.* 29 (1 Suppl 2): 87–92.

93 Reynolds, N.A. and Wagstaff, A.J. (2004). Cetuximab: in the treatment of metastatic colorectal cancer. *Drugs* 64 (1): 109–118. discussion 19-21.

94 Zondor, S.D. and Medina, P.J. (2004). Bevacizumab: an angiogenesis inhibitor with efficacy in colorectal and other malignancies. *Ann. Pharmacother.* 38 (7–8): 1258–1264.

95 Hoy, S.M. and Wagstaff, A.J. (2006). Panitumumab: in the treatment of metastatic colorectal cancer. *Drugs* 66 (15): 2005–2014. discussion 15-6.

96 Zhang, B. (2009). Ofatumumab. *MAbs* 1 (4): 326–331.

97 Lipson, E.J. and Drake, C.G. (2011). Ipilimumab: an anti-CTLA-4 antibody for metastatic melanoma. *Clin. Cancer Res.* 17 (22): 6958–6962.

98 Foyil, K.V. and Bartlett, N.L. (2011). Brentuximab vedotin for the treatment of CD30+ lymphomas. *Immunotherapy* 3 (4): 475–485.

99 Keating, G.M. (2012). Pertuzumab: in the first-line treatment of HER2-positive metastatic breast cancer. *Drugs* 72 (3): 353–360.

100 Haddley, K. (2013). Trastuzumab emtansine for the treatment of HER2-positive metastatic breast cancer. *Drugs Today (Barc)* 49 (11): 701–715.

101 Rogers, K.A. and Jones, J.A. (2014). Obinutuzumab for the treatment of chronic lymphocytic leukemia. *Drugs Today (Barc)* 50 (6): 407–419.

102 Poole, R.M. and Vaidya, A. (2014). Ramucirumab: first global approval. *Drugs* 74 (9): 1047–1058.

103 Hoffman, L.M. and Gore, L. (2014). Blinatumomab, a Bi-specific anti-CD19/CD3 BiTE® antibody for the treatment of acute lymphoblastic leukemia: perspectives and current pediatric applications. *Front. Oncol.* 4: 63.

104 Gunturi, A. and McDermott, D.F. (2015). Nivolumab for the treatment of cancer. *Expert Opin. Invest. Drugs* 24 (2): 253–260.

105 Robert, C., Ribas, A., Wolchok, J.D. et al. (2014). Anti-programmed-death-receptor-1 treatment with pembrolizumab in ipilimumab-refractory advanced melanoma: a randomised dose-comparison cohort of a phase 1 trial. *Lancet* 384 (9948): 1109–1117.

106 Greillier, L., Tomasini, P., and Barlesi, F. (2015). Necitumumab for non-small cell lung cancer. *Expert Opin. Biol. Ther.* 15 (8): 1231–1239.

107 (2015). Dinutuximab approved for high-risk neuroblastoma. *Cancer Discovery* 5 (6): Of5.

108 Lokhorst, H.M., Plesner, T., Laubach, J.P. et al. (2015). Targeting CD38 with daratumumab monotherapy in multiple myeloma. *N. Engl. J. Med.* 373 (13): 1207–1219.

109 Markham, A. (2016). Elotuzumab: first global approval. *Drugs* 76 (3): 397–403.

110 Eli Lilly and Company (2016). Olaratumab approved for soft-tissue sarcoma. *Cancer Discovery* 6 (12): 1297.

111 Inman, B.A., Longo, T.A., Ramalingam, S., and Harrison, M.R. (2017). Atezolizumab: a PD-L1-blocking antibody for bladder cancer. *Clin. Cancer Res.* 23 (8): 1886–1890.

112 Kantarjian, H.M., DeAngelo, D.J., Stelljes, M. et al. (2016). Inotuzumab ozogamicin versus standard therapy for acute lymphoblastic leukemia. *N. Engl. J. Med.* 375 (8): 740–753.

113 Cordes, L.M. and Gulley, J.L. (2017). Avelumab for the treatment of metastatic Merkel cell carcinoma. *Drugs Today (Barc)* 53 (7): 377–383.

114 Baron, J. and Wang, E.S. (2018). Gemtuzumab ozogamicin for the treatment of acute myeloid leukemia. *Expert Rev. Clin. Pharmacol.* 11 (6): 549–559.

115 Syed, Y.Y. (2017). Durvalumab: first global approval. *Drugs* 77 (12): 1369–1376.

116 Markham, A. and Duggan, S. (2018). Cemiplimab: first global approval. *Drugs* 78 (17): 1841–1846.

117 Dhillon, S. (2018). Moxetumomab pasudotox: first global approval. *Drugs* 78 (16): 1763–1767.

118 Deeks, E.D. (2019). Polatuzumab vedotin: first global approval. *Drugs* 79 (13): 1467–1475.

119 Lattanzi, M. and Rosenberg, J.E. (2020). The emerging role of antibody-drug conjugates in urothelial carcinoma. *Expert Rev. Anticancer Ther.* 20 (7): 551–561.

120 Keam, S.J. (2020). Trastuzumab deruxtecan: first approval. *Drugs* 80 (5): 501–508.

121 Dhillon, S. (2020). Isatuximab: first approval. *Drugs* 80 (9): 905–912.

122 Syed, Y.Y. (2020). Sacituzumab govitecan: first approval. *Drugs* 80 (10): 1019–1025.

123 Hoy, S.M. (2020). Tafasitamab: first approval. *Drugs* 80 (16): 1731–1737.

124 Wang, B., Wu, C., Zhong, Q. et al. (2021). Belantamab mafodotin for the treatment of multiple myeloma. *Drugs Today (Barc)* 57 (11): 653–663.

125 Markham, A. (2021). Margetuximab: first approval. *Drugs* 81 (5): 599–604.

126 Markham, A. (2021). Dostarlimab: first approval. *Drugs* 81 (10): 1213–1219.

127 Zurko, J. and Hamadani, M. (2021). Loncastuximab tesirine for diffuse large B-cell lymphoma. *Drugs Today (Barc)* 57 (12): 733–743.

128 Syed, Y.Y. (2021). Amivantamab: first approval. *Drugs* 81 (11): 1349–1353.

129 Markham, A. (2021). Tisotumab vedotin: first approval. *Drugs* 81 (18): 2141–2147.

130 Paik, J. (2022). Nivolumab plus relatlimab: first approval. *Drugs* 82 (8): 925–931.

131 (2023). Teclistamab approved for myeloma. *Cancer Discov.* 13 (1): OF1.

132 Llovet, J.M., Castet, F., Heikenwalder, M. et al. (2022). Immunotherapies for hepatocellular carcinoma. *Nat. Rev. Clin. Oncol.* 19 (3): 151–172.

133 Tallent, A. (2023). FDA gives nod to mirvetuximab soravtansine. *Cancer Discov.* 13: 1, 8.

134 Reichert, J.M. and Dhimolea, E. (2012). The future of antibodies as cancer drugs. *Drug Discovery Today* 17 (17–18): 954–963.

135 Kamen, L., Myneni, S., Langsdorf, C. et al. (2019). A novel method for determining antibody-dependent cellular phagocytosis. *J. Immunol. Methods* 468: 55–60.

136 Ludwig, D.L., Pereira, D.S., Zhu, Z. et al. (2003). Monoclonal antibody therapeutics and apoptosis. *Oncogene* 22 (56): 9097–9106.

137 Chen, S., Li, X., Wang, H. et al. (2022). Anti-VEGFR2 monoclonal antibody(MSB0254) inhibits angiogenesis and tumor growth by blocking the signaling pathway mediated by VEGFR2 in glioblastoma. *Biochem. Biophys. Res. Commun.* 604: 158–164.

138 Haunschild, C.E. and Tewari, K.S. (2020). Bevacizumab use in the frontline, maintenance and recurrent settings for ovarian cancer. *Future Oncol.* 16 (7): 225–246.

139 Leget, G.A. and Czuczman, M.S. (1998). Use of rituximab, the new FDA-approved antibody. *Curr. Opin. Oncol.* 10 (6): 548–551.

140 Plosker, G.L. and Figgitt, D.P. (2003). Rituximab: a review of its use in non-Hodgkin's lymphoma and chronic lymphocytic leukaemia. *Drugs* 63 (8): 803–843.

141 Kesavan, M., Eyre, T.A., and Collins, G.P. (2019). Front-line treatment of high grade B cell non-Hodgkin lymphoma. *Curr. Hematol. Malig. Rep.* 14 (4): 207–218.

142 Decaup, E., Rossi, C., Gravelle, P. et al. (2019). A tridimensional model for NK cell-mediated ADCC of follicular lymphoma. *Front. Immunol.* 10: 1943.

143 Stolz, C. and Schuler, M. (2009). Molecular mechanisms of resistance to Rituximab and pharmacologic strategies for its circumvention. *Leuk Lymphoma* 50 (6): 873–885.

144 Marcus, R. and Hagenbeek, A. (2007). The therapeutic use of rituximab in non-Hodgkin's lymphoma. *Eur. J. Haematol. Suppl.* 67: 5–14.

145 Gebbia, V., Giuliani, F., Valori, V.M. et al. (2007). Cetuximab in squamous cell head and neck carcinomas. *Ann. Oncol.* 18 (Suppl 6): vi5–vi7.

146 Mazzarella, L., Guida, A., and Curigliano, G. (2018). Cetuximab for treating non-small cell lung cancer. *Expert Opin. Biol. Ther.* 18 (4): 483–493.

147 Díaz-Serrano, A., Sánchez-Torre, A., and Paz-Ares, L. (2019). Necitumumab for the treatment of advanced non-small-cell lung cancer. *Future Oncol.* 15 (7): 705–716.

148 Stremitzer, S., Sebio, A., Stintzing, S., and Lenz, H.J. (2014). Panitumumab safety for treating colorectal cancer. *Expert Opin. Drug Saf.* 13 (6): 843–851.

149 Ross, J.S., Fletcher, J.A., Linette, G.P. et al. (2003). The Her-2/neu gene and protein in breast cancer 2003: biomarker and target of therapy. *Oncologist* 8 (4): 307–325.

150 Piccart-Gebhart, M.J. (2001). Herceptin: the future in adjuvant breast cancer therapy. *Anticancer Drugs* 12 (Suppl 4): S27–S33.

151 Baselga, J. and Albanell, J. (2001). Mechanism of action of anti-HER2 monoclonal antibodies. *Ann. Oncol.* 12 (Suppl 1): S35–S41.

152 Gianni, L., Pienkowski, T., Im, Y.H. et al. (2012). Efficacy and safety of neoadjuvant pertuzumab and trastuzumab in women with locally advanced, inflammatory, or early HER2-positive breast cancer (NeoSphere): a randomised multicentre, open-label, phase 2 trial. *Lancet Oncol.* 13 (1): 25–32.

153 Robert, M., Frenel, J.S., Bourbouloux, E. et al. (2020). Pertuzumab for the treatment of breast cancer. *Expert Rev. Anticancer Ther.* 20 (2): 85–95.

154 Diaz, R.J., Ali, S., Qadir, M.G. et al. (2017). The role of bevacizumab in the treatment of glioblastoma. *J. Neuro-Oncol.* 133 (3): 455–467.

155 Rosen, L.S., Jacobs, I.A., and Burkes, R.L. (2017). Bevacizumab in colorectal cancer: current role in treatment and the potential of biosimilars. *Targeted Oncol.* 12 (5): 599–610.

156 Zhang, T., Xin, Q., and Kang, J.M. (2021). Bevacizumab for recurrent glioblastoma: a systematic review and meta-analysis. *Eur. Rev. Med. Pharmacol. Sci.* 25 (21): 6480–6491.

157 Popper, H.H. (2016). Progression and metastasis of lung cancer. *Cancer Metastasis Rev.* 35 (1): 75–91.

158 Nagy, J.A., Dvorak, A.M., and Dvorak, H.F. (2007). VEGF-A and the induction of pathological angiogenesis. *Annu. Rev. Pathol.* 2: 251–275.

159 Ferrara, N., Hillan, K.J., and Novotny, W. (2005). Bevacizumab (Avastin), a humanized anti-VEGF monoclonal antibody for cancer therapy. *Biochem. Biophys. Res. Commun.* 333 (2): 328–335.

160 Reckamp, K.L., Redman, M.W., Dragnev, K.H. et al. (2022). Phase II randomized study of ramucirumab and pembrolizumab versus standard of care in advanced non-small-cell lung cancer previously treated with immunotherapy-lung-MAP S1800A. *J. Clin. Oncol.* 40 (21): 2295–2306.

161 Koppe, M.J., Postema, E.J., Aarts, F. et al. (2005). Antibody-guided radiation therapy of cancer. *Cancer Metastasis Rev.* 24 (4): 539–567.

162 Lin, M., Paolillo, V., Le, D.B. et al. (2021). Monoclonal antibody based radiopharmaceuticals for imaging and therapy. *Curr. Probl. Cancer* 45 (5): 100796.

163 Rizzieri, D. (2016). Zevalin® (ibritumomab tiuxetan): After more than a decade of treatment experience, what have we learned? *Crit. Rev. Oncol. Hematol.* 105: 5–17.

164 Krasner, C. and Joyce, R.M. (2001). Zevalin: 90 yttrium labeled anti-CD20 (ibritumomab tiuxetan), a new treatment for non-Hodgkin's lymphoma. *Current Pharm. Biotechnol.* 2 (4): 341–349.

165 White, C.A. (2003). Rituxan immunotherapy and zevalin radioimmunotherapy in the treatment of non-Hodgkin's lymphoma. *Current Pharm. Biotechnol.* 4 (4): 221–238.

166 Wiseman, G.A., Leigh, B., Erwin, W.D. et al. (2002). Radiation dosimetry results for Zevalin radioimmunotherapy of rituximab-refractory non-Hodgkin lymphoma. *Cancer* 94 (4 Suppl): 1349–1357.

167 Van Der Weyden, C., Dickinson, M., Whisstock, J., and Prince, H.M. (2019). Brentuximab vedotin in T-cell lymphoma. *Expert Rev. Hematol.* 12 (1): 5–19.

168 Li, B.T., Shen, R., Buonocore, D. et al. (2018). Ado-trastuzumab emtansine for patients with HER2-mutant lung cancers: results from a phase II basket trial. *J. Clin. Oncol.* 36 (24): 2532–2537.

169 Darvin, P., Toor, S.M., Sasidharan Nair, V., and Elkord, E. (2018). Immune checkpoint inhibitors: recent progress and potential biomarkers. *Exp. Mol. Med.* 50 (12): 1–11.

170 Walia, H.K., Sharma, P., Singh, N., and Sharma, S. (2022). Immunotherapy in small cell lung cancer treatment: a promising headway for future perspective. *Curr. Treat Options Oncol.* 23 (2): 268–294.

171 Mannie, M.D. (2001). T cell-mediated antigen presentation: a potential mechanism of infectious tolerance. *Immunol. Res.* 23 (1): 1–21.

172 Keir, M.E., Butte, M.J., Freeman, G.J., and Sharpe, A.H. (2008). PD-1 and its ligands in tolerance and immunity. *Annu. Rev. Immunol.* 26: 677–704.

173 Woo, S.R., Corrales, L., and Gajewski, T.F. (2015). Innate immune recognition of cancer. *Annu. Rev. Immunol.* 33: 445–474.

174 van Houtum, E.J.H., Büll, C., Cornelissen, L.A.M., and Adema, G.J. (2021). Siglec signaling in the tumor microenvironment. *Front. Immunol.* 12: 790317.

175 Oaknin, A., Tinker, A.V., Gilbert, L. et al. (2020). Clinical activity and safety of the anti-programmed death 1 monoclonal antibody dostarlimab for patients with recurrent or advanced mismatch repair-deficient endometrial cancer: a nonrandomized phase 1 clinical trial. *JAMA Oncol.* 6 (11): 1766–1772.

176 Shuvo, P.A., Tahsin, A., Rahman, M.M., and Emran, T.B. (2022). Dostarlimab: the miracle drug for the treatment of colorectal cancer. *Ann. Med. Surg. (Lond)* 81: 104493.

177 Kwok, G., Yau, T.C., Chiu, J.W. et al. (2016). Pembrolizumab (Keytruda). *Hum. Vaccines Immunother.* 12 (11): 2777–2789.

178 Finkelmeier, F., Waidmann, O., and Trojan, J. (2018). Nivolumab for the treatment of hepatocellular carcinoma. *Expert Rev. Anticancer Ther.* 18 (12): 1169–1175.

179 Rizzo, A., Ricci, A.D., and Brandi, G. (2021). Durvalumab: an investigational anti-PD-L1 antibody for the treatment of biliary tract cancer. *Expert Opin. Invest. Drugs* 30 (4): 343–350.

180 Piedimonte, G., King, K.A., Holmgren, N.L. et al. (2000). A humanized monoclonal antibody against respiratory syncytial virus (palivizumab) inhibits RSV-induced neurogenic-mediated inflammation in rat airways. *Pediatr. Res.* 47 (3): 351–356.

181 Kummerfeldt, C.E. (2014). Raxibacumab: potential role in the treatment of inhalational anthrax. *Infect. Drug Resist.* 7: 101–109.

182 Džunková, M., D'Auria, G., Xu, H. et al. (2016). The monoclonal antitoxin antibodies (actoxumab-bezlotoxumab) treatment facilitates normalization of the gut microbiota of mice with *Clostridium difficile* infection. *Front. Cell. Infect. Microbiol.* 6: 119.

183 Greig, S.L. (2016). Obiltoxaximab: first global approval. *Drugs* 76 (7): 823–830.

184 Markham, A. (2018). Ibalizumab: first global approval. *Drugs* 78 (7): 781–785.

185 Markham, A. (2021). REGN-EB3: first approval. *Drugs* 81 (1): 175–178.

186 Lee, A. (2021). Ansuvimab: first approval. *Drugs* 81 (5): 595–598.

187 Mazumdar, S. (2009). Raxibacumab. *MAbs* 1 (6): 531–538.

188 Hou, A.W. and Morrill, A.M. (2017). Obiltoxaximab: adding to the treatment arsenal for *Bacillus anthracis* infection. *Ann. Pharmacother.* 51 (10): 908–913.

189 Blair, H.A. (2020). Ibalizumab: a review in multidrug-resistant HIV-1 infection. *Drugs* 80 (2): 189–196.

190 Misasi, J., Gilman, M.S., Kanekiyo, M. et al. (2016). Structural and molecular basis for Ebola virus neutralization by protective human antibodies. *Science* 351 (6279): 1343–1346.

191 Saxena, D., Kaul, G., Dasgupta, A., and Chopra, S. (2021). Atoltivimab/maftivimab/odesivimab (Inmazeb) combination to treat infection caused by *Zaire ebolavirus*. *Drugs Today (Barc)* 57 (8): 483–490.

192 Coller, B.S., Anderson, K., and Weisman, H.F. (1995). New antiplatelet agents: platelet GPIIb/IIIa antagonists. *Thromb. Haemost.* 74 (1): 302–308.

193 Genetta, T.B. and Mauro, V.F. (1996). ABCIXIMAB: a new antiaggregant used in angioplasty. *Ann. Pharmacother.* 30 (3): 251–257.

194 Usta, C., Turgut, N.T., and Bedel, A. (2016). How abciximab might be clinically useful. *Int. J. Cardiol.* 222: 1074–1078.

195 Dantzer, J.A. and Wood, R.A. (2018). The use of omalizumab in allergen immunotherapy. *Clin. Exp. Allergy* 48 (3): 232–240.

196 Loureiro, C.C., Amaral, L., Ferreira, J.A. et al. (2018). Omalizumab for severe asthma: beyond allergic asthma. *Biomed Res. Int.* 2018: 3254094.

197 Kawakami, T. and Blank, U. (2016). From IgE to omalizumab. *J. Immunol.* 197 (11): 4187–4192.

198 Seyed Jafari, S.M., Feldmeyer, L., Bossart, S. et al. (2020). Case report: combination of omalizumab and dupilumab for recalcitrant bullous pemphigoid. *Front. Immunol.* 11: 611549.

199 Radonjic-Hoesli, S., Hofmeier, K.S., Micaletto, S. et al. (2018). Urticaria and angioedema: an update on classification and pathogenesis. *Clin. Rev. Allergy Immunol.* 54 (1): 88–101.

200 Voulgari, P.V. and Drosos, A.A. (2006). Adalimumab for rheumatoid arthritis. *Expert Opin. Biol. Ther.* 6 (12): 1349–1360.

201 Wasserman, A.M. (2011). Diagnosis and management of rheumatoid arthritis. *Am. Fam. Physician* 84 (11): 1245–1252.

202 Lu, X., Hu, R., Peng, L. et al. (2021). Efficacy and safety of adalimumab biosimilars: current critical clinical data in rheumatoid arthritis. *Front. Immunol.* 12: 638444.

203 Deeks, E.D. (2016). Certolizumab pegol: a review in inflammatory autoimmune diseases. *BioDrugs* 30 (6): 607–617.

204 Melo, A.T., Campanilho-Marques, R., and Fonseca, J.E. (2021). Golimumab (anti-TNF monoclonal antibody): where we stand today. *Hum. Vaccines Immunother.* 17 (6): 1586–1598.

205 Lichtenstein, L., Ron, Y., Kivity, S. et al. (2015). Infliximab-related infusion reactions: systematic review. *J. Crohns Colitis* 9 (9): 806–815.

206 Onrust, S.V. and Wiseman, L.R. (1999). Basiliximab. *Drugs* 57 (2): 207–213. discussion 14.

207 Garnett, W.R. and Yunker, N. (2001). Treatment of Crohn's disease with infliximab. *Am. J. Health Syst. Pharm.* 58 (4): 307–316. quiz 17-9.

208 Scheinfeld, N. (2003). Adalimumab (HUMIRA): a review. *J. Drugs Dermatol.* 2 (4): 375–377.

209 Lanier, B.Q., Corren, J., Lumry, W. et al. (2003). Omalizumab is effective in the long-term control of severe allergic asthma. *Ann. Allergy Asthma Immunol.* 91 (2): 154–159.

210 Keeley, K.A., Rivey, M.P., and Allington, D.R. (2005). Natalizumab for the treatment of multiple sclerosis and Crohn's disease. *Ann. Pharmacother.* 39 (11): 1833–1843.

211 Rosenfeld, P.J., Brown, D.M., Heier, J.S. et al. (2006). Ranibizumab for neovascular age-related macular degeneration. *N. Engl. J. Med.* 355 (14): 1419–1431.

212 Zareba, K.M. (2007). Eculizumab: a novel therapy for paroxysmal nocturnal hemoglobinuria. *Drugs Today (Barc)* 43 (8): 539–546.

213 Baker, D.E. (2009). Certolizumab pegol for the treatment of Crohn's disease. *Expert Rev. Clin. Immunol.* 5 (6): 683–691.

214 Chien, A.L., Elder, J.T., and Ellis, C.N. (2009). Ustekinumab: a new option in psoriasis therapy. *Drugs* 69 (9): 1141–1152.

215 Church, L.D. and McDermott, M.F. (2009). Canakinumab, a fully-human mAb against IL-1beta for the potential treatment of inflammatory disorders. *Curr. Opin. Mol. Ther.* 11 (1): 81–89.

216 Mazumdar, S. and Greenwald, D. (2009). Golimumab. *MAbs* 1 (5): 422–431.

217 Tanaka, T., Ogata, A., and Narazaki, M. (2010). Tocilizumab for the treatment of rheumatoid arthritis. *Expert Rev. Clin. Immunol.* 6 (6): 843–854.

218 Lewiecki, E.M. (2010). Treatment of osteoporosis with denosumab. *Maturitas* 66 (2): 182–186.

219 Burness, C.B. and McCormack, P.L. (2011). Belimumab: in systemic lupus erythematosus. *Drugs* 71 (18): 2435–2444.

220 Markham, A. and Patel, T. (2014). Siltuximab: first global approval. *Drugs* 74 (10): 1147–1152.

221 Poole, R.M. (2014). Vedolizumab: first global approval. *Drugs* 74 (11): 1293–1303.

222 Burness, C.B. (2015). Idarucizumab: first global approval. *Drugs* 75 (18): 2155–2161.

223 Sanford, M. and McKeage, K. (2015). Secukinumab: first global approval. *Drugs* 75 (3): 329–338.

224 Keating, G.M. (2015). Mepolizumab: first global approval. *Drugs* 75 (18): 2163–2169.

225 Dahagam, C., Goud, A., Abdelqader, A. et al. (2016). PCSK9 inhibitors and their role in high-risk patients in reducing LDL cholesterol levels: alirocumab. *Future Cardiol.* 12 (2): 149–157.

226 Markham, A. (2015). Evolocumab: first global approval. *Drugs* 75 (13): 1567–1573.

227 Markham, A. (2016). Reslizumab: first global approval. *Drugs* 76 (8): 907–911.

228 Puig, L. (2017). Brodalumab: the first anti-IL-17 receptor agent for psoriasis. *Drugs Today (Barc)* 53 (5): 283–297.

229 Markham, A. (2017). Guselkumab: first global approval. *Drugs* 77 (13): 1487–1492.

230 Santini, G., Mores, N., Malerba, M. et al. (2017). Dupilumab for the treatment of asthma. *Expert Opin. Invest. Drugs* 26 (3): 357–366.

231 Scott, L.J. (2017). Sarilumab: first global approval. *Drugs* 77 (6): 705–712.

232 Gelfand, J.M., Cree, B.A.C., and Hauser, S.L. (2017). Ocrelizumab and other CD20(+) B-cell-depleting therapies in multiple sclerosis. *Neurotherapeutics* 14 (4): 835–841.

233 Oldenburg, J., Mahlangu, J.N., Kim, B. et al. (2017). Emicizumab prophylaxis in hemophilia A with inhibitors. *N. Engl. J. Med.* 377 (9): 809–818.

234 Matera, M.G., Rogliani, P., Calzetta, L. et al. (2017). Benralizumab for the treatment of asthma. *Drugs Today (Barc)* 53 (12): 633–645.

235 Lamb, Y.N. (2018). Burosumab: first global approval. *Drugs* 78 (6): 707–714.

236 Wedi, B. (2019). Lanadelumab to treat hereditary angioedema. *Drugs Today (Barc)* 55 (7): 439–448.

237 Markham, A. (2018). Erenumab: first global approval. *Drugs* 78 (11): 1157–1161.

238 Lamb, Y.N. (2018). Galcanezumab: first global approval. *Drugs* 78 (16): 1769–1775.

239 Bangert, C. and Kopp, T. (2018). Tildrakizumab for the treatment of psoriasis. *Immunotherapy* 10 (13): 1105–1122.

240 Al-Salama, Z.T. (2019). Emapalumab: first global approval. *Drugs* 79 (1): 99–103.

241 Lionetto, L., Curto, M., Cisale, G.Y. et al. (2019). Fremanezumab for the preventive treatment of migraine in adults. *Expert Rev. Clin. Pharmacol.* 12 (8): 741–748.

242 McKeage, K. (2019). Ravulizumab: first global approval. *Drugs* 79 (3): 347–352.

243 Duggan, S. (2018). Caplacizumab: first global approval. *Drugs* 78 (15): 1639–1642.

244 McClung, M.R. (2018). Romosozumab for the treatment of osteoporosis. *Osteoporos Sarcopenia* 4 (1): 11–15.

245 Gu, C. and Yang, J. (2019). Risankizumab for the treatment of psoriasis. *Expert Rev. Clin. Pharmacol.* 12 (9): 851–857.

246 Markham, A. (2019). Brolucizumab: first approval. *Drugs* 79 (18): 1997–2000.

247 Blair, H.A. (2020). Crizanlizumab: first approval. *Drugs* 80 (1): 79–84.

248 Dhillon, S. (2020). Eptinezumab: first approval. *Drugs* 80 (7): 733–739.

249 Markham, A. (2020). Teprotumumab: first approval. *Drugs* 80 (5): 509–512.

250 Frampton, J.E. (2020). Inebilizumab: first approval. *Drugs* 80 (12): 1259–1264.

251 Heo, Y.A. (2020). Satralizumab: first approval. *Drugs* 80 (14): 1477–1482.

252 Markham, A. (2021). Naxitamab: first approval. *Drugs* 81 (2): 291–296.

253 Markham, A. (2021). Evinacumab: first approval. *Drugs* 81 (9): 1101–1105.

254 Duggan, S. (2021). Tralokinumab: first approval. *Drugs* 81 (14): 1657–1663.

255 Deeks, E.D. (2021). Anifrolumab: first approval. *Drugs* 81 (15): 1795–1802.

256 Hoy, S.M. (2022). Tezepelumab: first approval. *Drugs* 82 (4): 461–468.

257 Dhillon, S. (2022). Sutimlimab: first approval. *Drugs* 82 (7): 817–823.

258 Shirley, M. (2022). Faricimab: first approval. *Drugs* 82 (7): 825–830.

259 Blair, H.A. (2022). Spesolimab: first approval. *Drugs* 82 (17): 1681–1686.

260 Pugliese, D., Privitera, G., Rogai, F. et al. (2021). Two-year effectiveness and safety of golimumab in ulcerative colitis: an IG-IBD study. *United Eur. Gastroenterol. J.* 9 (1): 102–109.

261 Hemperly, A. and Vande Casteele, N. (2018). Clinical pharmacokinetics and pharmacodynamics of infliximab in the treatment of inflammatory bowel disease. *Clin. Pharmacokinet.* 57 (8): 929–942.

262 Love, T.J. and Kavanaugh, A. (2018). Golimumab in the treatment of psoriatic arthritis. *Expert Rev. Clin. Immunol.* 14 (11): 893–898.

263 Markatseli, T.E., Papagoras, C., Nikoli, A. et al. (2014). Certolizumab for rheumatoid arthritis. *Clin. Exp. Rheumatol.* 32 (3): 415–423.

264 Khanna, R., Mosli, M.H., and Feagan, B.G. (2016). Anti-integrins in ulcerative colitis and Crohn's disease: what is their place? *Dig. Dis.* 34 (1–2): 153–159.

27

Microbial Alkaline Protease: Production, Purification, and Applications

Degafneh Tadesse[1], Abate Ayele[1,2], Gamachis Korsa[1,2], and Chandran Masi[1,2,3]

[1] *Addis Ababa Sciences and Technology University, Department of Biotechnology, Akaki Kality, P.O. Box 16417, Addis Ababa 1000, Ethiopia*
[2] *Addis Ababa Science and Technology University, Center of Excellence for Biotechnology and Bioprocess, P.O. Box 16417, Addis Ababa 1000, Ethiopia*
[3] *Dhanalakshmi Srinivasan Engineering College (Autonomous), Department of Food Technology, Perambalur, Tamil Nadu, India*

27.1 Introduction

The development of environmentally friendly/green technologies based on enzymes is given great priority in light of polluting chemical-based manufacturing and production techniques [1, 2]. Because they decompose organically and are flexible, enzymes are ecological biocatalysts that have less detrimental impacts on the environment [3]. According to Dabhi et al. [4], protease is an enzyme that initiates protein catabolism by hydrolyzing the peptide bonds that link the amino acids in the polypeptide chain that makes up proteins. This process is known as proteolysis. Proteases are among the most valuable commercial enzymes and account for 60% of the market for all enzymes [5, 6]. The Enzyme Commission group categorizes proteases into class three (hydrolases) and subgroup four (which hydrolyze peptide bonds). Based on the ideal pH range, proteases are classified as acidic, neutral, or alkaline. In nature, alkalophilic bacteria have a broad distribution and are practically ubiquitous [7]. Due to its nonpathogenic and nonhazardous sources, alkaline protease is environmentally friendly. Plants, animals, and microbes can all produce proteolysis enzymes [8]. Even though all of this may be a source of proteolytic enzymes, microorganisms are where the enzyme is found in a sustainable form [9]. Its applications include bleaching, dehairing, and the deproteinization of prawn waste to produce chitin, as well as the recovery of silver from old X-ray films [10].

Several steps are involved in the production of microbial enzymes in industry. Microorganisms that can produce enzymes are isolated, screened for, and identified at the beginning of the process. Next, process variables like fermentation conditions, culture parameters, and medium components are optimized. To be commercialized, the enzymes must first be purified and characterized [3, 11]. However, because they are biological molecules, enzymes are quite vulnerable to hostile industrial

Microbial Enzymes: Production, Purification, and Industrial Applications, First Edition.
Edited by Dinesh Yadav, Pankaj Chowdhary, Gautam Anand, and Rajarshi Kumar Gaur.

processes. As a result, enzymes that are stable under extreme conditions are required for industrial processes [12].

Microbial peptidases have been the preferred source to synthesize novel proteases due to their advantages over sources from plants or animals [3]. The protease must then be purified, a labor-intensive process after it has been developed. To purify enzymes, a variety of techniques and methods are currently available. Whether an enzyme is extracellular or intracellular determines the method and technique to be used [13, 14].

27.1.1 Alkalophiles and Alkaline Proteases

The term "alkalophiles" refers to organisms that can grow above pH 10, with optimal growth occurring around pH 9, but cannot grow at pH 7 or lower. In contrast, halotolerant organisms can grow at pH levels higher than 10, but their best rates of growth occur nearer to neutrality [15]. The two groups of obligate and facultative alkalophiles have been produced from the extreme alkalophiles. While facultative alkalophiles can grow at neutral pH, obligate alkalophiles cannot, and their growth is best at pH 10 or higher [16]. Additionally, they have been divided into two broad groups: alkalophiles and alkalotolerants. Alkalophilic microorganisms are widespread and can be found in almost all environments without being constrained by alkalinity [17]. These environments typically have pH levels between 10 and above. The effluents from industries like food, textiles, tanneries, potato processing plants, paper mills, calcium carbonate kilns, detergent manufacturing, and other industrial processes are what cause human-made alkaline environments [18]. All microorganisms follow a normal distribution pattern based on the pH dependence for their optimal growth, and the majority of these microorganisms are known to proliferate well at near-neutral pH values [19]. The number of microorganisms declines as the pH moves farther from this neutral range. According to Puissant et al. [20], the ratio of alkalophilic bacteria to neutrophilic bacteria in soil varies from 1/10 to 1/100. However, some neutrophilic organisms can develop even in unfavorable pH environments. This is mainly attributable to the unique physiological and metabolic systems that they have developed by changing the characteristics of the bioenergetic membranes and transport mechanisms, which enable their survival and proliferation under such challenging circumstances [21]. The term pH-dependent extremophiles may also be used to describe these microorganisms. A wide variety of microorganisms called alkalophiles survive and thrive best in extremely alkaline environments.

27.1.2 Sources of Microbial Alkaline Proteases

Animals, plants, and microorganisms are all capable of producing alkaline proteases. Microorganisms have recently produced more proteases due to their ability to produce such a wide variety of enzymes [22]. They produce roughly two-thirds of all proteases in the world. Nearly two-thirds of the proteases used in industry

Figure 27.1 Alkalophilic sites of alkaline proteases. Source: Sharma et al. [24]/with permission of Elsevier.

are made by microorganisms [23]. In contrast, a few naturally occurring alkaline environments, such as soda soils, lakes, and deserts, support several of such species as shown in Figure 27.1 [24]. Microbial proteases have advantages over a range of animal and plant resources, such as the ability to manipulate genetic information, grow quickly, and require less space to grow [7]. Specific microorganisms can only produce proteases with desired characteristics. In comparison to plants and animals, microbes require less time and less stress to grow and maintain. Some microorganisms can secrete protease by themselves without being induced. In a planned bioreactor, proteases are produced in large quantities by the fermentation of microorganisms [25].

27.2 Alkaline Protease Production

Different fermentation processes, such as solid-state fermentation (SSF) and submerged-state fermentation, can produce alkaline protease. Fermentation media is required to be properly optimized to produce commercially viable enzymes. The production of enzymes is influenced by various factors, including pH, nitrogen source, carbon source, metal ions, temperature, and inhibitors [25, 26].

Table 27.1 Alkaline protease from bacteria by solid-state fermentation.

Microorganism	Substrate	Proteolytic production	References
Bacterial proteolytic enzymes			
Bacillus cereus strain AT	Cow dung	4813 ± 62 U/g	[28]
Bacillus halodurans	Wheat bran and saw dust	397.09 U/g	[29]
Bacillus subtillus KHS 1	Green husk, wheat bran, and soybean meal	6596 U/g	[30]
Bacillus subtilis IH-72	Wheat bran and guar meal	89.15 U/g	[31]
Bacillus sp. (PE-11)	Wheat bran	178 U/g	[32]

27.2.1 Solid-state Fermentation

SSF is a type of fermentation process that uses a solid substrate for the growth of microorganisms in the absence or almost absence of free water [24, 27]. Here, a solid substrate serves as both a nutrient source for the culture and a base for the microbial cells. This kind of method is preferred in countries with abundant biomass and agricultural waste because these materials can be used as inexpensive raw materials, as presented in Table 27.1 [29].

27.2.2 Submerged Fermentation

A liquid fermentation medium with soluble nutrients is used in the submerged fermentation (SmF) process, in which the substrate is suspended or dissolved in water [33–35]. The advantages of this process include easier sterilization and process control. Proteases are typically produced using SmF due to the advantages of consistent enzyme production characteristics with defined medium and process conditions, as presented in Table 27.2 [34].

27.2.2.1 Optimization of Fermentation Media for Protease Production

SmF and, to a lesser extent, SSF processes are used to produce alkaline proteases [15, 40]. The medium composition is optimized in the commercial production of alkaline proteases to maintain a balance between the different medium components and to reduce the number of unused components after fermentation [16].

27.2.2.2 Effect of Different Production Parameters on Activity and Stability of Alkaline Protease

Effect of pH Alkaliphilic microorganisms rely extensively on extracellular pH for cell growth and enzyme production [16, 24]. A pH of around 10 is ideal for these microorganisms to grow. The distribution of inside and outside weak bases that are not transported by cells, as well as the optimal pH of intercellular enzymes, can be used to estimate the cytoplasmic pH of these microorganisms. The ideal pH ranges

Table 27.2 Alkaline protease from bacteria by submerged fermentation.

Microorganism	Substrate	Proteolytic production	References
Bacterial proteolytic enzymes			
Bacillus licheniformis ALW1	Molasses, wheat bran	22.903 U/ml	[34]
Paenibacillus sp. TKU047	Shrimp head powder (SHP)	2.98 U/ml	[33]
Bacillus cereus	Sucrose and NH_4Cl	75.79 Units/ml/min	[36]
Bacillus sp.	Nutrient agar and soybean protein	98.36 U/ml	[17]
Bacillus cereus FT 1	Lactose and casein	187 U/ml	[37]
Bacillus subtilis ASASBT	Starch and gelatin	86.51 U/mg	[38]
Bacillus licheniformis NK	Gut wastes of Sardinella longiceps	68.56 U/ml	[15]
Bacillus licheniformis LBA 46	Agro-industrial by-products	3000 U/ml	[39]

from 9 to 11 for the production of alkaline proteases [41, 42]. Each organism has a different alkaline protease at a particular pH level. Therefore, pH is a crucial factor that affects the production of enzymes and should be properly optimized [43]. Table 27.3 shows the optimal pH requirements of various microorganisms.

Effect of Temperature Temperature is another critical factor that must be controlled for optimal cell growth and protease enzyme production. Temperatures between 40 and 70 °C are optimal for ATPase activity [16].

Alkaline Proteases from Actinomycetes Streptomyces strains are the preferred source of actinomycetes. While most research on actinomycetes has focused on antibiotic production, there have been few reports on their enzymes. Actinomycetes are terrestrial microorganisms that are typically isolated from soils for alkaline protease production, as presented in Table 27.4 [56].

Fungal Proteases Due to their high diversity, a wide range of substrate specificity, and stability in harsh environments, fungal proteases have attracted the attention of researchers. They also have the advantage of facilitating the separation of mycelium by straightforward filtration. The SSF process makes it simple to make fungal proteases. According to Jisha et al. [57], fungi proteases are also used to alter the proteins in food. Due to their wide range of substrate specificity, stability in unfavorable conditions, high diversity, and ability to separate mycelium by simple filtration, proteases isolated from fungi are of interest to researchers [58].

Table 27.3 Optimum T^0 and pH for different bacterial spp.

No	Bacterial species	Source of isolation	Optimum temperature (°C)	Optimum pH	References
1.	*Bacillus licheniformis NH1*	Fishery wastewaters	65–70	10.0–11.0.	[44]
2.	*Streptomyces ambofaciens DP2*	Milk processing plants and slaughterhouses	50	8	[45]
3.	*Staphylococcus sciuri*	Poultry soil samples	37	8	[43]
4.	*Bacillus cereus FT 1*	*Organic waste containing soil*	35	9.5	[37]
5.	*Bacillus* sp.	Diary industry, effluent, market waste, and sewage waste	50	8	[46]
6.	*Bacillus subtilis*	Soil	45	10	[41]
7.	*Bacillus cereus FT1*	Soil	65	9.5	[37]
8.	*Bacillus tequilensis P15*	Marine soil	50	8	[47]
9.	*Citricoccus* sp.	*Agricultural soil*	40	10	[42]
10.	*Streptomyces* sp.	Water and sediment samples	45	8.5	[48]
11.	*Paenibacillus dendritiformis* (BT7)	Tannery effluents	40	9	[49]

Table 27.4 Alkaline protease from Actinomycetes species.

No	Actinomycetes species	Source of isolation	Optimum temperature (°C)	Optimum pH	References
1.	*Nocardiopsis dassonvillei*	—	60	10	[50]
2.	*Nocardiopsis dassonvillei* OK-18	—	70	9	[51]
3.	*Streptomyces* sp. Al-Dhabi-82	Soil samples	40	9	[52]
4.	*Saccharomonospora viridis* strain Hw G550	Harsh environments	50–60	8	[53]
5.	*Streptomyces* sp. GS-1	Water and sediment samples	50	8	[48]
6.	*Nocardiopsis alba* OM-4	Salt-enriched soil	60–70	10	[54]
7.	*Nocardiopsis alba* TATA-13	Salt-enriched soil	60–70	10	[54]
8.	*Streptomyces* sp. LCJ12A	Soil of Pichavaram Mangrove Forest	35	10	[55]

Since they are generally recognized as genetically regarded safe (GRAS) strains, proteases derived from fungal sources have an advantage over those derived from bacterial sources [59, 60]. In comparison to bacteria, fungi produce a wider range of enzymes. For instance, *Aspergillus oryzae* produces acid, neutral, and alkaline proteases. The broad substrate specificity and wide pH range of the fungal proteases allow for their activity. They are less heat-tolerant than bacterial enzymes and react at a slower rate. In an SSF process, it is simple to produce fungus enzymes. Fungal acid proteases are stable between pH 2.6 and 6.0 and perform best between pH 4 and 4.5. Due to their limited pH and temperature specificities, they are particularly useful in the cheese-making industry [61].

The importance of these enzymes and their numerous applications in various industries encourages researchers to investigate acid protease with increased activity from fungi. The current global demand for industrial enzymes has resulted in a scarcity of plant and animal proteases, sparking interest in microbial proteases [6]. Numerous reports on Ethiopian fungal acid proteases and the country's diverse ecological niche [62], the potential isolate was successfully identified and assigned to the genus *Aspergillus* using macroscopic and microscopic characteristics. Acid proteases are an important class of enzymes used in the food and beverage industries. The fungal isolates were extracted from grape and dairy farm soil using potato dextrose agar, and they were then screened for the production of proteases using the clear zone on skim milk agar as a basis, as presented in Table 27.5 [77]. The current study focuses on the precise categorization of proteases, the production of alkaline proteases from various fungi via fermentation (both submerged and solid state), and their potential applications in the detergent, leather, food, and pharmaceutical industries, as well as their critical roles in waste management, silver recovery processes, and silk degumming [78].

27.3 Purification of Alkaline Proteases

First, using centrifugation, filtration, or differential sedimentation, the culture is separated from the fermentation medium. Following that, the supernatant is concentrated by ultrafiltration, and the protein from the biologically crude mixture is recovered by precipitation with salts or organic solvents. Ammonium sulfate is frequently used in salt precipitation to purify enzymes because it is straightforward, highly soluble, does not denaturize proteins, and does not produce heat. The disposal of ammonium sulfate, however, must be monitored because it is corrosive [79]. Thermostability is one of the most important and distinguishing features of industrial enzymes, which has the advantage of lowering microbial contaminants. Recovery of highly pure proteins is an overall objective of purification. Additionally, the purification procedure increases the specific activity of enzymes, making them more specific for various industrial applications [80]. Due to its simplicity, high solubility, resistance to denaturing proteins, and lack of heat production, ammonium sulfate is commonly employed in salt precipitation to purify enzymes. However, because ammonium sulfate is caustic, disposal must be carefully monitored [79].

Table 27.5 Alkaline protease from fungi.

Fungal isolate	Fermentation type	pH	Temperature (°C)	Type of protease	References
Beauveria sp. MTCC 5184	SMF	9.0	50	Serine	[63]
Trametes cingulate CTM10101	SMF	9.0	60	Serine	[64]
Aspergillus niger	—	ND	30	—	[65]
Aspergillus sp.	—	5	28	—	[66]
Penicillium citrinum	SSF	7.73	30	Serine	[67]
Aspergillus terreus	SSF	10.0	45	Serine	[68]
Aspergillus foetidus	—	—	—	Acidic protease	[69]
Penicillium chrysogenum X5	SMF	10.0	80	Serine	[70]
Cupressus torulosa D. Don	SMF	7	27	—	[71]
Penicillium rubidurum	SMF	8.0	40	Unidentified	[72]
Aspergillus ochraceus BT21	SMF	9.0	50	Serine	[73]
Penicillium bilaiae	—	6.26	24.5	—	[74]
Trichoderma longibrachiatum	SMF	9.0	40	Unidentified	[72]
Xylaria curta	SMF	ND	28 °C	—	[75]
Aspergillus ochraceus	—	8	35 °C	—	[76]

To further purify the enzyme, chromatography techniques such as ion exchange chromatography (IEC), gel filtration chromatography (GFC), affinity chromatography, hydrophobic interaction chromatography, and dye ligand chromatography need to be used. To purify enzymes, a variety of techniques and methods are currently available. Whether an enzyme is extracellular or intracellular determines the method and technique to be used [13, 81, 82].

In the study, purified protease from *A. oryzae* Y1 was shown to have several comparative advantages. Because it has a higher molecular mass than *Bacillus megaterium* (25,28 kDa), the purified protease from Y1 was found to be inconsistent, in contrast to other neutral proteases. The total activity and total protein of the crude enzyme revealed noticeably high specific activities of 439062U and 1934.7 mg, respectively. This is significantly higher than the previously reported enzyme activities in *A. oryzae* CH93 (14.7 U/g) [83, 84]. *Bacillus subtilis* FBL-1 fermentation broth that had undergone ammonium sulfate precipitation had 2.9 times more specific protease activity. The specific protease activity of an eluted protein fraction from the column chromatography using DEAE-Cellulose and Sephadex G-75 was increased by 94.2 and 94.9-fold, respectively. A purified protease band at about 37.6 kDa was visible on an SDS-PAGE. Because of its resistance to a wide range of chemicals, this enzyme has the potential to be used as a biocatalyst in industrial applications such as brewing and grain starch isolation [41, 85].

Protein from the cell-free dialysis was precipitated in the first step using ammonium sulfate at a saturation level of 60%. By using liner sodium chloride as an ingredient in the wash step and chromatography on DEAE-cellulous until fraction no 41, this led to a purification of the protease that was 2.3 times as effective with a yield of 9.78% of the original activity. The experiment revealed that a protease had been purified 8.94-fold to a specific activity of 30.21 U/mg protein. The neutral protease from *A. oryzae* Y1 was purified using ammonium sulfate precipitation and DEAE Sepharose Fast Flow chromatography, yielding a 10.0-fold increase in specific activity (2264.3 U/mg) and a 21% recovery rate. The estimated molecular weight of the purified protease was 45 kDa [86]. According to Chander and Puri [61], protease can be purified from senesced leaves of the weed Lantana camara using a two-step process involving ammonium sulfate precipitation and Sephadex G-250 gel permeation chromatography. Senesced leaves from Lantana camara yielded 6.19% and a Sephadex G-250 fraction that increased 28.31-fold. SDS-PAGE analysis revealed that the enzyme has a low molecular weight of 43 kDa. Metal ions such as Cu^{2+}, Zn^{2+}, Mg^{2+}, Co^{2+}, and Mn^{2+} strongly activate protease activity. When casein was used as the substrate, it remained active at 60 °C and pH 10.5 for an hour of incubation.

The protease was purified using ammonium sulfate precipitation and Sephadex G-100 GFC for *Bacillus cereus* VITSN0 [87]. The purification produced 1.3-fold more purified protease with 51.5 U/mg specific activity with a total yield of 37.5%. A single band of approximately 36 kDa on SDS-PAGE confirmed the molecular weight of the purified protease. The animal blood stain was successfully removed from cotton fabric and significantly dehaired goat skin by alkaline protease [80, 88, 89].

In a different study, the same *A. ochraceus* protease was completely purified using IEC, gel filtration, and precipitation by ammonium sulfate using Sephacryl S-200, DEAE-Sepharose, and CM-Sepharose columns [73, 79]. The six samples obtained after the extraction step were partially purified by dialysis. The ammonium sulfate purification and dialysis techniques, as expected, produced the highest and lowest band intensities. Kiwellin (20 kDa) and Thaumatin-like protein (22 kDa) were also found in proteins prepared using all methods. The ammonium sulfate purification also had the highest protease activity (26 U/mg protein) and was selected for additional investigation [90, 91].

27.4 Applications of Alkaline Protease in Different Industries

All proteolytic enzymes have specific features in terms of temperature, pH, ion requirement, specificity, activity, and stability. These features determine its use in

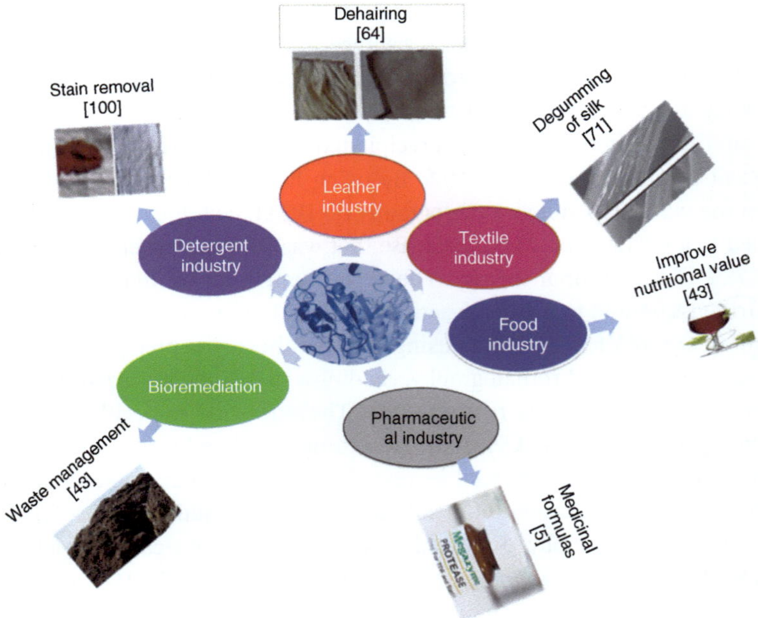

Figure 27.2 Applications of alkaline protease in different industries. Source: Shanmugavel et al. [92]/with permission of International Journal of Biosciences and Nanosciences; Manavalan et al. [93]/MDPI/CC BY 4.0; More et al. [94]/with permission of Taylor and Francis; Aladdin et al. [95]/with permission of Der Pharmacia Lettre; Furhan and Sharma [96]/with permission of International Journal of Advanced Biotechnology and Research.

bio-manufacturing sectors such as those producing food, leather, detergents, and pharmaceuticals, as shown in Figure 27.2 [97].

Silver recovery: Alkaline proteases are used to recover silver from used X-ray films. The gelatin layers of the used X-ray film contain approximately 1.5–2.0% (by weight) silver. Because burning film to recover silver causes significant pollution. Both polyester and silver film bases can be recycled via enzymatic hydrolysis of the gelatin layers on X-ray film [57, 98, 99]. The stripping techniques can use proteolytic enzymes made from various microorganisms to recover silver. The suspension layer of silver, which contains the protein gelatin, is broken down using a proteolytic enzyme like protease [8, 100].

Food industry: Alkaline proteases are frequently employed in the production of cheese, baking, soya hydrolysates, and meat tenderization, among other things. Proteases are frequently included in tonics, particularly those intended to treat indigestion [57, 101]. Proteases are used in a variety of processes in the food industry, including baking, cheese-making, meat tenderization, and the preparation of hydrolysates [101, 102]. These days, proteases are the most essential component of our food. They enhance flavor, nutritional value, and digestibility while reducing allergenic chemicals [97]. The utilization of proteases during the production of soy sauce boosts both the yield and nutritional value. Alkalase treatment of soy proteins at pH 8 yields hydrolysates that are soluble, have a high protein yield, and have less bitterness [103]. Proteases are now widely used to improve the quality and tenderness of meat. Low-gluten flour must also be prepared to make biscuits, and protease is an important component of this process [97, 104]. Proteases are utilized in the baking industry to swiftly prepare the dough and lower dough viscosity [105]. Protease is primarily used in the dairy industry to make cheese by hydrolyzing particular peptide bonds to produce casein and macro peptides [6, 97]. The color and texture of various dairy products can also be changed and improved using some proteases [106, 107].

Leather Industry: Industries related to tanning are to blame for environmental contamination. Therefore, the use of hydrolyzing enzymes that resemble proteases is a greener method of processing leather than other methods [108, 109]. Proteases are a successful substitute for toxic chemicals like sodium sulfide in enhancing leather quality and lowering environmental pollution [110–112]. Due to its elastolytic and keratinolytic activities, alkaline protease is being used more frequently in developing leather industries [14, 113]. The influencing qualities of alkaline protease are very useful in the leather processing industries. Protease is found to be useful in the soaking, bating, and dehairing stages of skin and hide preparation. Enzymatic removal of unwanted colors aids in the production of clean hide [13, 114, 115]. Proteases are used to selectively hydrolyze noncollagenous skin constituents and remove non-fibrillar proteins such as albumins and globulins. Collagen, a protein found in skins and hides in interaction with other globular and fibrous proteins, is the main protein used in the production of leather. To prepare leather, noncollagenous material must be removed; the degree to which this is done determines the final leather's softness and durability [8, 116].

Detergents Industry: According to Gürkök [117], enzymes are an essential part of medical cleaning products, automatic dishwashing detergents, laundry spot removers, and powder and liquid detergents. One of the most crucial components of all types of detergents, including those used for home laundry, contact lens cleaning solutions, and denatured alcohol, are proteases. The enzymes increase the effectiveness of detergents for removing protein from clothing that has been soiled by perspiration, grass, milk, egg, or other proteins. The cleaning power of conventional detergents is increased by the introduction of detergent enzymes [109]. The most widespread application of industrial enzymes is as additives in detergents. About 25% of all enzyme sales globally are proteases found in laundry detergents [118, 119]. Detergents' ability to remove difficult stains is improved by the use of enzymes in their formulations, which also makes them environmentally safe [104]. Detergent enzymes are desirable as hard surface cleaner additives because they must function on protein substrates bonded to solid surfaces. They may also help with proteinaceous stains, which are frequent in laundry. The efficiency of alkaline proteases in eliminating blood stains from cotton fabric [49].

Pharmaceutical Industry: Proteases are a unique medicinal class with a wide range of applications. They are crucial in the development of various medications that combat serious deadly disorders like cancer, microbe-related infections, inflammation, and dissolving clots [102, 120]. Proteases are being employed to treat conditions such as cystic fibrosis, sepsis, digestive disorders, and others. New pharmacological molecules called proteases are being developed to treat both acute and chronic inflammation. Due to their wide substrate affinity, proteases may have more use as anti-inflammatory medications. Numerous proteases with microbial and plant origins have been discovered and tested for their ability to reduce inflammation [121]. The Serratia species generate a type of protease known as serratio peptidase, which is primarily used to treat inflammation and effectively relieve pain [122]. According to Thakur et al. [97], collagenase and Escherichia coli asparaginase both contribute significantly to the removal of asparagine from the blood in various forms of lymphocytic leukemia, burns, and wounds. *B. subtilis* nattokinase is also effective in preventing cardiovascular disease. Due to their fibrinolytic activity, alkaline proteases produced by *Bacillus* sp. CK-114 also has thrombolytic effects [97].

Degumming of Silk: Traditionally, soap or an alkaline solution was used to degum silk. Proteases are employed as an alternative to these chemicals because using soap or alkali is a crude treatment and these chemicals are not eco-friendly [97]. A proteinaceous substance called sericin contains 20–30% raw silk. Silk fibers become rough when sericin is present, but they become very soft after it is removed [8, 97]. Protease is replacing the more expensive, conventional way of degumming silk since it is less expensive. According to [123], protease-based silk degumming has a greater efficiency as seen in the removal of sericin and reduced energy consumption. The main degumming agents utilized include trypsin, papain, and bacterial proteases. This enzyme makes the yarn stronger without harming the environment [124].

Waste management: Chemical use in industry is detrimental to the surroundings and the environment. An eco-friendly alternative to this risky chemical use is urgently needed for waste management [125]. The keratin structure of chicken feathers, which makes up 5% of the bird's body weight, provides a rich source of proteins for food and feed. The keratinolytic process can convert poultry waste into feed and food [13, 126]. The development of industrial technology that is less damaging to the environment is necessary because of the buildup of pollutants brought on by human activities [127]. The use of bacterial protease for waste treatment or the bioremediation of hydrocarbons is one well-known use of contemporary biotechnology. Additionally, several advantages to using enzymes over using traditional chemical catalysts [128]. The management of trash from homes and processing companies, as well as the cleaning of hair-clogged pipes, are fascinating potential uses for bacterial proteases [129]. Additionally, it is utilized to eliminate offensive odors from homes and public areas, as well as to degrade waste of keratinous material in domestic garbage. These proteases can solubilize proteins in wastes, particularly waste feathers from poultry slaughterhouses, and recover liquid concentrates or dry solids with nutritional value for fish or cattle [130]. Bacterial proteases are now commercially employed in the bioremediation process and as a probiotic agent in aquaculture by including them in the feed of fish and shrimp [131].

27.5 Future Prospects of Using Microbial Alkaline Proteases

Nowadays, the majority of industrial processes take place in harsh environments where enzymes are unstable in conditions of extremely high temperature, high or low pH, and high concentrations of organic solvents and detergents. Only a small class of proteases, however, is recognized as a commercial resource [132]. Numerous criteria determine whether alkaline protease is suitable for use in different industrial applications. The production of proteases is impacted by strain development and media design [15]. It can also be made using immobilized cell systems in batch or repeated batch fermentations. The fermentation media needs to be appropriately tuned to produce alkaline proteases that are commercially viable [26]. Other crucial elements are temperature, metal ions, pH, nitrogen source, carbon source, and inhibitors [16]. According to Jisha et al. [57], the detergent, pharmaceutical, leather, food, and agricultural industries all depend heavily on proteases. Proteases make up around 60% of all industrial enzyme sales, which are currently projected to be worth over 3 billion USD worldwide. Microbial alkaline proteases already play an essential role in various industries, including detergent, leather, feed, chemical, medical, food, and waste treatment. Their potential, however, is much greater, and their use in novel processes is likely to increase shortly.

Furthermore, because of its thermostability, alkali stability, detergent compatibility, and resistance to heavy metals, the protease is a good candidate for potential uses in a variety of biotechnological sectors such as detergent, leather, food/feed, photography, and so on. Additionally, the enzyme might be used as a model system to shed light on the molecular underpinnings of thermostability and alkali stability as well as open the door to the development of new enzymes [1]. The development of novel-designed proteases that are selectively controlled by small molecules has the potential to significantly alter cell cycle progression and, possibly, cell death [133].

To increase the yield of protease enzyme from microbial sources, scientists used a variety of methods, including cloning, overexpression, fed-batch, and chemostat fermentation, parameter optimization using the one factor at a time method, and statistical techniques such as response surface methodology. Continuous efforts are being made to increase protease enzyme production using both traditional methods such as UV or chemicals and cutting-edge methods such as genetic engineering, protein engineering, metagenomics, and gene editing using clustered regularly interspaced short palindromic repeats (CRISPR) [134].

Research is being conducted on their medicinal potential for preventing the spread of diseases like cancer and epidemics like AIDS and malaria. Over the last few decades, we have gained a better understanding of these enzymes' potential applications in fields other than food technology, such as textiles, leather, detergent, agriculture, and the pharmaceutical industry. The "era of OMICS" has also provided future opportunities for using these enzymes in nanotechnology and site-specific or targeted drug delivery systems [135].

27.6 Conclusions

Proteases have been widely commercialized by numerous companies around the world and have a wide range of applications in industries such as food, pharmaceuticals, cosmetics, and so on. Enzymatic processes have played important roles in a variety of bioprocesses for many sectors, as this review has shown. Thermostable, cold-active, and halophilic features of microbial proteases are considered important characteristics relevant in a variety of bioprocesses from a biotechnological perspective. Additionally, they can modify the metabolism of microbes. About 75% of commercial proteases used today come from microorganisms, which have a variety of uses and unique properties. As a result, biotechnological processes may be improved, leading to a more precise breakdown of the studied proteins while also meeting the industry's growing demand. It appears that less research has been done on the topic of designing proteases for new or combining catalytic properties with lengthy half-lives. The protease-based industry anticipates getting modified fusion proteases that combine several actions into one.

References

1 Khajuria, V., Sharma, K., Slathia, P. et al. (2015). Production of a detergent-compatible alkaline protease from *Bacillus cereus* K-3. *J. Mater. Environ. Sci.* 6 (8): 2089–2096. http://www.jmaterenvironsci.com/Document/vol6/vol6_N8/253-JMES-1621-2015-Bajaj.pdf.

2 Suberu, Y., Akande, I., Samuel, T. et al. (2019). Cloning, expression, purification and characterisation of serine alkaline protease from *Bacillus subtilis* RD7. *Biocatal. Agric. Biotechnol.* 20: 101264. https://doi.org/10.1016/j.bcab.2019.101264.

3 Souza, T.S.P.D., de Andrade, C.J., Koblitz, M.G.B., and Fai, A.E.C. (2023). Microbial peptidase in food processing: Current state of the art and future trends. *Catal. Lett.* 153 (1): 114–137. https://doi.org/10.1007/s10562-022-03965-w.

4 Dabhi, U., Rona, R., and Kumar, D. (2017). Immobilization and characterization of an alkaline protease from *Aspergillus niger*. *Int. J. Multidiscip. Curr. Res.* 5: 925–929.

5 Ahmed, S.A. and Abood, N.H. (2017). Effect of some growth factors on protease production by *Rhizopus* oryzae. *Al-J. Al-Nahrain Univ.* 20 (2): 90–95. https://anjs.edu.iq/index.php/anjs/article/view/84/56.

6 Mamo, J. and Assefa, F. (2018). The role of microbial aspartic protease enzyme in food and beverage industries. *J. Food Qual.* 2018 (15): https://doi.org/10.1155/2018/7957269.

7 Tebyanian, H., Mirhosseiny, S.H., Bakhtiari, A. et al. (2018). Effect of physical and chemical factors in the production of alkaline protease enzyme by *Bacillus* strains. *Int. Lett. Nat. Sci.* 71: 10–16. https://doi.org/10.18052/www.scipress.com/ILNS.71.10.

8 Naveed, M., Nadeem, F., Mehmood, T. et al. (2021). Protease—a versatile and eco-friendly biocatalyst with multi-industrial applications: an updated review. *Catal. Lett.* 151: 307–323. https://doi.org/10.1007/s10562-020-03316-7.

9 Gemechu, G., Masi, C., Tafesse, M., and Kebede, G. (2020). A review of the bacterial alkaline proteases. *J. Xidian Univ.* 14 (11): 632–634. https://doi.org/10.37896/jxu14.11/022.

10 Masi, C., Vivek, P., Sowmya, V. et al. (2014). Production and process optimization of protease using various bacterial species—a review. *Int. J. ChemTech Res.* 6 (9): 4268–4275.

11 Niyonzima, F.N., Veena, S.M., and More, S.S. (2020). Industrial production and optimization of microbial enzymes. In: *Microbial Enzymes: Roles and Applications in Industries*, 115–135. https://doi.org/10.1007/978-981-15-1710-5_5.

12 Singh, S., Gupta, P., Sharma, V. et al. (2014). Multifarious potential applications of keratinase of *Bacillus subtilis* K-5. *Biocatal. Biotransform.* 32 (5–6): 333–342. https://doi.org/10.3109/10242422.2014.978306.

13 Razzaq, A., Shamsi, S., Ali, A. et al. (2019). Microbial proteases applications. *Front. Bioeng. Biotechnol.* 7: 110. https://doi.org/10.3389/fbioe.2019.00110.

14 Solanki, P., Putatunda, C., Kumar, A. et al. (2021). Microbial proteases: ubiquitous enzymes with innumerable uses. *3 Biotech* 11 (10): 428. https://doi.org/10.1007/s13205-021-02928-z.

15 Ramkumar, A., Sivakumar, N., Gujarathi, A.M., and Victor, R. (2018). Production of thermotolerant, detergent stable alkaline protease using the gut waste of *Sardinella longiceps* as a substrate: optimization and characterization. *Sci. Rep.* 8 (1): 12442. https://doi.org/10.1038/s41598-018-30155-9.

16 Mushtaq, H., Jehangir, A., Ganai, S.A. et al. (2021). Biochemical characterization and functional analysis of heat stable high potential protease of *Bacillus amyloliquefaciens* strain HM48 from soils of Dachigam National Park in Kashmir Himalaya. *Biomolecules* 11 (1): 117. https://doi.org/10.3390/biom11010117.

17 Elyasi Far, B., Yari Khosroushahi, A., and Dilmaghani, A. (2020). In silico study of alkaline serine protease and production optimization in *Bacillus* sp. khoz1 closed *Bacillus safensis* isolated from honey. *Int. J. Pept. Res. Ther.* 26: 2241–2251. https://doi.org/10.1007/s10989-020-10016-8.

18 Ozdenefe, M.S., Dincer, S., Unal, M.U. et al. (2017). Optimization of culture conditions for alkaline protease production from waste breads using *Bacillus subtilis*. *Rom. Biotechnol. Lett.* 22 (3): 12597–12610.

19 Ash, K. and Mishra, S.K. (2023). Protease enzymes: present status and future perspectives for industrial sector. *Int. J. Curr. Microbiol. Appl. Sci.* 12 (2): 311–323. http://dx.doi.org/10.20546/ijcmas.2023.1202.029.

20 Puissant, J., Jones, B., Goodall, T. et al. (2019). The pH optimum of soil exoenzymes adapts to long-term changes in soil pH. *Soil Biol. Biochem.* 138: 107601. https://doi.org/10.1016/j.soilbio.2019.107601.

21 Musa, H., Kasim, F.H., Gunny, A.A.N., and Gopinath, S.C. (2018). Salt-adapted moulds and yeasts: Potentials in industrial and environmental biotechnology. *Process Biochem.* 69: 33–44. https://doi.org/10.1016/j.procbio.2018.03.026.

22 Bezerra, V.H.S., Cardoso, S.L., Fonseca-Bazzo, Y. et al. (2021). Protease produced by endophytic fungi: a systematic review. *Molecules* 26 (22): 7062. https://doi.org/10.3390/molecules26227062.

23 Hailemichael, F. (2021). Production and industrial application of microbial aspartic protease: a review. *Int. J. Food Eng. Technol.* 5 (2): 85–90. https://doi.org/10.11648/j.ijfet.20210502.17.

24 Sharma, K.M., Kumar, R., Panwar, S., and Kumar, A. (2017). Microbial alkaline proteases: optimization of production parameters and their properties. *J. Genet. Eng. Biotechnol.* 15 (1): 115–126. https://doi.org/10.1016/j.jgeb.2017.02.001.

25 Gurumallesh, P., Alagu, K., Ramakrishnan, B., and Muthusamy, S. (2019). A systematic reconsideration on proteases. *Int. J. Biol. Macromol.* 128: 254–267. https://doi.org/10.1016/j.ijbiomac.2019.01.081.

26 Sharma, M., Gat, Y., Arya, S. et al. (2019). A review on microbial alkaline protease: an essential tool for various industrial approaches. *Ind. Biotechnol.* 15 (2): 69–78. https://doi.org/10.1089/ind.2018.0032.

27 Dhillon, A., Sharma, K., Rajulapati, V., and Goyal, A. (2017). Proteolytic enzymes. In: *Current Developments in Biotechnology and Bioengineering*, 149–173. Elsevier https://doi.org/10.1016/B978-0-444-63662-1.00007-5.

28 Vijayaraghavan, P., Lazarus, S., and Vincent, S.G.P. (2014). De-hairing protease production by an isolated *Bacillus cereus* strain AT under solid-state fermentation using cow dung: Biosynthesis and properties. *Saudi J. Biol. Sci.* 21 (1): 27–34. https://doi.org/10.1016/j.sjbs.2013.04.010.

29 Balachandran, C., Vishali, A., Nagendran, N.A. et al. (2021). Optimization of protease production from *Bacillus halodurans* under solid state fermentation using agrowastes. *Saudi J. Biol. Sci.* 28 (8): 4263–4269. https://doi.org/10.1016/j.sjbs.2021.04.069.

30 Ramakrishna, D.P.N., Reddy, N.G., and Gopal, S.V.R. (2012). Solid state fermentation for the production of alkaline protease by *Bacillus Subtilis* KHS-1 (MTCC No-10110) using different agro-industrial residues. *Int. J. Pharm. Pharm. Sci.* 4: 512–517.

31 Mukhtar, H. and Haq, I. (2013). Comparative evaluation of agroindustrial byproducts for the production of alkaline protease by wild and mutant strains of *Bacillus subtilis* in submerged and solid-state fermentation. *The Scientific World Journal* 2013: https://doi.org/10.1155/2013/538067.

32 Ellaiah, P., Adinarayana, K., Rajyalakshmi, P., and Srinivasulu, B. (2003). Optimization of process parameters for alkaline protease production under solid-state fermentation by alkalophilic *Bacillus* sp. *Asian J. Microbiol., Biotechnol. Environ. Sci.* 5 (1): 49–54.

33 Doan, C.T., Tran, T.N., Wen, I.H. et al. (2019). Conversion of shrimp head waste for the production of a thermotolerant, detergent-stable, alkaline protease by *Paenibacillus* sp. *Catalysts* 9 (10): 798. https://doi.org/10.3390/catal9100798.

34 Emran, M.A., Ismail, S.A., and Hashem, A.M. (2020). Production of detergent stable thermophilic alkaline protease by *Bacillus licheniformis* ALW1. *Biocatal. Agric. Biotechnol.* 26: 101631. https://doi.org/10.1016/j.bcab.2020.101631.

35 Johnvesly, B. and Naik, G.R. (2001). Studies on the production of thermostable alkaline protease from thermophilic and alkaliphilic *Bacillus* sp. JB-99 in a chemically defined medium. *Process Biochem.* 37 (2): 139–144. https://doi.org/10.1016/S0032-9592(01)00191-1.

36 Ayantunji, Y.J., Omole, R.K., Olojo, F.O., and Awojobi, K.O. (2020). Optimization of alkaline protease production in submerged fermentation using *Bacillus cereus* isolated from an abattoir wastewater in Ile-Ife, Nigeria. *J.Adv. Biol. Biotechnol.* 23 (3): 1–15.

37 Asha, B. and Palaniswamy, M. (2018). Characterization of crude and partially purified thermo active and thermo stable alkaline protease produced by *Bacillus cereus* FT1. *Pharm. Sci. Res.* 10 (1): 180–187. https://hero.epa.gov/hero/index.cfm/reference/details/reference_id/8165352.

38 Sujatha, A. and Subash, A. (2018). Isolation and purification of an extracellular protease from *Bacillus subtilis* ASASBT isolated from termite soil. *Int. J. Pharm. Sci. Res.* 9 (11): 4812–4819.

39 Aguilar, J.G.D.S., de Castro, R.J., and Sato, H.H. (2019). Alkaline protease production by *Bacillus licheniformis* LBA 46 in a bench reactor: Effect of temperature and agitation. *Braz. J. Chem. Eng.* 36 (2): 615–625. https://doi.org/10.1590/0104-6632.20190362s20180014.

40 Patil, N.S. and Kurhekar, J.V. (2020). Optimization of protease production by *Bacillus isronensis* strain KD3 isolated from dairy industry effluent. *Nat. Environ. Pollut. Technol.* 19 (3): 1257–1264. https://doi.org/10.46488/NEPT.2020.v19i03.041.

41 Pant, G., Prakash, A., Pavani, J.V.P. et al. (2015). Production, optimization and partial purification of protease from *Bacillus subtilis*. *J. Taibah Univ. Sci.* 9 (1): 50–55. https://doi.org/10.1016/j.jtusci.2014.04.010.

42 Verma, J. and Pandey, S. (2019). Characterization of a partially purified alkaline protease secreted by halophilic bacterium *Citricoccus* sp. isolated from agricultural soil of northern India. *Biocatal. Agric. Biotechnol.* 17: 605–612. https://doi.org/10.1016/j.bcab.2019.01.020.

43 Abu-Khudir, R., Salem, M.M., Allam, N.G., and Ali, E.M. (2019). Production, partial purification, and biochemical characterization of a thermotolerant alkaline metallo-protease from *Staphylococcus sciuri*. *Appl. Biochem. Biotechnol.* 189: 87–102. https://doi.org/10.1007/s12010-019-02983-6.

44 El Hadj-Ali, N., Agrebi, R., Ghorbel-Frikha, B. et al. (2007). Biochemical and molecular characterization of a detergent stable alkaline serine-protease from a newly isolated *Bacillus licheniformis* NH1. *Enzyme Microb. Technol.* 40 (4): 515–523.

45 Bajaj, B.K. and Sharma, P. (2011). An alkali-thermotolerant extracellular protease from a newly isolated *Streptomyces* sp. DP2. *New Biotechnol.* 28 (6): 725–732. https://doi.org/10.1016/j.nbt.2011.01.001.

46 Boominadhan, U., Rajakumar, R., Sivakumaar, P.K.V., and Joe, M.M. (2009). Optimization of protease enzyme production using *Bacillus* sp. isolated from different wastes. *Bot. Res. Int.* 2 (2): 83–87.

47 Bose, A., Chawdhary, V., Keharia, H., and Subramanian, R.B. (2014). Production and characterization of a solvent-tolerant protease from a novel marine isolate *Bacillus tequilensis* P15. *Ann. Microbiol.* 64: 343–354. https://doi.org/10.1007/s13213-013-0669-y.

48 Sarkar, G. and Suthindhiran, K. (2020). Extraction and characterization of alkaline protease from *Streptomyces* sp. GS-1 and its application as a dehairing agent. *Biocatal. Agric. Biotechnol.* 25: 101590. https://doi.org/10.1016/j.bcab.2020.101590.

49 Masi, C., Tadesse, D., and Ayele, A. (2022). Potential use of proteolytic bacteria *Paenibacillus dendritiformis* (BT7) isolated from Batu tannery effluents for the detergent industry. *Karbala Int. J. Mod. Sci.* 8 (4): 670–681. https://doi.org/10.33640/2405-609X.3267.

50 Dwivedi, P., Sharma, A.K., and Singh, S.P. (2021). Biochemical properties and repression studies of an alkaline serine protease from a haloalkaliphilic actinomycete, *Nocardiopsis dassonvillei* sub-sp. albirubida OK-14. *Biocatal. Agric. Biotechnol.* 35: 102059. https://doi.org/10.1016/j.bcab.2021.102059.

51 Sharma, A.K., Kikani, B.A., and Singh, S.P. (2020). Biochemical, thermodynamic and structural characteristics of a biotechnologically compatible alkaline protease from a haloalkaliphilic, *Nocardiopsis dassonvillei* OK-18. *Int. J. Biol. Macromol.* 153: 680–696. https://doi.org/10.1016/j.ijbiomac.2020.03.006.

52 Al-Dhabi, N.A., Esmail, G.A., Ghilan, A.K.M. et al. (2020). Characterization and fermentation optimization of novel thermo-stable alkaline protease from *Streptomyces* sp. Al-Dhabi-82 from the Saudi Arabian environment for eco-friendly and industrial applications. *J. King Saud Univ. Sci.* 32 (1): 1258–1264. https://doi.org/10.1016/j.jksus.2019.11.011.

53 Darwesh, O.M., El-Hawary, A.S., El Kelany, U.S., and El-Sherbiny, G.M. (2019). Nematicidal activity of thermostable alkaline protease produced by *Saccharomonospora viridis* strain Hw G550. *Biotechnol. Rep.* 24: e00386. https://doi.org/10.1016/j.btre.2019.e00386.

54 Thakrar, F.J., Kikani, B.A., Sharma, A.K., and Singh, S.P. (2018). Stability of alkaline proteases from haloalkaliphilic actinobacteria probed by circular dichroism spectroscopy. *Appl. Biochem. Microbiol.* 54: 591–602. https://doi.org/10.1134/S0003683818100022.

55 Parthasarathy, M. and Gnanadoss, J.J. (2020). Purification and characterization of extracellular alkaline protease from *Streptomyces* sp. LCJ12A isolated from Pichavaram mangroves. *J. Appl. Biol. Biotechnol.* 8 (1): 15–20. http://dx.doi.org/10.7324/JABB.2020.80103.

56 Hameş-Kocabaş, E.E. and Uzel, A. (2007). Alkaline protease production by an actinomycete MA1-1 isolated from marine sediments. *Ann. Microbiol.* 57: 71–75. https://doi.org/10.1007/BF03175053.

57 Jisha, V., Smitha, R.B., Pradeep, S. et al. (2013). Versatility of microbial proteases. *Adv. Enzyme Res.* 1 (3): 39–51. http://dx.doi.org/10.4236/aer.2013.13005.

58 Mandal, S. and Banerjee, D. (2019). Proteases from endophytic fungi with potential industrial applications. In: *Recent Advancement in White Biotechnology*

Through Fungi: Diversity and Enzymes Perspectives, 319–359. https://doi.org/10.1007/978-3-030-10480-1_10.

59 Benluvankar, V., Jebapriya, G.R., and Gnanadoss, J.J. (2015). Protease production by *Penicillium* sp. LCJ228 under solid state fermentation using groundnut oilcake as substrate. *Life* 50: 12–19.

60 Sharma, N. (2019). A review on fungal alkaline protease. *J. Emerging Technol. Innovative Res.* 6 (6): 1–14.

61 Chander, M. and Puri, P. (2019). Recent advances in microbial production of proteases. *Int. J. Res. Anal. Rev.* 6 (1): 64–76. ISSN 2348-1269.

62 Mamo, J., Kangwa, M., Fernandez-Lahore, H.M., and Assefa, F. (2020). Optimization of media composition and growth conditions for the production of milk-clotting protease (MCP) from *Aspergillus oryzae* DRDFS13 under solid-state fermentation. *Braz. J. Microbiol.* 51: 571–584. https://doi.org/10.1007/s42770-020-00243-y.

63 Shankar, S., Rao, M., and Laxman, R.S. (2011). Purification and characterization of an alkaline protease by a new strain of *Beauveria* sp. *Process Biochem.* 46: 579–585. https://doi.org/10.1016/j.procbio.2010.10.013.

64 Benmrad, M.O., Moujehed, E., Elhoul, M.B. et al. (2016). A novel organic solvent-and detergent-stable serine alkaline protease from *Trametes cingulata* strain CTM10101. *Int. J. Biol. Macromol.* 91: 961–972. https://doi.org/10.1016/j.ijbiomac.2016.06.025.

65 Galeano, R.M.S., Franco, D.G., Chaves, P.O. et al. (2021). Plant growth promoting potential of endophytic *Aspergillus niger* 9-p isolated from native forage grass in Pantanal of Nhecolândia region, Brazil. *Rhizosphere* 18: 100332. https://doi.org/10.1016/j.rhisph.2021.100332.

66 Matias, R.R., Sepúlveda, A.M.G., Batista, B.N. et al. (2021). Degradation of *Staphylococcus aureus* biofilm using hydrolytic enzymes produced by amazonian endophytic fungi. *Appl. Biochem. Biotechnol.* 193: 2145–2161. https://doi.org/10.1007/s12010-021-03542-8.

67 Xiao, Y.Z., Wu, D.K., Zhao, S.Y. et al. (2015). Statistical optimization of alkaline protease production from *Penicillium citrinum* YL-1 under solid-state fermentation. *Prep. Biochem. Biotechnol.* 45 (5): 447–462. https://doi.org/10.1080/10826068.2014.923450.

68 Abu-Tahon, M.A., Arafat, H.H., and Isaac, G.S. (2020). Laundry detergent compatibility and dehairing efficiency of alkaline thermostable protease produced from *Aspergillus terreus* under solid-state fermentation. *J. Oleo Sci.* 69 (3): 241–254. https://doi.org/10.5650/jos.ess19315.

69 Souza, P.M., Werneck, G., Aliakbarian, B. et al. (2017). Production, purification and characterization of an aspartic protease from *Aspergillus foetidus*. *Food Chem. Toxicol.* 109: 1103–1110. https://doi.org/10.1016/j.fct.2017.03.055.

70 Benmrad, M.O., Moujehed, E., Elhoul, M.B. et al. (2018). Production, purification, and biochemical characterization of serine alkaline protease from *Penicillium chrysogenium* strain X5 used as excellent bio-additive for textile processing. *Int. J. Biol. Macromol.* 119: 1002–1016. https://doi.org/10.1016/j.ijbiomac.2016.06.025.

71 Rajput, K., Chanyal, S., and Agrawal, P.K. (2016). Optimization of protease production by endophytic fungus, *Alternaria alternata* isolated from gymnosperm tree-Cupressus torulosa D Don. *World J. Pharm. Pharm. Sci.* 5: 1034–1054.

72 Chandra Behera, B., Kumar Sethi, B., Mohapatra, S. et al. (2021). Bio-production of alkaline protease by *Trichoderma longibrachiatum* and *Penicillium rubidurum* using different agro-industrial products. *Novel Res. Microbiol. J.* 5 (3): 1241–1255. https://doi.org/10.21608/nrmj.2021.178300.

73 El-Khonezy, M.I., Elgammal, E.W., Ahmed, E.F., and Abd-Elaziz, A.M. (2021). Detergent stable thiol-dependant alkaline protease produced from the endophytic fungus *Aspergillus ochraceus* BT21: purification and kinetics. *Biocatal. Agric. Biotechnol.* 35: 102046. https://doi.org/10.1016/j.bcab.2021.102046.

74 Ben Mefteh, F., Frikha, F., Daoud, A. et al. (2019). Response surface methodology optimization of an acidic protease produced by *Penicillium bilaiae* isolate TDPEF30, a newly recovered endophytic fungus from healthy roots of date palm trees (*Phoenix dactylifera* L.). *Microorganisms* 7 (3): 74. https://doi.org/10.3390/microorganisms7030074.

75 Meshram, V., Saxena, S., Paul, K. et al. (2017). Production, purification and characterisation of a potential fibrinolytic protease from endophytic *Xylaria curta* by solid substrate fermentation. *Appl. Biochem. Biotechnol.* 181: 1496–1512. https://doi.org/10.1007/s12010-016-2298-y.

76 Elgammal, E.W., El-Khonezy, M.I., Ahmed, E.F., and Abd-Elaziz, A.M. (2020). Enhanced production, partial purification, and characterization of alkaline thermophilic protease from the endophytic fungus *Aspergillus ochraceus* BT21. *Egyptian Pharmaceutical Journal* 19 (4): 338.

77 Usman, A., Mohammed, S., and Mamo, J. (2021). Production, optimization, and characterization of an acid protease from a filamentous fungus by solid-state fermentation. *Int. J. Microbiol.* 2021: https://doi.org/10.1155/2021/6685963.

78 Pawar, K.S., Singh, P.N., and Singh, S.K. (2023). Fungal alkaline proteases and their potential applications in different industries. *Front. Microbiol.* 14: 1138401. https://doi.org/10.3389/fmicb.2023.1138401.

79 Gimenes, N.C., Silveira, E., and Tambourgi, E.B. (2021). An overview of proteases: production, downstream processes and industrial applications. *Sep. Purif. Rev.* 50 (3): 223–243. https://doi.org/10.1080/15422119.2019.1677249.

80 Abdullah, R., Asim, M., Nadeem, M. et al. (2022). Production, optimization, purification, kinetic analysis, and applications of alkaline proteases produced from *Bacillus subtilis* through solid-state fermentation of agricultural byproducts. *Kuwait J. Sci.* 49 (4): 1–15. https://doi.org/10.48129/kjs.12103.

81 Banerjee, G. and Ray, A.K. (2017). Impact of microbial proteases on biotechnological industries. *Biotechnol. Genet. Eng. Rev.* 33 (2): 119–143. https://doi.org/10.1080/02648725.2017.1408256.

82 Chandrasekaran, S., Kumaresan, S.S.P., and Manavalan, M. (2015). Production and optimization of protease by filamentous fungus isolated from paddy soil in Thiruvarur District Tamilnadu. *J. App. Biol. Biotech.* 3 (6): 066–069. https://doi.org/10.7324/JABB.2015.3610.

83 Asker, M.M., Mahmoud, M.G., El Shebwy, K., and Abd el Aziz, M.S. (2013). Purification and characterization of two thermostable protease fractions from *Bacillus megaterium*. *J. Genet. Eng. Biotechnol.* 11 (2): 103–109. https://doi.org/10.1016/j.jgeb.2013.08.001.

84 Salihi, A., Asoodeh, A., and Aliabadian, M. (2017). Production and biochemical characterization of an alkaline protease from *Aspergillus oryzae* ch93. *Int. J. Biol. Macromol.* 94: 827–835. https://doi.org/10.1016/j.ijbiomac.2016.06.023.

85 Si, J.-B., Jang, E.-J., Charalampopoulos, D., and Wee, Y.-J. (2018). Purification and characterization of microbial protease produced extracellularly from *Bacillus subtilis* FBL-1. *Biotechnol. Bioprocess Eng.* 23 (2): 176–182. https://doi.org/10.1007/s12257-017-0495-3.

86 Ao, X.L., Yu, X., Wu, D.T. et al. (2018). Purification and characterization of neutral protease from *Aspergillus oryzae* Y1 isolated from naturally fermented broad beans. *AMB Express* 8 (1): 1–10. https://doi.org/10.1186/s13568-018-0611-6.

87 Sundararajan, S., Kannan, C.N., and Chittibabu, S. (2011). Alkaline protease from *Bacillus cereus* VITSN04: potential application as a dehairing agent. *J. Biosci. Bioeng.* 111 (2): 128–133. https://doi.org/10.1016/j.jbiosc.2010.09.009.

88 Madhavi, J., Srilakshmi, J., Rao, M.R., and Rao, K.R.S.S. (2011). Efficient leather dehairing by bacterial thermostable protease. *Int. J. Bio-Sci. Bio-Technol.* 3 (1): 11–26. https://www.earticle.net/Article/A167003.

89 Ullah, N., Rehman, M.U., Sarwar, A. et al. (2022). Purification, characterization, and application of alkaline protease enzyme from a locally isolated *Bacillus cereus* strain. *Fermentation* 8 (11): 628. https://doi.org/10.3390/fermentation8110628.

90 Mousavi, B., Azizi, M.H., and Abbasi, S. (2022). Antidiabetic bio-peptides of soft and hard wheat glutens. *Food Chem.: Mol. Sci.* 4: 100104. https://doi.org/10.1016/j.fochms.2022.100104.

91 El-Khonezy, M.I., El-Gammal, E.W., Atwa, N.A., and El-Abd, M.A. (2015). Partial purification and characterization of an alkaline serine protease produced by *Streptomyces griseus* NCRRT and its antifungal effect on *Fusarium solani*. *World Appl. Sci. J.* 33 (5): 831–842.

92 Shanmugavel, M., Vasantharaj, S., Saathiyavimal, S., and Gnanamani, A. (2016). Application of an alkaline protease in biological waste processing: an eco-friendly approach. *Int. J. Biosci. Nanosci.* 3: 19–24.

93 Manavalan, T., Manavalan, A., Ramachandran, S., and Heese, K. (2020). Identification of a novel thermostable alkaline protease from *Bacillus megaterium*-TK1 for the detergent and leather industry. *Biology* 9 (12): 472. https://doi.org/10.3390/biology9120472.

94 More, S.V., Chavan, S., and Prabhune, A.A. (2018). Silk degumming and utilization of silk sericin by hydrolysis using alkaline protease from *Beauveria* Sp. (MTCC 5184): a green approach. *J. Nat. Fibers* 15 (3): 373–383. https://doi.org/10.1080/15440478.2017.1330718.

95 Aladdin, A., Alsaheb, R.A., Pareek, A. et al. (2017). Biotechnological aspects and pharmaceutical applications of bacterial proteases. *Pharm. Lett.* 9 (2): 9–20.

96 Furhan, J. and Sharma, S. (2014). Isolation, screening and characterization of cold active alkaline protease from Wular lake of Kashmir region. *Int. J. Adv. Biotechnol. Res.* 4 (1): 576–581.

97 Thakur, N., Goyal, M., Sharma, S., and Kumar, D. (2018). Proteases: industrial applications and approaches used in strain improvement. *Biol. Forum–Int. J.* 10 (1): 158–167.

98 Anbesaw, M.S. (2021). Characterization and potential application of bromelain from pineapple (*Ananas* comosus) waste (peel) in recovery of silver from X-ray films. *Int. J. Biomater.* 2021: https://doi.org/10.1155/2021/9964337.

99 Lakshmi, B.K.M. and Hemalatha, K.P.J. (2016). Eco-friendly recovery of silver from used X-ray films by alkaline protease of *Bacillus cereus* strain S8. *Front. Environ. Microbiol.* 2 (6): 45–48. https://doi.org/10.11648/j.fem.20160206.14.

100 Asgher, M., Bashir, F., and Iqbal, H.M. (2018). Protease-based cross-linked enzyme aggregates with improved catalytic stability, silver removal, and dehairing potentials. *Int. J. Biol. Macromol.* 118: 1247–1256. https://doi.org/10.1016/j.ijbiomac.2018.06.107.

101 Singh, R., Singh, A., and Sachan, S. (2019). Enzymes used in the food industry: friends or foes? In: *Enzymes in Food Biotechnology*, 827–843. Academic Press https://doi.org/10.1016/B978-0-12-813280-7.00048-7.

102 Srilakshmi, J., Madhavi, J., Lavanya, S., and Ammani, K. (2015). Commercial potential of fungal protease: past, present and future prospects. *J. Pharm. Chem. Biol. Sci.* 2 (4): 218–234.

103 Sun, X.D. (2011). Enzymatic hydrolysis of soy proteins and the hydrolysates utilisation. *Int. J. Food Sci. Technol.* 46 (12): 2447–2459. https://doi.org/10.1111/j.1365-2621.2011.02785.x.

104 Souza, P.M.D., Bittencourt, M.L.D.A., Caprara, C.C. et al. (2015). A biotechnology perspective of fungal proteases. *Braz. J. Microbiol.* 46: 337–346. https://doi.org/10.1590/S1517-838246220140359.

105 Zadeike, D., Jukonyte, R., Juodeikiene, G. et al. (2018). Comparative study of *ciabatta crust crispness* through acoustic and mechanical methods: Effects of wheat malt and protease on dough rheology and crust crispness retention during storage. *LWT* 89: 110–116. https://doi.org/10.1016/j.lwt.2017.10.034.

106 Ben Amira, A., Besbes, S., Attia, H., and Blecker, C. (2017). Milk-clotting properties of plant rennets and their enzymatic, rheological, and sensory role in cheese making: a review. *Int. J. Food Prop.* 20 (1): S76–S93. https://doi.org/10.1080/10942912.2017.1289959.

107 Aruna, K., Shah, J., and Birmole, R. (2014). Production and partial characterization of alkaline protease from Bacillus tequilensis strains CSGAB0139 isolated from spoilt cottage cheese. *Int. J. Appl. Biol. Pharm.* 5 (3): 201–221.

108 Karn, S.K. and Kumar, A. (2015). Hydrolytic enzyme protease in sludge: recovery and its application. *Biotechnol. Bioprocess Eng.* 20: 652–661. https://doi.org/10.1007/s12257-015-0161-6.

109 Varia, A.D., Shukla, V.Y., and Tipre, D.R. (2019). Alkaline protease versatile enzyme. *Int. J. Res. Anal. Rev.* 6 (2): 208–217.

110 Dettmer, A., Cavalli, É., Ayub, M.A., and Gutterres, M. (2013). Environmentally friendly hide unhairing: enzymatic hide processing for the replacement of sodium sulfide and delimig. *J. Cleaner Prod.* 47: 11–18. https://doi.org/10.1016/j.jclepro.2012.04.024.

111 Wanyonyi, W.C. and Mulaa, F.J. (2019). Alkaliphilic enzymes and their application in novel leather processing technology for next-generation tanneries. In: *Alkaliphiles in Biotechnology, Advances in Biochemical Engineering/Biotechnology*, vol. 172 (ed. G. Mamo and B. Mattiasson). Cham: Springer https://doi.org/10.1007/10_2019_95.

112 Zhang, Y., Liu, H., Tang, K. et al. (2021). Effect of different ions in assisting protease to open the collagen fiber bundles in leather making. *J. Cleaner Prod.* 293: 126017. https://doi.org/10.1016/j.jclepro.2021.126017.

113 Khambhaty, Y. (2020). Applications of enzymes in leather processing. *Environ. Chem. Lett.* 18 (3): 747–769. https://doi.org/10.1007/s10311-020-00971-5.

114 Kanagaraj, J., Panda, R.C., and Kumar, V. (2020). Trends and advancements in sustainable leather processing: Future directions and challenges—a review. *J. Environ. Chem. Eng.* 8 (5): 104379. https://doi.org/10.1016/j.jece.2020.104379.

115 Saran, S., Chib, S., and Saxena, R.K. (2019). Biotechnology of leather: an alternative to conventional leather processing. *High Value Ferment. Prod.: Hum. Welfare* 2: 23–47. https://doi.org/10.1002/9781119555384.

116 Ammasi, R., Victor, J.S., Chellan, R., and Chellappa, M. (2020). Alkaline protease for efficacious rehydration of skin matrix by a novel *Bacillus crolab* MTCC 5468 in sustainable leather production: a green approach. *Biotechnol. Lett* 42: 249–267. https://doi.org/10.1007/s10529-019-02769-0.

117 Gürkök, S. (2019). Microbial enzymes in detergents: a review. *Int. J. Sci. Eng. Res.* 10 (9): 75–81.

118 Hamza, T.A. (2017). Bacterial protease enzyme: a safe and good alternative for industrial and commercial use. *Int. J. Chem. Biochem. Sci.* 3 (1): 1–10. http://www.aiscience.org/journal/ijcbs.

119 Sanchez, S. and Demain, A.L. (2011). Enzymes and bioconversions of industrial, pharmaceutical, and biotechnological significance. *Org. Process Res. Dev.* 15 (1): 224–230. https://doi.org/10.1021/op100302x.

120 Pezzani, R., Jimenez-Garcia, M., Capo, X. et al. (2023). Anticancer properties of bromelain: State-of-the-art and recent trends. *Front. Oncol.* 12: 1068778. https://doi.org/10.3389/fonc.2022.1068778.

121 Verma, M.K. and Pulicherla, K.K. (2016). Enzyme promiscuity in earthworm serine protease: substrate versatility and therapeutic potential. *Amino Acids* 48: 941–948. https://doi.org/10.1007/s00726-015-2162-3.

122 McCarty, S.M., Cochrane, C.A., Clegg, P.D., and Percival, S.L. (2012). The role of endogenous and exogenous enzymes in chronic wounds: a focus on the implications of aberrant levels of both host and bacterial proteases in wound healing. *Wound Repair Regener.* 20 (2): 125–136. https://doi.org/10.1111/j.1524-475X.2012.00763.x.

123 El-Sayed, H., Mowafi, S., El-Fiky, A.F., and Khalil, E.M. (2022). Low-temperature water-saving bio-degumming of natural silk using thermophilic protease. *Sustainable Chem. Pharm.* 27: 100681. https://doi.org/10.1016/j.scp.2022.100681.

124 Thirupathaiah, Y., Chandel, A.K., and Sivaprasad, V. (2018). Potential applications of enzymes in sericulture. In: *Sustainable Biotechnology-Enzymatic Resources of Renewable Energy*, 463–472. https://doi.org/10.1007/978-3-319-95480-6_18.

125 Chisholm, J.M., Zamani, R., Negm, A.M. et al. (2021). Sustainable waste management of medical waste in African developing countries: a narrative review. *Waste Manage. Res.: J. Sustainable Circ. Econ.* 39 (9): 1149–1163. https://doi.org/10.1177/0734242X211029175.

126 Srivastava, B., Khatri, M., Singh, G., and Arya, S.K. (2020). Microbial keratinases: an overview of biochemical characterization and its eco-friendly approach for industrial applications. *J. Cleaner Prod.* 252: 119847. https://doi.org/10.1016/j.jclepro.2019.119847.

127 Saravanan, A., Kumar, P.S., Jeevanantham, S. et al. (2021). Effective water/wastewater treatment methodologies for toxic pollutants removal: processes and applications towards sustainable development. *Chemosphere* 280: 130595. https://doi.org/10.1016/j.chemosphere.2021.130595.

128 Bhattacharya, A. and Gupta, A. (2022). Current trends in the applicability of thermophiles and thermozymes in bioremediation of environmental pollutants. In: *Microbial Extremozymes*, 161–176. Academic Press https://doi.org/10.1016/B978-0-12-822945-3.00013-0.

129 Petek, B. and Marinšek Logar, R. (2021). Management of waste sheep wool as valuable organic substrate in European Union countries. *J. Mater. Cycles Waste Manage.* 23: 44–54. https://doi.org/10.1007/s10163-020-01121-3.

130 Pandian, S., Sundaram, J., and Panchatcharam, P. (2012). Isolation, identification and characterization of feather degrading bacteria. *Eur. J. Exp. Biol.* 2: 274–282.

131 Nisar, U., Peng, D., Mu, Y., and Sun, Y. (2022). A solution for sustainable utilization of aquaculture waste: a comprehensive review of biofloc technology and aqua mimicry. *Front. Nutr.* 8: 1231. https://doi.org/10.3389/fnut.2021.791738.

132 Li, Q., Yi, L., Marek, P., and Iverson, B.L. (2013). Commercial proteases: present and future. *FEBS Lett.* 587 (8): 1155–1163. https://doi.org/10.1016/j.febslet.2012.12.019.

133 Gerry, C.J. and Schreiber, S.L. (2020). Unifying principles of bifunctional, proximity-inducing small molecules. *Nat. Chem. Biol.* 16: 369–378. https://doi.org/10.1038/s41589-020-0469-1.

134 Rehman, R., Ahmed, M., Siddique, A. et al. (2017). Catalytic role of thermostable metalloproteases from *Bacillus subtilis* KT004404 as dehairing and destaining agent. *Appl. Biochem. Biotechnol.* 181: 434–450. https://doi.org/10.1007/s12010-016-2222-5.

135 Zhao, Y., Yu, X., and Li, J. (2020). Manipulation of immune–vascular crosstalk: new strategies towards cancer treatment. *Acta Pharm. Sin. B* 10 (11): 2018–2036. https://doi.org/10.1016/j.apsb.2020.09.014.

28

Microbial Lipases in Modern Detergency: Sources, Production, and Application

Shashwat Katiyar and Nand Lal

Chhatrapati Shahu Ji Maharaj University, School of Life Sciences & Biotechnology, Kalyanpur, Kanpur, Uttar Pradesh 208024, India

28.1 Introduction

The detergency process is a surprisingly complex process and a good detergency requires the synergism of many simultaneous processes. A detergent removes dirt and contaminants from a surface by solubilizing, suspending, or emulsifying the cleaning formulation. Most of the industries are currently manufacturing microbial enzymes based detergents as they involve in process of cleaning with an environmental friendly, significant, and lower the energy consumption. More than half of the supplies of such detergents are produced in developing countries. Cellulases, proteases, amylases, and lipases are the major class of detergent enzymes; each of these provides various benefits for applied uses in washing laundry and dishwashing. The enzymatic detergents are effective at diverse temperatures and environments, and prove to be least toxic and almost noncorrosive in comparison to other detergent formulations.

28.2 Detergent Features

Detergents are amphiphilic in nature; the molecules with an amphiphilic nature have partly hydrophilic and partly hydrophobic properties. The amphiphilic nature of detergents is responsible for mixing the hydrophobic substances like oil and grease with the water [1]. These molecules form a structure in which the globular head, having a hydrophilic nature, aggregates in the aqueous solution called micelles; this structure eliminates the unfavorable proximity to the water and hydrophobic tails and yet allows the interaction of solvent with dissolved molecules.

Microbial Enzymes: Production, Purification, and Industrial Applications, First Edition.
Edited by Dinesh Yadav, Pankaj Chowdhary, Gautam Anand, and Rajarshi Kumar Gaur.

Amphiphiles in a dilute aqueous solution do not form micelles until they surpass the critical micelle concentration [2]. The main components are:

28.2.1 Surfactants

Surfactants (sodium alkylbenzene sulfonates, sodium stearate, and potassium alcohol sulfates) area class of chemical compounds that decrease the value of surface tension between two liquids, between a liquid and a gas, or interfacial tension between a liquid and a solid. Surfactants have emulsifying properties that make a substance/dirt insoluble in water and easy to remove. Surfactants have a hydrophobic (water-hating) tail and a hydrophilic (water-loving) head. The hydrophobic tail of each surfactant is surrounded by soil. The hydrophilic head is surrounded by water. Depending on the charge of the hydrophilic head of the surfactant is classified as anionic (sulfates, sulfonates, and gluconates), nonionic (cocamide, ethoxylates, and alkoxylates), cationic (alkyl ammonium chlorides), or amphoteric (betaines and amino oxides).

28.2.2 Builders

Builders act as enhancers for the surfactants. These builders are called water softeners as they deactivate Ca and Mg ions in water. For example, zeolites trap the divalent ions in the solid particles that facilitate the process of removing dirt. There are builders like phosphate-containing builders that can also be used in detergents e.g. sodium triphosphate. Builders have several functions including the process of softening, emulsifying, and buffering. Builders soften water by the process of deactivating hardness minerals (metal ions like magnesium and calcium). They do this through one of the two ways: (i) sequestration, which involves holding of metal ions in solution and (ii) precipitation, occurred by removing metal ions from the solution as insoluble materials.

28.2.3 Cobuilders

Cobuilders are known to facilitate the mechanism of action of builders. Certain organic polymers are being used as cobuilders, e.g., polycarboxylate.

28.2.4 Dye-transfer Inhibitors

Dye-transfer inhibition during laundering can be performed by catalytic bleaching of the migrating dyes in the wash-liquor. The rate of the bleaching reaction onto the acceptor fabric should be significantly higher as compared to the rate of dye adsorption. These common dye transfer inhibitors such as chroma band S-100 are known to prevent the original textile colors from being rinsed off into the washing water [3].

28.3 Enzymes in Detergents

A lot of additives are used to modify the detergents as per desired needs. Some of the additives of detergents include sequestering builders (citrate, polyphosphates), precipitating builders and alkaline agents (sodium carbonates and sodium silicates), bleaching agents (hydrogen peroxide, sodium perborate, and sodium per carbonate), processing aids (alcohol, water, xylene sulfonate, and sodium sulfate), and corrosion inhibitor (sodium silicate). These additives have shown various toxic effects that are causing adverse effects on human exposure indirectly. There are mainly two types of detergents used by the industries:

(I) Phosphate-containing detergents: The detergents which carry phosphates in their components are highly caustic.
(II) Detergents carrying surfactants: Detergents that have many substances in their compositions are highly toxic and would be harmful agents to use in food and brewery industries [4].

To avoid the use of these traditional chemicals, the enzymes are often used in modern detergency as these are more stable even at low temperatures [5] and safe for human health. Enzymes show the crucial role in making and modifying the detergents that are being used in several industries for specific purposes. Widely used classes of enzymes in modern detergency are proteases, lipases, amylases, and cellulases. Each class of these enzymes has its specific way of functioning, so these are used via different industries according to their desired need [3]. These detergent enzymes are beneficial in industrial areas as they need less time of washing, less use of water, and low temperature to work fast in comparison to other normal detergents [6]. Being lesser toxic agents than others, they are preferably chosen by most industries. Redox enzymes like peroxidases and oxidases are also being studied so that they can be the lead component in detergents for bleaching and utilizing less harsh chemicals. Most of the enzymatic detergents are hydrolases, the enzymes that catalyze the cleavage of substrates by water, e.g., proteases, lipases, amylases, cellulases, etc. [7]. These enzymes' mechanisms of action are very specific according to the type of stains and dirt (Table 28.1) [8, 9].

The enzymes involved in catalytic reactions like hydrolysis or transesterification reactions or in triacylglycerol synthesis have high importance in several industrial segments such as cosmetics, pharmaceuticals, and food. Lipases come under the class of triacylglycerol hydrolases that have physiological importance and industrial abilities [10]. The enzymes in detergent do not require cofactors for their functioning.

Table 28.1 The enzymes in detergent and their specific actions according to the dirt.

Specific enzymatic actions and types of dirt	
Lipases	Decomposition of fatty materials like sauces, oil, butter, etc.
Amylases	Remove the stains that are related to starch
Proteases	Remove the stains based on proteins like blood, egg, and grass, and adhere strongly to textile fibers to remove the stains
Cellulases	Intercalate the structure of cellulose fibers of a cotton cloth
Mannases	Removing stains of food
Pectinases	Removing stains of fruits

28.4 Lipases and Their Characteristics

Lipases are considered as monomeric proteins with a molecular weight of 19–60 kDa. The enzyme lipases catalyze the hydrolysis of oils and fats to give glycerol and free fatty acids as their end product. The physical properties of enzymes depend on some factors like the chain length of fatty acids, the position of fatty acids in the backbone of glycerol, and the degree of unsaturation [11, 12]. At pH 7, up to 4, and at 8, the lipases are stable in organic solvents. Lipases are active and most of the lipases catalyze many useful reactions like esterification.

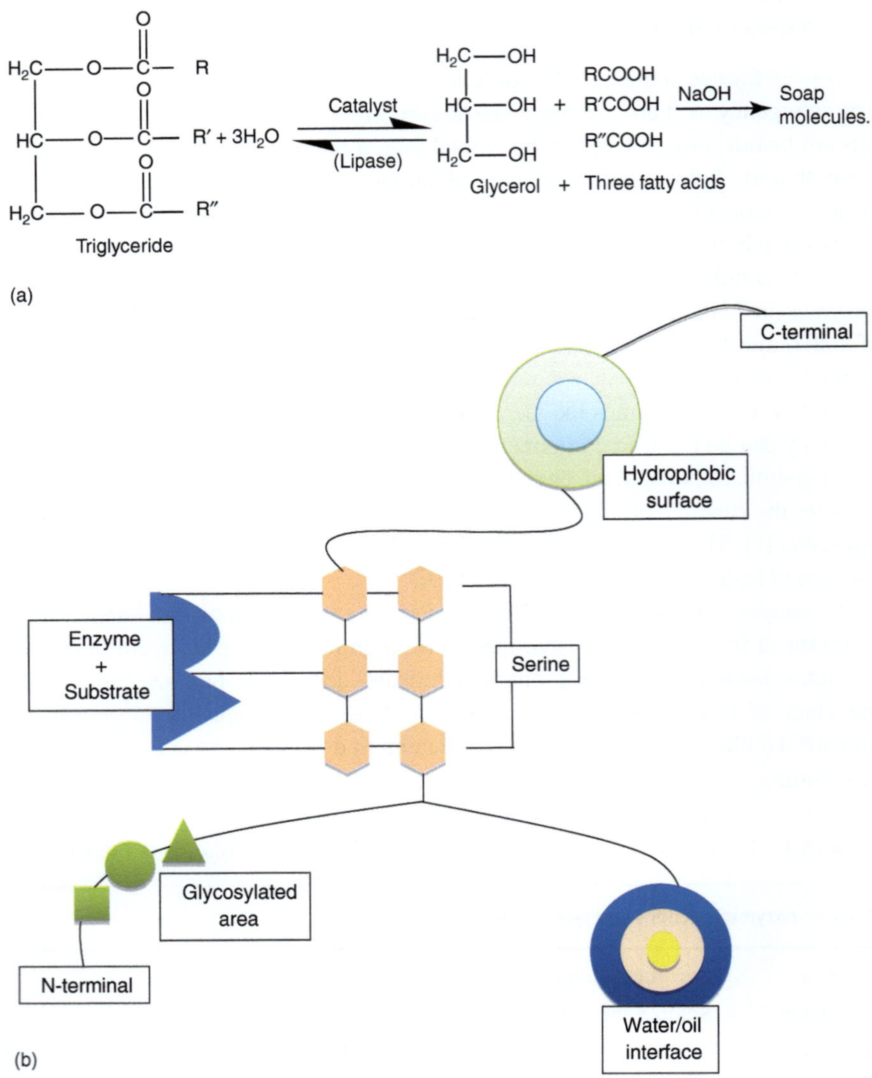

Figure 28.1 (a) Enzymatic action of lipases on triglyceride. (b) Industrial application of microbial lipases.

Lipase action does not require cofactors, but the calcium ions stimulate the action of lipases [13]. Lipases hydrolyze the triglycerides into glycerol and fatty acid; however, microbial lipases are very important because of their industrial applications (Figure 28.1) [14].

28.5 Microbial Lipases: Sources, Production, and Purification

Lipases can be produced from various sources like microbes, animals, and plants. Microbial enzymes find diverse industrial applications and have a low cost of manufacturing. They are easily available with more stability than plant and animal lipases. Microbial lipases can be obtained from natural resources as they have abilities to adapt to different habitats like contaminated soil, alkaline lakes, hot spring, etc. and due to such adaptations, microbial lipases carry special features. Most lipases used at the industrial level are fungal and bacterial lipases. Common microorganism genera that are involved in the production of lipases are: *Acinetobacter* [15–17], *Bacillus* [18–22], *Pseudomonas* [23–25], *Cryptococcus* [26], *Aspergillus* [27], *Trichosporon* [28], *Streptomyces* [29], *Staphylococcus* [30, 31], *Talaromyces* [32], *Fusarium* [33–35], and *Burkholderia* [36]. Fermentation is the main strategy employed for the production of lipases from microbes. There are two types of fermentation processes that can be used to produce microbial lipases:

(1) Submerged fermentation
(2) Solid-state fermentation

Submerged fermentation allows a significant number of extracellular enzymes and is considered as frequently used technique, whereas solid-state fermentation uses cheap or cost-effective substrates. It was observed when *Acinetobacter* species were grown and evaluated for production of lipases using both fermentation processes, the producer strain gave more lipase yield in solid-state fermentation than submerged fermentation [37].

Some lipases that are used in detergents are produced by stimulation via surfactants present in the media used for fermentation. For example, the lipases obtained from *Bacillus flexus* strain *XJU-1* is produced by the stimulation via nonionic surfactant Tween-80, which makes the bacteria release lipase [38]. The production of lipases used in detergents is affected by several factors, such as nitrogen and carbon sources present in the media to provide nutrition and osmoticum, and also affected by physicochemical parameters like incubation period, pH, incubation temperature, agitation, and the size of inoculum.

28.5.1 Carbon Sources

In the carbon sources, various oils are included like coconut oil, neem oil, olive oil and soybean oil, and carbohydrates like fructose, glucose, sucrose, mannitol, etc. are included as carbon sources. In a few cases, oils are used in combination with carbohydrates to increase the secretion of lipases. Detergent lipases require a low concentration of oil for their secretion. If more oil concentration is used, then the production of lipases decreases due to low oxygen transfer, which leads to the undergrowth of microbial cells [18, 39].

28.5.2 Inoculum Size

For the production of detergent lipases, the inoculum size should range from 0.6% to 5% for commercial-based lipase production. The size of inoculum varies with the type of bacteria used to grow. Lipase production from *Fusarium solani N4-2* requires 4% of the inoculum level for sufficient growth [33, 35]. Lipase production from *Trichosporon asahii* MSR 54 requires 6% of inoculum level to show a sufficient growth [28].

28.5.3 pH

The optimum level of pH for the production of microbial lipases should range from 7.0 to 11.0. At pH = 6, *Fusarium* species [27], *Cryptococcus* species [26], and the species of *Acinetobacter* [15, 16] produce detergent lipases in higher amounts. Production of detergent lipases requires pH according to the specific strains of microbes/producer organism.

28.5.4 Incubation Temperature

Most of the lipases used for the detergent purpose are produced from fungus and require a temperature between 25 and 30 °C whereas the bacterial detergent lipases require a maximum incubation temperature around the range of 30–40 °C [32, 38]. Lipase from *Bacillus licheniformis* B42 [18] and *Streptomyces griseochromogenes* [40] require an optimum temperature of 55 °C.

28.5.5 Nitrogen Source

Mainly amino acids are used as the nitrogen source for the media during fermentation. Phenylalanine is used for the production of lipase by *Streptomyces* species and ammonium molybdate is also used as a nitrogen source by *Geobacillus stearothermophilus* B78 [18].

28.5.6 Incubation Time

Optimal incubation time for detergent lipases production is in the range of 24–48 hours in case of bacteria, whereas it ranges from 52 to 120 in case of fungal lipase production. However, a higher incubation time of 72 hours was observed in the production of the detergent lipase of bacteria (Actinomycetes, *G. stearothermophilus,* and *B. licheniformis*) [29, 41]. The short incubation times make the fermentation cost-effective.

28.5.7 Purification

Mostly ammonium sulfate is used to purify lipases because of its lower cost and it does not change the enzymatic structure. Some enzymes are purified through precipitation using acetone. The other purification methods involve chromatography techniques like ion exchange chromatography and gel filtration [20]. Ultrafiltration technique is also used to purify the enzymes. Enzymes can also be purified by using the specific substrates [28]. Although lipases used for food application are purified by various steps, including culture broth elimination in the fermentation process by filtration and centrifugation process [42–44]. The significant outcome is obtained from the pre-purification steps involving (i) aqueous two-phase systems, (ii) uses of polyvinyl alcohol polymers as stationary phases, (iii) hydrophobic interaction chromatography, (iv) immuno purification, and (v) membrane separation procedures [45, 46].

28.6 Diverse Industrial Applications of Microbial Lipases

28.6.1 Lipases in Modern Detergency

The most industrially significant field of utilization of hydrolytic lipases is their inclusion primarily for removal of dirt and oil stains from fabric, and domestic and industrial utensils. The utilization of enzymes in modern detergency is in its prime and detergents largely contain the same constituents and their amounts depend upon the detergency methods. Recently, various types of enzymes including amylase, lipase, cellulase, and protease are commonly used to improve modern days' detergency [47]. Detergent lipases are particularly preferred to require the following properties: (i) capability to perform in relatively rough washing environment (such as pH 10–11, 30–60 °C); (ii) ability to effect against damaging surfactants and enzymes like such as proteases and linear alkyl-benzene sulfonates; (iii) a low substrate requirement (specific to hydrolyze fatty acids of diverse combinations); which are significant characteristics of many modern detergent formulations. Additionally, the drift toward conditions like washing in lower temperatures has become a major issue during the removal of grease stains, specifically for cotton and silk fabrics. Few specific lipases are able to remove greasy spots like sauces, lipstick, oils, butter, etc. [48]. The detergent enzymes can also minimize the environmental exposure of detergent, considering all are biodegradable, leaving no toxic residues on the life of aquatic organisms and have no negative effect on the recycling of water [49].

The common detergent constituents are not environment friendly and hazardous to generally aquatic flora and fauna, so to substitute these hazardous chemicals, lipases are being used in the detergents [48, 50, 51]. As lipases are active in ambient temperatures, they are always preferred to remove the lipid molecules from the substrates present in mud. The muddy fabric dirt can easily be removed by lipase-containing detergents, which is why currently, many of the companies or industries prefer enzymatic detergents [20, 48]. Lipases obtained from *Pseudomonas ADT3* are considered highly valuable lipases used in detergents [52].

Bacillus sonorensis produces a type of lipase that can remove the corn oil strain from a colorless fabric [39, 53]. The addition of cold-active lipases in detergents allows cloth washing at even low temperatures [54].

Thermally stable lipases and alkaline lipases are produced from *Pseudomonas aeruginosa strain* BUP2 that work efficiently in the detergents used for different specific activities of industries [55]. *Pseudomonas alcaligenes* M-1produces alkaline lipases that specifically remove the fatty stains [56]. For the formulations of commercially produced detergents, the high-temperature optimum lipases are required that are produced from *Pseudomonas mendocina* and *Pseudomonas glumae*. Lipo-prime is the chief example of lipase-containing detergent [57]. The Alkaline lipases from *T. asahii* MSR-54have the capability to remove oily stains at ambient temperatures [58].

28.6.1.1 Lipases Cleaning in the Textile Industries

To increase the performance and quality of raw materials in textile industries, lipases play a crucial role. Anhydrous alkaline lipases are used to remove the oil stains on wool fabrics [59, 60]. Degumming and dewaxing on silk fibers are mainly done by lipases and proteases in a definite quantity for better results [61]. Sometimes, amylases are also used along with lipases to remove the strains of starch. The lipase treatments give the fabric wettability, glossy and a modified appearance, and also lightweight [62].

28.6.1.2 Lipases and Proteases Cleaning in Dairy Industries

Lipases are used in boosting the flavor of cheese, modifying the fatty acid chain and performing hydrolysis reactions of fats in milk, etc. [63, 64]. These enzymes are also involved in regulating the ripening and softening of cheese with unique flavors generated using free fatty acids [65, 66]. Specific lipases are used to produce a unique flavor of cheese; the enzymes involved in the production of cheese are *Aspergillus oryzae*, *Aspergillus niger*, *Mucor miehei*, etc. Overusing enzymes causes more enzymatic reactions, which might influence the productivity and the enzyme's undesirable substrate specificity [67, 68]. Fungal lipases and proteases result in better flavor after three months of ripening of cheddar cheese. Providing better flavor lipases release fatty acids from triglycerides [69, 70]. Using the combination of lipases and proteases in cleaning the plates during the pasteurization of sweet milk surfactant leads to the formation of emulsifiers that help in cleaning (Figure 28.2) [3]. The combinatorial effect of lipase and protease together is the breakdown of oils, fats, and protein chains.

28.6.2 Other Applications of Lipases

28.6.2.1 Lipases in Fat and Oil Industries

Fats and oil are the primary constituents of any food. Lipases modify the fats and oil by changing the fatty acids in glycerides or by interchanging with another new fatty acid. Interesterification and esterification reactions are performed using lipases to add value to the product. Immobilized lipase membrane reactors are assembled

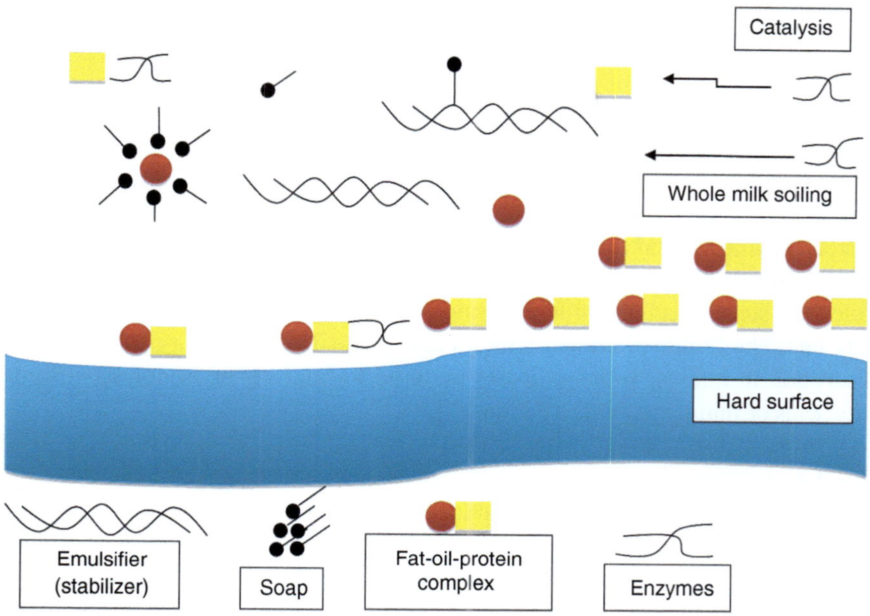

Figure 28.2 The combinatorial effects of both enzymes.

for the hydrolysis of fats and oil [71, 72]. Microbial phospholipases are highly selective and are used in the removal of phospholipids in vegetable oils [73, 74]. Oils and fats that contain polyunsaturated fatty acids like eicosapentaenoic and docosahexaenoic acids also involve the use of these enzymes. Lipases have an important role in oil-based industry for altering or modifying structural lipids and specific enzymatic reactions are carried out in the optimal conditions [75, 76].

28.6.2.2 Lipases in Cosmetics and Personal Care Products

The modification/innovation in cosmetic products is driving the growth of cosmetic industries. Lipases from *Rhizomucor meithei* are used as biocatalysts [77, 78] in cosmetics. Personal care essentials like wax esters are also being manufactured by using enzymatic lipases. Lipases obtained from *Caulerpa cylindracea* (an invasive microalgae) are used in the batch bioreactors [79]. The manufacturing rate has been improved using lipases than using conventional techniques, and this upgradation resulted in improved product and made the process cost-effective. In hair stressing, the use of lipases is seen and also serves as one of the constituents of topical emulsions of anti-obese nature. Lipases are also used for aroma production in perfumeries. In the preparation of emulsifiers, lipase activity is very essential as it helps in the production of propylene glycerol mono fatty acids that are pearling agent to cosmetics as well as in foods [80, 81].

28.6.2.3 Lipases in Tea Processing and Food Industries

Tea is included in commonly used beverages and lipid is considered as noticeable substance that should be in the reduced form. Enzymatic hydrolysis of lipids during the production of black tea causes the generation of a volatile product. Lipases from *Rhizomucor miehei* are found to reduce the total lipid content effectively from tea [82, 83].

Immobilization of lipases prevents the loss of its enzymatic activity and also makes it more thermostatically stable [84]. The idea behind the use of immobilized lipases is that the enzyme can easily be isolated from the substrate and can be reused for a new substrate molecule. Reusing the enzyme is the great benefit of using an immobilized enzyme as it takes lower costs. Improvisation of food quality and cleansing of oily equipment makes the use of lipases in food industries [85]. Many lipids like oleic acid, stearic acid, palmitic acid, and linoleic acid are mainly found in human milk fats. The profile of human milk fat affects the digestive ability and intestinal absorption in infants. So here, lipases are used to catalyze the acidolysis of some fatty acids or mainly palmitic acid [86, 87].

28.6.2.4 In Bioremediation

Decontamination of samples from industrial effluents is necessary that are hazardous to the environment [88]. Lipases from organisms like *Bacillus subtilis* COM-B6, *Staphylococcus pasteurii* COM-4A, and *Arthrobacter* species are known to cut pollutants effectively [89–91]. The *Pseudomonas* species are used for microbial remediation of fats and lipids [92, 93]. In the acidic environment, the species of *Bukholderia* have shown the ability to degrade edible oils. lipases from *Pseudomonas, Bacillus,* and *Halomonas* species are used to treat high concentrations of oil and gaseous contaminants in wastewater [94–96]. Fungal lipases from *Geotrichum candidum* are also used in the mill of olive for treatment of wastewater [97]. Alkaline and Acid active lipases are used to remove fats and grease from the skin as well. Acid-active lipases are stored in the state of pickle, act as a cleanser for skin cells, and improve the skin texture [98].

28.6.2.5 In Pharmaceutical and Medicinal Industries

A number of microbial lipases are being used in the pharmaceutical industries as constituents of drugs, as therapeutic medicines and treatments, as a diagnostic tool and to modify the medicinal devices. As constituents, thermally stable lipases have the ability to catalyze trans-esterification reactions for palm oil. Lipases are also used in the production of ethyl docosahexaenoate, aryl aliphatic glycolipids, etc. and other therapeutic drugs [99]. Lipases isolated from *Bacillus* are used in the production of enantiopure compounds in pharmaceuticals [100]. Lipases are also a constituent of anti-obese creams. Fungal lipase obtained from *Candida rugosa* is involved in the production of lovastatin drugs that reduce serum cholesterol levels [101]. Adipocytokines as lipoprotein lipases are synthesized and released by adipose tissues after communicating with the rest of the body [102]. Lipases are also used in the treatment of cancer as they act as tumor suppressors. It is noticed that if these lipoprotein lipases are removed, the growth of tumor is found to gradually increase [103]. Lipases are also considered as a cure for scalp diseases of skin, loss of hairs, etc. Propyl gallate, tyrosol acetate, etc., are manufactured by using *Staphylococcus* lipases as they have antioxidant properties [104].

The detection of tuberculosis is another medical condition for which microbial lipases are utilized as diagnostic tools (lipases from *Mycobacterium tuberculosis* are used for detecting TB) [105]. Lipases are also involved in the detection of acute pancreatitis and cancers [106, 107]. Lipases from *Chromobacterium,Pseudomonas,* and *Rhizopus* species are immobilized on a methacrylic polymer bead to hydrolyze approximately 90% of fats pass through cylindrical cartridges developed by Alcresta Therapeutics [108, 109].

28.7 Conclusion and Future Perspectives

The versatile microbial lipase enzymes are capable and conceptually dynamic and consist of an extensive range of commercial and industrial applications involving the production of modified molecules. The unique lipase, such as triacylglycerol acyl hydrolase enzymes, catalyze the alcoholysis esterification and hydrolysis reactions. The detergent industry is one of the biggest markets for enzymes, particularly lipases, and the need for biocatalysts is consistently rising. Uses of microbial enzymes can improve the working performance of domestic and commercial purpose detergents by expediting the getting rid of challenging stains on the surface and have a significant positive effect on the environment. Basically, the purpose of enzymes in detergent is to decrease the uses of chemicals in the detergent industry and also lower the energy utilization in response to minimizing washing duration, water usage, and temperature. The problem arising due to fats or lipids are being faced in several biotech industries and these problems are also resulting in decreased biomass production and also quality of products. Microorganisms have the ability to degrade lipids even in a diverse range of conditions by producing several lipolytic enzymes. Lipases have significant roles as they act as modulators in pharmaceuticals to handle the lifestyle diseases like obesity. There is a lot of interest in finding novel microbial strains with distinct lipase capabilities throughout the world. The identification and development of additional enzymes from extreme organisms (psychrophilic, thermophiles, and hyperthermophiles) will increase the number of enzymes that can be added to detergents and perform in various conditions. Recombinant DNA technology is a different strategy for enhancing the characteristics of enzymes for certain purposes. However, in low-income nations, enzyme detergent use is not very common. Developing nations must continue to advance with these changes. To develop the awareness about the environmental, economical and health benefits the use of enzyme detergents needs to be increased.

References

1 Pharr, D. (2017). Green analytical chemistry – the use of surfactants as a replacement of organic solvents in spectroscopy. *Phys. Sci. Rev.* 2 (7): 20170006. https://doi.org/10.1515/psr-2017-0006.

2 Voet, D. and Voet, J.G. (2010). *Lipids and Membranes, Biochemistry*, 4e, 394–397. Wiley.
3 Olsen, H.S. and Falholt, P. (1998). The role of enzymes in modern detergency. *J. Surfactants Deterg.* 1: 555–567. https://doi.org/10.1007/s11743-998-0058-7.
4 Bajpai, D. and Tyagi, V.K. (2007). Laundry detergents: an overview. *J. Oleo Sci.* 56: 327–340.
5 Palmowski, L., Baskaran, K., Wilson, H. et al. (2005). Clean in Place - A Review of Current Technology and its Use in the Food and Beverage Industry. Report for General Circulation October.
6 Ole, K., Borchert, T., and Fuglsang, C. (2002). Industrial enzyme applications. *Curr. Opin. Biotechnol.* 13 (4): 345–351. https://doi.org/10.1016/s0958-1669(02)00328-2.
7 Cowan, D. (2010). Lipases for the production of food components. In: *Enzymes in Food Technology*, 2e (ed. R.J. Whitehurst and M. van Oort). Blackwell Publishing Ltd.
8 Hasan, F., Shah, A.A., Javed, S. et al. (2010). Enzymes used in detergents: lipases. *Afric J. Biotechnol.* 9 (31): 4836–4844. https://doi.org/10.5897/AJBx09.026.
9 Keshwani, A., Malhotra, B., and Kharkwal, H. (2015). Natural polymer based detergents for stain removal. *World J. Pharm. Sci.* 4 (4): 490–508.
10 Fickers, P., Marty, A., and Nicaud, J.M. (2011). The lipases from *Yarrowia lipolytica*: genetics, production, regulation, biochemical characterization and biotechnological applications. *Biotechnol. Adv.* 29: 632–644. https://doi.org/10.1016/j.biotechadv.2011.04.005. PMID: 21550394.
11 Carpen, A., Bonomi, F., Iametti, S. et al. (2019). Effects of starch addition on the activity and specificity of food-grade lipases. *Biotechnol. Appl. Biochem.* 66 (4): 607–616. https://doi.org/10.1002/bab.1761. PMID: 31056790.
12 Tong, X., Busk, P.K., and Lange, L. (2016). Characterization of a new sn-1, 3-regioselective triacylglycerol lipase from *Malbranchea cinnamomea*. *Biotechnol. Appl. Biochem.* 63 (4): 471–478. https://doi.org/10.1002/bab.1394. PMID: 25959497.
13 Silveira, E.A., Moreno-Perez, S., Basso, A. et al. (2017). Modulation of the regioselectivity of *Thermomyces lanuginosus* lipase via biocatalyst engineering for the Ethanolysis of oil in fully anhydrous medium. *BMC Biotech.* 17 (1): 88. https://doi.org/10.1186/s12896-017-0407-9.
14 Gopinath, S.C.B., Anbu, P., Lakshmipriya, T. et al. (2013). Strategies to characterize fungal lipases for applications in medicine and dairy industry. *Biomed. Res. Int.* 154549. https://doi.org/10.1155/2013/154549.
15 Saisubramanian, N., Sivasubramanian, S., Nandakumar, N. et al. (2008). Two step purification of *Acinetobacter* sp. lipase and its evaluation as a detergent additive at low temperatures. *Appl. Biochem. Biotechnol.* 150: 139–156. https://doi.org/10.1007/s12010-008-8143-1.
16 Wang, H., Shao, J., Wei, Y.J. et al. (2011). A novel low temperature alkaline lipase from *Acinetobacter johnsoniiLP28* suitable for detergent formulation. *Food Technol. Biotechnol.* 49: 96–102.

17 Wang, H., Zhong, S., Ma, H. et al. (2012). Screening and characterization of a novel alkaline lipase from *Acinetobacter calcoaceticus* 1-7 isolated from Bohai bay in China for detergent formulation. *Braz. J. Microbiol.* 43: 148–156. https://doi.org/10.1590/S1517-83822012000100016.

18 Bayoumi, R.A., El-louboudey, S.S., Sidkey, N.M. et al. (2007). Production, purification and characterization of thermo-alkalophilic lipase for application in bio-detergent industry. *J. Appl. Sci. Res.* 3: 1752–1765.

19 Niyonzima, F.N. and More, S.S. (2013). Screening and identification of a novel alkaline lipase producing bacterium. *Int. J. Pharm. Bio Sci.* 4: 1037–1045.

20 Lailaja, V.P. and Chandrasekaran, M. (2013). Detergent compatible alkaline lipase produced by marine *Bacillus smithii* BTMS 11. *World J. Microbiol. Biotechnol.* 29: 1349–1360. https://doi.org/10.1007/s11274-013-1298-0.

21 Nerurkar, M., Manasi, J., Sujata, P. et al. (2013). Application of lipase from marine bacteria *Bacillus sonorensis* as an additive in detergent formulation. *J. Surfactants Deterg.* 16: 435–443. https://doi.org/10.1007/S11743-012-1434-0.

22 Amara, A.A., Salem, S.S., and Shabeb, M.S.A. (2009). The possibility to use bacterial protease and lipase as a detergent. *Global J. Biotechnol. Biochem.* 4: 104–114.

23 Kanimozhi, S. and Perinbam, K. (2011). Application of an alkaline lipase from *Pseudomonas* sp. Lp1 as bio-detergent. *Adv. Biotech.* 10: 28–31.

24 Mobarak-Qamsari, E., Kasra-Kermanshahi, R., and Moosavinejad, Z. (2011). Isolation and identification of a novel, lipase producing bacterium, *Pseudomonas aeruginosa* KM110. *Iran J. Microbiol.* 3: 92–98.

25 Khoo, M.L. and Ibrahim, C.O. (2009). Lipase from thermoalkalophilic *Pseudomonas* species as an additive in potential laundry detergent formulations. *Malays. J. Microbiol.* 5: 1–5.

26 Thirunavukarasu, K., Edwinoliver, N.G., Anbarasan, S. et al. (2008). Removal of triglyceride soil from fabrics by a novel lipase from *Cryptococcus* sp. S-2. *Process Biochem.* 43: 701–706. https://doi.org/10.1016/j.procbio.2008.02.011.

27 Saisubramanian, N., Edwinoliver, N.G., Nandakumar, N. et al. (2006). Efficacy of lipase from *Aspergillus niger* as an additive in detergent formulations: a statistical approach. *J. Ind. Microbiol. Biotechnol.* 33: 669–676. https://doi.org/10.1007/s10295-006-0100-9.

28 Kumar, S.S., Kumar, L., Sahai, V. et al. (2009). A thiol-activated lipase from *Trichosporon asahii* MSR 54: detergent compatibility and presoak formulation for oil removal from soiled cloth at ambient temperature. *J. Ind. Microbiol. Biotechnol.* 26: 427–432. https://doi.org/10.1007/s10295-008-0513-8.

29 Aly, M.M., Tork, S., Al-Garni, S.M. et al. (2012). Production of lipase from genetically improved *Streptomyces exfoliates LP10* isolated from oil-contaminated soil. *Afr. J. Microbiol. Res.* 6: 1125–1137. https://doi.org/10.5897/AJMR11.1123.

30 Cherif, S., Mnif, S., Hadrich, F. et al. (2011). A newly high alkaline lipase: an ideal choice for application in detergent formulations. *Lipids Health Dis.* 10: 221–228. https://doi.org/10.1186/1476-511X-10-221.

31 Chauhan, M., Chauhan, R.S., and Garlapati, V.K. (2013). Evaluation of a new lipase from *Staphylococcus* sp. for detergent additive capability. *Biomed Res. Int.* 1–6. https://doi.org/10.1155/2013/374967.

32 Romdhane, I.B., Fendri, A., Gargouri, Y. et al. (2010). A novel thermoactive and alkaline lipase from *Talaromyces thermophilus* fungus for use in laundry detergents. *Biochem. Eng. J.* 53: 112–120. https://doi.org/10.1016/j.bej.2010.10.002.

33 Gulati, R., Isar, J., Kumar, V. et al. (2005). Production of a novel alkaline lipase by *Fusarium globulosum* using neem oil, and its applications. *Pure Appl. Chem.* 77 (1): 251–262. https://doi.org/10.1351/pac200577010251.

34 Liu, R., Jiang, X., Mou, H. et al. (2009). A novel low-temperature resistant alkaline lipase from a soda lake fungus strain *Fusarium solani* N4-2 for detergent formulation. *Biochem. Eng. J.* 46: 265–270. https://doi.org/10.1016/j.bej.2009.05.016.

35 Prazeres, J.N., Cruz, J.A.B., and Pastore, G.M. (2006). Characterization of alkaline lipase from *Fusarium oxysporum* and the effect of different surfactants and detergents on the enzyme activity. *Braz. J. Microbiol.* 37: 505–509. https://doi.org/10.1590/S1517-83822006000400019.

36 Wang, H.K., Liu, J.R., Lu, F.P. et al. (2009). A novel alkaline and low-temperature lipase of *Burkholderia cepacia* isolated from Bohai in China for detergent formulation. *Ann. Microbiol.* 59: 105–110. https://doi.org/10.1007/BF03175606.

37 Khoramnia, A., Ebrahimpour, A., Beh, B.K. et al. (2011). Production of a solvent, detergent, and thermotolerant lipase by a newly isolated *Acinetobacter* sp. in submerged and solid-state fermentations. *J. Biomed. Biotechnol.* 2011: 702179. https://doi.org/10.1155/2011/702179.

38 Niyonzima, F.N., More, S.S., and Muddapur, U. (2013). Optimization of fermentation culture conditions for alkaline lipase production by *Bacillus flexus* XJU-1. *Curr. Trends Biotechnol. Pharm.* 7: 793–803.

39 Nerurkar, M., Vaidyanathan, J., Adivarekar, R. et al. (2013). Use of a natural dye from *Serratia marcescens* subspecies *Marcescens* in dyeing of textile fabrics. *Octa J. Environ. Res.* 1 (2): 129–135.

40 Gunalakshmi, B., Sahu, M., Sivakumar, K. et al. (2008). Investigation on lipase producing actinomycete strain LE-1, isolated from shrimp pond. *Res. J. Microbiol.* 3: 73–81. https://scialert.net/fulltext/?doi=jm.2008.73.81.

41 Nagarajan, J., Nawawi, N.M., and Ibrahim, A.L. (2014). *Rhodococcus UKMP-5M*, an endogenous lipase producing actinomycete from Peninsular Malaysia. *Biologia* 69: 123–132. https://doi.org/10.2478/s11756-013-0308-x.

42 Chandra, P., Enespa, S.R. et al. (2020). Microbial lipases and their industrial applications: a comprehensive review. *Microb. Cell Fact.* 19: 169. https://doi.org/10.1186/s12934-020-01428-8.

43 Koutinas, A.A., Wang, R., and Webb, C. (2004). Restructuring upstream bioprocessing: technological and economic aspects for production of a generic microbial feedstock from wheat. *Biotechnol. Bioeng.* 85 (5): 524–538. https://doi.org/10.1002/bit.10888.

44 Chen, P., Min, M., Chen, Y. et al. (2010). Review of biological and engineering aspects of algae to fuels approach. *Int. J. Agric. Biol. Eng.* 2 (4): 1–30. https://doi.org/10.3965/j.issn.1934-6344.2009.04.001-030.

45 Kuczewski, M., Fraud, N., Faber, R. et al. (2010). Development of a polishing step using a hydrophobic interaction membrane adsorber with a PER. C6®-derived recombinant antibody. *Biotechnol. Bioeng.* 105 (2): 296–305. https://doi.org/10.1002/bit.22538.

46 Ghose, S., Tao, Y., Conley, L. et al. (2013). Purification of monoclonal antibodies by hydrophobic interaction chromatography under no-salt conditions. *MAbs* 5 (5): 795–800. https://doi.org/10.4161/mabs.25552.

47 Ito, S., Kobayashi, T., Ara, K. et al. (1998). Alkaline detergent enzymes from alkaliphiles: Enzymatic properties, genetics and structures. *Extremophiles* 2: 185–190. https://doi.org/10.1007/s007920050059.

48 Jaeger, K.E. and Reetz, M.T. (1998). Microbial lipases from versatile tools for biotechnology. *Trends Biotechnol.* 16: 396–403. https://doi.org/10.1016/s0167-7799(98)01195-0.

49 Berhanu, A. and Amare, G. (2012). Microbial lipases and their industrial applications: review. *Biotechnology* 11: 100–118. https://doi.org/10.3923/biotech.2012.100.118.

50 Bardach, J., Fujiya, M., and Holl, A. (1967). Investigations of external chemoreceptors of fishes. In: *Olfaction and Taste II* (ed. T. Hayashi), 647–665. Pergamon.

51 Pettersson, A., Adamsson, M., and Dave, G. (2000). Toxicity and detoxification of Swedish detergents and softener products. *Chemosphere.* 41 (10): 1611–1620. https://doi.org/10.1016/s0045-6535(00)00035-7.

52 Dey, A., Chattopadhyay, A., Mukhopadhyay, S.K. et al. (2014). Production, partial purification and characterization of an extracellular psychrotrophic lipase from *Pseudomonas* sp. ADT3. *J. Bioremed. Biodegred.* 5 (6): 242. https://doi.org/10.4172/2155-6199.1000242.

53 Fujii, T., Tatara, T., and Minagawa, M. (1986). Studies on applications of lipolytic enzyme in detergency I. Effect of lipase from *Candida cylindracea* on removal of olive oil from cotton fabric. *J. Am. Oil Chem. Soc.* 63 (6): 796–799. https://doi.org/10.1007/BF02541967.

54 Li, Y., Li, J., Li, W. et al. (2014). A state-of-the-art review on magnetorheological elastomer devices. *Smart Mater. Struct.* 23 (12): 123001. https://doi.org/10.1088/0964-1726/23/12/123001.

55 Unni, K.N., Priji, P., Sajith, S. et al. (2016). *Pseudomonas aeruginosa* strain BUP2, a novel bacterium inhabiting the rumen of Malabari goat, produces an efficient lipase. *Biologia.* 71 (4): 378–387. https://doi.org/10.1515/biolog-2016-0057.

56 Ogierman, M.A., Fallarino, A., Riess, T. et al. (1997). Characterization of the *Vibrio cholerae* El Tor lipase operon lip AB and a protease gene downstream of the hly region. *J. Bacteriol.* 179 (22): 7072–7080. https://doi.org/10.1128/jb.179.22.7072-7080.1997.

57 Bacha, A.B., Al-Assaf, A., Moubayed, N.M. et al. (2018). Evaluation of a novel thermo-alkaline *Staphylococcus aureus* lipase for application in detergent formulations. *Saudi J. Biol. Sci.* 25 (3): 409. https://doi.org/10.1016/j.sjbs.2016.10.006.

58 Contesini, F.J., Lopes, D.B., Macedo, G.A. et al. (2010). *Aspergillus* sp. lipase: potential biocatalyst for industrial use. *J. Mol. Catal. B: Enzym.* 67 (3–4): 163–171. https://doi.org/10.1016/j.molcatb.2010.07.021.

59 Uddin, F. (2019). Introductory chapter: textile manufacturing processes. In: *Textile Manufacturing Processes [Internet]* (ed. F. Uddin). London: IntechOpen https://doi.org/10.5772/intechopen.87968.

60 Al-Zuhair, S. and Taher, H. (2016). *Supercritical Fluids Technology in Lipase Catalysed Processes*. Boca Raton: CRC Press.

61 Shen, J. (2019). Enzymatic treatment of wool and silk fbers. In: *Advances in Textile Biotechnology* (ed. A. Cavaco-Paulo, V.A. Nierstrasz, and Q. Wang), 77–105. Woodhead Publish.

62 Kalantzi, I., Shimmield, T.M., Pergantis, S.A. et al. (2013). Heavy metals, trace elements and sediment geochemistry at four Mediterranean fish farms. *Sci. Total Environ.* 444: 128–137. https://doi.org/10.1016/j.scitotenv.2012.11.082.

63 Balcao, V.M. (1998). Malcata FX lipase catalyzed modification of milk fat. *Biotechnol. Adv.* 16 (2): 309–341. https://doi.org/10.1016/s0734-9750(97)00064-5.

64 Ray, A. (2012). Application of lipase in industry. *Asian J. Pharm. Technol.* 2 (2): 33–37.

65 Hamdy, S., Hamdy Shaaban, H.S., Mahmoud, K.A. et al. (2017). Preparation of Ras cheese favour concentrate using lipolyzed cream and skim milk curd. *Int. J. Dairy Sci.* 12 (4): 275–281. https://doi.org/10.3923/ijds.2017.275.281.

66 Wolf, I.V., Meinardi, C.A., and Zalazar, C.A. (2009). Production of favour compounds from fat during cheese ripening by action of lipases and esterases. *Protein Pept. Lett.* 16 (10): 1235–1243. https://doi.org/10.2174/092986609789071289.

67 Girelli, A.M., Astolf, M.L., and Scuto, F.R. (2020). Agro-industrial wastes as potential carriers for enzyme immobilization: areview. *Chemosphere* 244: 125368. https://doi.org/10.1016/j.chemosphere.2019.125368.

68 Li, S., Yang, X., Yang, S. et al. (2012). Technology prospecting on enzymes: application, marketing and engineering. *Comput. Struct. Biotechnol. J.* 2 (3): e201209017. https://doi.org/10.5936/csbj.201209017.

69 De Wit, M., Osthof, G., Viljoen, B.C. et al. (2005). A comparative study of lipolysis and proteolysis in Cheddar cheese and yeast-inoculated Cheddar cheeses during ripening. *Enzyme Microb. Technol.* 37 (6): 606–616. https://doi.org/10.1016/j.enzmictec.2005.03.028.

70 Grummer, J., Bobowski, N., Karalus, M. et al. (2013). Use of potassium chloride and favor enhancers in low sodium Cheddar cheese. *J. Dairy Sci.* 96 (3): 1401–1418. https://doi.org/10.3168/jds.2012-6057.

71 Otzen, D. (2011). Protein–surfactant interactions: a tale of many states. *Biochem. Biophys. Acta* 1814 (5): 562–591. https://doi.org/10.1016/j.bbapap.2011.03.003.

72 Damude, H.G. and Zhu, Q. (2012). US. Patent No. 8,119,860. Washington, DC: U.S. Patent and Trademark Office, 21.02.2012.

73 Singhania, T., Sinha, H., Das, P. et al. (2015). Efficientdegumming of rice bran oil by immobilized PLA1 from *Thermomyces lanuginosus*. *Food Technol. Biotechnol.* 53 (1): 91–95. https://doi.org/10.17113/ftb.53.01.15.3740.

74 Cerminati, S., Eberhardt, F., Elena, C.E. et al. (2017). Development of a highly efficient oil degumming process using a novel phosphatidylinositol-specific phospholipase C enzyme. *Appl. Microbiol. Biotechnol.* 101 (11): 4471–4479. https://doi.org/10.1007/s00253-017-8201-0.

75 Osório, N.M., Ferreira-Dias, S., Gusmão, J.H. et al. (2001). Response surface modelling of the production of ω-3 polyunsaturated fatty acids-enriched fats by a commercial immobilized lipase. *J. Mol. Catal. B: Enzym.* 11 (4–6): 677–686. https://doi.org/10.1016/S1381-1177(00)00079-5.

76 Feltes, M.M., de Oliveira Pitol, L., Correia, J.G. et al. (2009). Incorporation of medium chain fatty acids into fish oil triglycerides by chemical and enzymatic interesterification. *Grasas Aceites* 60 (2): 168–176. https://doi.org/10.3989/gya.074708.

77 Longo, M.A. and Sanromán, M.A. (2006). Production of food aroma compounds: microbial and enzymatic methodologies. *Food Technol. Biotechnol.* 44 (3): 335–353.

78 Knezevic, Z., Milosavic, N., Bezbradica, D. et al. (2006). Immobilization of lipase from *Candida rugosa* on Eupergit® C supports by covalent attachment. *Biochem. Eng. J.* 30 (3): 269–278. https://doi.org/10.1016/j.bej.2006.05.009.

79 Lehtinen, T., Efmova, E., Santala, S. et al. (2018). Improved fatty aldehyde and wax ester production by overexpression of fatty acyl-CoA reductases. *Microb. Cell Fact.* 17: 19. https://doi.org/10.1186/s12934-018-0869-z.

80 Saford, B., Api, A.M., Barratt, C. et al. (2015). Use of an aggregate exposure model to estimate consumer exposure to fragrance ingredients in personal care and cosmetic products. *Regul. Toxicol. Pharm.* 72 (3): 673–682. https://doi.org/10.1016/j.yrtph.2015.05.017.

81 Nohynek, G.J., Antignac, E., Re, T. et al. (2010). Safety assessment of personal care products/cosmetics and their ingredients. *Toxicol. Appl. Pharmacol.* 243 (2): 239–259.

82 Clough, P.M. (2001). Specialty vegetable oils containing y-linolenic acid and stearidonic acid. In: *Structured and Modified Lipids*, 1e, vol. 4 (ed. F.D. Gunstone), 75–107. Boca Raton: CRC Press.

83 Haghi, A.K. (ed.) (2011). *Food Science: Research and Technology*. Boca Raton: CRC Press.

84 Reis, C.L., Sousa, E.Y., Serpa, J.D. et al. (2019). Design of immobilized enzyme biocatalysts: drawbacks and opportunities. *Quím. Nova* 42 (7): 768. https://doi.org/10.21577/0100-4042.20170381.

85 Nguyen, H.H. and Kim, M. (2017). An overview of techniques in enzyme immobilization. *Appl. Sci. Converg. Technol.* 26 (6): 157–163. https://doi.org/10.5757/ASCT.2017.26.6.157.

86 Sahin, N., Akoh, C.C., and Karaali, A. (2005). Lipase-catalyzed acidolysis of tripalmitin with hazelnut oil fatty acids and stearic acid to produce human milk fat substitutes. *J. Agric. Food. Chem.* 53 (14): 5779–5783. https://doi.org/10.1021/jf050465e.

87 Basso, A. and Serban, S. (2019). Industrial applications of immobilized enzymes – a review. *Mol. Catal.* 479: 110607. https://doi.org/10.1016/j.mcat.2019.110607.

88 Yang, T., Fruekilde, M.B., and Xu, X. (2003). Applications of immobilized *Thermomyces lanuginosa* lipase in interesterification. *J. Am. Oil Chem. Soc.* 80 (9): 881–887. https://doi.org/10.1007/s11746-003-0789-7.

89 Lailaja, V.P. (2007). Alkaline lipase production by marine *Bacillus smithii* BTMS. PHD Thesis, Cochin University of Science and Technology, pp. 1–197.

90 MacLean, E., Broger, T., Yerlikaya, S. et al. (2019). A systematic review of biomarkers to detect active tuberculosis. *Nat. Microbiol.* 4 (5): 748–758. https://doi.org/10.1038/s41564-019-0380-2.

91 Behera, A.R., Veluppal, A., and Dutta, K. (2019). Optimization of physical parameters for enhanced production of lipase from *Staphylococcus hominis* using response surface methodology. *Environ. Sci. Pollut. Res.* 26 (33): 34277–34284. https://doi.org/10.1007/s11356-019-04304-0.

92 Olusesan, A.T., Azura, L.K., Abubakar, F. et al. (2009). Phenotypic and molecular identification of a novel thermophilic *Anoxybacillus* sp.: a lipase-producing bacterium isolated from a Malaysian hotspring. *World J. Microbiol. Biotechnol.* 25 (11): 1981–1988. https://doi.org/10.1007/s11274-009-0097-0.

93 Gao, L.L., Lu, Y.C., Zhang, J.L. et al. (2019). Biotreatment of restaurant wastewater with an oily high concentration by newly isolated bacteria from oily sludge. *World J. Microbiol. Biotechnol.* 35 (11): 179. https://doi.org/10.1007/s11274-019-2760-4.

94 Chandra, P. and Singh, D.P. (2014). Removal of Cr(VI) by a halotolerant bacterium *Halomonas* sp. CSB 5 isolated from sāmbhar Salt Lake, Rajasthan (India). *Cell Mol. Biol.* 60 (5): 64–72. https://doi.org/10.14715/cmb/2014.60.5.12.

95 Chandra, P., Rawat, A.P., and Singh, D.P. (2016). Isolation of alkaliphilic bacterium *Citricoccus alkalitolerans* CSB1: an efficient biosorbent for bioremediation of tannery waste water. *Cell Mol. Biol.* 62 (3): 135. https://doi.org/10.4172/1165-158X.1000135.

96 Azhdarpoor, A., Mortazavi, B., and Moussavi, G. (2014). Oily wastewaters treatment using *Pseudomonas* sp. isolated from the compost fertilizer. *J. Environ. Health Sci. Eng.* 12 (1): 77. https://doi.org/10.1186/2052-336X-12-77.

97 Martini, V.P., Glogauer, A., Müller-Santos, M. et al. (2014). First co-expression of a lipase and its specific foldase obtained by metagenomics. *Microb. Cell Fact.* 13 (1): 171. https://doi.org/10.1186/s12934-014-0171-7.

98 Galante, Y.M. and Formantici, C. (2003). Enzyme applications in detergency and in manufacturing industries. *Curr. Org. Chem.* 7 (13): 1399–1422. https://doi.org/10.2174/1385272033486468.

99 Gherardini, J., Wegner, J., Chéret, J. et al. (2019). Transepidermal UV radiation of scalp skin *ex vivo* induces hair follicle damage that is alleviated by the topical treatment with caffeine. *Int. J. Cosmet. Sci.* 41 (2): 164–182. https://doi.org/10.1111/ics.12521.

100 Guncheva, M. and Zhiryakova, D. (2011). Catalytic properties and potential applications of *Bacillus* lipases. *J. Mol. Catal. B: Enzym.* 68 (1): 1–21. https://doi.org/10.1016/j.molcatb.2010.09.002.

101 Tietz, N.W. and Shuey, D.F. (1993). Lipase in serum, the elusive enzyme: an overview. *Clin. Chem.* 39 (5): 746–756. https://doi.org/10.1093/CLINCHEM/39.5.746.

102 Frühbeck, G. (2008). Overview of adipose tissue and its role in obesity and metabolic disorders. In: *Adipose Tissue Protocols* (ed. K. Yang), 1–22. Humana Press.

103 Barrett, J.C. (1993). Mechanisms of multistep carcinogenesis and carcinogen risk assessment. *Environ. Health Perspect.* 100: 9–20. https://doi.org/10.1289/ehp.931009.

104 Horchani, H., Aissa, I., Ouertani, S. et al. (2012). Staphylococcal lipases: biotechnological applications. *J. Mol. Catal. B: Enzym.* 76: 125–132. https://doi.org/10.1016/j.molcatb.2011.11.018.

105 Brust, B., Lecoufe, M., Tuaillon, E. et al. (2011). *Mycobacterium tuberculosis* lipolytic enzymes as potential biomarkers for the diagnosis of active tuberculosis. *PLoS One* 6 (9): e25078. https://doi.org/10.1371/journal.pone.0025078.

106 Lerner, A. (1989). Acute pancreatitis in children and adolescents. In: *Textbook of Gastroenterology and Nutrition in Infancy* (ed. E. Lebenthal), 897–906. New York: Raven Press.

107 Suzuki, M., Sai, J.K., and Shimizu, T. (2014). Acute pancreatitis in children and adolescents. *World J. Gastrointest. Pathophysiol.* 5 (4): 416–426. https://doi.org/10.4291/wjgp.v5.i4.416.

108 Erskine, J.M., Lingard, C.D., Sontag, M.K. et al. (1998). Enteral nutrition for patients with cystic fibrosis: comparison of a semi-elemental and nonelemental formula. *J. Pediatr.* 132 (2): 265–269. https://doi.org/10.1016/s0022-3476(98)70443-3.

109 Hemmerich, J., Adelantado, N., Barrigón, J.M. et al. (2014). Comprehensive clone screening and evaluation of fed-batch strategies in a microbioreactor and lab scale stirred tank bioreactor system: application on *Pichia pastoris* producing *Rhizopus oryzae* lipase. *Microb. Cell Fact.* 13 (1): 36. https://doi.org/10.1186/1475-2859-13-36.

29

Production of Inulin Oligosaccharides from Microbial Inulinases and Their Applications

Priyanka, Hemant Ghai, and Wamik Azmi

Himachal Pradesh University, Department of Biotechnology, Summerhill, Shimla, Himachal Pradesh 171005, India

29.1 Introduction

Food culture has experienced a significant shift on a global scale. Food habits have changed as a result of modernization [1]. Diet is now regarded not just for the body's energy requirements, but also for the improvement of health. Gut bacteria play a critical role in human health by metabolizing diverse dietary substrates [2]. Dietary carbohydrates, in particular, are known to be important drivers of the structure and function of the gut microbiota [3]. Food companies have a strong desire to develop food products that go beyond the traditional role of providing basic nourishment and essential nutrients. They aspire to create functional foods that offer additional health benefits. As a result, functional foods are designed not just to satiate hunger and provide essential nutrients, but also to proactively address nutrition-related ailments and enhance the overall physical and mental well-being of individuals. In 2010, Vergari et al. presented a comprehensive overview of functional food products and the market [4]. In 2008, the global functional foods industry had a substantial market value exceeding US$80 billion. The United States held a prominent position in the nutraceuticals market, owning a share of 35%, followed closely by Japan with 25%. The European sector, which continues to expand, currently holds a value of US$8 billion [4]. It is noteworthy that India and China serve as major producers of traditional functional food items and nutraceuticals. They are the two largest countries in the world to produce these types of food products. Until the 1980s, oligosaccharides were promoted as low-calorie agents, but they have lately acquired popularity in the pharmaceutical and food sectors. They are valued at around $200 per kilo, and inulin has now been presented as a substrate for the synthesis of oligosaccharides by selective hydrolysis by endoinulinase [5].

Nondigestible dietary components are of two types which change colonic microbiota: prebiotics (encourage the development and/or activity of bacteria in the gut) and probiotics (supplementation of live microbes) [6]. Prebiotics are nondigestible substances that improve host health by modulating microbial metabolism and

Microbial Enzymes: Production, Purification, and Industrial Applications, First Edition.
Edited by Dinesh Yadav, Pankaj Chowdhary, Gautam Anand, and Rajarshi Kumar Gaur.

the makeup and/or activity of the gut microbiota [7]. Prebiotics, such as fructooligosaccharides (FOS) and inulooligosaccharides (IOS) are gaining popularity owing to their numerous health benefits, low caloric content, noncariogenic nature, and safety for individuals with diabetes. These short-chain carbohydrates have multifunctional properties and can reduce diabetes, cardiovascular diseases, cancer, infections, inflammation, and obesity. The bioavailability of nutritionally essential minerals, including calcium, magnesium, and iron, is also improved by prebiotic intake [6]. Most recently, synbiotics (products containing both prebiotics and probiotics that work together) are being used to maintain a healthy microbial population in the gut. In a synbiotic, the prebiotic must have a beneficial influence on the development of the particular probiotic [8]. In addition, a diverse range of products are derived from inulinases, such as high-fructose syrup manufacturing, FOS, inulin oligosaccharides, and various vital metabolites like bioethanol, 2,3-butanediol, organic acids, single-cell oil, single-cell proteins, among others, which establishes it as an important industrial-scale enzyme [9]. Inulinases can be produced through both submerged and solid-state fermentations using a variety of substrates and microorganisms [6, 10, 11]. In recent years, due to the numerous applications of inulinases, many researchers have begun exploring enzyme immobilization techniques to enhance stability and yield.

Immobilization of inulinase has been done utilizing several techniques and a variety of supports, with substantial advances in terms of stability and storage of

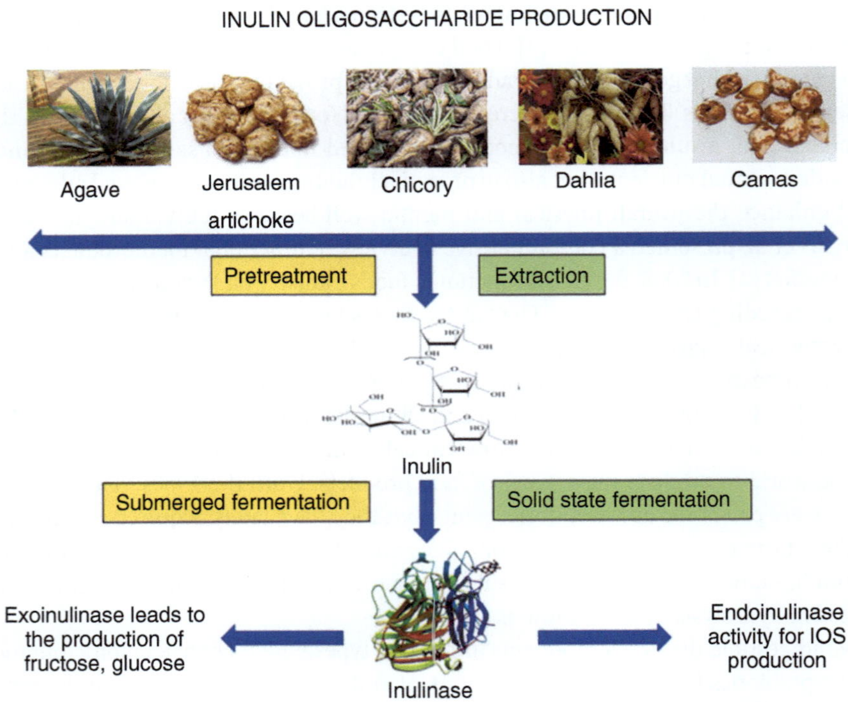

Figure 29.1 Overview of inulin oligosaccharide production. Source: Paul Moore/Adobe Stock; Edward Westmacott/Adobe Stock Photos; Ruud Morijn/Adobe Stock Photos.

the immobilized enzyme being made with each iteration [12]. The utilization of immobilized recombinant endoinulinase, possessing improved thermostability and extended operational lifespan compared to its free form, has emerged as a promising approach for the industrial production of IOS. To fully exploit the industrial applications of endoinulinases, it is crucial to establish high-efficiency expression systems, develop large-scale preparation methods, and formulate cost-effective inulinase formulations. Research has already been conducted on the cloning, overexpression, and characterization of highly active endoinulinase genes from various microorganisms, aiming to facilitate the production of IOS (Figure 29.1).

29.2 Substrate: Inulin

Humans have been more conscious of their eating habits in recent years, and functional foods have become progressively vital in maintaining human health [1]. Inulin is a major part of our daily dietary intake for millennia due to its nutritious qualities while also providing important technical advantages [10]. Considering Western and American diets, daily inulin consumption is projected to be 1–10 and 2.5 g per day, respectively. Yet, inulin intake is greater (3–11 g) per day in the European diet [13].

Inulin functions as a possible prebiotic in food processing industries maintaining a high degree of polymerization (DP) [1]. Inulin has been granted GRAS certification in the United States and is widely used. Naturally occurring in around 36,000 plant species, inulin finds its highest abundance in chicory roots [14]. Inulin is a fructan-type plant polysaccharide made of fructose units. The fructose units are connected by β-(2→1)-D-fructosyl-fructose bond. Its chemical structure consists of terminal D-glucopyranosyl residue which is joined through an α-(1→2) bond [15]. In the early 1800s, Valentine Rose, a German scientist, made the discovery of inulin in the roots of Elecampane (*Inula helenium*), then Thomson titled it inulin in 1817 [14]. Many plants, such as *Asparagus officinalis* (Shatwaar), *Helianthus tuberosus* (Jerusalem artichoke), *Asparagus racemosus* (Safed musli), *Dahlia pinnata* (Dahlia), *Taraxacum officinale* (Dandelion), *Cichoriumintybus* (Chicory), etc. contain a significant amount of inulin in their bulbs, tubers, and tuberous roots [13]. A list of some inulin-rich feedstocks is mentioned in Table 29.1. Endoinulinase selectively hydrolyzes inulin-containing raw materials, which serve as a feedstock for producing IOS such as inulotriose and inulotetraose [5].

Inulin, a versatile compound, not only enhances the flavor of food but also offers a range of physiological benefits. The utilization of inulin-rich feedstocks has led to the production of a wide array of valuable products, including high-fructose syrup, inulinases, IOS, biofuels, organic acids, single-cell oil, single-cell proteins, mannitol, sorbitol, 2,3-butanediol, pullulan, and more [13]. In the pharmaceutical field, inulin finds diverse applications, such as protein stabilization, modified drug delivery systems that enhance dissolution rates and enable targeted drug administration and physiological and disease-modifying effects of inulin [16]. Moreover, inulin plays

Table 29.1 Inulin-rich feedstocks [14, 15].

S. no.	Inulin feedstocks	Scientific name	Plant part	Content of inulin (%)
1.	Garlic	*Allium sativum*	Tuber, wet Tuber, dried	12.5–23.5 >75%
2.	Barley grains	*Hordeum vulgare*	Grains	18–20
3.	Asparagus raw	*Asparagus officinalis*	Root, wet	2~3
4.	Sweet leaf	*Stevia rebaudiana*	Root	18–23
5.	Salsify	*Tragopogonporrifolius* L.	Root, wet	4~11
6.	Jerusalem artichoke/ sunchoke	*Helianthus tuberosus* L.	Tubers, wet	8.16~13.46
7.	Agave	*Agave* sp.	Stem	12–15
8.	Dahlia	*Dahlia pinnata*	Tubers, wet Root, dried	6–9.5 59
9.	Chicory	*Cichoriumintybus* L.	Root, dried	65–79
10.	Yacon	*Smallanthussonchifolius*	Root, wet Tubers, wet	7–8 1.1–7.5
11.	Onion	*Allium cepa* L.	Tubers, dried	48
12.	Suma	*Pfalia glomerate*	Roots	11.45

a crucial role in plant physiology. It serves as a reserve energy resource and regulates cold resistance in various plant species, including onion, garlic, wheat, banana, leek, asparagus, chicory, and others. Additionally, inulin demonstrates its ability to modulate plant growth under conditions of water scarcity caused by drought or low temperatures [13]. Inulin, with its diverse applications and remarkable properties, remains a valuable and versatile compound in the fields of nutrition, medicine, and plant biology.

29.2.1 Inulin Structure and Chemical Properties

Plants exhibit a rich diversity of fructans, showcasing diverse polymerization degrees (DP) and chemical structures [17]. Inulin, a linear fructan structure, comprises β-D-fructosyl residues interconnected by glycosidic bonds, often terminating with a single glucose unit linked via an α-D-glucopyranosyl or α-(1→2) bond, similar to sucrose [15]. The presence of β-(2-1)-D-fructosyl fructose bonds in inulin renders it resistant to digestion in the human small intestine. Instead, it serves as a fermentable substrate for the intestinal microflora in the large intestine [14]. Inulin molecules display a diverse range of polymerization degrees, encompassing a spectrum from 2 to 60, with an average of approximately 10–12. Represented as GFn, the formula of inulin signifies the presence of a terminal glucose unit (G), fructosyl residue (F), and the number of fructose residues (n) [15]. Within the inulin macromolecule, the glucose unit adopts a pyranose form in a ($^4C_1$ conformation), while fructose is present in a furanose form [18]. Extraction of native inulin predominantly involves fresh plant materials, ensuring careful measures are taken to prevent acid hydrolysis and inhibit the plant's inulinase activity, but no fractionation method is used to remove the smaller oligosaccharides and monomers that are naturally present, as is the case with commercially available inulin [15]. Plant-derived inulin exhibits remarkable variability in terms of chain length, structure, and polydispersity. These characteristics are influenced by factors such as plant species, life cycle stage, harvesting date, and extraction and post-extraction methodologies [19].

29.3 Inulin Oligosaccharides

Iso-malto-oligosaccharides, xylo-oligosaccharides, cello-oligosaccharides, galacto-oligosaccharides, and FOS are different types of food-grade oligosaccharides getting much importance nowadays [20]. FOS are produced by transfructosylation from sucrose or by enzymatic hydrolysis of inulin in controlled conditions. Inulin can be partly reduced to IOS, a type of oligosaccharide, rather than being degraded to monosaccharides. Specifically, the FOS derived from inulin are referred to as inulin oligosaccharides (IOS). Fructosyltransferase is the key enzyme responsible for commercial FOS synthesis [1]. The fructosyltransferase enzyme is responsible for producing FOS such as 1-kestose (GF2), nystose (GF3), and fructofuranosylnystose (GF4) [21]. However, a limitation of this biological process is the simultaneous synthesis of glucose, fructose, and sucrose. This drawback results in higher extraction costs for FOS, degradation of their quality, limitations in their applications, lower yields, and the need for additional separation steps, ultimately reducing the profitability of the process [21]. Present FOS synthesis from sucrose utilizing immobilized fungal fructosyltransferases is inefficient owing to end-product inhibition, which results in a significant reduction in enzyme activity.

29.3.1 Inulin Oligosaccharides (IOS): Production

Inulin emerges as a highly desirable substrate for enzymatic production of functional oligosaccharides, particularly those rich in fructose units (inulo- or fructo-oligosaccharides), when employing purified endoinulinase. However, two crucial challenges must be addressed to achieve this objective. First, the utilization of more cost-effective agricultural commodities, such as chicory or Jerusalem artichoke, which are abundant in inulin, as substrates. Second, the development of an efficient and scalable industrial process for isolating endoinulinase. Overcoming these hurdles holds the key to unlocking the full potential of inulin in producing high-content oligosaccharides with valuable functional properties.

29.3.1.1 Inulinase Structure and Properties

Inulinases are a type of hydrolytic enzyme that belongs to the glycoside hydrolase family 32, and they have been classified based on their ability to hydrolyze inulin [6]. Inulinases have risen in recent years in the current biotechnological epoch because of their diverse range of products, which include producing inulinoligosaccharides, high-fructose syrup, FOS, and several other significant metabolites like bioethanol, organic acids, single-cell oil, 2,3-butanediol, single-cell proteins, etc. [9]. Inulinase-shydrolyze β-(2→1) fructosyl linkage and are produced by microorganisms such as bacteria, fungi, and yeast. Inulin is the second most frequent plant polymer in nature, behind starch. *Aspergillus* sp., *Penicillium* sp., *Kluyveromyces* sp., and *Bacillus* sp. have been among the most effective inulinase producers [6]. The structural and biochemical properties of a biocatalyst are influenced by a variety of elements such as the microbial source, origin, amino-acid sequence, and so on. Inulinases are found in a wide range of microbes, plants, and mammals [9]. In nature, there exist two distinct types of inulinases: exoinulinases and endoinulinases. Exoinulinases (EC 3.8.1.80), also referred to as β-D-fructanfructohydrolases or β-D-fructosidases, catalyze the hydrolysis of β-fructofuranosidic bonds, liberating the terminal fructose unit from inulin [11]. On the other hand, endoinulinases (EC 3.2.1.7) are responsible for the production of inulotriose, inulotetraose, and inulopentaose [11]. It is worth noting that exoinulinases also exhibit invertase activity (EC 3.2.1.26, fructofuranosidase), indicating their capability to degrade both sucrose and fructans using a single active site.

29.3.1.2 Microbial Inulinase Production: Bacteria, Fungi, and Yeasts

The commercial viability of inulinase production from animal and plant sources is hindered by their low enzyme yields. As a result, alternative sources such as filamentous fungi (*Aspergillus* sp., *Penicillium* sp., and *Rhizoctonia solani*), yeasts (*Kluyveromyces* sp., *Pichia* sp., and *Cryptococcus* sp.), and bacteria (*Streptomyces* sp. and *Xanthomonas* sp.) have emerged as preferred options for inulinase production. Inulin-hydrolyzing enzymes have been discovered in various phylogenetically distinct microorganisms, including bacteria, filamentous fungi, yeasts, and actinomycetes [11].

Fungal Inulinases Filamentous fungi are highly preferred as a microbial source for inulinase production due to their unique attributes, such as their ability to thrive in low pH environments and utilize inexpensive substrates even at high temperatures. Notably, certain filamentous fungi have been found to exhibit a synergistic effect by combining both exo- and endoinulinases during the process of fructan hydrolysis [22]. Recent discoveries have revealed a novel inulinase-producing strain called *Penicillium amphipolaria* KAS 2555, which was isolated from detritus mangrove soil. This strain has demonstrated the effective utilization of *Saccharum arundinaceum* as a substrate for inulinase fermentation through solid-state fermentation techniques [23]. Furthermore, the wild environment has proven to be a rich source of coprophilous fungal strains, with 61 strains belonging to *Neocosmospora*, *Trichoderma*, *Aspergillus*, *Mucor*, and *Fusarium* species being identified and purified [24]. Solid-state fermentation has shown promising results in enhancing the production of both inulinase and invertase enzymes, as observed in the case of *Aspergillus brasiliensis* [25]. Additionally, numerous strains of *Aspergillus niger*, a leading producer of inulinase, have demonstrated remarkable inulinase titers when cultivated on inulin-rich vegetal extracts [26]. To broaden the scope of inulinase production, successful expression of inulinases from *A. niger* F0602, *Aspergillus ficuum* JNSP5-06, and *Penicillium janthinellum* has been achieved in the yeast *Pichia pastoris,* highlighting the potential of genetic engineering approaches [27]. Moreover, the development of fungal recombinant strains has proven to be a successful strategy for enhancing inulinase production and improving stability under varying pH and temperature conditions compared to native strains [22]. These advancements hold significant promise for the future industrial applications of inulinase and its derivatives.

Bacterial Inulinases The limited availability of data regarding the origins of bacterial inulinases, compared to other microbial sources, can be attributed to recurrent mutational aberrations in single-cellular technology and the relatively low enzyme output. However, there is a growing interest in bacterial inulinase manufacturing due to the inherent advantages offered by their simple molecular structure and remarkable thermostability [6]. Bacterial strains such as *Bacillus* sp., *Streptomyces* sp., *Xanthomonas* sp., and *Clostridium* sp. have been extensively explored for their ability to produce highly active inulinases under extreme conditions, including high temperatures, alkaline or acidic environments, and high salinity. An intriguing example is the discovery of *Lactobacillus paracasei* B41, which was isolated from the Bulgarian traditional beverage known as "boza." This bacterial strain has demonstrated its ability to hydrolyze chicory flour inulin, effectively converting it into lactic acid with an impressive enzyme activity of 232 U/ml [28]. Moreover, a novel bacterial inulinase producer, *Marinimicrobium* sp., was identified from a marine solar saltern located in the Yellow Sea, China. This strain exhibits remarkable inulolytic activity even under challenging conditions, such as high temperatures (55 °C) and alkaline pH (9.0) [29]. The significant progress being made in bacterial inulinase research opens up new avenues for exploring their biotechnological applications, and further investigations are warranted to fully harness their potential in various industrial sectors.

Yeast Inulinases From the dawn of civilization till now, yeasts, a diverse group of eukaryotic fungus that typically lives as a unicellular organism, have had a wide range of uses and a dramatic influence on the industrial, biotechnological, medical, and environmental arenas [30]. *Diploidyeast, Kluyveromyces marxianus, Meyerozyma guilliermondii, Cryptococcus aureus, Zygosaccharomyces cerevisiae* producer of exoinulinase. *Pichia guillermondii* produces 60 U/ml exoinulinase. A study with 14 yeast strains *Kluyveromyces* sp., *Debaryomyces* sp., *Candida* sp., and *Schizosaccharomyces* sp. was done and revealed that the strain *K. marxianus* ATCC 36907 possesses high ability to synthesize inulinase [11].

29.3.2 Mechanism of Hydrolysis of Inulin by Exo-and Endoinulinases

There has been a growing interest in the potential of inulinase due to its vital role in hydrolyzing inulin, a process essential for the production of fuel ethanol, fructose, and FOS. These products hold significant importance in the food and pharmaceutical industries [31]. Inulinases can be classified into two types: exo- and endo-acting enzymes, both of which target the β-2,1 linkage present in inulin. The GH32 family encompasses a diverse range of more than 370 members from various species, including invertases, levanases (EC 3.2.1.65), and transfructosidases such as sucrose: sucrose 1-fructosyltransferase (EC 2.4.1.99) and fructan-fructan 1-fructosyltransferase (EC 2.4.1.100). Exoinulinases primarily yield fructose as the major end product, while endoinulinases produce FOS along with minor amounts of monosaccharides [32]. Enzymatic synthesis of FOS is currently achieved through two main pathways: utilizing sucrose and employing fructosyltransferases or employing inulin and employing endoinulinases [33]. Exoinulinases (EC 3.2.1.80) sequentially cleave the β-2,1 linkage starting from the nonreducing end of inulin, releasing terminal fructosyl units and generating fructose along with a molecule of glucose. On the other hand, endoinulinases (EC 3.2.1.7) act randomly, hydrolyzing the internal linkages of inulin to produce FOS. A study was conducted to investigate the characteristics of exoinulinase such as molecular mass, effect of pH,

Table 29.2 Reaction conditions for activity of different endo inulinases for production of inulin oligosaccharides (IOS).

Source of endoinulinase	pH	Reaction-temperature	Incubation-time	Feedstock used	DP of formedoligosaccharides	References
Recombinant *Pichia pastoris*	6	60	8	400 g/linulin	2–5	[34]
Aspergillus arachidicola	5.5	60	24	150 g/linulin	3–4	[21]
Pseudomonas mucidolens	7.0	50	30	—	2–5	[22]
Saccharomyces cerevisiae	—	40	24	200 g/l	3–6	[35]
Recombinant *Yarrowialipolytica*	4.5	35	72	600 g/l	3–4	[36]
Recombinant *Bacillus subtilis*	7.4	32	48	20 g/linulin	3–5	[37]
Recombinant *Saccharomyces cerevisiae*	5	40 °C	24	200 g/l chicory	3–6	[35]
Recombinant *Escherichia coli*	4.6	55	24	15 g/linulin	3–7	[38]
Recombinant *Escherichia coli*	5	55	24	50 g/linulin	3–4	[39]
Aspergillus ficuum	5	45	72	50 g/linulin	2–8	[40]
Xanthomonas campestris	6.0	50	2	5 g/linulin	3–5	[39]
Bacillus safensis AS-08	5.5	50	15 min	20 g/linulin	—	[41]
Aspergillus niger	6.0	60	8 h	400 g/linulin	3–6	[20]

effect of temperature, inhibitory effect of D-fructose, etc. from *Aspergillus terreus* in comparison to inulinases produced by other microorganisms [32]. Microbial endoinulinases, also known as 2,1-β-D-fructan-fructan hydrolases (EC 3.2.1.7), specifically target and hydrolyze the internal linkages within inulin, resulting in the release of intermediate products such as inulotriose (F3), inulotetraose (F4), and inulopentaose (F5) [24]. These findings underscore the importance of exploring the potential applications of inulinases and their enzymatic capabilities in various industrial sectors.

The pricing of an enzymatic bioprocess is a critical need for its commercialization. In order to attain this goal, low-cost inulin-rich plant extracts, strategic statistical optimization, over-expression of inulinase, and high-cell density fermentations are being investigated [11]. The reaction conditions for the activity of different endo inulinases for production of inulin oligosaccharides (IOS) are described in Table 29.2; types of feedstocks, fermentation type, and action of inulinases are described in Table 29.3.

29.4 Strategies to Enhance Production of Inulin Oligosaccharides

29.4.1 Strain Improvement for Enhanced Inulin Oligosaccharide Production

In recent years, there has been significant interest in the study of exo- and endoinulinases derived from bacterial and fungal strains, with extensive research conducted on their heterologous expression in yeast and bacterial systems [11]. However, despite their potential benefits, the widespread use of commercial endoinulinases in the scaled-up production of FOS (IOSs) has been hindered by the complex conditions and high costs associated with their manufacturing process. Furthermore, the secretion of both endoinulinase and exoinulinase by the majority of strains presents a challenge in developing a method for IOS production from wild-type strains [37]. To overcome these limitations, yeasts have emerged as attractive hosts for heterologous inulinase expression, offering the advantages of high cell densities and well-established recovery techniques. Among the commonly used yeast hosts for this purpose are *P. pastoris, Yarrowia lipolytica, S. cerevisiae,* and *Kluyveromyces lactis* [11]. Notably, successful synthesis of endoinulinase has been achieved in *Escherichia coli* (*E. coli*) BL21 (DE3) through the heteroexpression of the endoinulinase-encoding gene from *A. ficuum*. Optimization of conditions for IOS production from inulin resulted in an impressive yield of 94.41%, with the identified hydrolysis products primarily consisting of DP3 to DP7 [38]. Similarly, the expression of the endo-inulinase gene (inul) from *Pseudomonas* sp. in *E. coli* HB101 demonstrated a high IOS yield of 78% [37]. Moreover, the characterization and expression of the endo-inulinase gene inu3B in *E. coli* led to the production of a soluble protein with effective catalytic activity against inulin, remarkable thermostability, and broad pH tolerance. The resulting FOS products predominantly comprised DP2, DP3, and DP4 [57]. These valuable findings contribute

Table 29.3 Types offeedstocks, fermentation type, and action of inulinases.

Microorganism	Feedstock	Fermentation	Inulinase action	Maximal inulinase activity (IU/ml)	References
Bacteria					
Achromobacter sp.	Inulin	SmF	Exoinulinase	0.33	[42]
Bacillus safensis	Inulin Dahlia tubers extract	SmF SmF	Endoinulinase	12.56 28.67	[43]
Bacillus sp.	Jerusalem artichoke tubers extract	SmF	Exoinulinase	≈8.90	[44]
Bacillus subtilis	Dahlia tubers extract	SmF	Exoinulinase	0.025	[45]
Streptomyces sp.	Jerusalem artichoke Garlic bulb	SmF SSF	Endoinulinase Endoinulinase	1.60 89	[42, 46]
Streptomyces rochei	Inulin	SmF	Endoinulinase	1.00	[46]
Xanthomonas campestris	Garlic peel Onion peel	SSF SSF	Endoinulinase Endoinulinase	117 101	[42]
Fungi					
Aspergillus niger	Jerusalem artichoke and bean	SSF	Exoinulinase	11.13	[42]
Aspergillus terreus	Garlic waste	SSF	Exoinulinase	0.022 ± 0.031	[47]
Aspergillus terreus	Artichoke leaves	SSF	Exoinulinase	4.433 ± 0.121	[47]
Aspergillus versicolor	Chicory roots	SSF	Exoinulinase	0.177 ± 0.125	[47]
Aspergillus ficuum	Inulin	SmF	Exoinulinase	25	[48]
Aspergillus fumigatus	Inulin	SmF	Exoinulinase	7.97	[49]
Aspergillus tamarii	Dahlia tubers extract	SmF	Exoinulinase	57.07	[50]
Aspergillus tritici	Raw asparagus inulin	SmF	Endoinulinase	25.01	[1]
Aspergillus tubingensis	Chicory roots powder	SmF	Exoinulinase	21.90	[51]
Mucor circinelloides	Inulin	SmF	Exoinulinase	23.55	[52]
Yeasts					
Cryptococcus aureus	Inulin	SmF	Exoinulinase	52.37, 85	[53]
Kluyveromycesmarxianus	*Dahlia* tubers extract	SmF	Exoinulinase	25.30	[54]
Pichia guilliermondii	Inulin	SmF	Exoinulinase	39.56	[34]
Rhodotorulaglutinis	Leek powder	SmF	Exoinulinase	30.89	[55]
Yarrowialipolytica	Inulin	SmF	Endoinulinase	62.85	[56]

to the expanding knowledge and potential applications of inulinase in various biotechnological fields.

29.4.2 Immobilized Inulinases for Enhanced Inulin Oligosaccharide Production

Immobilization is the process of converting a soluble enzyme into an insoluble form, either with or without the use of a carrier [58]. This technique enables the confinement or localization of enzyme molecules within a specific spatial region while preserving their catalytic activities. Immobilized enzymes present numerous advantages over their native counterparts, including improved stability, simplified product recovery and purification, the potential for repeated utilization, and the facilitation of continuous process technology [59].

29.4.2.1 Covalent Binding Method

The covalent coupling of enzymes to a support involves several steps, including support functionalization, enzyme coupling to the activated support, and the removal of excess and unattached molecules [58]. In the context of inulinase immobilization for the production of fructose and FOS, a wide range of supports has been explored, including cellulose-based supports, insoluble protein-based supports, silica-based supports, magnetic-based supports, chitin-based supports, and polymeric supports. Some research investigated the covalent immobilization of inulinase from the marine-derived fungus *A. terreus* on novel gel beads composed of alginate and carboxymethyl cellulose. The study aimed to evaluate the catalytic properties of both the free and immobilized enzymes, shedding light on their potential applications [60].

29.4.2.2 Entrapment Method

Entrapment is a highly advantageous one-step procedure that minimizes the potential loss of enzyme activity during immobilization. Physical entrapment within a polymer or gel matrix, such as alginate, is a commonly employed method for immobilizing enzymes. Among the various techniques available, the sol–gel approach is frequently utilized for this purpose. In a study conducted, an experimental design technique was employed to optimize the immobilization of inulinase from *K. marxianus* NRRL Y-7571 using a combination of alginate and activated coal as supports [61]. By employing the experimental design tool, the researchers identified the optimum conditions for immobilization, resulting in a remarkable specific activity of 2063.5 U/mg of protein using sodium alginate, glutaraldehyde, and activated coal at concentrations of 20 g/l, 50 ml/l, and 30 g/l, respectively. The immobilization process exhibited exceptional efficiency, with a 100% yield achieved after a 24-hour refrigeration treatment. Furthermore, the gel beads demonstrated a high enzyme loading capacity of 668 U/g, highlighting the efficacy of immobilizing inulinase on alginate-chitosan beads as a viable and promising method for enzyme immobilization.

29.4.2.3 Encapsulation Method

Encapsulation involves the formation of spherical particles through the encapsulation of enzymes within a semipermeable membrane. This technique is highly effective and is preferred due to its simplicity and the absence of a chemical bond between the enzyme and the support, thus minimizing the risk of enzyme dissipation from the carrier [58]. To further enhance the performance of the resulting capsules, functional groups can be introduced to the surface of the capsules. In the context of immobilizing inulinase, two methods have been utilized to prepare alginate gel beads with encapsulation: the one-step method and the two-step method. Comparative studies have demonstrated that the one-step method yields superior results for inulinase immobilization, and this method has been further optimized [62].

29.5 Applications of Inulin Oligosaccharides (IOS)

Inulin oligosaccharides, a type of storage oligosaccharide, have not yet been fully explored for their potential applications. They offer the opportunity to produce valuable products such as fructose, FOS, ethanol, gluconic acid, sorbitol, and more [63]. Endoinulinase plays a crucial role in selectively hydrolyzing inulin into IOS, including inulotriose and inulotetraose, which have various industrial uses [64]. The conversion process holds promising advantages from an industrial perspective, thanks to its favorable reaction conditions and simplified kinetics [11]. Inulin oligosaccharides share functional similarities with other oligosaccharides and can be utilized as dietary supplements, prebiotics, fibers, functional sweeteners, pet food ingredients, bioethanol feedstocks, and more (Figure 29.2). Additionally, fructose, a readily fermentable low-calorie sweetener, shares structural and functional similarities with inulin oligosaccharides (IOS), making them suitable for incorporation into functional foods and nutraceuticals [1]. The significant medicinal relevance of short-chain FOS and inulin oligosaccharides (IOS) has led to a rapid increase in their manufacturing output. FOS have been categorized as prebiotics due to their bifidogenic origin and health-promoting properties, which have been recommended by healthcare practitioners when consumed in appropriate amounts [39]. Some important properties of FOS include:

1) Low sweetness intensity, about one-third of sucrose, which makes them suitable when sucrose's high sweetness needs to be avoided.
2) Low calorie levels are due to their resistance to hydrolysis by digestive enzymes and they are not extensively utilized as an energy source in the body, making them suitable for consumption by diabetic patients.
3) Inulin oligosaccharides are not utilized by *Streptococcus mutans* to produce acids and insoluble β-glucan, which are known to contribute to the development of dental caries.
4) Prebiotics, such as FOS, promote the growth of beneficial bifidobacteria while inhibiting the proliferation of potentially harmful microorganisms that can lead to diarrhea [24].

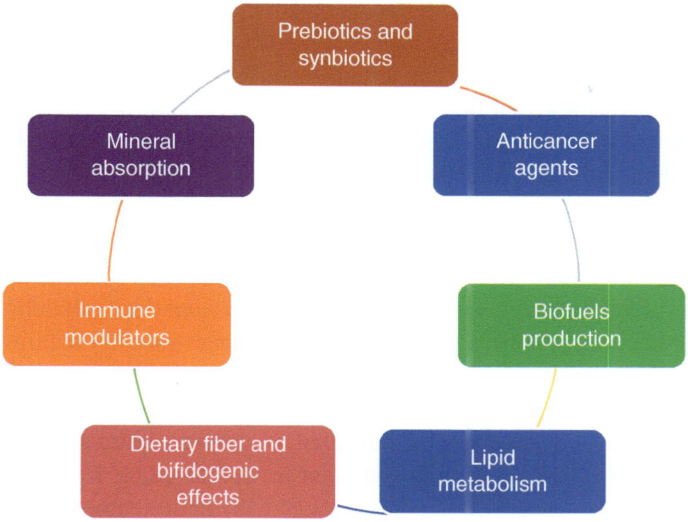

Figure 29.2 Applications of inulin oligosaccharides (IOS).

Fructans are naturally occurring compounds found in plants, and they exist as mixtures with varying degrees of polymerization (DP) and different chemical structures [24]. Fructosyltransferases are responsible for synthesizing FOS such as 1-kestose (GF2), nystose (GF3), and fructofuranosylnystose (GF4). The composition of fructans in plants depends on factors like the plant species, environmental conditions, and stage of development. FOS are characterized as low-molecular-weight linear molecules consisting of 2–20 fructose monomers connected by glycosidic bonds, with a terminal glucose component. These structural features make FOS resistant to degradation by digestive enzymes in the upper gastrointestinal system, classifying them as natural fibers [39]. Inulin and FOS have various sources, as discussed earlier. Acid hydrolysis is a commonly used method to synthesize fructose and FOS with a DPof less than 10 from simple and cost-effective sources. However, this technique has drawbacks such as the need for prolonged refluxing, expensive acid-resistant equipment, and the generation of hazardous waste [39]. Alternatively, inulinases offer an enzymatic approach for producing high-purity fructose and a mixture of IOS, including inulobiose, inullotriose, inullotetraose, inulopentaose, and minor amounts of glucose. Enzyme-based processes have advantages over traditional chemical methods, as they operate at lower temperatures, generate fewer hazardous waste materials, and produce lower emissions and by-products [24].

29.5.1 Inulin-derived Oligosaccharides as Prebiotics

During a meeting of the International Scientific Association of Probiotics and Prebiotics (ISAPP) in London in November 2008, the concept of prebiotics was introduced. Prebiotics were defined as fermented ingredients that bring about favorable changes in the composition and activity of the gut microbiome, resulting in various health benefits [7, 9]. Specifically, short-chain FOS containing fructosyl units linked by a β-(2,1) linkage (with a range of 2–8 fructosyl units) were found to exhibit optimal bifidogenic activity. The stimulation of bifidobacteria growth has been associated with improved digestion, enhanced absorption of nutrients, increased availability of vitamins, and crucially, prevention of gut colonization by harmful pathogens and putrefactive bacteria [24].

In a study, the prebiotic role of chicory FOS was demonstrated using two types of FOS: fibruline instant and fibrulose [65]. They observed that different strains of *Bifidobacterium* (*B. longum, B. infantis,* and *B. angulatum*) efficiently utilized the fructose oligomers present in commercial chicory FOS, confirming their suitability as prebiotics. To qualify as a prebiotic, a food ingredient must meet three key requirements: resistance to hydrolysis and absorption in the upper gastrointestinal system, selectivity as a substrate for specific probiotic strains, and the ability to positively influence the composition and activity of the intestinal microflora toward a healthier state [10]. Inulin and FOS are naturally abundant in various edible fruits and vegetables. Many companies now produce FOS through enzymatic synthesis from inulin. This enzymatic synthesis yields a mixture of fructans consisting of different types of oligofructose, including F_n and GF_n. Interestingly, studies have shown that F_n fructans exhibit similar prebiotic effects in humans compared to GF_n fructans. FOS derived from inulin are considered long-chain fructans [33].

29.5.2 Inulin-derived Oligosaccharides as Dietary Fibers

Dietary fiber encompasses a diverse array of nondigestible and nonabsorbable compounds that are primarily located in the small intestine. When specific fibers are digested by beneficial bacteria residing in the hindgut microbiota, they are recognized as prebiotics, as highlighted by Rezende and co-workers in 2021 [66]. Within the large intestine, FOS undergo digestion by bacteria, resulting in the production of short-chain fatty acids (SCFAs) like acetate, propionate, and butyrate, which can be readily absorbed. Notably, several studies have revealed intriguing benefits of FOS, including potential enhancements in calcium uptake within the gut, stimulation of *Bifidobacterium* sp. growth in the colon, reduction of iron intake by enteric pathogens, and improved absorption of essential minerals such as vitamin D and E, particularly in the presence of inulin [67].

29.5.3 Inulin-derived Oligosaccharides in Controlling Diabetes

Diabetes has a profound impact on the quality and longevity of life for individuals affected by this condition. Shockingly, over 50% of the 4 million diabetes-related deaths occur in people under the age of 60 [68]. Diabetes mellitus (DM) is a chronic metabolic disorder characterized by inadequate insulin production or utilization by the body. If left unmanaged, diabetes can lead to severe complications, including heart disease, kidney failure, blindness, and even death [39]. The prevalence of diabetes is on the rise globally, with the seventh edition of the International Diabetes Federation Diabetes Atlas reporting a staggering 425 million diagnosed cases in 2017. Projections indicate that this number will soar to 629 million by 2045. Addressing this growing epidemic is of utmost importance.

Recent research sheds light on the potential of functional oligosaccharides, such as FOS, in managing diabetes [24]. Their study demonstrated that a daily dose of 20 g of FOS could effectively reduce baseline hepatic glucose production in healthy individuals, without interfering with insulin-stimulated metabolism. This finding opens up new possibilities for utilizing FOS as a beneficial dietary component for diabetes management. Guidelines from the World Health Organization (WHO) advocate for limiting free sugar intake to no more than 10% of the total energy intake across all age groups. In this context, functional oligosaccharides offer promising prospects for diabetes prevention. Their nondigestible nature and resistance to human digestive enzymes make them an ideal candidate for regulating blood sugar levels [68].

In the pursuit of safer and more sustainable production methods, *Aspergillus oryzae* has been employed to generate mono- to pentasaccharides. These compounds can serve as food components without the risk of harmful microbial metabolite formation, showcasing their potential for application in diabetes-friendly diets. Moreover, a study has been conducted utilizing FOSs in diabetic rats to assess their viability as a non-nutrient sweetener. The results were promising, as FOSs not only avoided elevating blood sugar levels but also exhibited the potential to mitigate blood protein loss, thereby offering multifaceted benefits for individuals with diabetes. These findings underscore the importance of exploring functional oligosaccharides, such as FOS, as a valuable adjunct in diabetes management strategies. Their unique properties and positive effects on blood sugar regulation and related complications provide a foundation for further investigation and potential therapeutic applications.

29.5.4 Inulin-derived Oligosaccharides as Synbiotics

The composition and activity of the colonic microbiota play a crucial role in maintaining gut health, not only in healthy individuals but also in those with gastrointestinal problems [69]. To enhance the benefits of microbial dietary supplements, a combined approach of probiotics and prebiotics, known as "synbiotics," has gained attention [3]. Synbiotics involve the use of live beneficial microbes (probiotics) along with selective substrates (prebiotics) that work together to promote their survival and colonization in the gastrointestinal tract. Among the prebiotics, inulin and FOSs are commonly utilized, especially when paired with probiotics, to improve gut health [1]. Fructans, in particular, have been found to stimulate the growth of existing microflora in the colon while facilitating the establishment and growth of new probiotic strains. This approach has shown promising results, such as the reduction of diarrhea in infants through the addition of a combination of milk-derived oligosaccharides (OS) and *Bifidobacterium lactis* to infant formula. Furthermore, a study demonstrated the effectiveness of a synbiotic combination of *B. lactis* HN019 and prebiotic oligosaccharides in reducing the incidence of dysentery symptoms, pneumonia, and respiratory infections in children [70]. In the context of synbiotic food options, a study has extensively reviewed the diversity of products available, particularly in dairy items such as yogurt, ice cream, infant formula, cheese, skim milk, bread buns, chocolates, candy, and soy beverages. This comprehensive review provides valuable insights into the concentrations of probiotics and prebiotics in these products, shedding light on their potential in promoting gut health and overall well-being [8].

29.5.5 Inulin-derived Oligosaccharides in Lipid Metabolism

The chronic effects of a diet containing short-chain FOS on plasma lipids and fatty acid synthase (FAS) activity in insulin-resistant rats were investigated. The inclusion of short-chain FOS in the diet was found to have a preventive effect on lipid disorders and reduce FAS activity in the liver. These findings suggest that the addition of FOS can help improve lipid metabolism in insulin-resistant individuals. Prebiotics such as FOS have been shown to contribute to hypocholesterolemia through two mechanisms. First, they decrease cholesterol absorption and enhance its excretion through feces. Second, they promote the production of SCFAs through selective fermentation by intestinal bacterial microflora. These SCFAs have been associated with various health benefits, including the regulation of cholesterol levels. Further, studies using rat models have demonstrated that feeding them with inulin or oligofructose leads to a significant reduction in serum concentrations of triacylglycerols (TAG) and phospholipids. This highlights the potential of these prebiotic compounds to lower lipid levels and support overall cardiovascular health. Overall, the consumption of FOS and other prebiotics holds promise as a dietary approach to improve lipid profiles and potentially reduce the risk of lipid-related disorders. Further research is needed to explore the underlying mechanisms and to determine the optimal dosage and duration of prebiotic supplementation for maximum lipid-lowering effects.

29.5.6 Inulin-derived Oligosaccharides as Anti-cancer Agents

According to global cancer data from 2012, there were approximately 14.1 million new cases of cancer and an alarming 8.2 million cancer-related deaths. While the importance of a balanced diet in cancer prevention and management has been well-established, the role of dietary supplements in cancer therapy remains uncertain in terms of their potential benefits for cancer recovery [71]. Although the significance of a balanced diet has been demonstrated in cancer prevention and management, it is uncertain whether utilizing dietary supplements during cancer therapy is beneficial in cancer recovery [71]. Studies conducted on mice have shown promising results, demonstrating that these prebiotic compounds can reduce tumor formation, inhibit tumor growth, and even impede metastasis. Colorectal cancer (CRC), which ranks as the third most prevalent cancer worldwide, has seen a recent surge in emerging countries due to various environmental and lifestyle factors. Factors such as lack of physical exercise, poor dietary habits, disruption of circadian rhythm, and increased alcohol consumption have been identified as contributors to this concerning trend [72]. Investigations in both animal models and humans have shed light on the potential of inulin-type fructans in reducing the risk of colon cancer. These fructans have been found to minimize exposure to genotoxic carcinogens within the gut, as well as mitigate their detrimental effects. Moreover, inulin-type fructans have displayed significant capabilities in inhibiting the progression of pre-neoplastic and neoplastic lesions, thereby holding promise as a preventive measure against colon cancer. Prebiotics have emerged as a valuable tool in addressing dysbiosis, a condition characterized by an imbalance in gut microbiota. By selectively promoting the growth of beneficial bacteria, prebiotics contribute to the synthesis of SCFAs, modulation of anti-inflammatory immune responses, maintenance of the intestinal epithelial barrier, and induction of pro-apoptotic processes and other cellular functions associated with gut health [72]. SCFAs, in particular, have shown potential as preventive agents against CRC by inhibiting histone deacetylases, triggering apoptosis in tumor colonocytes, and reducing the number of colon polyps and hyperplastic Peyer's patches in the small intestine mucosa [73]. Experiments showed that a 15% supplementation of experimental animals' basal diets led to a significant decrease in colon tumors. Such supplementation has led to a considerable decrease in colon tumors, hindered the proliferation of malignant tumors in mice, and even reduced the rate of lung metastases from intramuscularly implanted malignant tumors [24]. Nevertheless, further research is warranted to elucidate the underlying mechanisms and determine the optimal strategies for integrating prebiotics into cancer therapy protocols.

29.5.7 Inulin-derived Oligosaccharides in Biofuels

The worldwide exploitation of fossil fuels has led to environmental damage, including oil reserve depletion, poor air quality, global warming, and unpredictable climates. Inulin-containing agricultural and industrial waste, such as agave, asparagus, coffee, chicory, and garlic, have gained attention as potential feedstocks for biofuel production [21]. Microorganisms like *K. marxianus*, *Y. lipolytica*, *Rhodotorula glutinis*, and *S. cerevisiae* can convert these waste materials into valuable biofuels and bioproducts [74]. This approach offers a sustainable alternative to fossil fuels and contributes to mitigating their negative impacts.

29.5.7.1 Bioethanol Production from Wastes Containing Inulin

Inulinases haveand have been used for ethanol production. Exoinulinase facilitates the removal of terminal fructose residues from inulin, generating fructose and glucose, which can be readily converted to ethanol by *S. cerevisiae*. Alternatively, *K. marxianus* can directly convert inulin to ethanol, as it possesses active inulinase and alcohol dehydrogenase. Acid or enzyme hydrolysis, followed by fermentation with *S. cerevisiae* or direct fermentation with *K. marxianus,* enables efficient ethanol production from fructans. Utilizing renewable inulin-containing nongrain materials, such as *Jerusalem artichokes*, holds potential for the bioenergy industry [75, 76]. Specific *S. cerevisiae* strains capable of converting inulin to ethanol without pretreatment are being investigated [77]. The transcription level of SUC2 is crucial for inulinase activity and inulin catabolism in *S. cerevisiae* strains, with sequence variations in the SUC2 promoter influencing its expression [78]. Higher expression of SUC2 enhances inulin degradation and ethanol yield [79].

29.5.7.2 Biodiesel Production from Inulin Waste

Recently, it has been observed that certain oleaginous yeast strains, namely *R. toruloides* 2F5 and *T. cutaneum* CGMCC 2.1374, exhibit the unique ability to directly utilize inulin for microbial lipid fermentation. These strains not only possess the capacity to produce and secrete enzymes responsible for inulin hydrolysis but also have the capability to accumulate intracellular lipids. This microbial lipid, with a composition resembling plant oil, holds great potential as an alternative feedstock for biodiesel production [56, 78, 80].

29.5.7.3 Other Types of Fuels from Inulin Waste

In recent studies, there has been growing interest in utilizing inulin-containing waste for the production of various biofuels such as butanol, jet fuels, and biogas. Acidic or enzymatic hydrolysis of inulin can yield high concentrations of fructose, which can be further converted into 5-hydroxymethylfurfural (HMF) through a dehydration process. HMF serves as a key intermediate in the production of biofuels, particularly jet fuels. Notably, HMF has been successfully transformed into dihydroxymethylfuran (DMF) using a copper-ruthenium (CuRu) catalyst, offering a higher energy density and boiling point compared to ethanol, making it an attractive alternative to conventional fuels [13]. Furthermore, butanol (n-butanol) has gained attention as a promising biofuel with several advantages over ethanol. *Jerusalem artichokes* (*H. tuberosus L.*) have shown potential as an economical and alternative carbon source for butanol fermentation [81]. In a study utilizing inulinase from *A. niger* (Novozymes Inc.) and fermentation with *Clostridium saccharobutylicum* DSM 13864, optimal conditions of pH 4.8, 48 °C, and an inulin substrate concentration of 60 g/L resulted in 94.5% inulin hydrolysis within 24 hours. The study also achieved an 85% theoretical yield of acetone–butanol–ethanol (ABE) [82]. However, research on biogas production from inulin-containing waste remains limited.

29.6 Commercial Statistics of Inulin Oligosaccharide Production with Future Perspectives

As a consequence of growing demand for the product as a cost-effective digestive aid, the global market for FOS is expected to reach USD 1.04 billion by 2025. Anxiety, sleeplessness, stress, nervousness, and a lack of energy are all likely to be linked to digestive issues[3]. In 2018, more than 35% of Americans experienced a digestive health issue, according to the CDC,which is expected to offer tremendous commercial viability for the ingredient. Dietary supplements are projected to be the fastest-expanding category in terms of applicability. The use of nutritional supplements by people and animals has grown dramatically in recent years, and this trend is anticipated to continue in the future years. In the forecast period of 2020–2027, the inulin and FOS market is anticipated to develop at a

6.20% annual pace. Fonterra Co-operative Group, Royal Cosun, New Francisco (Yunfu City) Biotechnology Corporation Limited, Dana Dairy Group, Glycosyn, Dextra Laboratories Limited, Glycom A/S, Tereos, Ingredion Incorporated, Royal FrieslandCampina N.V., Südzucker AG, Cargill are the market leaders secured in the inulin and FOS business [4]. The growth of the inulin and FOS industries is projected to be driven by the need to reduce the use of some artificial sweeteners. More prebiotic demand, along with increased government aid, is expected to boost growth. In the long run, rising interest in gastric wellness and increased demand for low-calorie sweeteners are expected to fuel commodities growth.

29.7 Conclusion

Oligosaccharides are sugars made from a variety of low-cost and plentiful sources, and because of the health benefits, and accessible sources, they have been regarded as a luxury. These substances have a huge market that is still growing. The poor yields of FOS are the major disadvantage of the manufacturing method. IOSs are already recognized for their bifidogenic impact, health benefits, and as one of the most often manufactured and utilized oligosaccharides in the food sector. To increase the performance of the enzymes involved in the production of FOS and IOS, new techniques such as molecular methods must be investigated. Plants that contain inulin are a low-cost, plentiful, and renewable source of inulin for large-scale synthesis of prebiotic oligosaccharides. The majority of publications on the use of inulinases to produce microbial products from inulin/inulin-rich raw materials are mostly from laboratory-scale reactors. Immobilized recombinant endoinulinase has greater thermostability and longer service life than free endoinulinase, which would increase its potential for commercial IOS synthesis. Further attempts are needed to create cheaper enzyme technologies through the characterization of novel endoinulinase producers, thermostability and process optimization research, genetic engineering, and fast purification systems in order to create this technology industrially viable. Furthermore, the bioprocess will be strengthened by the microorganism's capacity to utilize agro-industrial waste and a low-cost technique for the purification of generated oligosaccharides. Thus, new prospective prebiotic substances could be created using this information in conjunction with enzyme engineering to improve consumer quality of life.

References

1 Singh, R.S., Singh, R.P., and Kennedy, J.F. (2016). Recent insights in enzymatic synthesis of fructooligosaccharides from inulin. *Int. J. Biol. Macromol.* 85: 565–572.

2 Yan, Y.L., Hu, Y., and Ganzle, M.G. (2018). Prebiotics, FODMAPs and dietary fiber—conflicting concepts in development of functional food products? *Curr. Opin. Food Sci.* 20: 30–37.

3 Mohanty, D., Misra, S., Mohapatra, S., and Sahu, P.S. (2018). Prebiotics and synbiotics: recent concepts in nutrition. *Food Biosci.* 26: 152–160.

4 Vergari, F., Tibuzzi, A., and Basile, G. (2010). An overview of the functional food market: from marketing issues and commercial players to future demand from life in space. *Adv. Exp. Biol.* https://doi.org/10.1007/978-1-4419-7347-4_23.

5 Flores, A.C., Morlett, J.A., and Rodriguez, R. (2016). Inulin potential for enzymatic obtaining of prebiotic oligosaccharides. *Crit. Rev. Food Sci. Nutr.* 56: 1893–1902.

6 Singh, R.S. and Singh, R.P. (2017). Inulinases. In: *Current Developments in Biotechnology and Bioengineering* (ed. A. Pandey, S. Nagi, and C.R. Soccol), 423–446. Elsevier.

7 Davani-Davari, D., Negahdaripour, M., Karimzadeh, I. et al. (2019). Prebiotics: definition, types, sources, mechanisms, and clinical applications. *Foods* 8: 92–118.

8 Gonzalez-Herrera, S.M., Bermudez-Quinones, G., Ochoa-Martinez, L.A. et al. (2021). Synbiotics: a technological approach in food applications. *J. Food Sci. Technol.* 58: 811–824.

9 Singh, R.S., Singh, T., Hassan, M., and Kennedy, J.F. (2020). Updates on inulinases: structural aspects and biotechnological applications. *Int. J. Biol. Macromol.* 164: 193–210.

10 Kango, N. and Jain, S.C. (2011). Production and properties of microbial inulinases: recent advances. *Food Biotechnol.* 25: 165–212.

11 Rawat, H.K., Soni, H., Treichel, H., and Kango, N. (2017). Biotechnological potential of microbial inulinases: recent perspective. *Crit. Rev. Food Sci. Nutr.* 57: 3818–3829.

12 Neeraj, G., Ravi, S., Somdutt, R. et al. (2018). Immobilized inulinase: a new horizon of paramount importance driving the production of sweetener and prebiotics. *Crit. Rev. Biotechnol.* 38: 409–422.

13 Singh, R.S., Singh, T., and Larroche, C. (2019). Biotechnological applications of inulin-rich feedstocks. *Bioresour. Technol.* 273: 641–653.

14 Shoaib, M., Shehzad, A., Omar, M. et al. (2016). Inulin: properties, health benefits and food applications. *Carbohydr. Polym.* 147: 444–454.

15 Wan, X., Guo, H., Liang, Y. et al. (2020). The physiological functions and pharmaceutical applications of inulin: a review. *Carbohydr. Polym.* 246: 116589.

16 Mensink, M.A., Frijlink, H.W., van der Voort, M.K., and Hinrichs, W.L. (2015). Inulin, a flexible oligosaccharide. II: review of its pharmaceutical applications. *Carbohydr. Polym.* 134: 418–428.

17 Apolinario, A.C., de Lima Damasceno, B.P., de Macedo Beltrao, N.E. et al. (2014). Inulin-type fructans: a review on different aspects of biochemical and pharmaceutical technology. *Carbohydr. Polym.* 101: 368–378.

18 Flores-Maltos, D.A., Mussatto, S.I., Contreras-Esquivel, J.C. et al. (2016). Biotechnological production and application of fructooligosaccharides. *Crit. Rev. Biotechnol.* 36: 259–267.

19 Roberfroid, M., Gibson, G.R., Hoyles, L. et al. (2010). Prebiotic effects: metabolic and health benefits. *Br. J. Nutr.* 104: S1–S63.

20 Xu, Y., Zheng, Z., Xu, Q. et al. (2016). Efficient conversion of inulin to inulooligosaccharides through endoinulinase from *Aspergillus niger*. *J. Agric. Food. Chem.* 64: 2612–2618.

21 Jiang, X., Zhu, Y., Zhang, W. et al. (2019). Efficient production of inulooligosaccharides from inulin by endoinulinase from *Aspergillus arachidicola*. *Carbohydr. Polym.* 208: 70–76.

22 Paul, I. and Kumar, C.G. (2020). Fungal biofactories as potential inulinase sources for production of fructooligosaccharides. In: *New and Future Developments in Microbial Biotechnology and Bioengineering* (ed. J. Singh and P. Gehlot), 183–210. Elsevier.

23 Das, D., Bhat, R., and Selvaraj, R. (2020). Optimization of inulinase production by a newly isolated *Penicillium amphipolaria* strain using solid-state fermentation of hardy sugarcane stems. *Biocatal. Agric. Biotechnol.* 30: 101875.

24 Ojwach, J., Kumar, A., Mutanda, T., and Mukaratirwa, S. (2020). Fructosyltransferase and inulinase production by indigenous coprophilous fungi for the biocatalytic conversion of sucrose and inulin into oligosaccharides. *Biocatal. Agric. Biotechnol.* 30: 101867.

25 Guerrero-Urrutia, C., Volke-Sepulveda, T., Figueroa-Martinez, F., and Favela-Torres, E. (2021). Solid-state fermentation enhances inulinase and invertase production by *Aspergillus brasiliensis*. *Process Biochem.* 108: 169–175.

26 Rawat, H.K., Ganaie, M.A., and Kango, N. (2015). Production of inulinase, fructosyltransferase and sucrase from fungi on low-value inulin-rich substrates and their use in generation of fructose and fructo-oligosaccharides. *Antonie van Leeuwenhoek* 107: 799–811.

27 Chen, M., Lei, X., Chen, C. et al. (2015). Cloning, overexpression, and characterization of a highly active endoinulinase gene from *Aspergillus fumigatus* Cl1 for production of inulo-oligosaccharides. *Appl. Biochem. Biotechnol.* 175: 1153–1167.

28 Petrova, P., Velikova, P., Popova, L., and Petrov, K. (2015). Direct conversion of chicory flour into L(+)-lactic acid by the highly effective inulinase producer *Lactobacillus paracasei* DSM 23505. *Bioresour. Technol.* 186: 329–333.

29 Li, A.X., Guo, L.Z., and Lu, W.D. (2012). Alkaline inulinase production by a newly isolated bacterium *Marinimicrobium* sp. LS-A18 and inulin hydrolysis by the enzyme. *World J. Microbiol. Biotechnol.* 28: 81–89.

30 Karim, A., Gerliani, N., and Aider, M. (2020). *Kluyveromyces marxianus*: an emerging yeast cell factory for applications in food and biotechnology. *Int. J. Food Microbiol.* 333: 108818.

31 Ramapriya, R., Thirumurugan, A., Sathishkumar, T., and Manimaran, D.R. (2018). Partial purification and characterization of exoinulinase produced from *Bacillus* sp. *J. Genet. Eng. Biotechnol.* 16: 363–367.

32 Coitinho, J.B., Guimaraes, V.M., de Almeida, M.N. et al. (2010). Characterization of an exoinulinase produced by *Aspergillus terreus* CCT 4083 grown on sugar cane bagasse. *J. Agric. Food. Chem.* 58: 8386–8391.

33 Singh, R.S. and Singh, R.P. (2010). Production of fructooligosaccharides from inulin by endoinulinases and their prebiotic potential. *Food Technol. Biotechnol.* 48: 435–450.

34 He, M., Wu, D., Wu, J., and Chen, J. (2014). Enhanced expression of endoinulinase from *Aspergillus niger* by codon optimization in *Pichia pastoris* and its application in inulooligosaccharide production. *J. Ind. Microbiol. Biotechnol.* 41: 105–114.

35 Wang, D., Li, F.L., and Wang, S.A. (2016). A one-step bioprocess for production of high-content fructo-oligosaccharides from inulin by yeast. *Carbohydr. Polym.* 151: 1220–1226.

36 Han, Y.Z., Zhou, C.C., Xu, Y.Y. et al. (2017). High-efficient production of fructo-oligosaccharides from inulin by a two-stage bioprocess using an engineered *Yarrowia lipolytica* strain. *Carbohydr. Polym.* 173: 592–599.

37 Jiang, R., Qiu, Y., Huang, W. et al. (2019). One-step bioprocess of inulin to product inulo-oligosaccharides using *Bacillus subtilis* secreting an extracellular endo-inulinase. *Appl. Biochem. Biotechnol.* 187: 116–128.

38 Wang, P., Ma, J., Zhang, Y. et al. (2016). Efficient secretory overexpression of endoinulinase in *Escherichia coli* and the production of inulooligosaccharides. *Appl. Biochem. Biotechnol.* 179: 880–894.

39 Takur, S., Khan, A.A., and Azmi, W. (2020). Potential of oligosaccharides from inulin in human nutrition and health. *Ann. Phytomed.* 2020 (9): 141–146.

40 Zhengyu, J., Jing, W., Bo, J., and Xueming, X. (2005). Production of inulooligosaccharides by endoinulinases from *Aspergillus ficuum*. *Food Res. Int.* 38: 301–308.

41 Singh, S.P., Jadaun, J.S., Narnoliya, L.K., and Pandey, A. (2017). Prebiotic oligosaccharides: special focus on fructooligosaccharides, its biosynthesis and bioactivity. *Appl. Biochem. Biotechnol.* 183: 613–635.

42 Das, D., Bhat, M.R., and Selvaraj, R. (2019). Review of inulinase production using solid-state fermentation. *Ann. Microbiol.* 69: 201–209.

43 Singh, R., Singh, R., and Yadav, M. (2013). Molecular and biochemical characterization of a new endoinulinase producing bacterial strain of *Bacillus safensis* AS-08. *Biologia* 68: 1028–1033.

44 Gavrailov, S. and Ivanova, V. (2016). Effects of nitrogen and carbon sources on the production of inulinase from strain *Bacillus* sp. SG113. *Acta Sci. Nat.* 3: 68–73.

45 Singh, R.S., Chauhan, K., and Kennedy, J.F. (2017). A panorama of bacterial inulinases: production, purification, characterization and industrial applications. *Int. J. Biol. Macromol.* 96: 312–322.

46 Laowklom, N., Chantanaphan, R., and Pinphanichakarn, P. (2012). Production, purification and characterization of inulinase from a newly isolated *Streptomyces* sp. CP01. *Nat. Resour.* 03: 137–144.

47 Abd El Aty, A.A., Wehaidy, H.R., and Mostafa, F.A. (2014). Optimization of inulinase production from low cost substrates using Plackett–Burman and Taguchi methods. *Carbohydr. Polym.* 102: 261–268.

48 Chen, H.Q., Chen, X.M., Chen, T.X. et al. (2011). Extraction optimization of inulinase obtained by solid state fermentation of *Aspergillus ficuum* JNSP5-06. *Carbohydr. Polym.* 85: 446–451.

49 Gill, P.K., Manhas, R.K., and Singh, P. (2006). Hydrolysis of inulin by immobilized thermostable extracellular exoinulinase from *Aspergillus fumigatus*. *J. Food Eng.* 76: 369–375.

50 Garuba, E.O. and Onilude, A. (2018). Immobilization of thermostable exo-inulinase from mutant thermophilic *Aspergillus tamarii*-U4 using kaolin clay and its application in inulin hydrolysis. *J. Genet. Eng. Biotechnol.* 16: 341–346.

51 Trivedi, S., Divecha, J., and Shah, A. (2012). Optimization of inulinase production by a newly isolated *Aspergillus tubingensis* CR16 using low cost substrates. *Carbohydr. Polym.* 90: 483–490.

52 Singh, R.S., Chauhan, K., Kaur, R., and Kaur, R. (2018). Inulinase production in shake-flask fermentations from *Mucor circinelloides* BGPUP-9. *J. Appl. Biol. Biotechnol.* 6: 18–25.

53 Sheng, J., Chi, Z., Li, J. et al. (2007). Inulinase production by the marine yeast *Cryptococcus aureus* G7a and inulin hydrolysis by the crude inulinase. *Process Biochem.* 42: 805–811.

54 Sokolenko, G.G. and Karpechenko, N.A. (2015). Expression of inulinase genes in the yeasts *Saccharomyces cerevisiae* and *Kluyveromyces marxianus*. *Mikrobiologiia* 84: 37–42.

55 Tasar, O.C., Erdal, S., and Algur, O.F. (2015). Utilization of leek (*Allium ampeloprasum* var. porrum) for inulinase production. *Prep. Biochem. Biotechnol.* 45: 596–604.

56 Zhao, C.H., Cui, W., Liu, X.Y. et al. (2010). Expression of inulinase gene in the oleaginous yeast *Yarrowia lipolytica* and single cell oil production from inulin-containing materials. *Metab. Eng.* 12: 510–517.

57 Bao, M., Niu, C., Xu, X. et al. (2019). Identification, soluble expression, and characterization of a novel endo-inulinase from *Lipomyces starkeyi* NRRL Y-11557. *Int. J. Biol. Macromol.* 137: 537–544.

58 da S Pereira, A., CPL, S., Moraes, L. et al. (2021). Polymers as encapsulating agents and delivery vehicles of enzymes. *Polymers* 13: 4061–4088.

59 Mohamed, T.M., El-Souod, S.M., Ali, E.M. et al. (2014). Immobilization and characterization of inulinase from *Ulocladium atrum* on nonwoven fabrics. *J. Biosci.* 39: 785–793.

60 Awad, G.E., Wehaidy, H.R., Abd El Aty, A.A., and Hassan, M.E. (2017). A novel alginate–CMC gel beads for efficient covalent inulinase immobilization. *Colloid. Polym. Sci.* 295: 495–506.

61 Missau, J., Scheid, A.J., Foletto, E.L. et al. (2014). Immobilization of commercial inulinase on alginate–chitosan beads. *Sustainable Chem. Processes* 2: 1–6.

62 Danial, E.N., Elnashar, M.M., and Awad, G.E. (2010). Immobilized inulinase on grafted alginate beads prepared by the one-step and the two-steps methods. *Ind. Eng. Chem. Res.* 49: 3120–3125.

63 Li, X., Zhang, Q., Wang, W., and Yang, S.T. (2021). A novel inulin-mediated ethanol precipitation method for separating endo-inulinase from inulinases for inulooligosaccharides production from inulin. *Front. Bioeng. Biotechnol.* 9: 679720.

64 Naidoo, K., Kumar, A., Sharma, V. et al. (2015). Purification and characterization of an endoinulinase from *Xanthomonas campestris* pv. *phaseoli* KM 24 mutant. *Food Technol. Biotechnol.* 53: 146–153.

65 Durieux, A., Fougnies, C., Jacobs, H., and Simon, J.P. (2001). Metabolism of chicory fructooligosaccharides by bifidobacteria. *Biotechnol. Lett* 23: 1523–1527.

66 Rezende, E.S.V., Lima, G.C., and Naves, M.M.V. (2021). Dietary fibers as beneficial microbiota modulators: a proposed classification by prebiotic categories. *Nutrition* 89: 111217.

67 Costa, G., Vasconcelos, Q., Abreu, G. et al. (2020). Changes in nutrient absorption in children and adolescents caused by fructans, especially fructooligosaccharides and inulin. *Arch. Pediatr.* 27: 166–169.

68 Zhu, D., Yan, Q., Liu, J. et al. (2019). Can functional oligosaccharides reduce the risk of diabetes mellitus? *FASEB J.* 33: 11655–11667.

69 Meyer, D. and Stasse-Wolthuis, M. (2009). The bifidogenic effect of inulin and oligofructose and its consequences for gut health. *Eur. J. Clin. Nutr.* 63: 1277–1289.

70 Sazawal, S., Dhingra, U., Hiremath, G. et al. (2010). Prebiotic and probiotic fortified milk in prevention of morbidities among children: community-based, randomized, double-blind, controlled trial. *PLoS One* 5: e12164.

71 Mazraeh, R., Azizi-Soleiman, F., Jazayeri, S.M.H.M., and Noori, S.M.A. (2019). Effect of inulin-type fructans in patients undergoing cancer treatments: a systematic review. *Pak. J. Med. Sci.* 3: 575–580.

72 Mahdavi, M., Laforest-Lapointe, I., and Masse, E. (2021). Preventing colorectal cancer through prebiotics. *Microorganisms* 9: 1325–1340.

73 Fernandez, J., Ledesma, E., Monte, J. et al. (2019). Traditional processed meat products re-designed towards inulin-rich functional foods reduce polyps in two colorectal cancer animal models. *Sci. Rep.* 9: 14783–14799.

74 Gautam, S.P., Bundela, P.S., Pandey, A.K. et al. (2012). Diversity of cellulolytic microbes and the biodegradation of municipal solid waste by a potential strain. *Int. J. Microbiol.* 2012: 325907.

75 Chi, Z.M., Zhang, T., Cao, T.S. et al. (2011). Biotechnological potential of inulin for bioprocesses. *Bioresour. Technol.* 102: 4295–4303.

76 Gao, J., Yuan, W., Li, Y. et al. (2015). Transcriptional analysis of *Kluyveromyces marxianus* for ethanol production from inulin using consolidated bioprocessing technology. *Biotechnol. Biofuels* 8: 1–17.

77 Yang, F., Liu, Z., Dong, W. et al. (2014). Ethanol production using a newly isolated *Saccharomyces cerevisiae* strain directly assimilating intact inulin with a high degree of polymerization. *Biotechnol. Appl. Biochem.* 61: 418–425.

78 Yang, F., Liu, Z.C., Wang, X. et al. (2015). Invertase Suc2-mediated inulin catabolism is regulated at the transcript level in *Saccharomyces cerevisiae*. *Microb. Cell Fact.* 14: 59–68.

79 Wang, S.A. and Li, F.L. (2013). Invertase SUC2 is the key hydrolase for inulin degradation in *Saccharomyces cerevisiae*. *Appl. Environ. Microbiol.* 79: 403–406.

80 Wang, Z.P., Fu, W.J., Xu, H.M., and Chi, Z.M. (2014). Direct conversion of inulin into cell lipid by an inulinase-producing yeast *Rhodosporidium toruloides* 2F5. *Bioresour. Technol.* 161: 131–136.

81 Sarchami, T. and Rehmann, L. (2015). Optimizing acid hydrolysis of *Jerusalem artichoke*-derived inulin for fermentative butanol production. *Bioenergy Res.* 8: 1148–1157.

82 Sarchami, T. and Rehmann, L. (2014). Optimizing enzymatic hydrolysis of inulin from *Jerusalem artichoke* tubers for fermentative butanol production. *Biomass Bioenergy* 69: 175–182.

30

Characterization of Phytopathogen's Tannase as a Virulence Factor

Richa Naredi[1] *and Kanti P. Sharma*[2]

[1] *Mody University of Science and Technology, Department of Biosciences, School of Liberal Arts and Sciences, Lakshmangarh, Sikar, Rajasthan 332311, India*
[2] *Central University of Haryana, Department of Nutrition Biology, School of Interdisciplinary and Applied Sciences, Jant-Pali, Mahendergarh, Haryana 123031, India*

30.1 Introduction

Earth's maximum biomass is formed by the plants. They are primary producers in the food web; thus, many animals depend on them for food and also for shelter and oxygen. An increase in biotic and abiotic stress harshly affects the crop yield [1, 2]. Biotic stress conditions cause plant diseases, resulting in a loss in crop productivity. This finally results in problem of hunger and starvation, especially in developing and underdeveloped nations. Virulent pathogens, susceptible plant hosts, and the presence of favorable conditions for pathogen growth are among the major factors responsible for the disease occurrences in plants. Thus, the demand for the protection of plant crops for better food quality and quantity becomes a major concern for the scientific community [3].

Virulence is the ability of pathogenic microorganisms to enter the host body, replicate their eluding host immune system and infect the host to cause disease [4]. Pathogens attach themselves to the plant surface and then penetrate into it. Hereby, they reproduce and assemble and finally exit by leaving the host infected or dead. Cell-wall-degrading enzymes and host-specific or non-host-specific toxins are released by the pathogens. These, along with host immune system damaging or signaling mechanism disturbing pathogen proteins, help the pathogen in establishing disease successfully in the plants. Enzymes like cellulase, pectinase, or xylanase are virulence factors in plant pathogen bacteria like *Erwinia*, *Agrobacterium*, *Xanthomonas*, *Clavibacter*, etc. These enzymes help the bacteria to degrade cell walls of plants. [5]. Like pectic enzyme degrades pectin present in plant's primary cell walls [6]. Pectinase in plants is produced during the process of ripening, but some microbes form pectinase when they attack the plants or the fruits [7].

Microbial Enzymes: Production, Purification, and Industrial Applications, First Edition.
Edited by Dinesh Yadav, Pankaj Chowdhary, Gautam Anand, and Rajarshi Kumar Gaur.

Plants produce a variety of secondary metabolites such as flavonoids, lignins, alkaloids, phenols, anthocyanins, etc., which synergistically help plant's defense system against microorganisms, pests and herbivores [8, 9]. Tannins are also one of the secondary metabolites and help in the defense mechanism [10]. These are water-soluble compounds present universally in the plant kingdom. These are toxic elements for microorganisms because of their ability to precipitate proteins, carbohydrate, and other macromolecules. However, literature reports some few microorganisms like *Pseudomonas*, *Pantonea*, *Lactobacillus*, *Bacillus*, and *Enterobacter*. Fungi (*Trichoderma*, *Aspergillus*, *Rhizopus*, etc. and yeasts use tannase to protect them from the harmful effects of the tannins [11].

Tannase enzyme is also known as Tannin acyl hydrolase (EC 3.1.1.20). It belongs to the superfamily of esterases and is active in both acidic and basic pH at temperatures ranging from 25 to 60 °C. It is well known for detannification of products like fruit juices, beers, oaknut wines, and soft drinks like coffee [12]. Tannase is used to make instant tea and coffee, which are soluble in cold water [13]. It has been reported that green tea produced in the presence of tannase enzyme is healthier and has more antioxidant properties, and helps in removing more carcinogenic and mutagenic from the preserved foods than the normal green tea [14].

Inhibition of pathogens is essential. Natural and chemical inhibitors both contain the extracted molecules that inhibit the interaction of plants and microbes, but the natural inhibitors have more qualities as they are easy to degrade, cheaper in rate, easily available, no side effects, etc. India is a hub of many medicinal plants. The most common plants are *Azadirachta indica* (Neem), *Ocimum tenuiflorum* (Tulsi), *Withania somnifera* (Ashwagandha), and *Zingiber officinale* (Ginger) [15]. These are known for their antimicrobial, anti-inflammatory, anticarcinogenic, and antioxidant properties, among others. Neem leaves have many properties [16] and are very effective as inhibitor, as earlier, they have also been used as an inhibitor to control collar rot disease [17]. Due to the increasing pollution and nonbiodegradable fertilizers, pesticides, and herbicides, soil quality is deteriorating day-by-day. Thus, there is an urgent demand for products that can act as pesticides as well as improve the quality of soil. If not, then not degrade its quality. Bio-pesticides and herbicides made from medicinal plants can replace chemical-based products. Neem-based bio-pesticides are widely utilized [18].

Tannase is an enzyme causing hydrolysis of tannins and thus might be responsible for the dilution of plant defense. Literature reveals that tannase of microorganisms was explored for its various applications in the food and beverages industry. Literary reports about the use of tannase of pathogens as a virulence factor are scanty or nil. Thus, the present study was undertaken to characterize tannase as a virulence factor in pathogens and identification of its inhibitors to improve plant tolerance against phytopathogens with the following objectives:

- To isolate microorganisms for tannase activity from diseased plant.
- To estimate the pathogenicity of the isolate microorganisms.
- To identify natural inhibitors of pathogens

30.2 Material and Methods

The study was focused to characterize tannase enzymes of pathogens as a virulence factor. It includes a collection of disease samples from plant sources, isolation of bacteria, examining tannase activity among the isolates, checking of pathogenicity of tannase-positive isolates, followed by identification of natural inhibitors against pathogen's and their tannase activity.

30.2.1 Isolation of Bacteria

Diseased fruits from Amla (*Phyllanthus emblica*), Orange (*Citrus sinensis*), and Jujube (*Ziziphus mauritiana*) were used as a sample to isolate microorganisms. Bacterial isolation was performed by following the method of Tripathi et al. [19]. The enrichment process was also followed for the isolation of bacteria. The following medium (Table 30.1) was used for the isolation of tannase-producing plant pathogens. The medium contains tannic acid as a sole source of carbon.

After plating the sample on a tannic acid agar medium, plates were kept in an incubator for 48 hours at 37 °C for bacterial growth. The observed growth was checked for homogeneity through Gram staining and the mixed culture was purified by normal and quadrant streaking. Isolates were further checked for their growth and amount of tannase activity in tannic acid broth medium (Table 30.2).

Table 30.1 Tannic acid agar medium composition (100 ml).

Components	Amount (g)
Potassium di-hydrogen phosphate	0.05
Di-potassium hydrogen phosphate	0.05
Magnesium sulfate	0.05
Ammonium nitrate	1
Tannic acid	0.1
Agar agar	1.8

Table 30.2 Tannic acid broth medium composition (100 ml).

Components	Amount (g)
Potassium di-hydrogen phosphate	0.05
Di-potassium hydrogen phosphate	0.05
Magnesium sulfate	0.05
Ammonium nitrate	1
Tannic acid	0.1

A loop-full bacterial culture was inoculated in tannic acid broth medium for quantification of tannase activity. The culture was grown for 24 hours in a shaking incubator at 120 rpm at 37 °C.

30.2.2 Bacterial Growth and Enzyme Assay

The bacterial growth was evaluated on the basis of optical density (600 nm) and weight of the pellet. In an Eppendorf tube, 1 ml of the culture was taken and centrifuged at 5000 rpm for 5 minutes. The pellet's wet weight was recorded. Tannase enzyme activity was determined by the method given by Sharma et al. [20]. Culture supernatant was used as a source of the enzyme. About 50 ml of grown culture was centrifuged at 5000 rpm for 15 minutes. Resting cells were used for the pathogenicity test.

30.2.3 Pathogenicity Test

Surface sterilization and pathogenicity test were conducted as described by Ruinelli et al. [21] and Bedford et al. [22] respectively. The leaves of *P. emblica*, *C. sinensis*, and *Z. mauritiana* were surface sterilized by washing them under running tap water for five minutes followed by rinsing with 70% ethanol for one minute. Leaves were disinfected by dipping into 6.5% sodium hypochlorite solution for five minutes followed by washing twice in sterile distilled water for one minute each. The washed leaves were kept for air drying on facing abaxial side upward under aseptic conditions. The resting cells were suspended in 0.8% potassium chloride (KCl). Tannase-positive bacterial isolates from *P. emblica*, *C. sinensis*, and *Z. mauritiana* were used for the pathogenicity test and to know the effect of inhibition of tannase and its correlation with pathogen's virulence. The leaves were pricked with the help of a sterile needle. The isolate's resting cell suspension was taken in a sterile 2-ml syringe and inoculated in leaves through the prick at ten different places by applying a little pressure against the leaves. The ability to cause disease by the isolated pathogen is determined by determining the pathogenicity score (amount of necrosis or no necrotic area).

30.2.4 Tannase Inhibition and Virulence

It was performed by following the method given by Iyanuloluwa, et al. [23] *A. indica* (Neem) leaves were taken to look for inhibitors. Neem leaves were plucked and dried overnight in a hot air oven at 70 °C and grinded in a laboratory blender. The powder was mixed (1 : 6 ratio) with sterile distilled water, heated to boil, and cooled. The aqueous extract was filtered through Whatman filter paper 1 and stored in 4 °C till used. To know the effect of plant's extract on tannase enzyme activity, it was mixed equally with the citrate buffer (125 μl + 125 μl), and tannase activity was determined as done earlier. Pathogenicity test was done as earlier to know the inhibitory effect of aqueous plant's leaf extract on disease occurrences. Sterile syringe was taken, which was filled with resting cells suspended in 5 ml of 0.8% KCl solution and inoculated in Amla, Orange, and Jujube leaves and incubation was done on 0.5% water agar mixed with aqueous *A. indica* leaves extract (1 : 1 ratio) in a sealed petri plate sealed at 25 °C for a week.

30.3 Results and Discussion

Today's world population crossed 7 billion; it is very requisite to fulfill the great requirement of food. It is our foremost work to identify and demolish pathogens before they harm the crops. Some of the fruit plants are expensive enough to lose even a single crop. On average, losses of fruit crops in developing countries are around 22.5% per year [24]. So it is very important to avoid the pathogens and their interaction with plant molecules.

Tannase enzyme, one of the factors causing pathogenicity, degrades tannin. Tannins are the secondary metabolite that forms 10% of the dry weight of tree leaves. Since its presence in leaves in great amounts and its toxic nature for insects and other microorganisms, tannins are known for their plant defense mechanisms. This is how tannins can defend plants, but some pathogens are resistant to tannins due to the presence of tannase enzymes.

Pathogens like bacteria, fungi, and yeast form the tannase enzyme continuously and in great amounts which degrade tannin or tannic acid, making it easier for pathogens to attack the plant immune system. Keeping plants protected from pathogens can be done in various ways. Plant-based medicines or extracts can have the untapped potential to avoid the interaction of pathogens with plants and to cure diseases.

The study was planned to characterize tannase as a virulence factor and identification of its inhibitors from plant sources. It included isolates of microorganisms from disease plants and their parts followed by screening with reference to tannase enzyme activity in them. Tannase producer microorganisms were subjected to a pathogenicity test. Further, the potential of *A. indica* leaves aqueous extract was explored for its potential to reduce the occurrences of plant diseases by inhibiting the tannase enzyme of plant pathogens. It showed the following result.

Upon plating and followed by incubation, petri plates showed the growth of microorganisms (Table 30.3). Petri plate inoculated with *P. emblica* and *C. sinensis* diseased fruits sample showed growth of Gram-negative bacteria of coccobacilli shape and named as isolate A and B, respectively. The petri plate inoculated with *Z. mauritiana* diseased fruit samples showed Gram-negative bacilli and named as isolate C. Literature also suggests the role of various Gram-negative bacteria as causative agents in the disease of the above plants [25–28].

Table 30.4 shows the growth of isolates in tannic acid broth medium. In this medium tannic acid acts as a sole source of carbon. The growth of the above bacteria in tannic acid broth medium is attributed to the presence of their ability to use tannic acid as a sole source of carbon. It is due to the production of tannase enzyme. Sharma [10] suggested the role of plant pathogens to use their tannase enzyme to overcome the toxicity of plant tannins.

Table 30.3 Morphological characteristics of the bacterial isolates from various plant sources.

S. no.	Plant source	Gram character	Shape	Isolate name
1	*Phyllanthus emblica*	Negative	Coccobacilli	A
2	*Citrus sinensis*	Negative	Coccobacilli	B
3	*Ziziphus mauritiana*	Negative	Bacilli	C

Table 30.4 Growth of Isolates.

S. no.	Isolate	Isolates source	OD_{660}	Weight (wet) of the pellet (g)	Colony forming units/ml (cfu/ml)
1.	A	*Phyllanthus emblica*	0.745	0.020	8690
2.	B	*Citrus sinensis*	0.768	0.020	8980
3.	C	*Ziziphus mauritiana*	0.790	0.031	9570

30.4 Correlation Between Inhibition of Tannase Activity and Pathogenicity

Further to know the correlation between tannase activity of pathogen and its virulence, tannase activity was determined in the presence or absence of *A. indica* leaf extract. The experiments resulted in a decrease in enzyme activity (Table 30.5). It may be due to the presence of tannase inhibitor molecule in the plant leaves extract. In addition to the above, the amount of necrosis was also reduced when the bacterial isolates were subjected to a pathogenicity test in the presence of plant leaf extract. This suggests the plant leaf extract may possess an inhibitory molecule that affects both tannase activity and pathogen's virulence. Literature also reports the antimicrobial activity of *A. indica* leaf extract in the inhibition of bacterial growth and reproduction [29].

Table 30.5 Comparison of tannase activity with or without inhibitor.

S. no.	Isolate	Isolates source	Tannase activity (micro mol/ml/minute)	Tannase activity with inhibitor (micro mol/ml/minute)
1.	A	*Phyllanthus emblica*	0.80	0.70
2.	B	*Citrus sinensis*	0.71	0.61
3.	C	*Ziziphus mauritiana*	0.75	0.51

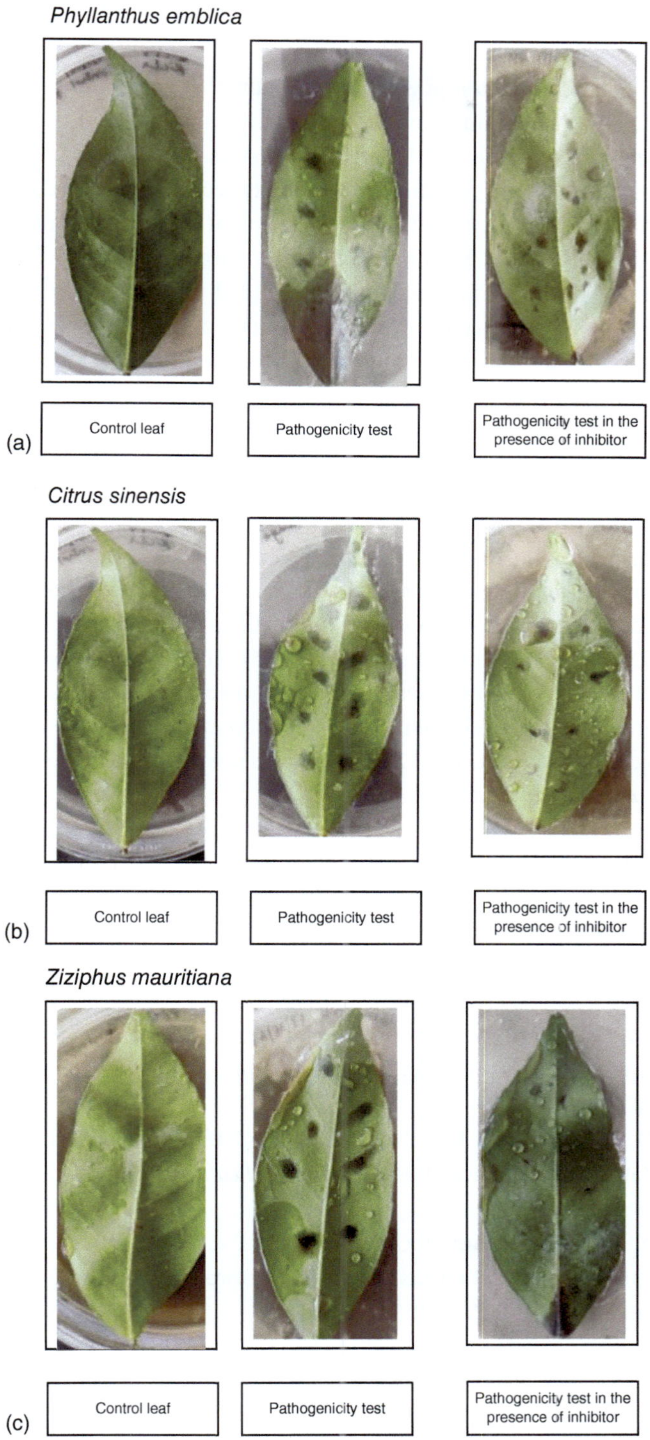
Phyllanthus emblica
Control leaf
Pathogenicity test
Pathogenicity test in the presence of inhibitor
(a)
Citrus sinensis
Control leaf
Pathogenicity test
Pathogenicity test in the presence of inhibitor
(b)
Ziziphus mauritiana
Control leaf
Pathogenicity test
Pathogenicity test in the presence of inhibitor
(c)

30.5 Conclusion

In the present study, an attempt was made to show that tannase enzyme is a virulent factor in plant pathogens and how we can inhibit pathogen's ability to cause disease by inhibiting tannase activity of them. The results of the study demonstrate that the activity of tannase enzyme and pathogenicity score was reduced in the presence of plant leaf extract. Thus, it may be concluded plant leaf extract contains molecules that work as inhibitors of bacterial isolates' tannase activity and also inhibit their ability to cause disease. Thus, it can be concluded that inhibition of tannase may inhibit phytopathogen's virulence and thus tannase of them may work as a virulence factor and *A. indica*'s leaves aqueous extract can be utilized to reduce the disease occurrences by reducing pathogen's tannase enzyme activity.

References

1 Mahalingam, R. (2015). Consideration of combined stress: a crucial paradigm for improving multiple stress tolerance in plants. In: *Combined Stresses in Plants* (ed. R. Mahalingam), 1–25. Springer International Publishing.

2 Ramegowda, V. and Senthil Kumar, M. (2015). The interactive effects of simultaneous biotic and abiotic stresses on plants: mechanistic understanding from drought and pathogen combination. *J. Plant Physiol.* 176: 47–54.

3 Strange, R.N. and Scott, P.R. (2005). Plant disease: a threat to global food security. *Annu. Rev. Phytopathol.* 43: 83–116.

4 Cross, A.S. (2008). What is a virulence factor? *Crit. Care* 12: 196.

5 Aguilar-Marcelino, L., Mendoza-de-Gives, P., Al-Ani, L.K.T. et al. (2020). Using molecular techniques applied to beneficial microorganisms as biotechnological tools for controlling agricultural plant pathogens and pest. In: *Molecular Aspects of Plant Beneficial Microbes in Agriculture* (ed. V. Sharma, R. Salwan, and L. Tawfeeq), 333–349. USA: Academic Press.

6 Hoondal, G., Tiwari, R., Tewari, R. et al. (2002). Microbial alkaline pectinases and their industrial applications: a review. *Appl. Microbiol. Biotechnol.* 59: 409–418.

7 Silva, D., Tokuioshi, K., Da Silva, M.E. et al. (2005). Production of pectinase by solid state fermentation with *Penicillium viridicatum* RFC3. *Process Biochem.* 40: 2885–2889.

8 Ribeiro, I.C.D.O., Mariano, E.G.A., Careli, R.T. et al. (2018). Plants of the Cerrado with antimicrobial effects against *Staphylococcus* spp. and *Escherichia coli* from cattle. *BMC Vet. Res.* 14: 32.

9 Samoilova, Z., Smirnova, G., Muzyka, N., and Oktyabrsky, O. (2014). Medicinal plant extracts variously modulate susceptibility of *Escherichia coli* to different antibiotics. *Microbiol. Res.* 169: 307–313.

10 Sharma, K.P. (2019). Tannin degradation by phytopathogen's tannase: a Plant's defense perspective. *Biocatal. Agric. Biotechnol.* 21: 101342.

11 Sharma, K.P. and John, P.J. (2011). Purification and characterization of Tannase and Tannase gene from *Enterobacter* sp. *Process Biochem.* 46: 240–244.

12 Sharma, S., Agarwal, L., and Saxena, R.K. (2007). Statistical optimization for tannase production from *Aspergillus niger* under submerged fermentation. *Indian J. Microbiol.* 47: 132–138.

13 Thiyonila, B., Kannan, M., Reneeta, N.P. et al. (2020). Influence of Tannase from *Serratia marcescens* strain IMBL5 on enhancing antioxidant properties of green tea. *Biocatal. Agric. Biotechnol.* 27: 101675.

14 Lu, M.J. and Chen, C. (2007). Enzymatic tannase treatment of green tea increases in vitro inhibitory activity against N-nitrosation of dimethylamine. *Process Biochem.* 42: 1285–1290.

15 Mashhadi, N.S., Ghiasvand, R., Askari, G. et al. (2013). Antioxidative and inti-inflammatory effects of ginger in health and physical activity: review of current evidence. *Int. J. Prev. Med.* 4: S36–S42.

16 Subapriya, R. and Nagini, S. (2005). Medicinal properties of neem leaves: a review. *Curr. Med. Chem.* 5: 149–146.

17 Khan, I.H., Javaid, A., AI-Taie, A.H., and Ahmed, D. (2020). Use of neem leaves as soil amendment for the control of collar rot disease of chickpea. *Egypt. J. Biol. Pest Control* 30: 98.

18 Chaudhary, S., Kanwar, R.K., Sehgal, A. et al. (2017). Progress on *Azadirachta indica* based biopesticides in replacing synthetic toxic pesticides. *Plant Biotechnol.* 2017: 3389.

19 Tripathi, A.D., Sharma, K., and Lakshmi, B. (2016). Study on tannase producing *Bacillus megaterium* isolated from tannery effluent. *Int. J. Adv. Res. Biol. Sci.* 3: 28–35.

20 Sharma, S., Bhat, T.K., and Dawra, R.K. (2000). Spectrophotometric method for assay of tannase using rhodamine. *Anal. Biochem.* 279: 85–89.

21 Ruinelli, M., Blom, J., Smits, T.H.M., and Pothier, J.F. (2019). Comparative genomics and pathogenicity potential of members of the *Pseudomonas syringae* species complex on *Prunus* spp. *BMC Genomics* 20: 172.

22 Bedford, K.E., Sholberg, P.L., and Kappel, F. (2003). Use of detached leaf bioassay for screening sweet cherry cultivars for bacterial canker resistance. *Genet. Breed. Tree Fruits Nuts* 622: 365.

23 Iyanuloluwa, O., Adamu, K.Y., and Audu, J.A. (2019). Antibacterial and antifungal activities of aqueous leaves extract of some medicinal plants. *GSC Biol. Pharm. Sci.* 09: 62–69.

24 Global Food Losses and Food Waste (2011). Extent, Causes and prevention. Food and Agriculture Organization Düsseldorf, Germany.

25 Hasan, M.F., Islam, M.A., and Sikdar, B. (2020). First report of *Serratia marcescens* associated with black rot of *Citrus sinensis* fruit, and evaluation of its biological control measures in Bangladesh. *F1000Research* 9: 1371.

26 Myung, I., Moon, S.Y., Jeong, I.H. et al. (2010). A new disease, bacterial fruit rot of jujube, caused by *Xanthomonas arboricola* in Korea. *New Dis. Rep.* 22: 12.

27 Wu, T., Zhang, J., Zhang, W. et al. (2011). Occurrence and control of jujube-fruit shrink disease in Hami area. *Acta Agric. Jiangxi* 6: 28.

28 Zhang, C., Liu, M.J., Zhou, J.Y., and Zhao, J. (2008). Advances in research on Chinese jujube fruit shrink disease. *Hebei J. Forestry Orchard Res.* 23: 62–65.

29 Harjai, K., Bala, A., Gupta, R.K., and Sharma, R. (2013). Leaf extract of *Azadirachta indica* (Neem): a potential antibiofilm agent for *Pseudomonas aeruginosa*. *Pathog. Dis.* 69: 62–65.

31

Mycozyme-based Functional Oligosaccharides

Suresh Nath[1], Hemant K. Rawat[2], Aamir Khan[2], and Naveen Kango[1]

[1] *Dr. Harisingh Gour Vishwavidyalaya (A Central University), Enzyme Technology and Molecular Catalysis Laboratory, Department of Microbiology, University Road, Sagar, Madhya Pradesh 470003, India*
[2] *Dr. Harisingh Gour Vishwavidyalaya (A Central University), Department of Zoology, University Road, Sagar, Madhya Pradesh 470003, India*

31.1 Introduction

In the human gut, certain indigestible carbohydrate polymers escape absorption and undergo bacterial fermentation. This impacts the gut microbiome through altered bacterial composition and metabolic activities, even leading to the production of beneficial byproducts like short-chain fatty acids. The term "prebiotic" was first coined in [1] by Gibson and Roberfroid. These prebiotics are primarily nondigestible oligosaccharides (NDOs) sourced naturally or enzymatically manufactured. Due to the complexity of chemically synthesizing NDOs with their multitude of reactive hydroxyl groups, enzymatic production is the preferred method for large-scale production. Recently, there has been a growing interest in the use of mycozymes, derived from fungi, for generating health-promoting prebiotic oligosaccharides and nutraceuticals [2]. Compared to chemical methods, enzymes offer superior catalytic properties like high selectivity, specificity, mild operating conditions, efficient turnover, and biodegradability. Longstanding misconceptions about enzymes—expensive, fragile, and inefficient—are being shattered with the rise of their mass production through diverse fungal species. Not only are these biocatalysts readily available, but they offer a remarkable environmental advantage: cleaner, less toxic waste compared to traditional chemical processes. This makes them particularly valuable for the production of prebiotics, a class of beneficial carbohydrates like fructooligosaccharides (FOS), inulin, and xylooligosaccharides (XOS) (Figure 31.1). Notably, enzymatic bioprocesses, powered by fungal enzymes, have become the preferred method for industrially producing these essential prebiotics (Table 31.1).

Obtaining oligosaccharides typically involves extracting them from natural sources, chemically synthesizing them, or using enzymatic methods. While extracting FOS from plants is one option, the process can be cumbersome and time-consuming, with the final products composition fluctuating based on external factors.

Microbial Enzymes: Production, Purification, and Industrial Applications, First Edition.
Edited by Dinesh Yadav, Pankaj Chowdhary, Gautam Anand, and Rajarshi Kumar Gaur.

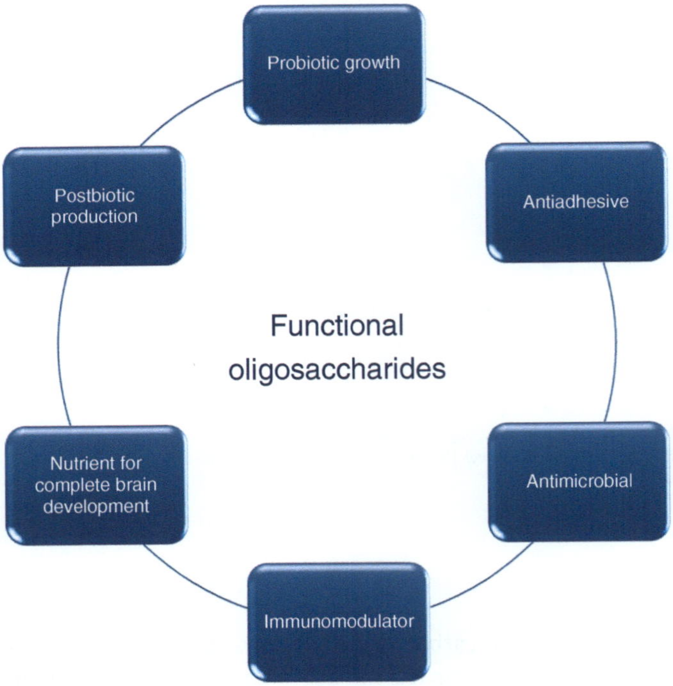

Figure 31.1 Functional properties of prebiotic oligosaccharides.

31.1.1 Chemical Synthesis

While chemical synthesis methods like O-trichloroacetimidate, thioglycosides, modified Koenigs–Knorr, tritylcyanothylidene condensation, and the orthoester method ensure consistent oligosaccharide composition, their inability to manipulate specific glycosidic linkages, stereochemistry, and regioselectivity calls for improved methodologies for precise oligosaccharide construction [23].

31.1.2 Enzymatic Method

Chemical approaches face various limitations in oligosaccharide generation, prompting a shift toward enzymatic bioprocesses as a highly promising alternative. Numerous enzymes, including fructosyltransferase, inulinase, mannanase, xylanase, β-galactosidase, and cellulase, play crucial roles in producing FOS, inulooligosaccharides (IOS), mannooligosaccharides (MOS), XOS, galactooligosaccharides (GOS), and chitooligosaccharides (COS), respectively (Table 31.2). The majority of prebiotic oligosaccharides are synthesized using enzymes classified under glycoside hydrolase (GH), glycosyltransferase (GT), and transglycosylase (TG) classes [24]. GH enzymes participate in the hydrolysis of acetal linkages in carbohydrates or between carbohydrates and noncarbohydrate moieties. GT enzymes facilitate the transfer of glycosidic moieties from activated donors to acceptor residues, with subclassification into inverting or retaining based on whether the

Table 31.1 Mycozyme producing functional oligosaccharides.

Functional oligosaccharides	Mycozymes	Fungus	Significance	References
Cello-oligosaccharides	*Endo*-glucanase	*Neurospora crassa* OR74A	HPLC analysis of the hydrolytic products confirmed the *endo*-β(1,4) mode of action of the enzyme. Moreover, such a pattern revealed that NcCel45A cannot hydrolyze efficiently oligosaccharides with a degree of polymerization smaller than six	[3]
	β-Glucosidase with cellobiohydrolase activity	*Rhizomucor miehei* NRRL 5382	Laminarin a polysaccharide made up of β-1,3-glucan with β-1,6 branches, was efficiently hydrolyzed	[4]
	β-Glucosidase	*Rhizomucor miehei* NRRL 5282	The enzyme hydrolyzed oligosaccharides having β- and α-(1,4) and β-(1,2) glycosidic linkages, such as cellobiose, lactose, maltose, and sophorose, respectively, but had no activity on cellulose, laminaribiose, sucrose, salicin, amygdalin, laminarin, and trehalose. No hydrolysis was detected on soluble polysaccharides with β-(1,3) glycosidic linkages (amygdalin and laminarin)	[5]
	Lytic polysaccharide monooxygenase	*Malbranchea cinnamomea*	High-performance anion exchange chromatography and mass spectrometry confirmed that purified protein was active against an array of cellulosic (avicel, carboxy methyl cellulose) and hemicellulosic (birch wood xylan, wheat arabinoxylan and rye arabinoxylan) substrates, releasing both oxidized and unoxidized cello-oligosaccharide and xylo-oligosaccharide products respectively	[6]
	Swollenin	*Trichoderma reesei*	Swollenin (SWOI), a protein recognized based on its sequence similarity with plant expansins, have activity on substrates containing β-1,4 glucosidic bonds, i.e., carboxymethyl cellulose, hydroxyethyl cellulose, and β-glucan and showed cellobiose as the main reaction product	[7]
Xylooligosaccharides	*Endo*-xylanase	*Thermomyces lanuginosus* VAPS-24	The produced XOS showed concentration-dependent antioxidant activities and probiotic growth promotion	[8]
Mannooligosaccharides	*Endo*-mannanase	*Aspergillus quadrilineatus*	MOS showed cytotoxic effect and reduced cell viability of Caco-2 cells. MOS also supported better *Lactobacilli* biofilm formation. *Lactobacilli* effectively fermented MOS to generate acetate and propionate as main short-chain fatty acids. Lactobacilli produced leucine, isoleucine, and valine as branched-chain amino acids	[9]
Galactooligosaccharides	β-Galactosidase	*Aspergillus oryzae*	GOS have been widely proven to have prebiotic properties similar to those oligosaccharides found in human breast milk	[10]
	Gamanase 1.5L and Depol 670L	*Aspergillus niger* and *Trichoderma reesei*	Potato Rhamnogalacturonan (RG) I and its hydrolysates are nondigestible and bifidogenic; however, hydrolysates were more selectively fermented by gut-beneficial bacteria	[11]

(Continued)

Table 31.1 (Continued)

Functional oligosaccharides	Mycozymes	Fungus	Significance	References
Fructooligosaccharides	Fructosyltransferase	*Aspergillus tamarii*	An efficient system for biotransformation of sucrose to fructooligosaccharides (FOS) was obtained using *Aspergillus tamarii* NKRC 1229 mycelial fructosyltransferase (m-FTase)	[12]
	β-Fructofuranosidase	*Aspergillus figiensis*	Increased thermostability of the engineered β-fructofuranosidase enzyme had a markedly beneficial effect on process productivity when producing FOS from sucrose as substrate	[13]
	Endo-inulinase	*Aspergillus tritici*	High substrate concentration, low enzyme dose, and short hydrolytic period justify the efficiency of the developed bioprocess for fructooligosaccharides synthesis from inulin by fungal inulinase	[14]
Pectic-oligosaccharides	Polygalacturonase	*Aspergillus aculeatus*	It could be used as a natural antibacterial agent in the food industry	[15]
	Nongalactosylated polygalacturonase	*Aspergillus niger*	The enzyme membrane reactor built in this study could be used in the conversion of pectin into high-value products, such as oligogalacturonic acid	[16]
	Viscozyme L (Pectinase)	*Aspergillus aculeatus*	Valorize onion skins, an under-utilized agricultural byproduct, into pectic oligosaccharides (POS), compounds with potential health benefits	[17]
	Pectate lyase	*Humicola insolens* Y1	The properties of PLHY1 make it valuable for application in the agro-food industry for the production of pectin oligosaccharides	[18]
	Endo-glucanase	*Chaetomium thermophilum*	CTendo45 is the first reported bifunctional enzyme in glycoside hydrolase family 45 from *C. thermophilum* that is able to hydrolyze both cellulose and pectin	[19]
Chitooligosaccharides	*Endo*-chitinase	*Trichoderma reesei*	*Endo*-chitinase Chit33 specificity on different chitinolytic materials allows the production of unexplored chitooligosaccharides with antioxidant activity	[20]
	Cellulase with chitosanolytic activity	*Trichoderma harzianum*	A two-stage degradation method combining H_2O_2 pretreatment and enzymatic hydrolysis was developed to produce ChOS from chitosan	[21]
	Alginate lyase	*Yarrowia lipolytica*	Green biotechnology for oligosaccharide production from seaweed	[21]
Alginate-oligosaccharides	Glucuronan lyase	*Trichoderma* sp. GL2	*Sinorhizobium meliloti* M5N1CS synthesizes a homopolymer of glucuronic acids β-(1,4) linked and variably C2 and/or C3 O-acetylated. To obtain β-(4,5)-unsaturated oligoglucuronans, various acetylated forms of this bacterial polymer were cleaved by a *Trichoderma* sp. GL2 glucuronan lyase	[22]

Table 31.2 Production strategy of functional oligosaccharides.

Functional oligosaccharides	Mycozymes	Substrate	Assay conditions			Product(s)	References
			T (°C)	pH	Time		
Cellooligosaccharides	*Endo*glucanase	Phosphoric acid swollen cellulose	50	5	1 h	Glc2 and Glc4	[3]
	β-Glucosidase with cellobiohydrolase activity	Glucose, cellobiose	40	5	60 h	Gentiobiose	[4]
	β-Glucosidase	Cellobiose	50	5	24 h	Cellotriose and trace amount of cellotetrose	[5]
	Lytic polysaccharide monooxygenase	Carboxymethyl cellulose	50	5	96 h	Cello oligosaccharides (G2–G8)	[6]
	Swollenin	Barley β-glucan	30	5	24 h	Cellobiose with traces of cellotriose	[7]
Xylooligosaccharides	*Endo*-xylanase	Xylan from corn cobs	45	5	8 h	Xylotriose and xylobiose	[8]
Mannooligosaccharides	*Endo*-mannanase	Defatted copra meal	50	5	1 h	MOS of DP 2-4	[9]
Galactooligosaccharides	β-Galactosidase	Casein whey, Greek yoghurt whey, and concentrated acid whey permeate	55	—	3 h	Glucose, galactose, lactose, DP3, DP4	[10]
	Gamanase 1.5L and Depol 670L	Potato galactan-rich rhamnogalacturonan I	40	5	2 h	GOS of DP 2–6	[11]
Fructooligosaccharides	Fructosyltransferase	Sucrose	20	7	24 h	Nystose and Kestose	[12]
	β-Fructofuranosidase	Sucrose from white and brown sugar, refinery and molasses	62	5	8 h	Oligomers with DP 2-4	[13]
	Endo-inulinase	Inulin	55	5.5	12 h	ketose (GF2), nystose (GF3) and fructofuranosylnystose (GF4)	[14]

(Continued)

Table 31.2 (Continued)

Functional oligosaccharides	Mycozymes	Substrate	Assay conditions			Product(s)	References
			T (°C)	pH	Time		
Pectic-oligosaccharides	Polygalacturonase	Mango peel pectin	60	4.5	1 h	POS of DP (1-4)	[15]
	Nongalactosylated polygalacturonase	Pectin	50	5	10 min	High DP oligosaccharides	[16]
	Viscozyme L (Pectinase)	Pectin from onion skin	45	4.5	15 min	POS of DP (2-4)	[17]
	Pectate lyase	Apple peel powder	37	10	16 h	POS of DP (4-6)	[18]
	Endoglucanase	Pectin	50	4	60 min	Galacturonic acid oligosaccharides	[19]
Chitooligosaccharides	*Endo*-chitinase	Colloidal chitin	45	5.5	30 min	COS DP 1–7	[20]
	Cellulase with chitosanolytic activity	Chitosan	55	5.65	12 h	GlcN DP 1-7	[21]
Alginate-oligosaccharides	Alginate lyase	Sun-dried *Laminaria japonica*	—	—	72 h	AOS DP 2-3	[21]
	Glucuronan lyase	Highly acetylated and deacetylated glucuronans	20	5.5	96 h	Di- and trisaccharide oligoglucuronan	[22]

stereochemistry of the glycosidic bond in the reaction product remains similar to the donor or changes. TGs engage in catalytic reactions similar to GHs, but the hydrolase versus transferase ratio differs among different TGs. The mechanism and biological role of TGs remain indistinguishable [25].

Commercial production of various oligosaccharides employs different enzymes based on the type of glycosidic linkage formation in the resulting oligosaccharide. Biocatalysis demonstrates exceptional performance in prebiotic oligosaccharide generation due to its substrate specificity and the production of pure products. Furthermore, the prebiotic and nutritional properties of oligosaccharides strongly depend on the three-dimensional stereochemistry of the glycosidic bond, a factor uncontrollable through chemical catalysis. Enzymatic oligosaccharide synthesis offers notable advantages, including selectivity, specificity, eco-friendliness, and energy-efficient catalysis with a high turnover number [25]. Additionally, various enzyme engineering approaches, such as immobilization, genetic engineering, codon optimization, and mutagenesis, have been consistently employed to enhance the catalytic properties of enzymes.

31.2 Functional Oligosaccharides

31.2.1 Cellooligosaccharides

Among dietary fibers, short-chain COS are gaining prominence as an emerging oligosaccharide due to their prebiotic qualities and low-calorie nature. COS typically consist of a linear chain of D-glucose, usually with a degree of polymerization (DP) of ≤ 6 monomers, linked by β-1,4-glycosidic bonds, making them soluble in water, unlike cellulose [26]. The prebiotic effects of cellobiose (DP2) and the smallest COS, cellotriose (DP3), have been assessed on probiotic bacteria such as *Bifidobacterium breve*, *Bacteroides vulgatus*, *Clostridium butyricum*, *Lactococcus*, and *Lactobacillus* spp. [27, 28]. Investigations into the modulation of gut microflora in calves' guts have also been conducted. COS are typically generated either through enzymatic synthesis using a bottom-up approach or by cellulose depolymerization using cellulases [28]. Enzymatic synthesis of COS using a bottom-up approach has been implemented by Zhong et al. [26, 28]. The cascade mechanism involves three glycoside phosphorylases—sucrose phosphorylase (ScP; GH 13 family), cellobiose phosphorylase (CbP; GH 94 family), and cellodextrin phosphorylase (CdP; GH 94 family)—resulting in the production of 88 mol% COS from glucose and sucrose substrates [26]. From sucrose, a maximum of 82 mol% (93 g/l) COS was generated, consisting of DP 3 (33%, w/w), DP 4 (34% w/w), DP 5 (24% w/w), and DP 6 (9% w/w) [28]. An alternative method for COS generation involves the depolymerization of cellulose using various cellulases. Cellulose, a glucose homopolymer with β-1,4-glycosidic bonds, is challenging to degrade due to its compact and highly crystalline nature in lignocellulosic forms. Cellulases, comprising *endo*-1,4-glucanase, cellobiohydrolases (*exo*-1,4-glucanases), and β-glucosidases, collaborate to hydrolyze cellulose into cellobiose and short-chain COS [29]. Controlled enzymatic depolymerization of cellulose has been demonstrated with varying combinations of cellulases, achieving a maximum of 49.7% (w/w) cellobiose with a cellobiose/glucose ratio of 9.4 [30]. Ávila et al. [31] highlighted strategies for COS production from lignocellulosic biomass using chemical and enzymatic catalysis approaches. Organosolv-pretreated forest residues from birch and spruce were hydrolyzed to cellobiose using a combination of four cellulases, resulting in a maximum of 22.3% cellobiose from birch lignocellulose [27].

31.2.2 Xylooligosaccharides

XOS are oligomers of xylose connected by β-(1,4)-xylosidic bonds, and they can exhibit various side groups such as acetylated, methylated, α-D-glucopyranosyl uronic acid, or arabinofuranosylated forms in their branched structures. While XOS are naturally present in fruits, vegetables, and honey, their concentrations are typically low, prompting industrial production through xylan hydrolysis. Xylans, which are hemicelluloses found in plant cell walls [32], serve as the source for XOS production, with variations in side groups, linkages, substitution patterns, and degree of polymerization depending on the xylan source and production process. XOS, alongside MOS, are gaining prominence as prebiotic ingredients in functional foods. However, the drawback lies in the high cost associated with the use of expensive commercial xylan as the raw material for XOS production. A potential solution is the utilization of lignocellulosic biomass as an alternative to xylan due to its renewability and abundance [33].

Recent advancements involve the enzymatic hydrolysis of agricultural wastes using a commercial enzyme mixture to produce XOS. For instance, arabinoxylan extracted from coffee husk (CH) and sugarcane straw (SS) through acidic hydrolysis followed by enzymatic catalysis yielded XOS with varying degrees of polymerization (DP). Optimization using a mixture of *endo*-xylanase, feruloyl esterase, and α-L-arabinofuranosidase resulted in high XOS yields from SS and CH xylan. The prebiotic potential of these XOS, particularly DP 2-4, was demonstrated through their enhanced fermentability with Lactobacillus and Bifidobacteria strains. Additionally, the XOS exhibited antioxidant activity, scavenging DPPH free radicals [8]. Another approach to improve XOS production involved a 2-step pretreatment (mild deacetylation followed by hydrothermal treatment) of SS, leading to increased hemicellulose solubilization and higher XOS yields. Recombinant strains expressing specific xylanases were employed for DP 2-3 XOS production from pretreated SS. Similarly, commercial enzyme mixtures were applied to generate XOS from sugarcane bagasse and straw mixture hydrolysis. Various studies highlight the potential of different enzymes and pretreatment methods in enhancing XOS production from diverse xylan sources. In conclusion, XOS represent a promising functional food ingredient with prebiotic and nutritional properties. Ongoing research focuses on optimizing production processes, exploring alternative raw materials, and understanding the diverse applications of XOS in the food industry.

31.2.3 Mannooligosaccharides

MOS are oligomers of mannose linked by glycosidic bonds, with α-MOS obtained from yeast cell wall hydrolysis and common β-MOS generated through the hydrolysis of plant β-mannans, found in locust bean gum (LBG), konjac gum (KG), and guar gum (GG) [34]. There are four types of mannans based on glycosidic linkage and branching patterns: linear mannans, galactomannans, glucomannan, and galactoglucomannans. Mannanases, including β-1,4-mannanase, β-mannosidase, α-galactosidase, and β-glucosidase, are employed to hydrolyze raw mannans into MOS, particularly β-MOS [35]. Various GH families, such as GH-5 and GH-26, from fungal sources like *Yunnania penicillate*, *Aspergillus nidulans*, *Aspergillus niger*, *Aspergillus oryzae*, and *Rhizomucor miehei*, have been used for MOS production. Recent studies have utilized β-mannanase genes from organisms like *A. niger* (AnMan26) and *Aspergillus sojae* to achieve high yields of MOS through partial hydrolysis of fenugreek gum and coffee extract mannan, respectively. The nutritional properties of MOS, considered an emerging prebiotic ingredient, are being explored, and they are being compared to FOS. Researchers have investigated the prebiotic potential of MOS obtained from LBG and palm kernel cake, evaluating its effects on gut microflora, particularly against *L. plantarum*. Additionally, studies have estimated the pro-health properties of MOS on shrimp survival and observed variations in gut microflora composition, including *Actinobacteria*, *Proteobacteria*, *Verrucomicrobia*, *Chloroflexi*, and *Firmicutes*. For detailed insights into the nutraceutical properties of MOS, one can refer to the work by Jana et al. [36].

31.2.4 Galactooligosaccharides

GOS consist of 2-8 galactose units connected by β-(1-4) and β-(1-6) glycosidic bonds, occasionally with β-(1-2) and β-(1-3) linkages [25, 37]. Typically, GOS, lactulose, and related oligosaccharides are synthesized through the transgalactosylation of lactose in saturated solutions using β-galactosidase (EC 3.2.1.23) [37]. β-Galactosidase facilitates the transfer of galactose from one lactose molecule to another, producing predominantly DP 3-8 GOS. Similar to other prebiotic oligosaccharides, GOS exhibit prebiotic potential by promoting the growth of *Lactobacillus* and *Bifidobacterium* spp., inhibiting pathogenic enteric bacteria. GOS are recognized as low-calorie, antidiabetic, and noncariogenic, remaining stable in acidic pH and high temperatures. Furthermore, GOS demonstrate anticolon cancer, cholesterol-lowering, immune-boosting, and pathogenicity-minimizing properties. Several studies have focused on GOS production using microbial β-galactosidases [38]. For instance, a *Kluyveromyces lactis* β-galactosidase yielded DP 2-4 GOS from lactose, achieving maximum yields of 40% and 49% with β-galactosidase and a mix of β-galactosidase and glucose oxidase, respectively. *Kluyveromyces marxianus* produced extracellular β-galactosidase, resulting in approximately 50% GOS generation from lactose hydrolysis. *A. oryzae* β-galactosidase synthesized lactulose-derived oligosaccharides through transgalactosylation, reaching a maximum of 62.4% in five hours at 60 °C. *K. marxianus* NCIM 3551 β-galactosidase catalyzed GOS production, achieving a maximum of 72.0 g/l GOS with a yield of 36% under optimal conditions [39]. Commercial galactosidases, such as Biocatalase, Lactozym Pure, and Lactase F, have also been utilized for GOS production, resulting in varying yields. Yeasts *Pichia kluyveri* and *Pseudozyma tsukubaensis* yielded GOS with maximum yields of 14.01% and 15.71% from lactose in 24hours. Engineered β-galactosidase producers demonstrated enhanced GOS yield and reduced incubation time. GOS offer various nutritional benefits, including promoting probiotic gut microflora, inhibiting pathogenic microbial adherence, reducing blood pressure and serum cholesterol, and contributing to anticolon cancer and immune regulation. Additionally, GOS play a crucial role in probiotic preservation methods like freeze-drying and pasteurization [38].

31.2.5 Fructooligosaccharides

FOS stand out as a prominent and widely recognized prebiotic ingredient in the realm of functional foods [40]. The production of FOS through fungal enzymes is a straightforward, cost-effective process with practical downstream processing capabilities from the biotransformation mixture. Industrial FOS production primarily involves the biotransformation of sucrose to FOS facilitated by fructosyltransferase (FTase). FTase (EC 2.3.1.99) initiates the hydrolysis of sucrose (GF) into fructose (F) and glucose (G) [12]. The liberated fructose is subsequently transferred to an acceptor molecule, which can be either water or any oligosaccharide molecule, resulting in the formation of FOS. FOS produced by FTase typically comprises short chains (DP 3-5) of fructose, such as kestose (GF2), nystose (GF3), or fructofuranosyl nystose (GF4) [41]. The structure of FOS involves fructose units linked by β-(2→1) or β-(2→6) glycosidic bonds, with a terminal glucose residue. In a broader context, fructans, which are fructose polymers featuring a terminal glucose molecule, represent a category of carbohydrates found in approximately 15% of flowering plants. Plant fructans function as storage carbohydrates in various plant parts, including tap roots (e.g. Chicory Roots), stems (e.g. Ginger), tubers (e.g. Jerusalem artichoke tubersDahlia, and Dandelion root), and fruits (e.g. Banana) [42]. These fructans accumulate as a protective response to abiotic and biotic stresses, such as drought and cold. Plants typically store fructans with approximately 10–200 fructosyl residues. Similarly, bacteria also store fructans as an energy source, forming a protective layer that helps them evade recognition by the host's immune system and provides resistance against bacteriostatic compounds [43].

Despite extensive discussions, a lingering puzzle surrounds the nomenclature of these enzymes. The challenge arises from their dual capability to exhibit both hydrolytic and transfructosylating potential [44]. This dual functionality makes it challenging to definitively categorize these enzymes into distinct classes, creating an ongoing debate in the scientific community. According to the nature of catalyzed bond, FOS synthesizing enzymes are grouped into the following types:

31.2.5.1 β-D-Fructofuranoside Fructohydrolase (FFase)

The enzyme FFase, also known as invertase or sucrase (EC 3.2.1.26), plays a crucial role in catalyzing the hydrolysis of sucrose, leading to the formation of glucose and fructose. This enzyme belongs to the glycoside hydrolase family 32 (GH 32) recognized for its activity on sucrose and related β-D-fructo-furanosides [45]. It is understood that FFase inherently possess both sucrose hydrolyzing and transfructosylation capabilities, although the ratio (Ut/Uh) of hydrolase (Uh) to transferase (Ut) varies among species. Among more than 25 fungal species examined, including *A. niger* GNCC 2613, *Aspergillus awamori* MTCC 2879, *Aspergillus ficuum* MTCC 7591, *A. niger* ATCC 26011, *Penicillium citrinum* MTCC 1256, and *Penicillium rugulosum* MTCC 3487, demonstrated potential as sources of invertases when cultivated on various inulin-rich plant extracts [46]. *Aspergillus terreus* exhibited extracellular invertase production on low-cost substrates. Two intracellular invertases, namely invertase 1 and invertase 2, were purified from *A. terreus*, each showing optimal activity under different conditions. Invertase 1 exhibited maximum activity at pH 3.0 and 60 °C, while invertase 2 was optimally active at pH 4.6 and 55 °C. Invertase 2 consisted of two protein subunits, each weighing 32 kDa [47]. A crystallized invertase with fructosyltransferase (FTase) activity was derived from *Aspergillus kawachii*, comprising a small N-terminal, a beta-propeller domain, a helical linker sequence, and a beta-sandwich C-terminal end [48]. *Aspergillus carbonarius* strains isolated from canned Peach syrup were studied as invertase producers, with the best producer strain *A. carbonarius* PC-4 demonstrating significant invertase production (6.71 U/ml) on pineapple crown after three days of solid-state fermentation [49]. The β-fructosidase from *A. oryzae*, a 95 kDa monomeric glycoprotein, was characterized. The enzyme coding sequence was cloned in *Escherichia coli* and expressed in *Pichia pastoris*. This enzyme specifically produced levan- and neolevan-type β-(2-6)-linked FOS at a high sucrose concentration (33%), achieving a maximum of 56% fructooligosaccharide yield [50].

31.2.5.2 Fructosyltransferase

FTase (EC 2.4.1.99) is responsible for catalyzing the transfructosylation process, where fructose produced from sucrose hydrolysis is transferred to an acceptor molecule. Transfructosylation mechanism involving the hydrolysis of the beta-2,1-glycosidic bond in sucrose, leading to the release of fructose. This liberated fructose is then transferred to the β-(2–1) or β-(2–6) position of an acceptor molecule other than water, such as sucrose or oligosaccharides. Numerous microbial species from plant, bacteria, and fungi groups have been identified as producers of fructosyltransferase through solid-state fermentation (SSF) or submerged fermentation [51]. Several fungi, including *Saccharomyces cerevisiae, Aureobasidium pullulans, Aureobasidium melanogenum, Kluyveromyces maraxianus, Xanthophyllomyces, Rhodotorula, Aspergillus, Penicillium,* with a focus on the *Aspergillus* and *Penicillium* genera, have been recognized as efficient fructooligosaccharide (FOS) producers based on fructosyltransferase activity. Large-scale FOS production often involves the use of free purified or immobilized fructosyltransferases, typically sourced from *A. niger*, *A. oryzae*, and *A. pullulans*. Fructosyltransferase can be found intracellularly, bound to the cell membrane, or extracellularly, secreted into the extracellular medium. In a screening of 25 fungal strains, predominantly from the *Aspergillus* and *Penicillium* genera, for fructosyltransferase, inulinase, and invertase on various plant sources rich in inulin, *P. citrinum* MTCC 1256 displayed the highest intracellular fructosyltransferase activity at 10.8 U/ml when cultured on Dandelion root extract medium. *P. rugulosum* MTCC 3487 and *A. niger* ATCC 26011 produced 3.58 and 2.2 U/ml intracellular fructosyltransferase on Dandelion tuber extract and Asparagus root extract, respectively [52]. To enhance fructosyltransferase production for commercial applications, researchers are exploring strategies such as cloning, overexpression, and mutation. Mutation techniques, including EtBr, EMS, and RSM, in *A. pullulans* NAC8 resulted in a sixfold increase in extracellular and a two-fold increase in intracellular fructosyltransferase. The beta-fructosyltransferase from *A. niger* PR-142 also exhibited a 1.5-fold increase in intracellular fructosyltransferase upon mutation with UV 253.7 nm.

31.2.5.3 Inulinase

Inulins are water-soluble fructans linked by β-2,1 bonds and naturally present in various plants such as dandelion root, asparagus taproot, chicory root, onion, and banana [53]. *Exo*-inulinase (EC 3.8.1.80; β-D-fructan fructohydrolase or β-D-fructosidase) is an enzyme that catalyzes the hydrolysis of the terminal fructose unit in inulin. The *exo*-hydrolysis of inulin leads to the release of fructose, forming high fructose syrup (up to 95%). This method is preferred over sucrose or starch hydrolysis and isomerization as it involves a two-step process and enzyme cocktail. A secretion expression of *exo*-inulinase from *A. niger* was achieved by co-expressing it with the gene hac1 from *S. cerevisiae*, responsible for folding and secreting eukaryotic proteins from the endoplasmic reticulum. Recombinant *P. pastoris* expressing *exo*-inulinase and hac1 resulted in 95% fructose generation from inulin [54]. The fructose liberated by *exo*-inulinase can be converted into various value-added products such as bioethanol, sorbitol, lactic acid, citric acid, single-cell oil, single-cell protein, biohydrogen, etc. [46, 53]. *Endo*-inulinase (EC 3.2.1.7; β-D-fructan fructanohydrolase) hydrolyzes the β-2,1 bonds within the inulin backbone, producing IOS similar to kestose, nystose, and fructofuranosylnystose, including inulotriose, inulotetraose, and inulopentaose as major products [46]. Low-degree polymerization FOS (agavins) obtained from *Agave angustifolia* hydrolysis, using a mixture of *exo*-inulinase prepared with *A. niger* and commercial *endo*-inulinase (Megazyme) in a 1 : 3 ratio, resulted in 33% hydrolysis at 60 °C. The obtained FOS mixture contained 10% different DP FOS, with DP7 and DP8 as major products. An engineered *Yarrowia lipolytica* strain, displaying a fusion gene composed of *endo*-inulinase from *A. niger* and an inulin-binding module from *Bacillus macerans*, produced 0.912 ± 0.012 gFOS/gInulin in two hours [55].

Due to their stability over a wide range of pH, temperature, and sucrose concentration, *endo*-inulinases from different fungal species, including *Aspergillus arachidicola, A. ficuum, Aspergillus fumigatus*, and *A. niger* CICIM F0620, have been reported for enhanced FOS generation with improved properties [56]. The *endo*-inulinase from *Lipomyces starkeyi* was cloned in pET22b (+) and expressed in *E. coli*, generating a 56 kDa recombinant inulinase that produced DP 3-5 FOS with optimum activity at pH 5.0–6.0 and 70 °C. Similarly, *A. arachidicola endo*-inulinase was cloned in pET-22b (+) and expressed.

31.3 Conclusion

Majorly explored oligosaccharides are FOS and GOS, while functional properties of MOS, COS, and XOS are being studied. Mycozymes (particularly hydrolases or transferases) are an excellent source for green and efficient production of these prebiotic oligosaccharides from raw lignocellulosic agro-wastes. Preparation yield, functional properties, and the efficacy of synthesis of nutraceutical oligosaccharides are prominently maintained by the source and catalytic factors of these mycozymes. Manufacturing development requires enriched catalytic factors such as stability over a broad range of pH and temperature, high product yield, consumption of agro-waste as substrate, and high shelf life. Mycozymes are appropriate with regard to these factors; thus, they are being a hot-spot for applied research on oligosaccharides for functional food industries.

References

1 Gibson, G.R. and Roberfroid, M. (1995). Dietary modulation of the human colonic microbiota-introducing the concept of prebiotics. *J. Nutr.* 125: 1401–1412.

2 Nath, S. and Kango, N. (2021). Recent developments in industrial mycozymes: a current appraisal. *Mycol.* https://doi.org/10.1080/21501203.2021.1974111.

3 Kadowaki, M.A. and Polikarpov, I. (2019). Structural insights into the hydrolysis pattern and molecular dynamics simulations of GH45 subfamily a endoglucanase from Neurospora crassa OR74A. *Biochimie.* https://doi.org/10.1016/j.biochi.2019.08.016.

4 Guo, Y., Yan, Q., Yang, Y. et al. (2015). Expression and characterization of a novel β-glucosidase, with transglycosylation and exo-β-1,3-glucanase activities, from *Rhizomucor miehei. Food Chem.* 175: 431–438. https://doi.org/10.1016/j.foodchem.2014.12.004.

5 Krisch, J., Bencsik, O., Papp, T. et al. (2012). Characterization of a β-glucosidase with transgalactosylation capacity from the zygomycete *Rhizomucor miehei. Bioresour. Technol.* 114: 555–560. https://doi.org/10.1016/j.biortech.2012.02.117.

6 Basotra, N., Dhiman, S.S., Agrawal, D. et al. (2019). Characterization of a novel lytic polysaccharide monooxygenase from *Malbranchea cinnamomea* exhibiting dual catalytic behavior. *Carbohydr. Res.* https://doi.org/10.1016/j.carres.2019.04.006.

7 Andberg, M., Penttilä, M., and Saloheimo, M. (2015). Swollenin from *Trichoderma reesei* exhibits hydrolytic activity against cellulosic substrates with features of both endoglucanases and cellobiohydrolases. *Bioresour. Technol.* 181: 105–113. https://doi.org/10.1016/j.biortech.2015.01.024.

8 Khangwal, I., Nath, S., Kango, N., and Shukla, P. (2020). Endo-xylanase induced xylooligosaccharide production from corn cobs, its structural features, and concentration-dependent antioxidant activities. *Biomass Convers. Biorefin.* 1–11. https://doi.org/10.1007/s13399-020-00997-3.

9 Suryawanshi, R.K. and Kango, N. (2020). Production of mannooligosaccharides from various mannans and evaluation of their prebiotic potential. *Food Chem.* 127428. https://doi.org/10.1016/j.foodchem.2020.127428.

10 Fischer, C. and Kleinschmidt, T. (2020). Synthesis of galactooligosaccharides by *Cryptococcus laurentii* and *Aspergillus oryzae* using different kinds of acid whey. *Int. Dairy J.* 104867. https://doi.org/10.1016/j.idairyj.2020.104867.

11 Khodaei, N. and Karboune, S. (2018). Optimization of enzymatic production of prebiotic galacto/galacto(arabino)-oligosaccharides and oligomers from potato rhamnogalacturonan I. *Carbohydr. Polym.* 181: 1153–1159. https://doi.org/10.1016/j.carbpol.2017.11.011.

12 Choukade, R. and Kango, N. (2019). Characterization of a mycelial fructosyltransferase from *Aspergillus tamarii* NKRC 1229 for efficient synthesis of fructooligosaccharides. *Food Chem.* 286: 434–440.

13 Coetzee, G., van Rensburg, E., and Görgens, J.F. (2019). Evaluation of the performance of an engineered β-fructofuranosidase from *Aspergillus fijiensis* to produce short-chain fructooligosaccharides from industrial sugar streams. *Biocatal. Agric. Biotechnol.* 101484. https://doi.org/10.1016/j.bcab.2019.101484.

14 Singh, R.S., Singh, T., and Kennedy, J.F. (2020). Purification, thermodynamics and kinetic characterization of fungal endoinulinase for the production of fructooligosaccharides from inulin. *Int. J. Biol. Macromol.* https://doi.org/10.1016/j.ijbiomac.2020.09.001.

15 Xue, L., Long, J., Lu, C. et al. (2021). Immobilization of polygalacturonase for the preparation of pectic oligosaccharides from mango peel wastes and assessment of their antibacterial activities. *Food Biosci.* 39: 100837. https://doi.org/10.1016/j.fbio.2020.100837.

16 Xu, Q., Liu, M., Liu, Q. et al. (2017). The inhibition of LPS-induced inflammation in RAW264.7 macrophages via the PI3K/Akt pathway by highly N-acetylated chitooligosaccharide. *Carbohydr. Polym.* 174: 1138–1143. https://doi.org/10.1016/j.carbpol.2017.07.051.

17 Baldassarre, S., Babbar, N., Van Roy, S. et al. (2018). Continuous production of pectic oligosaccharides from onion skins with an enzyme membrane reactor. *Food Chem.* 267: 101–110. https://doi.org/10.1016/j.foodchem.2017.10.055.

18 Wang, Z., Xu, B., Luo, H. et al. (2019). Production pectin oligosaccharides using *Humicola insolens* Y1-derived unusual pectate lyase. *J. Biosci. Bioeng.* https://doi.org/10.1016/j.jbiosc.2019.07.005.

19 Zhou, H., Li, T., Yu, Z. et al. (2019). A lytic polysaccharide monooxygenase from *Myceliophthora thermophila* and its synergism with cellobiohydrolases in cellulose hydrolysis. *Int. J. Biol. Macromol.* https://doi.org/10.1016/j.ijbiomac.2019.08.004.

20 Kidibule, P.E., Santos-Moriano, P., Plou, F.J., and Fernández-Lobato, M. (2020). Endo-chitinase Chit33 specificity on different chitinolytic materials allows the production of unexplored chitooligosaccharides with antioxidant activity. *Biotechnol. Rep.* 27: e00500. https://doi.org/10.1016/j.btre.2020.e00500.

21 Li, M., Han, J., Xue, Y. et al. (2019). Hydrogen peroxide pretreatment efficiently assisting enzymatic hydrolysis of chitosan at high concentration for chitooligosaccharides. *Polym. Degrad. Stab.* https://doi.org/10.1016/j.polymdegradstab.2019.04.011.

22 Delattre, C., Michaud, P., Lion, J.M. et al. (2005). Production of glucuronan oligosaccharides using a new glucuronan lyase activity from a *Trichoderma* sp. strain. 118 (4): 448–457. https://doi.org/10.1016/j.jbiotec.2005.04.014.

23 Rajagopalan, G. and Krishnan, C. (2019). Functional oligosaccharides: production and action. In: *Next Generation Biomanufacturing Technologies* (ed. N.K. Rathinam and R.K. Sani), 155–180. Washington, DC: ACS Publications, American Chemical Society.

24 Benkoulouche, M., Fauré, R., Remaud-Siméon, M. et al. (2019). Harnessing glycoenzyme engineering for synthesis of bioactive oligosaccharides. *Interface Focus* 9: 20180069.

25 Vera, C., Illanes, A., and Guerrero, C. (2020a). Enzymatic production of prebiotic oligosaccharides. *Curr. Opin. Food Sci.* 37: 160–170.

26 Zhong, C., Ukowitz, C., Domig, K., and Nidetzky, B. (2020a). Short-chain cello-oligosaccharides: intensification and scale-up of their enzymatic production and selective growth promotion among probiotic bacteria. *Agric. Food Chem.* 68: 8557–8567.

27 Karnaouri, A., Matsakas, L., Krikigianni, E. et al. (2019). Valorization of waste forest biomass toward the production of cello-oligosaccharides with potential prebiotic activity by utilizing customized enzyme cocktails. *Biotechnol. Biofuels* 12: 1–19.

28 Zhong, C., Duic, B., Bolivar, J.M., and Nidetzky, B. (2020b). Three-enzyme phosphorylase cascade immobilized on solid support for biocatalytic synthesis of cello-oligosaccharides. *ChemCatChem* 12: 1350–1358.

29 Kango, N., Jana, U.K., and Choukade, R. (2019). Fungal enzymes: sources and biotechnological applications. In: *Advancing Frontiers in Mycology & Mycotechnology* (ed. T. Satyanarayana, S. Deshmukh, and M. Deshpande), 515–538. Singapore: Springer.

30 Hrůzová, K., Matsakas, L., Karnaouri, A. et al. (2021). Valoriza-tion of outer tunic of the marine filter feeder Ciona intestinalis towards the production of second-generation biofuel and prebiotic oligosaccharides. *Biotechnol. Biofuels* 14: 32.

31 Ávila, P.F., Silva, M.F., Martins, M., and Goldbeck, R. (2021). Cello-oligosaccharides production from lignocellulosic biomass and their emerging prebiotic applications. *World J. Microbiol. Biotechnol.* 37: 73.

32 Carvalho, D.M., Martínez-Abad, A., Evtuguin, D.V. et al. (2017). Isolation and characterization of acetylated glucuronoarabinoxylan from sugarcane bagasse and straw. *Carbohydr. Polym.* 156: 223–234.

33 Amorim, C., Silverio, S.C., Silva, S.P. et al. (2019). Single-step production of arabino-xylooligosaccharides by recombinant *Bacillus subtilis* 3610 cultivated in brewers' spent grain. *Carbohydr. Polym.* 199: 546–554.

34 Jana, U.K., Kango, N., and Pletschke, B. (2021). Hemicellulose-derived oligosaccharides: emerging prebiotics in disease alleviation. *Front. Nutr.* 8: 670817.

35 Jana, U.K., Suryawanshi, R.K., Prajapati, B.P., and Kango, N. (2020). Prebiotic mannooligosaccharides: synthesis, characterization, and bioactive properties. *Food Chem.* 342: 128328.

36 Jana, U.K., Suryawanshi, R.K., Prajapati, B.P. et al. (2018). Production optimization and characterization of mannooligosaccharide generating β-mannanase from *Aspergillus oryzae*. *Bioresour. Technol.* 268: 308–314.

37 Vera, C., Guerrero, C., Aburto, C. et al. (2020b). Conventional and non-conventional applications of β-galactosidases. *Biochim. Biophys. Acta, Proteins Proteomics* 1868: 140271.

38 Guerrero, C., Vera, C., Conejeros, R., and Illanes, A. (2015). Transgalactosylation and hydrolytic activities of commercial preparations of β-galactosidase for the synthesis of prebiotic carbohydrates. *Enzyme Microb. Technol.* 70: 9–17.

39 Srivastava, P.K. and Kapoor, M. (2017). Production, properties, and applications of endo-β-mannanases. *Biotechnol. Adv.* 35: 1–19.

40 Ganaie, M.A., Gupta, U.S., and Kango, N. (2013). Screening of biocatalysts for transformation of sucrose to fructooligosaccharides. *J. Mol. Catal. B: Enzym.* 97: 12–17.

41 Choukade, R. and Kango, N. (2020). Applications of fungal inulinases. In: *Encyclopedia of Mycology, Reference Module in Life Sciences* (ed. O. Zaragoza and A. Casadevall), 337–347. Elsevier.

42 Rawat, H.K., Nath, S., Sharma, I., and Kango, N. (2024). Recent developments in the production of prebiotic fructooligosaccharides using fungal fructosyltransferases. *Mycol* 1–21: https://doi.org/10.1080/21501203.2024.2323713.

43 Hernández, L., Menéndez, C., Pérez, E.R. et al. (2018). Fructooligosaccharides production by *Schedonorus arundinaceus* sucrose:sucrose 1-fructosyltransferase constitutively expressed to high levels in *Pichia pastoris*. *J. Biotechnol.* 266: 59–71.

44 Choukade, R. and Kango, N. (2021). Production, properties and applications of fructosyltransferase: a current appraisal. *Crit. Rev. Biotechnol.* 41: 1178–1193.

45 Trollope, K.M., Van Wyk, N., Kotjomela, M.A., and Volschenk, H. (2015). Sequence and structure-based prediction of fructosyltransferase activity for functional subclassification of fungal GH32 enzymes. *FEBS J.* 282: 4782–4796.

46 Rawat, H.K., Soni, H., Treichel, H., and Kango, N. (2017). Biotechnological potential of microbial inulinases: recent perspective. *Crit. Rev. Food Sci. Nutr.* 57: 3818–3829.

47 Almeida, M., Guimaraes, V., Falkoski, D. et al. (2017). Purification and characterization of an invertase and a transfructosylase from Aspergillus terreus. *J. Food Biochem.* 42: https://doi.org/10.1111/jfbc.12551.

48 Nagaya, M., Kimura, M., Gozu, Y. et al. (2017). Crystal structure of a β-fructofuranosidase with high transfructosylation activity from *Aspergillus kawachii*. *Biosci. Biotechnol. Biochem.* 81: 1–10. https://doi.org/10.1080/09168451.2017.1353405.

49 do Nascimento, G.C., Batista, R.D., Santos, C.C.A.D.A. et al. (2019). β-fructofuranosidase and β -D-fructosyltransferase from new *Aspergillus carbonarius* PC-4 strain isolated from canned peach syrup: effect of carbon and nitrogen sources on enzyme production. *Scientific World J.* 2019: 6956202. https://doi.org/10.1155/2019/6956202.

50 Xu, L., Wang, D., Lu, L. et al. (2014). Purification, cloning, characterization, and N-glycosylation analysis of a novel β-fructosidase from *Aspergillus oryzae* FS4 synthesizing levan- and neolevan-type fructooligosaccharides. *PLoS One* 9: e114793. https://doi.org/10.1371/journal.pone.0114793.

51 Singh, S.P., Jadaun, J.S., Narnoliya, L.K., and Pandey, A. (2017). Prebiotic oligosaccharides: special focus on fructooligosaccharides, its biosynthesis and bioactivity. *Appl. Biochem. Biotechnol.* 183: 613–635.

52 Rawat, H.K., Ganaie, M.A., and Kango, N. (2015). Production of inulinase, fructosyltransferase and sucrase from fungi on low-value inulin-rich substrates and their use in generation of fructose and fructooligosaccharides. *Anto van Leeuwen.* 107: 799–811. https://doi.org/10.1007/s10482-014-0373-3.

53 Kango, N. and Jain, S.C. (2011). Production and properties of microbial inulinases: recent advances. *Food Biotechnol.* 25: 165–212.

54 Chen, P., Shrotri, A., and Fukuoka, A. (2021). Synthesis of cello-oligosaccharides by depolymerization of cellulose: a review. *Appl. Catal., A* 621: 118177.

55 Mao, W., Han, Y., Wang, X. et al. (2019). A new engineered endo-inulinase with improved activity and thermostability: application in the production of prebiotic fructo-oligosaccharides from inulin. *Food Chem.* 294: 293–301. https://doi.org/10.1016/j.foodchem.2019.05.062.

56 Chen, X., Wang, J., and Li, Q. (2015). Simultaneous determination of maltooligosaccharides in beer using HPLC-ELSD and their influence on beer foam stability. *J. Am. Soc. Brew. Chem.* 73: 78.

32

Microbial Laccases: Structure, Function, and Applications

Supriya Gupta[1], Aiman Tanveer[1], Shruti Dwivedi[1], Vivek Kumar Morya[2], Manoj Kumar Yadav[3], and Dinesh Yadav[1]

[1] *Deen Dayal Upadhyaya Gorakhpur University, Department of Biotechnology, Civil Lines, Gorakhpur, Uttar Pradesh 273009, India*
[2] *Hallym University, Department of Orthopaedic Surgery, Dongtan Sacred Heart Hospital, 22, Gwanpyeong-ro 170beon-gil, Dongan-gu, Anyang-si, Gyeonggi-do 14068, Republic of Korea*
[3] *SVP University of Agriculture and Technology, Department of Agriculture Biotechnology, Modipuram, Meerut, Uttar Pradesh 250110, India*

32.1 Introduction

Laccases are enzyme systems that have been extensively studied and are ubiquitously present in a wide range of organisms [1]. Originally identified in the secretion of *Rhus vernicifera*, a lacquer tree native to Japan [2], laccase belongs to the multi-copper oxidase (MCO) superfamily, which encompasses a wide variety of proteins with distinct substrate specificities and diverse biological functions [3]. Each glycosylated polyphenol oxidase molecule contains four copper ions, which facilitate the one-electron oxidation of phenolic and related substances, as well as the reduction of oxygen to water [4, 5]. Functioning as catalysts, laccases drive the oxidation of diphenols, polyphenols, diamines, and aromatic amines, among other organic and inorganic molecules. This oxidative process involves the acceptance of electrons by oxygen molecules [6], resulting in the generation of highly reactive independent radicals that undergo nonenzymatic processes such as hydration, disproportionation, and polymerization [7].

The production of optimal laccase levels is influenced by various factors, such as time, shaking conditions, pH, dissolved oxygen quantity, light intensity, and the presence of organic salts [8]. In plants, laccases are primarily involved in seed coat lignification and polyflavonoid synthesis. In fungi, they play a role in delignification, fruit body formation, pathogenesis, and pigmentation. In insects, laccases contribute to cuticle sclerotization, while bacterial laccases are involved in copper homeostasis, pathogenicity, morphogenesis, and melanization [9, 10].

Laccase enzymes are involved in numerous biological processes, including biotransformation, delignification, pathogenesis, purification, and morphogenesis, owing to their broad substrate specificity that enables the oxidation of both harmful

Microbial Enzymes: Production, Purification, and Industrial Applications, First Edition.
Edited by Dinesh Yadav, Pankaj Chowdhary, Gautam Anand, and Rajarshi Kumar Gaur.

and benign compounds [11–13]. These enzymes are widely utilized in industries such as medicine, chemistry, food, textiles, and paper due to their robust catalytic activity, environmental friendliness, and selectivity [11–13]. Laccase enzymes are also crucial in the degradation of xenobiotic compounds resulting from extensive agricultural and manufacturing activities, which impact soil and aquatic ecosystems. Several studies have demonstrated that white-rot fungi and their ligninolytic enzymes, including laccases, can convert or degrade various xenobiotics *in vitro*. There is a growing interest in investigating enzymatic remediation as an alternative detoxification method for contaminated aquatic and terrestrial habitats, and laccases play a significant role in this context due to their ability to oxidize a broad range of hazardous compounds, such as phenols, halogenated phenols, and aromatic amines [14]. This chapter aims to provide a comprehensive summary of laccase studies, including their mode of action, structural characteristics, and recent applications, while highlighting key innovations in the field.

32.2 Structure, Classification, and Mode of Action of Laccases

Laccases, enigmas within the MCO and cupredoxin superfamilies, enthrall scientists with their intricate structures and unmatched catalytic prowess. Their architectural story begins with the cupredoxin fold, a meticulously woven tapestry of β-sheets forming a Greek-key barrel, a testament to nature's exquisite design. This closed β-sheet fortress, often encompassing three domains, each echoing the cupredoxin motif, houses a minimum of seven β-strands and approximately 500 amino acids, a testament to their structural complexity. But nature, ever the innovator, also offers a streamlined version—the two-domain or small laccases, showcasing the remarkable diversity within this enzymatic family [10, 15]. The quest to understand laccase structures has been illuminated by X-ray crystallography, a technique that has unveiled a breathtaking level of structural conservation [15]. This conservation is reflected in the 180 laccase structures deposited in the Protein Data Bank, a treasure trove for exploring their intricacies [10]. Beyond this impressive repository, the Laccase and Multicopper Oxidase Engineering Database catalogs 16 distinct families, each a testament to the remarkable evolutionary journey of these enzymes [16].

But the true magic of laccases lies within their active site, a playground for two distinct copper-binding clusters. The T1-T2 cluster, perched near the protein surface, serves as a stage for the single-electron oxidation of substrates. Here, a well-rehearsed dance of cysteine and histidine residues orchestrates the transfer of electrons, a crucial first act in the laccase drama. Deep within the protein's core, a more intricate set unfolds: the trinuclear T2-T3-T3' cluster. This molecular structure facilitates the overwhelming reduction of oxygen to water. The molecular stability of this protein is further strengthened by two disulfide bridges (positioned between domains 1 and 3 and domains 1 and 2). These bridges act as anchors, ensuring the Greek-key motif retains its structural integrity, allowing laccases to tackle a

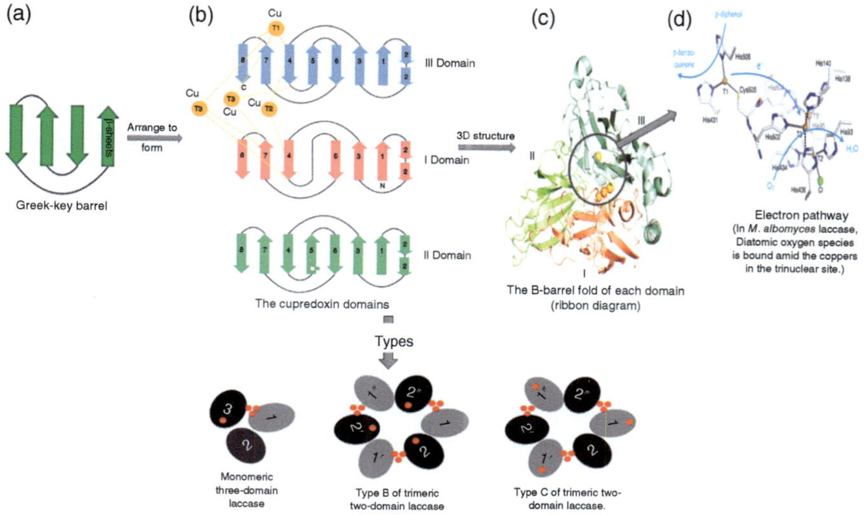

Figure 32.1 Structure of laccases in *M. albomyces*.

breathtakingly diverse repertoire of substrates, from simple phenols to complex lignin polymers. This unparalleled versatility has propelled laccases to the forefront of scientific inquiry. From unraveling the intricate ballet of lignin degradation in fungal ecosystems to exploring their potential in bioremediation, these enzymatic maestros continue to captivate researchers and inspire innovative solutions [10]. In the grand tapestry of life, laccases stand as a testament to nature's exquisite design and unwavering ingenuity, offering a glimpse into the boundless possibilities of enzymatic catalysis. Figure 32.1 provides a structural representation of laccases. The amino acid sequence in the T1Cu site comprises one cysteine and two histidine residues, while the T2Cu site consists of two histidine residues and water. The T3Cu site involves two copper ions and six histidine residues [17, 18].

Laccases, characterized by their unique spectroscopic properties, exhibit a remarkable diversity within their molecular architecture. The initial identification of these enzymes was marked by their distinctive blue color, attributed to the presence of T1 copper, a paramagnetic ion with a characteristic absorption peak at 610 nm. This iconic feature became the namesake for "blue laccases." However, not all members of this versatile family displayed the same hue. Those lacking intense blue coloration were termed "yellow" or "white" laccases. Upon further examination of the spectroscopic properties, we find T1 copper, which forms a trigonal coordination sphere with two histidines and a cysteine as its binding partners. The fourth ligand often adopts a variable role, contributing to the diverse array of substrates that these enzymes can tackle. The covalent bond between copper and cysteine serves as the pivotal orchestrator of the laccase's signature blue color, arising from its intense electrical absorption around 600 nm. This very site also acts as the catalytic hub for substrate oxidation, initiating the enzymatic activity.

Moving beyond the more prominent T1 copper, which is known for stealing the spotlight, we encounter its partner, the non-blue, paramagnetic T2 copper. Although less flashy than T1, T2 plays a crucial role in the electron relay system. Its presence is revealed through weak absorption in the visible light range (380–750 nm) and characteristic electron paramagnetic resonance (EPR) signals. Positioned in close proximity to T3 copper, T2 forms a crucial bridge in the catalytic pathway. Lastly, there is the enigmatic T3 copper, a spin-coupled diamagnetic pair exhibiting peak absorbance at 350 nm. This binuclear copper center lacks an EPR signal and undergoes electron absorption at 330 nm in its oxidized form. Interestingly, T3 copper also comprises the core of another protein family, including tyrosinases and hemocyanins [19].

Beyond their color spectrum, laccases can be further categorized based on their redox potential at the T1 site. This key characteristic results in three distinct categories: low, medium, and high redox potential laccases . Each category displays specialized substrate preferences and biocatalytic abilities, highlighting the remarkable adaptability of this enzyme family. The spectroscopic analysis of laccases provides a comprehensive understanding of their internal architectures and functional diversity. From the majestic blue dance of T1 copper to the intricate collaboration of T2 and T3, each spectroscopic feature narrates a chapter in the captivating story of these versatile biocatalysts. By deciphering this spectroscopic language, we can unlock the full potential of laccases in various fields, from bioremediation to biomanufacturing.

It has been suggested that an increase in the length of the Cu—N bond may impact the T1 site redox potential due to a reduction in the contribution of the free electron pair of the nitrogen atom [20]. In the high-potential laccase from *Trametes versicolor*, the short alpha-helix (residues 455–461) containing the T1 copper ligand His458 is farther from the copper ion compared to its location in the medium-potential laccase from *Craterellus cinereus*. This is likely due to the formation of a hydrogen bond between Glu460 and Ser113 of the first domain, causing the whole His458-containing helix to shift toward the first domain and increase the distance between the atoms Cu–N. In the laccase from *C. cinereus*, the position of Glu460 is occupied by methionine, which cannot form a hydrogen bond. The formation of this hydrogen bond (Ser-Glu) may significantly influence the T1 copper ion potential. This hypothesis is supported by the comparison of available amino acid sequences of laccases and their redox potentials. Laccases containing glutamic acid and serine at positions corresponding to Glu460 and Ser113 in the laccase from *T. versicolor* are high-potential ones [20, 21]. Laccases are enzymes that primarily accept electrons from reducing substrates at their T1 site. The efficiency of catalysis for oxidizing the majority of laccase substrates is determined by the potential of the T1 site copper ion in the enzyme. Laccases with high-potential T1 sites are promising for biotechnology. The range of compounds that can be oxidized with laccases can be expanded using redox mediators, which produce high-potential intermediates as a result of enzymatic oxidation [22]. Under diffusion-controlled conditions, these intermediates can chemically react with other compounds that cannot be oxidized by laccases alone. The oxidized mediator is reduced back to its initial state by the compound that was subjected to oxidation, creating a closed cycle [23–25].

32.3 Mode of Action of Laccases

The mechanisms underlying the processes of electron transport and oxygen reduction to water remain unclear. Initially, a reducing substrate is oxidized by laccases through the absorption of one electron by T1 Cu^{2+}, generating a free radical that is cationic in nature. This radical may undergo additional oxidation, either catalyzed by laccases (e.g. phenol to quinone) or through nonenzymatic reactions (e.g. hydration or polymerization) [6]. Laccases have also been known to produce reactive oxygen species when molecular oxygen is used as an electron acceptor, which can participate in subsequent oxidative processes and aid in the overall breakdown or transformation of organic compounds.

The reaction process of laccase is complex, as the oxidation of one substrate electron must be combined with the four-electron reduction of oxygen. This enzyme functions similarly to a battery, collecting electrons from several oxidation processes to reduce molecular oxygen. Therefore, the complete reduction of molecular oxygen to water requires the oxidation of four reducing substrate molecules [26].

At the T1 site, four monoelectronic oxidations extract electrons which are transferred to an O_2-bound trinuclear cluster. The T2 and T3 sites are involved in the reduction of molecular oxygen and the release of water. Laccases follow a "two-site Ping-Pong Bi-Bi" reaction mechanism, where products are liberated before binding to a new substrate. Blue copper oxidases' solvent channels appear to be well-suited for facilitating quick entry of O_2 molecules to the trinuclear cluster and the release of H_2O. Although several strategies have been proposed for this catalysis [27], the reductive phase of the cycle, which involves the reduction of the trinuclear cluster, remains a significant mystery.

The reduction of dioxygen has been the subject of extensive investigation, particularly in the context of blue copper-containing oxidases, such as laccases. Despite numerous studies on these enzymes, a consensus regarding the electron transfer pathway within the protein globule and the mechanism of dioxygen reduction remains elusive. It is generally hypothesized that the T1 site of laccases functions as the electron acceptor from reducing substrates, subsequently facilitating the transfer of electrons to the three-nuclear T2/T3 cluster. In this cluster, molecular oxygen is activated and undergoes reduction to water [21, 26].

Upon interaction with molecular oxygen, a completely reduced laccase can exist in various forms, with two extensively studied intermediates termed the peroxide intermediate and the native intermediate [28–30]. The native intermediate, in particular, plays a pivotal role in the catalytic cycle of laccase [1]. When reacting with $^{17}O_2$, this intermediate assumes the role of an oxygen radical, as confirmed by EPR, revealing the oxidation of all four copper ions in the native intermediate [98]. The structural configuration of this intermediate diverges from that of the "resting" enzyme, notably with the T2 site copper ion disconnected from ions of the T3 site.

Figure 32.2 illustrates a four-electron reduction of a dioxygen molecule to water, implicating the participation of laccase in this process [30]. The fully reduced three-nuclear T2/T3 copper cluster of laccase interacts with molecular oxygen, leading to the formation of the peroxide intermediate. Interestingly, when utilizing

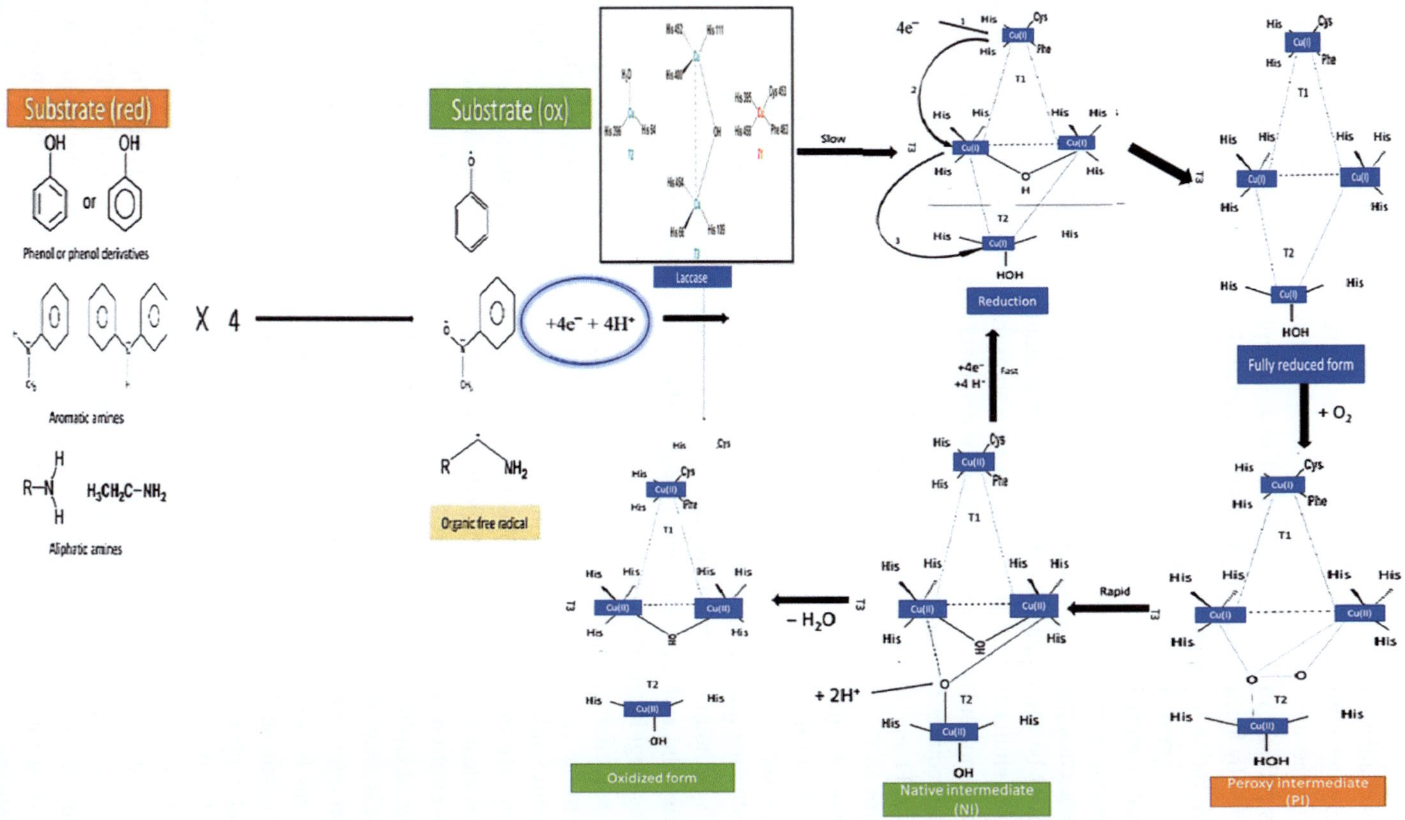

Figure 32.2 Catalytic cycle of laccase showing the mechanism of reduction and oxidation of the enzyme copper sites.

laccase with the T1 copper ion substituted by the redox-inactive mercury ion Hg^{2+}, a peroxide bridge forms between the reduced T2 and oxidized T3 sites [31, 32]. This intermediate transforms into a compound resembling the native intermediate of laccase, featuring four copper ions in the active site. The generation of the peroxide intermediate (in T1-Hg-laccase) and the native intermediate (in the native enzyme) is contingent on dioxygen concentration, and the second-order rate constants of these reactions are comparable. The proposed composition of the peroxide intermediate includes the O^{22-} ion, with one of its oxygen atoms bound to the T2 and T3 copper ions and the other coordinated with another copper ion of T3 [30, 33].

32.4 The Biological Function of Laccase Enzymes Based on Their Source

Laccases are found in a variety of organisms, including bacteria, fungi, plants, lichens, sponges, and animals, primarily arthropods [8, 34]. These enzymes play a significant role in the degradation of environmental pollutants, green catalysis, the degradation of xenobiotics, delignification, the treatment of dye, pulp bleaching, wastewater treatment, and the detoxification of the environment [8, 34]. Laccases' biological roles are closely tied to their origins, as well as their physiological and pathological functions [8]. Despite a literature survey, there is limited information available regarding the detailed properties and mode of action of laccases in different source organisms and their applications.

32.4.1 Bacterial Laccases

Bacterial laccases are widely distributed throughout the world due to their stability at high temperatures and pH levels, ease of gene manipulation, and stability in the presence of inhibitors, detergents, and other compounds. The first bacterial laccase was discovered in *Azospirillum lipoferum*, which was isolated from the plant's rhizosphere [8]. Laccase is most prevalent in the genera Bacillus and Streptomyces, which belong to the phyla Bacillota and Actinomycetes, respectively. Several species of bacteria, including *Bacillus subtilis, Bordetella campestris, Caulobacter crescentus, Escherichia coli, Streptomyces cyaneus, Streptomyces coelicolor, Streptomyces bikiniensis,* and *Streptomyces ipomoea*, have been identified as producing laccase [8, 34–40]. Bacterial laccases can be produced both extracellularly and intracellularly in some species, with *Streptomyces sp.* being a particularly efficient producer of extracellular laccases using agro-waste as a cheap substrate. Previous reports have suggested that bacterial laccases have a molecular weight ranging from 50 to 70 kDa [34]. The molecular weight of the laccase produced by *Streptomyces cyaneus* CECT 3335 was found to be ~69.5 kDa, while the minimum molecular weight of the monomeric protein produced by *Bacillus tequilensis* SN4 was ~32 kDa. The most important factor influencing the application of laccases is their biochemical properties, including their stability under a range of conditions such as pH, temperature, redox potential, metal ion, and organic solvents. Two thermostable laccases have been identified: *Streptomyces lavendulae* laccase with a half-life of 100 minutes at 70 °C, and *B. subtilis* laccase with a half-life of 112 minutes at 80 °C. Additionally, CotA laccases from *Bacillus pumilus* MK001 and *B. pumilus* W3 exhibited half-lives of 1 and 1.14 hours, respectively, at 80 °C. The half-life of *B. subtilis* WD23 spore-bound laccase is 2.5 hours at 80 °C, and its pH half-life is more than six months at pH 6.8 and 15 days at pH 9.0. This enzyme is also resistant to petroleum ether, acetone, ethyl acetate, and chloroform [41].

The identification of laccase-producing bacteria can be achieved through various techniques, including qualitative analysis based on color changes observed on a Petri plate, the decolorization of dye in bacterial culture media, and chromatography [42]. A more straightforward and basic approach is the SDS method, which utilizes substrates such as 4-amino-diethylaniline and 4-*tert*-butyl-catechol to yield different colors. However, the most accurate and quantitative method for analyzing laccase activity is the colorimetric method, which measures the production of color upon substrate action and calculates absorption based on the substrate used [43]. The biological function of laccase includes the degradation of azo dyes, xenobiotics degradation, detoxification, and bioremediation of industrial effluents. The mutant of bacterial laccases is utilized to oxidize the carcinogen benzo alpha pyrene in chemical plant sludge into a nontoxic effluent [44].

32.4.2 Fungus Laccases

The majority of discovered laccases are derived from fungi, with prevalent representation in deuteromycetes, ascomycetous, and basidiomycetous species [45, 46]. Notably, several *Trichoderma* species, recognized for cellulase production, have been identified as laccase producers [47]. Examples of laccase-producing *Trichoderma* species include *Trichoderma atroviride* [48], *Trichoderma longibrachiatum* [49], and *Trichoderma harzianum* [48]. Additionally, certain Trichoderma species induce laccase synthesis in white rot fungi [50]. Laccase characterization has primarily been conducted within basidiomycetes, with notable sources including *Phanerochaete chrysosporium, T. versicolor, Trametes hirsute, Trametes villosa, Trametes ochracea, Trametes gallica, Cerena maxima, Lentinus tigrinus, Coriolposis polyzona, Pleurotus osteatus, Stereum ostrea, Theliophora terristrus,* and *Lenzitis betulina* [51, 52].

Fungal laccases typically exhibit an isoelectric point around 4.0, with a range spanning 3–7, and an optimal temperature range between 40 and 70 °C [53]. Notably, these enzymes are commonly glycosylated, contributing to their stability [54]. Functionally, fungal laccases play crucial roles in plant disease, pigment synthesis, sporulation, and lignocellulosic material decomposition [55]. Contrary to certain observations, laccases from fungi, according to Munk et al. [56], do not necessitate mediators during lignin degradation. Fungal laccase production is predominantly extracellular due to high glycosylation, enhancing hydrophilicity and stability. However, certain white-rot fungi produce both extracellular and intracellular laccases, exhibiting similar isoenzyme patterns and isoelectric focusing [57]. Species such as *Suillus granulatus*, *P. chrysosporium*, and *Lentinula edodes* exemplify dual laccase production.

Fungal laccases are typically characterized by their lower molecular masses in comparison to plant laccases. They possess a range of biological functions, which include lignin degradation, the detoxification of pollutants, the decolorization of dyes, the biodegradation of xenobiotic compounds, the mediation of plant diseases, pigment synthesis, and sporulation. Marine fungi, such as *Cerrena unicolor, Diaporthe phaseolorum*, and *Pestalotiopsis* sp., have demonstrated the efficacy of their laccases in decolorizing textile dyes. Furthermore, studies by Bai et al. [58] have shown that spore-associated laccases play a role in melanin pigment synthesis, providing protection against hydrolytic enzymes, temperature fluctuations, and UV radiation.

32.4.3 Plant Laccases

The first reported laccase from plants was discovered in the Japanese lacquer tree, *Toxicodendron vernicifluum* (*R.vernicifera*), according to a study by Yoshida [2]. Laccases have been found in various plant species, including peach, sycamore, poplar, tobacco, *Liridendron tulipifera, Pinus taeda, Zea mays, Acer pseudoplatanus, Nicotiana tabacum, Lolium perenne, Populus trichocarpa, A. thaliana, Oryza sativa, Saccharumo cinarum, Brachypodium distachyon*, and *Brassica napus* [55]. Plant laccases are characterized by a high degree of glycosylation and carbohydrate-rich regions, with isoelectric points (pI) typically ranging from 5 to 9.5 and optimal activity at pH levels between 5 and 9 [59]. Despite their potential, research on plant laccases is limited. Plant laccases share the same molecular architecture and reaction mechanisms as fungal laccases, with a lower standard reduction potential ($E°$) of 0.41 V for *Rhus verniciflua* and pI values between 7.0 and 9.6 [60, 61]. Unlike their fungal and bacterial counterparts, plant laccases have a larger molecular weight, ranging from 60 to 130 kDa, and consist of approximately 500–600 amino acids [1, 60]. This increased size allows for a broader range of functionalities, including the ability to oxidize substrates independently, a trait not found in most fungal laccases [62]. The presence of multiple isoforms within a single plant species highlights their versatility. For instance, *P. trichocarpa* contains five distinct laccases in its xylem, while Arabidopsis thaliana has 17 isoforms and Pinus taeda has eight [63–65]. The existence of multiple isoforms of plant laccases indicates that each type plays a specialized role in the intricate processes of plant life, such as lignification, the process of constructing cell walls with lignin. Through the oxidation of phenolic monomers, plant laccases regulate the polymerization process, enhancing the rigidity and structural integrity of cell walls [66]. This essential role is critical for the plant's ability to withstand physical stress and microbial assault. In addition to their role in cell wall construction, plant laccases serve as nature's detoxifiers, effectively tackling a wide range of xenobiotic compounds, including pesticides, herbicides, and industrial pollutants [64]. These enzymes provide a natural defense against environmental threats, and their involvement in dye degradation processes makes them valuable tools in the textile industry for sustainable dye decolorization [44, 67].

Notably, plant laccases also play a crucial role in detoxifying phenolic chemicals in green algae, protecting the algae from harmful compounds. Although plant laccases have not been extensively studied in bioremediation, some practical applications have been reported, such as phytoremediation [63].

Laccases and other enzymes from *Asparagus densiflorus* have been shown to be effective in treating industrial textile effluents [63]. *A. densiflorus* demonstrated the ability to degrade dyes and reduce the levels of toxic heavy metals from soil using laccase-mediated processes [64]. Laccases from other plants have also been successfully tested for dye degradation using suspension cells and purified laccases [63, 64]. Studies have suggested that some laccases may be involved in the detoxification or degradation of herbicides [63–65, 68].

Plant laccases have been identified as integral components of diverse biological processes, including biosynthesis and polymerization of lignin, elongation, and stress response [63–65, 68]. Additionally, they participate in the formation of cell wall-associated polymers, providing structural support and contributing to the synthesis of ultraviolet (UV) absorbing compounds that shield algae from harmful solar radiation [65]. The broad range of enzymatic activities exhibited by plant laccases, encompassing lignification, xenobiotic detoxification, dye degradation, and algal defense, underscores their considerable significance in various biological processes and environmental applications [64]. As our understanding of these enzymes deepens, their potential to revolutionize various industries and contribute to a more sustainable future becomes increasingly apparent.

32.4.4 Animal Laccases

Animal laccases are widely distributed across various taxonomic groups, including arthropods, mollusks, and mammals, with an emphasis on insects. Extensive research has been conducted on these enzymes in insect species such as *Bombyx, Anopheles, Apis, Calliphora, Drosophila, Lucilia, Diploptera, Monochamus, Musca, Manduca, Papilio, Rhodnius, Phormia, Oryctes, Sexta, Schistocerca, Sarcophaga,* and *Tenebrio*. These organisms are classified under the orders Coleoptera, Diptera, Lepidoptera, and Hymenoptera. Genetic variations in human laccases, particularly those found in epithelial cells and termite intestines, have been linked to susceptibility to various diseases, including leprosy, juvenile idiopathic arthritis, ulcerative colitis, and Crohn's disease. Additionally, animal laccases have been found to play a protective role in the intestines of herbivorous insects, mitigating the toxic effects of lignin derivatives.

The molecular weight of animal laccases typically falls within the range of 70–100 kD, while the pH and isoelectric point (pI) values are observed to be within the ranges of 5–6.5 and 5.1–6.3, respectively [69, 70]. The primary functions attributed to animal laccases include detoxification of xenobiotics, pigmentation, sclerotization of the cuticle during the pupal, larval, and adult stages of insect development, and the delignification of food items. Specific instances of sclerotization have been reported in insects such as *Drosophila virilis, Reticulitermes flavipes,* and *Tribolium castaneum* [55, 71].

The cuticle of insects houses two MCO, each comprising four copper ions, which exhibit ortho- and para-diphenol oxidizing activities. Despite their pivotal roles in the development of insects, the involvement of laccases in various developmental stages remains limited. In sponge laccases, in addition to their role in the detoxification of xenobiotics, they also play a role in the delignification of lignin derivatives from their dietary sources. The oxidation of catechols by laccases is crucial in insect physiological processes such as tanning, wound healing, and immune responses [55]. Research on land crabs, including *Cardisoma haematocheir* and *Chiromantes dehaani,* has revealed guaiacol oxidase and cellulase-positive activity in their midgut glands [72]. Moreover, the salivary glands of *Nephotettix cincticeps* have been found to contain laccase, which secretes saliva involved in the detoxification of monolignols during feeding [7]. In *Manduca sexta*, laccase may play a vital role in the oxidation of harmful chemicals [70].

In summary, the roles of laccases in insects extend beyond detoxification and delignification, playing crucial roles in various physiological processes. Further research is necessary to fully understand the extent of their involvement in different developmental stages and physiological processes in insects.

32.4.5 Lichens Laccases

Lichens are a distinct category of organisms that exhibit a symbiotic association between fungi and either algae or cyanobacteria. The fungal component of lichens typically belongs to the ascomycetes, while the algae are primarily members of Chlorophyceae. The diversity of lichens includes various types, such as epiphytic, epilythic, and epigeic lichens. These organisms are known for their remarkable resilience, as they are capable of thriving under extreme natural conditions, and possess the ability to adapt their metabolic activities. In addition to producing laccases, lichens are also known to produce a variety of oxidoreductases and copper-containing phenol oxidases, such as tyrosinase.

The primary function of lichen laccases is related to the metabolism of phenolic compounds, such as solorinin, averantin, and averythrin, as well as the delignification process and other secondary compounds like lichen acids and solorinic acid. Certain lichen species, particularly those within the Peltigerales order (e.g., *S. crocea, Peltigera aphthosa*, and *Peltigera malacea*) and those outside the Peltigerales order (e.g., Usnea), have been identified as laccase producers. Lichen laccases play a vital role in the synthesis of humic substances and contribute to delignification processes [73–76]. Despite the reported laccase activity in various lichen types, the limited availability of reports can be attributed to the unique growth patterns and adaptive nature of lichens. Notably, there has been a scarcity of reports concerning lichen laccases since 2015, which highlights an important area for further investigation through dedicated research efforts.

The molecular weight of lichen laccases varies widely, ranging from low to high, with *P. malacea* exhibiting a weight of up to 340 kDa in the non-Peltigeralean lichen *S. crocea*. Notably, the metabolism of solorinin and solorinic in *S. crocea* is attributed to the physiological roles of laccase [77]. Table 32.1 provides an overview of various

Table 32.1 Laccase-producing organisms, their biochemical characterization, and applications.

S. no.	Organism	Substrate use	Temperature optima (°C)	pH optima	Molecular weight (kDa)	Application	References
1	*Rhus vernicifera*	ABTS	60	4	120	Lignification, degradation of bisphenol A.	[77, 78]
2	*Alcaligenes faecalis XF1*	Guaiacol, syringaldehyde, 2, 6-DMP, catechol, ABTS	80	8.0	~71 kDA	Decolorization of industrial effluent	[79]
3	*Phomaherbarum*	Agro-industrial residues	50 °C	8.0	298 kDa	Degradation of the dyes	[80]
4	*Bacillus amyloliquefaciens*	Aflatoxin	40 °C	6.0–8.0	35 kDa	Degradation of aflatoxin	[81]
5	*Kabatiella bupleuri*	ABTS	30–40 °C	3.5	70–75 kDa	Decolorization of synthetic dyes	[82]
6	*Bacillus* sp. MSK-01	ABTS and guaiacol	75 °C	4.5 and 8.0	32 kDa	Antiproliferative agent to cancer cells	[83]
7	*Bacillus aquimaris* AKRC02	Agro-industrial waste residues	45	7	65 kDa	Degrading environmental contaminants	[84]
8	*Gymnopusluxurians*	ABTS	55–65 °C	2.2	64 kDa	Decolorization of dyes	[85]
9	*Bacillus licheniformis* VNQ	Guaiacol and ABTS	55 °C	5.0	~48 kDa	Synthesis of bioactive 1,4-naphthoquinones	[86, 87]
10	*Trichoderma harzianum* S7113 (LacA and LacB)	ABTS	40 °C	9.0	63 and 48 kDa	Bisphenol A degradation	[88]
11	*Stropharia* sps. ITCC8422	Rice & wheat straw, Sugarcane bagasse	30–50 °C	5–11	100–135 kDa	Depolymerization of lignocellulosic biomass	[89]
12	*Bacillus* sps.	Millet husk	40 °C	7	63–75 kDa	Pesticides decomposition	[90]
13	*Fusarium oxysporum* HUIB02	ABTS & sodium acetate buffer	40 °C	3.5	≥100 kDa	Decolorization of dye	[91]

14	*Bacillus* sps. PC-3	ABTS	60 °C	7	36 kDa	Chitosan film functionalization	[92]
15	*Galactomyces geotrichum*	ABTS and guaiacol	45 °C	4.8	55 kDa	Detoxification and decolorization	[93]
16	*Ganoderma leucocontextum*	Guaiacol	40 °C	5	65 kDa	Decolorization, detoxification, compound degradation, and biosensor construction	[94]
17	*Ganoderma australe*	PDA-containing guaiacol	10–60 °C	5–8	48 kDa	Textile dye bioremediation	[95]
18	*Monilinia fructicola*	ABTS and sodium acetate buffer solution	30 °C	3–5	35 kDa	Construction of lab prototype of laccase-based bioreactor, biosensor, and bioelectrode	[96]
19	*Deconica castanella* CCIBt2781	ABTS, phenol red, veratryl alcohol	55 °C	2.5	64 kDa	Bioremediation of pentachlorophenol (PCP)	[97]
20	*Sphingobacterium ksn-11*	ABTS and syringaldazine	40 °C	4.5	90 kDa	Transformation of recalcitrant compounds (diclofenac)	[98]

organisms producing laccase enzymes, detailing their characterization and applications in industrial contexts. This comprehensive understanding of lichen laccases underscores their potential significance in both ecological and industrial contexts, warranting continued exploration and investigation.

32.5 Industrial Application of Laccases

The laccase enzyme demonstrates a remarkable breadth of utility across an array of industries, including food, textiles, paper, leather, pharmaceuticals, bioremediation, cosmetics, fine chemicals, and detergents. This extensive applicability is due to the enzyme's exceptional catalytic ability and its capacity to oxidize both phenolic and non-phenolic substances, some of which may possess toxic or nontoxic properties. Notably, the catalytic activity of laccase plays a critical role in mitigating the impact of various pollutants and recalcitrant compounds.

As a commercial product, laccase finds practical implementation in numerous industrial sectors, reflecting its efficacy and versatility. Its established utilization underscores its significance in current industrial processes, while its attributes position it as a promising candidate for future biotechnological endeavors. Ongoing research into the intricate mechanisms and substrate specificities of laccase continues to unveil its potential for innovative and sustainable applications in biotechnology. The role of industrial importance of laccases is represented in Figure 32.3.

32.5.1 Paper and Pulp Industry

The paper and pulp industry is one of the largest sectors globally, exerting a considerable influence on both the world economy and the environment. The current

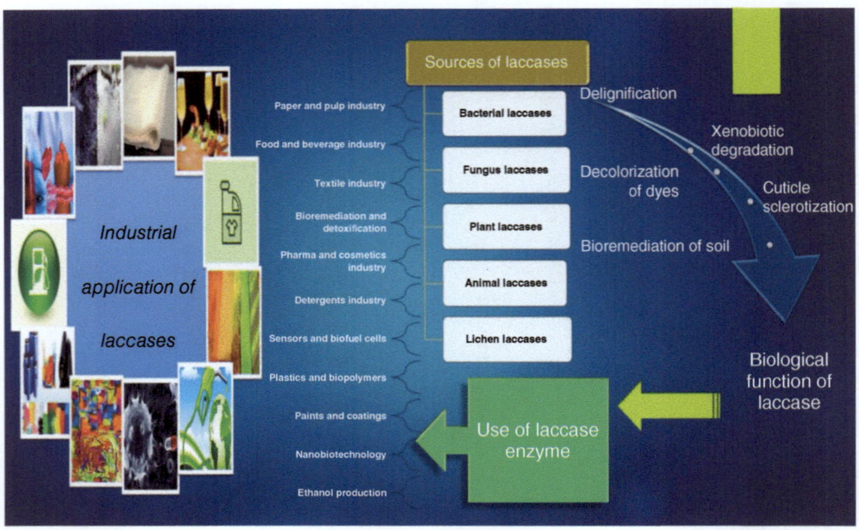

Figure 32.3 Biological function of laccases from different sources and its applications.

production and utilization of paper amount to approximately 300 million tonnes per day on a global scale, and projections indicate a surge in demand to reach 500 million tonnes by the year 2025. Notably, the predominant source for paper production is mature wood, contributing to 80% of the paper supply. However, reliance on mature wood poses significant environmental challenges due to heightened consumption of natural resources such as water, forests (as a primary source for wood pulp), and land. Furthermore, the industrial processes involved in paper manufacturing result in the release of harmful pollutants, attributed to the use of aggressive chemicals [99, 100]. The conventional physio-chemical processes in papermaking employ harsh chemicals, including sodium hydroxide, hydrogen peroxide, and sodium sulfide, under highly acidic conditions. This chemical-intensive approach imposes a substantial environmental burden, necessitating a transition toward more sustainable, biological alternatives. Bio-retting, bio-pulping, bio-deinking, bio-bleaching, and bio-refining emerge as pivotal solutions to mitigate environmental pollution, offering environmentally friendly alternatives to traditional processes such as retting, pulping, deinking, bleaching, and refining [101].

In the production of paper, raw materials such as wood undergo a pulping process to create pulp, which serves as the foundation for paper production. This process involves the removal of non-cellulosic components, primarily lignin. Plant laccases are responsible for the lignification of cell walls, while white-rot fungi play a crucial role in the degradation of plant lignin. Singh et al. [12] conducted extensive research on the involvement of laccases in the paper and pulp industry, highlighting their essential role in the removal and modification of lignin. The use of laccases represents a technological advancement in the development of biomass-based materials and chemical building blocks, as outlined by Zerva et al. [10]. This shift toward enzymatic processes not only reduces the environmental impact of the paper and pulp industry but also holds potential for sustainable and resource-efficient practices in the production of paper and related products.

32.5.2 Food and Beverage Industry

The food and beverage industry relies on enzymatic processes to address the transformation of various components, including polysaccharides, proteins with thiol groups, unsaturated fatty acids, and phenol-containing substances sourced from diverse origins. The exploration of laccase enzymes for cost-effective enhancement of the quality of food and beverage products has become a focus of research [102]. Laccases play a critical role in addressing issues of darkening or browning, turbidity, and haze formation in beverages, as they effectively remove phenolic compounds, improving color, stability, and shelf life. The enzymatic activity of laccases also facilitates the elimination of polyphenol complexes through oxidation, reducing oxygen concentration and increasing the overall shelf life of the product [10]. In the baking industry, laccases are employed as inducers to enhance the resilience of dough, impart softness, and increase the volume of bread, with *T. hirsute* laccases being particularly useful. These laccases catalyze cross-linking between ferulic acid and arabinoxylan within the dough matrix, affecting gluten content and structure, and contributing to the desired characteristics of bread, aligning with the objectives of the baking industry [5, 54]. The diverse applications of laccases in these food-related processes highlight their utility in optimizing product quality and characteristics, emphasizing their significance in food and beverage manufacturing.

32.5.3 Textile Industry

The textile industry, particularly in the chemical processing sector, is a significant contributor to global pollution due to the extensive use of chemicals and dyes in conventional processing methods. Conventional textile processing involves the application of various chemicals, exacerbating environmental concerns. However, laccase, a crucial enzyme, plays a pivotal role in mitigating the environmental impact associated with textile processing by offering sustainable and eco-friendly alternatives. Laccase finds application in diverse textile processes, including the bleaching of cotton, bio-stoning processes, decolorization of effluents, dye degradation, denim and cotton finishing, and enhancement of dye fixation in woolen and roving treatments of yarn regularity. Its versatility in various processes highlights its potential to address multiple challenges within the textile industry [67].

The utilization of laccase enzymes in textile processing offers an environmentally friendly solution to conventional methods, which are often resource-intensive and costly. This enzyme is particularly beneficial in finishing dyed cotton and denim fabrics, as well as in the removal of indigos commonly used in the denim industry. Fungal laccases, such as those found in *T. versicolor*, have demonstrated enhanced efficacy in the denim industry. Additionally, laccase plays a crucial role in the fixation of dyes in wool, the removal of azo dyes, and the improvement of the roving step to enhance yarn regularity. Through the oxidative combination of 3-methyl-2-benzothiazolinone hydrazine with phenols, laccase enzymes have the ability to produce red azo colors. Notably, laccase is increasingly being used to create novel colorants from phenolic and polyphenolic chemicals [10, 103]. One of the significant advantages of using laccase in textile processing is its potential to replace conventional chemicals, thereby reducing dependence on chemical inputs and minimizing the associated environmental impact. This alternative approach contributes to the conservation of resources, reduction of energy consumption, and decreased water usage in the textile industry [10]. Therefore, the integration of laccase in textile processes aligns with the growing demand for sustainable and environmentally friendly practices within industrial sectors.

32.5.4 Bioremediation and Detoxification

The process of industrialization, though providing employment opportunities, has unfortunately led to the depletion of resources and the generation of effluents containing hydrocarbons, nitrogen, phosphorus, and heavy metals. These effluents pose a significant threat to environmental components, including soil, crops, and human health, due to the presence of toxic chemicals. Effluents typically originate from various industrial activities, such as chemical washing, raw material processing, heating, extraction, and separation processes [104]. In response to the challenges posed by industrial effluents, the application of bioremediation, a process involving the use of living organisms and their products, has emerged as an effective strategy for toxin removal. Laccases, in particular, have garnered attention due to their ability to act on lignocellulosic substances containing both phenolic and nonphenolic compounds. This characteristic renders laccases instrumental in bioremediation efforts. Their proficiency in degrading recalcitrant compounds found in industrial effluents positions laccases as pivotal players in the detoxification and remediation of wastewater.

Recent advancements have showcased the application of laccases in coal biosolubilization. Notably, the *Fusarium oxysporum* LOCK 1134 strain has demonstrated the ability to biosolubilize lignite. Furthermore, the augmentation of this biosolubilization process has been achieved through the intervention of laccases, leading to the release of fulvic and humic acids [10]. This innovative application underscores the versatility of laccases in addressing environmental challenges associated with industrial activities, emphasizing their potential contributions to sustainable and eco-friendly approaches for effluent management and pollutant remediation.

32.5.5 Pharma and Cosmetics Industry

Laccase enzymes have emerged as valuable tools in diverse fields, including medical science, cosmetics, and agrochemicals, showcasing their versatility in various applications. In the medical realm, laccases have significant potential in the development of anticancer, antifungal, and antibiotic therapies, as well as in the detoxification of harmful compounds. One notable application of laccases is in the synthesis of bioactive molecules, such as the inhibition of fungal pathogens. For instance, laccase derived from Pseudomonas putida LUA15.1 has demonstrated inhibitory effects against six fungal pathogens, indicating its potential in antifungal drug development [105, 106]. Additionally, laccase catalysis has been used in the synthesis of a dimer product from sinapyl alcohol and ferulic acid, exhibiting antioxidative properties [105, 106].

In the field of agrochemicals, laccases have been employed in environmentally friendly and sustainable processes, such as the substitution of hydrogen peroxide with alkaline laccase, as reported by Saito et al. in 2012 [107]. This substitution represents a significant advancement and highlights the potential of laccases in agrochemical applications. Cosmetic applications also benefit from the enzymatic capabilities of laccases, which have been used to reduce melanin-derived blemishes in skin formulations, as reported by Tetsch et al. in 2005 and Nagai et al. in 2002 [108, 109]. This underscores the relevance of laccases in addressing dermatological concerns and promoting skin health. The diverse applications of laccases in medical science, cosmetics, and agrochemicals exemplify their potential as catalysts for various processes, ranging from drug development and detoxification to sustainable agrochemical practices and cosmetic formulations. The ongoing exploration of laccase functionalities continues to expand the scope of their practical applications in various scientific domains.

32.5.6 Detergents Industry

The utilization of detergents for stain removal constitutes a sustainable and environmentally responsible approach. In the detergent sector, enzymes fulfill a crucial function, and commonly utilized enzymatic agents comprise proteases, amylases, lipases, and cellulases. Conventional wisdom has not seen laccases as prevalent in the detergent industry; however, contemporary advancements have observed an emerging trend in their integration to enhance detergent efficacy [10]. The incorporation of laccases in this context signifies a paradigm shift toward the exploration of novel enzymatic functionalities to optimize detergent performance, representing a departure from the conventional enzyme types commonly employed in the industry. The integration of laccases in detergent formulations holds the potential for synergistically enhancing stain removal processes, thereby contributing to the ongoing development of sustainable and effective detergent technologies.

32.6 Sensors and Biofuel Cells

Laccase enzymes have proven to be indispensable components in the development of biosensors, thanks to their ability to detect a wide array of substances including catechol, polyphenols, dopamine, pharmaceutical residues, and various other analytes. Furthermore, laccases have also found application in biofuel cells, where they play crucial roles in strategic processes. Laccase enzymes have been demonstrated to significantly contribute to controlled evolution strategies in biofuel cells, such as in the case of the engineered variant of *E. coli* CueO MCO, denoted as D439T/L502K, which exhibits a substantially elevated onset potential compared to the wild-type enzyme. This enhanced electrocatalytic performance holds promise for optimizing biofuel cell functionality.

The exploration of laccase mutants has also yielded promising results. For instance, the K316N/D500G mutant of *B. licheniformis* CotA laccase has demonstrated catalytic proficiency in oxygen reduction at the fuel cell cathode, operating effectively within the electrochemical potential range of 0.59 V(SHE) at pH 8. These findings highlight the potential of laccases to serve as catalysts in the crucial cathodic reactions within biofuel cells, thereby contributing to their overall efficiency.

In biofuel cell applications, laccase's versatile functionality is utilized on both the cathode and anode sides, emphasizing its multifaceted role in enhancing electrocatalytic processes. The integration of laccases into biofuel cell architectures holds promise for advancing sustainable energy technologies and exemplifies the broader impact of enzymatic systems in bioelectrochemical applications.

32.7 Plastics and Biopolymers

Laccase enzymes possess a remarkable ability to generate a diverse array of functional polymers through oxidative reactions involving aromatic compounds.

One notable outcome of laccase-mediated synthesis is the production of the conductive polymer polyaniline . Moreover, laccase-mediated polymerization has played a significant role in modifying copolymers derived from xylylenediamines and catechol, as documented by Scheibel and Gitsov in 2019.

The transformative potential of laccases extends to the realm of lignocellulosic polymers, where their enzymatic action is frequently harnessed to enhance material properties. For instance, the grafting of octadecylamine onto jute fibers through laccase modification serves to impart improved hydrophobicity to the material. Through strategic alteration of lignocellulosic polymers, laccases can confer heightened strength, superior antimicrobial resistance, and modulated hydrophilic or hydrophobic characteristics to the resulting materials, as detailed in the work by Zerva et al. [10]. This versatile enzymatic approach holds great promise for tailoring the properties of various materials, thereby expanding the scope of applications in fields such as biotechnology and materials science.

32.8 Paints and Coatings

Laccase enzymes exhibit remarkable capabilities in synthesizing dyes, thereby contributing to the advancement of environmentally sustainable and green production processes. The diverse range of synthesized dyes includes phenoxazine derivatives, nontoxic dyes derived from benzene and naphthalene, resorcinol, 2,5-diaminobenzenesulfonic acid (2,5-DABSA), a dye specifically designed for protein gel staining, and coatings used in various applications. Laccase-synthesized dyes are particularly noteworthy in the formulation of paints and coatings, with phenoxazine derivatives, benzene- and naphthalene-derived nontoxic dyes, and resorcinol finding utility in these formulations and contributing to the development of eco-friendly alternatives.

The versatility of laccase-generated dyes extends to specific applications such as 2,5-DABSA, which serves as a dye for protein gel staining, demonstrating the adaptability of laccase-mediated synthesis in diverse scientific and industrial contexts. Beyond conventional applications, laccase-synthesized dyes are instrumental in the creation of paper-based lacquer paintings, where the eco-friendly nature of these dyes aligns with sustainable artistic practices. Additionally, laccase-generated dyes play a crucial role in the development of thermal insulation coatings tailored for exterior walls. This multifaceted utilization of laccase in dye synthesis not only underscores the enzyme's biotechnological significance but also exemplifies its potential to contribute to sustainable and green innovations across various sectors [10].

32.9 Nanobiotechnology

Laccases, due to their exceptional catalytic properties, have found diverse applications in nanotechnology, particularly in the modification of nanomaterials

Table 32.2 Recent advances for improving industrial applicability of laccases.

Enzymes	Recent advances in its application	References
Laccase	Lignin-degrading bacteria in paper mill sludge: Bacterial species with laccase activity and ability to degrade lignin *Agrobacterium tumefasciens, Klebsiella grimontii,* and *Beijeinckia fluminesia*	[110]
Laccase	Laccase immobilization using polymeric supports for wastewater treatment. Immobilization helps in implication on pollutant removal	[111]
Laccase	Molecular docking of Lac-CB10 helps in bioremediation of recalcitrant chemical compounds	[112]
Decolorizing peroxidase	Green and sustainable approach for decolorizing and detoxifying azo-dye	[113]
Peroxidases	Bioremediation of synthetic colorants from wastewater by microbial nanocomposite	[114]
Laccase	Newly isolated bacteria L11(16S Rdna). Showed high performance in multiple dye degradation	[115]
Laccase	Laccase mimicking Mn-Cu hybrid nanoflowers for visual detection of phenolic and degradation of dyes	[116]
Manganses peroxidase	Newly constructed manganese peroxidase-producing yeast consortium for tolerating lignin and decolorizing wastewater	[117]
Laccase	*Pseudomonas putida* strain MTCC7525 secreted laccase, which showed reduction in the toxicity of wastewater	[118]
Manganese peroxidase	Decolorization of dyes from wastewater by *Trametes hirsuta* PW17-41, MnP being the main enzymes, and FTIR analysis	[119]
Laccase, manganese peroxidase, and lignin peroxidase	Alteration in the genomic profile of bacteria by mutagens leads to detoxification by the production of oxidoreductase enzyme	[42]
Peroxidase	High percentage of COD, color, and phenolic compound removal by *Aspergillus uvarum* and *Phanerochaete chrysosporium* in treatment of kraft black liquor	[52]
Laccase	Reduction in organic pollutants of paper industry by use of multi-metal tolerant *Streptomyces tuirus* OS1 strain and production of biomass with enriched protein content	[120]
Peroxidase	Dye-decolorizing peroxidase from *Bacillus amyloliquefaciens* acts as a potential biocatalyst in lowering pollutants and biodegradation	[121]

Table 32.2 (Continued)

Enzymes	Recent advances in its application	References
Laccase, manganese, and lignin peroxidase.	Bioremediation and kraft lignin degradation of pulp and paper mill wastewater by use of *Bacillus cereus*	[84, 122]
Peroxidase and laccase	Synthetic dye and PAH degradation by plant peroxidase and microbial laccase	[123]
Laccase	Natural polysaccharides like chitosan and alginate proved to be green supporting materials were used in laccase immobilization. Helped in biosensing and biodegradation	[124]
Laccase	Immobilization of laccase on functionalized graphene oxide generates a nano-biocatalytic system for bioremediation	[125]
Laccase	Native fungal strains of *Aspergillus niger, Aspergillus flavus,* and *Penicillium digitatum* were used for decolorization and COD removal of cardboard recycling effluents	[126]
Lignin peroxidase	Bio-bleaching of high-quality paper and chemical pulp. Decolorization of kraft mill effluent	[127]

across various industries. One notable application involves the utilization of nanosized colloidal particles formed through the oxidation of lignin, which serves as promising platforms for a range of applications. In the field of environmental remediation, hybrid nanoflowers incorporating laccases have emerged as efficient nanobiocatalysts, specifically designed for the degradation of dyes. These hybrid nanoflowers harness the catalytic prowess of laccases to effectively break down recalcitrant compounds. The integration of laccases into nanostructures not only enhances the catalytic activity of the enzyme but also imparts elevated tolerance to high temperatures and extreme pH conditions. This augmentation addresses challenges associated with the low biodegradation and removal rates of xenobiotics, offering a viable solution for environmental management. This application of laccases in nanotechnology highlights their versatility and adaptability in addressing contemporary challenges, making them valuable contributors to the advancement of environmentally friendly technologies and industrial processes. The synergistic interplay between laccases and nanomaterials showcases their potential for sustainable solutions in the fields of biocatalysis and environmental science. Advances for improving the efficacy of laccase in industries are summarized in Table 32.2.

32.10 Ethanol Production

The production of fuel alcohol from the lignocellulosic components of sugarcane involves the hydrolysis of diluted acid. This process, however, is hindered by the presence of inhibitory phenolic compounds, which can impede efficient fuel production. To address this issue, Larsson et al. conducted a study in which they demonstrated the use of laccase enzyme, heterologously expressed from *T. versicolor* in yeast during fermentation. This strategic incorporation of laccase resulted in a notable enhancement in the generation of gasoline ethanol from sugarcane's sustainable raw material. The laccase enzyme played a crucial role in mitigating the inhibitory effects of phenolic compounds, thereby improving the overall efficiency of fuel alcohol production [128].

32.11 Conclusions

Based on scientific evidence, it is postulated that laccase evolved as one of the earliest copper-containing enzymes during the oxygenation phase of the biosphere. This enzyme exhibits versatility across a spectrum of organic and inorganic substrates, fulfilling a diverse array of catalytic functions. Laccases are ubiquitously distributed in nearly all living organisms, encompassing bacteria, fungi, plants, animals, and lichens. Notably, the functional roles of laccases exhibit organism-specific variations. In plants, laccases contribute to lignification processes, participating in the synthesis and reinforcement of lignin. Conversely, bacterial and fungal laccases are instrumental in delignification, aiding in the breakdown of lignin components. Furthermore, laccases play a role in pigmentation processes in animals, adding another layer of diversity to their biological functions.

The broad applicability of laccases extends to various industrial sectors, where their multifaceted functionalities find utility. In essence, laccase emerges as a versatile enzymatic tool with applications spanning different biological contexts and industrial processes. As an enzyme with diverse functionalities, laccase holds promise as a multipurposed biocatalyst, demonstrating its significance and impact across various fields of science and technology.

References

1 Dwivedi, U.N., Singh, P., Pandey, V.P., and Kumar, A. (2011). Structure-function relationship among bacterial, fungal and plant laccases. *J. Mol. Catal. B: Enzym.* 68: 117–128. doi.org/10.1016/j.molcatb.2010.11.002.

2 Yoshida, H. (1883). Chemistry of lacquer (Urushi). Part I. Communication from the chemical society of Tokio. *J. chem. Soc. Trans.* 43: 472–486. https://doi.org/10.1039/CT8834300472.

3 Nunes, C.S. and Kunamneni, A. (2018). Laccases—properties and applications. *Enzyme Hum. Anim. Nutr.* 133–161. https://doi.org/10.1016/B978-0-12-805419-2.00007-1.

4 Karla, M., Mirna, G., and Marco, R. (2020). *Laccases in Food Industry: Bioprocessing, Potential Industrial and Biotechnological Applications.* Frontiers in Bioengineering and Biotechnology 10.3389/fbioe.2020.00222.

5 Mayolo-Deloisa, K., González-González, M., and Rito-Palomares, M. (2020). Laccases in food industry: bioprocessing, potential industrial and biotechnological applications. *Front. Bioeng. Biotechnol.* 8: 222.

6 Solomon, E.I., Sundaram, U.M., and Machonkin, T.E. (1996). Multicopper oxidases and oxygenases. *Chem. Rev.* 96 (7): 2563–2606.

7 Hattori, M., Konishi, H., Tamura, Y. et al. (2005). Laccase-type phenoloxidase in salivary glands and watery saliva of the green rice leafhopper, *Nephotettix cincticeps*. *J. Insect Physiol.* 51 (12): 1359–1365.

8 Agarwal, N., Solanki, V.S., Gacem, A. et al. (2022). Bacterial laccases as biocatalysts for the remediation of environmental toxic pollutants: a green and eco-friendly approach—a review. *Water* 14 (24): 4068.

9 Zhang, L., Cui, H., Zou, Z. et al. (2019). Directed evolution of a bacterial laccase (CueO) for enzymatic biofuel cells. *Angew. Chem. Int. Ed.* 58 (14): 4562–4565.

10 Zerva, A., Simić, S., Topakas, E., and Nikodinovic-Runic, J. (2019). Applications of microbial laccases: patent review of the past decade (2009–2019). *Catalysts* 9 (12): 1023.

11 Sharma, P., Goel, R., and Capalash, N. (2007). Bacterial laccases. *World J. Microbiol. Biotechnol.* 23: 823–832.

12 Singh, G., Singh, S., Kaur, K. et al. (2019). Thermo and halo tolerant laccase from Bacillus sp. SS4: evaluation for its industrial usefulness. *J. Gen. Appl. Microbiol.* 65 (1): 26–33.

13 Sitarz, A.K., Mikkelsen, J.D., and Meyer, A.S. (2016). Structure, functionality and tuning up of laccases for lignocellulose and other industrial applications. *Crit. Rev. Biotechnol.* 36 (1): 70–86.

14 Strong, P.J. and Claus, H. (2011). Laccase: a review of its past and its future in bioremediation. *Crit. Rev. Env. Sci. Technol.* 41 (4): 373–434.

15 Hakulinen, N. and Rouvinen, J. (2015). Three-dimensional structures of laccases. *Cell. Mol. Life Sci.* 72: 857–868.

16 Sirim, D., Wagner, F., Wang, L. et al. (2011). The laccase engineering database: a classification and analysis system for laccases and related multicopper oxidases. *Database* 2011: bar006.

17 Kumar, A. and Chandra, R. (2020). Ligninolytic enzymes and its mechanisms for degradation of lignocellulosic waste in environment. *Heliyon* 6 (2).

18 Shleev, S., Tkac, J., Christenson, A. et al. (2005). Direct electron transfer between copper-containing proteins and electrodes. *Biosens. Bioelectron.* 20 (12): 2517–2554.

19 Claus, H. and Decker, H. (2006). Bacterial tyrosinases. *Syst. Appl. Microbiol.* 29 (1): 3–14.

20 Piontek, K., Antorini, M., and Choinowski, T. (2002). Crystal structure of a laccase from the fungus *Trametes versicolor* at 1.90-Å resolution containing a full complement of coppers. *J. Biol. Chem.* 277 (40): 37663–37669.

21 Shleev, S., Reimann, C.T., Serezhenkov, V. et al. (2006a). Autoreduction and aggregation of fungal laccase in solution phase: possible correlation with a resting form of laccase. *Biochimie* 88 (9): 1275–1285.

22 Christenson, A., Dimcheva, N., Ferapontova, E.E. et al. (2004). Direct electron transfer between ligninolytic redox enzymes and electrodes. *Electroanalysis* 16 (13–14): 1074–1092.
23 Bourbonnais, R., Leech, D., and Paice, M.G. (1998). Electrochemical analysis of the interactions of laccase mediators with lignin model compounds. *Biochimica et Biophysica Acta (BBA)-General Subjects* 1379 (3): 381–390.
24 Fabbrini, M., Galli, C., and Gentili, P. (2002). Comparing the catalytic efficiency of some mediators of laccase. *J. Mol. Catal. B Enzym* 16 (5–6): 231–240.
25 Xu, F. (1997). Effects of redox potential and hydroxide inhibition on the pH activity profile of fungal laccases. *J. Biolumin. Chemilumin.* 272 (2): 924–928. https://doi.org/10.1074/jbc.272.2.924.
26 Messerschmidt, A., Ladenstein, R., Huber, R. et al. (1992). Refined crystal structure of ascorbate oxidase at 1.9 Å resolution. *J. Mol. Biol.* 224 (1): 179–205.
27 Torres-Duarte, C., Roman, R., Tinoco, R., and Vazquez-Duhalt, R. (2009). Halogenated pesticide transformation by a laccase–mediator system. *Chemosphere* 77 (5): 687–692.
28 Bento, I., Martins, L.O., Lopes, G.G. et al. (2005). Dioxygen reduction by multi-copper oxidases; a structural perspective. *Dalton Trans.* 21: 3507–3513.
29 Quintanar, L., Yoon, J., Aznar, C.P. et al. (2005). Spectroscopic and electronic structure studies of the trinuclear Cu cluster active site of the multicopper oxidase laccase: nature of its coordination unsaturation. *JACS* 127 (40): 13832–13845.
30 Shleev, S., Persson, P., Shumakovich, G. et al. (2006b). Laccase-based biosensors for monitoring lignin. *Enzyme Microb. Technol.* 39 (4): 835–840.
31 Palmer, A.E., Lee, S.K., and Solomon, E.I. (2001). Decay of the peroxide intermediate in laccase: reductive cleavage of the O–O bond. *JACS* 123 (27): 6591–6599.
32 Shin, W., Sundaram, U.M., Cole, J.L. et al. (1996). Chemical and spectroscopic definition of the peroxide-level intermediate in the multicopper oxidases: relevance to the catalytic mechanism of dioxygen reduction to water. *JACS* 118 (13): 3202–3215.
33 Rulíšek, L., Solomon, E.I., and Ryde, U. (2005). A combined quantum and molecular mechanical study of the O_2 reductive cleavage in the catalytic cycle of multicopper oxidases. *Inorg. Chem.* 44 (16): 5612–5628.
34 Guan, Z.B., Luo, Q., Wang, H.R. et al. (2018). Bacterial laccases: promising biological green tools for industrial applications. *Cell. Mol. Life Sci.* 75: 3569–3592.
35 Arias, M.E., Arenas, M., Rodríguez, J. et al. (2003). Kraft pulp biobleaching and mediated oxidation of a nonphenolic substrate by laccase from *Streptomyces cyaneus* CECT 3335. *Appl. Environ. Microbiol.* 69: 1953–1958.
36 Chauhan, P.S., Goradia, B., and Saxena, A. (2017). Bacterial laccase: recent update on production, properties and industrial applications. *3 Biotech* 7 (5): 323.
37 Ece, S., Lambertz, C., Fischer, R., and Commandeur, U. (2017). Heterologous expression of a Streptomyces cyaneus laccase for biomass modification applications. *AMB Express* 7: 86–98.

38 Moya, R., Hernández, M., García-Martín, A.B. et al. (2010). Contributions to a better comprehension of redox-mediated decolouration and detoxification of azo dyes by a laccase produced by Streptomyces cyaneus CECT 3335. *Bioresour. Technol.* 101: 2224–2229.

39 Sherif, M., Waung, D., Korbeci, B. et al. (2013). Biochemical studies of the multicopper oxidase (small laccase) from *Streptomyces coelicolor* using bioactive phytochemicals and site-directed mutagenesis. *Microb. Biotechnol.* 6: 588–597.

40 Skálová, T., Dohnálek, J., Østergaard, L.H. et al. (2009). The structure of the small laccase from Streptomyces coelicolor reveals a link between laccases and nitrite reductases. *J. Mol. Biol.* 85: 1165–1178.

41 Kameshwar, A.K.S. and Qin, W. (2016). Lignin degrading fungal enzymes. In: *Production of Biofuels and Chemicals from Lignin*, 81–130. Singapore: Springer.

42 Bhayana, T., Saxena, A., Gupta, S., and Dubey, A.K. (2023). Enhanced decolourisation and degradation of azo dyes using wild versus mutagenic improved bacterial strain: a review. *Vegetos* 36 (1): 28–37. https://doi.org/10.1007/s42535-022-00496-y.

43 Pointing, S.B. (1999). Qualitative methods for the determination of lignocellulolytic enzyme production by tropical fungi. *Fungal Diversity* 2: 17–33.

44 Yadav, A., Yadav, P., Singh, A.K. et al. (2021). Decolourisation of textile dye by laccase: process evaluation and assessment of its degradation bioproducts. *Bioresour. Technol.* 340: 125591.

45 Giardina, P., Faraco, V., Pezzella, C. et al. (2010). Laccases: a never-ending story. *Cell. Mol. Life Sci.* 67: 369–385.

46 Kiiskinen, L.L., Rättö, M., and Kruus, K. (2004). Screening for novel laccase-producing microbes. *J. Appl. Microbiol.* 97 (3): 640–646.

47 Gochev, V.K. and Krastanov, A.I. (2007). Isolation of laccase producing *Trichoderma* spp. *Bulg. J. Agric. Sci.* 13 (2): 171.

48 Hölker, U., Dohse, J., and Höfer, M. (2002). Extracellular laccases in ascomycetes Trichoderma atroviride and Trichoderma harzianum. *Folia Microbiol.* 47: 423–427.

49 Velázquez-Cedeño, M.A., Farnet, A.M., Ferré, E., and Savoie, J.M. (2004). Variations of lignocellulosic activities in dual cultures of *Pleurotus ostreatus* and *Trichoderma longibrachiatum* on unsterilized wheat straw. *Mycologia* 96 (4): 712–719.

50 Velázquez-Cedeño, M., Farnet, A.M., Billette, C. et al. (2007). Interspecific interactions with *Trichoderma longibrachiatum* induce *Pleurotus ostreatus* defence reactions based on the production of laccase isozymes. *Biotechnol. Lett* 29: 1583–1590.

51 Singh, D. and Gupta, N. (2020). Microbial laccase: a robust enzyme and its industrial applications. *Biologia* 75: 1183–1193.

52 Díaz, A.I., Laca, A., Lima, N., and Díaz, M. (2022). Treatment of kraft black liquor using basidiomycete and ascomycete fungi. *Process Saf. Environ. Prot.* 168: 67–76. https://doi.org/10.1016/j.psep.2022.09.065.

53 Debaste, F., Flahaut, S., Penninckx, M., and Songulashvili, G. (2018). Using laccases for food preservation. In: *Food Packaging and Preservation*, 501–541. Academic Press.

54 Osma, J.F., Toca-Herrera, J.L., and Rodríguez-Couto, S. (2010). Uses of laccases in the food industry. *Enzyme Res.* 2010: 918761.

55 Janusz, G., Pawlik, A., Świderska-Burek, U. et al. (2020). Laccase properties, physiological functions, and evolution. *Int. J. Mol. Sci.* 21 (3): 966.

56 Munk, L., Sitarz, A.K., Kalyani, D.C. et al. (2015). Can laccases catalyze bond cleavage in lignin? *Biotechnol. Adv.* 33 (1): 13–24.

57 Singh Arora, D. and Kumar Sharma, R. (2010). Ligninolytic fungal laccases and their biotechnological applications. *Appl. Biochem. Biotechnol.* 160: 1760–1788.

58 Bai, Y., Ali, S., Liu, S. et al. (2023). Characterization of plant laccase genes and their functions. *Gene Ther.* 852: 147060.

59 Berthet, S., Thevenin, J., Baratiny, D. et al. (2012). Role of plant laccases in lignin polymerization. In: *Advances in Botanical Research*, vol. 61, 145–172. Academic Press.

60 Morozova, O.V., Shumakovich, G.P., Gorbacheva, M.A. et al. (2007). "Blue" laccases. *Biochemistry (Moscow)* 72: 1136–1150.

61 Frasconi, M., Favero, G., Boer, H. et al. (2010). Kinetic and biochemical properties of high and low redox potential laccases from fungal and plant origin. *Biochim. Biophys. Acta, Proteins Proteomics* 1804 (4): 899–908.

62 Thurston, C.F. (1994). The structure and function of fungal laccases. *Microbiology* 140 (1): 19–26.

63 Watharkar, A.D., Kadam, S.K., Khandare, R.V. et al. (2018). *Asparagus densiflorus* in a vertical subsurface flow phytoreactor for treatment of real textile effluent: a lab to land approach for in situ soil remediation. *Ecotoxicol. Environ. Saf.* 161: 70–77.

64 Arregui, L., Ayala, M., Gómez-Gil, X. et al. (2019). Laccases: structure, function, and potential application in water bioremediation. *Microb. Cell Fact.* 18 (1): 1–33.

65 Huang, M.T., Lu, Y.C., Zhang, S. et al. (2016). Rice (*Oryza sativa*) laccases involved in modification and detoxification of herbicides atrazine and isoproturon residues in plants. *J. Agric. Food. Chem.* 64 (33): 6397–6406.

66 Tobimatsu, Y. and Schuetz, M. (2019). Lignin polymerization: how do plants manage the chemistry so well? *Curr. Opin. Biotechnol.* 56: 75–81.

67 Mojsov, K.D. (2014). Biotechnological applications of laccases in the textile industry. *Savremene Tehnol.* 3 (1): 76–79.

68 Chiaiese, P., Palomba, F., Galante, C. et al. (2012). Transgenic tobacco plants expressing a fungal laccase are able to reduce phenol content from olive mill wastewaters. *Int. J. Phytorem.* 14 (9): 835–844.

69 Bajpai, P. (1999). Application of enzymes in the pulp and paper industry. *Biotechnol. Progr.* 15 (2): 147–157.

70 Dittmer, N.T., Suderman, R.J., Jiang, H. et al. (2004). Characterization of cDNAs encoding putative laccase-like multicopper oxidases and developmental expression in the tobacco hornworm, *Manduca sexta*, and the malaria mosquito, Anopheles gambiae. *Insect Biochem. Mol. Biol.* 34 (1): 29–41.

71 Arakane, Y., Muthukrishnan, S., Beeman, R.W. et al. (2005). Laccase 2 is the phenoloxidase gene required for beetle cuticle tanning. *Proc. Natl. Acad. Sci. U. S. A.* 102: 11337–11342.

72 Miyake, K., Ura, K., Chida, S. et al. (2019). Guaiacol oxidation activity of herbivorous land crabs, *Chiromantes haematocheir* and *Chiromantes dehaani*. *J. Biosci. Bioeng.* 128 (3): 316–322.

73 Beckett, R.P., Minibayeva, F.V., and Liers, C. (2013). On the occurrence of peroxidase and laccase activity in lichens. *Lichenologist* 45 (2): 277–283.

74 Laufer, Z., Beckett, R.P., and Minibayeva, F.V. (2006). Co-occurrence of the multicopper oxidases tyrosinase and laccase in lichens in sub-order peltigerineae. *Ann. Bot.* 98: 1035–1042.

75 Lisov, A.V., Zavarzina, A.G., Zavarzin, A.A., and Leontievsky, A.A. (2007). Laccases produced by lichens of the order Peltigerales. *FEMS Microbiol. Lett.* 275 (1): 46–52.

76 Zavarzina, A.G. and Zavarzin, A.A. (2006). Laccase and tyrosinase activities in lichens. *Microbiology* 75: 546–556.

77 Forootanfar, H. and Faramarzi, M.A. (2015). Insights into laccase producing organisms, fermentation states, purification strategies, and biotechnological applications. *Biotechnol. Progr.* 31 (6): 1443–1463.

78 Patel, S.K., Gupta, R.K., Kim, S.Y. et al. (2021). *Rhus vernicifera* laccase immobilization on magnetic nanoparticles to improve stability and its potential application in bisphenol A degradation. *Indian J. Microbiol.* 61: 45–54.

79 Mehandia, S., Sharma, S.C., and Arya, S.K. (2020). Isolation and characterization of an alkali and thermostable laccase from a novel Alcaligenes faecalis and its application in decolorization of synthetic dyes. *Biotechnol. Rep.* 25: e00413. https://doi.org/10.1016/j.btre.2019.e00413.

80 Debnath, R., Mistry, P., Roy, P. et al. (2021). Partial purification and characterization of a thermophilic and alkali-stable laccase of Phoma herbarum isolate KU4 with dye-decolorization efficiency. *Prep. Biochem. Biotechnol.* 51 (9): 901–918.

81 Xiong, D., Wen, J., Lu, G. et al. (2022). Isolation, purification, and characterization of a laccase-degrading aflatoxin B1 from *Bacillus amyloliquefaciens* B10. *Toxins* 14: 250. http://dx.doi.org/10.3390/toxins14040250.

82 Wiśniewska, K.M., Twarda-Clapa, A., and Białkowska, A.M. (2021). Screening of novel laccase producers—isolation and characterization of cold-adapted laccase from *Kabatiella bupleuri* G3 capable of synthetic dye decolorization. *Biomolecules* 11 (6): 828.

83 Sondhi, S., Kaur, R., and Madan, J. (2021). Purification and characterization of a novel white highly thermo stable laccase from a novel *Bacillus* sp. MSK-01 having potential to be used as anticancer agent. *Int. J. Biol. Macromol.* 170: 232–238.

84 Kumar, A., Singh, A.K., Bilal, M., and Chandra, R. (2022). Sustainable production of thermostable laccase from agro-residues waste by *Bacillus aquimaris* AKRC02. *Catal. Lett.* 152 (6): 1784–1800.

85 Sun, Y., Liu, Z.L., Hu, B.Y. et al. (2021). Purification and characterization of a thermo-and pH-stable laccase from the litter-decomposing fungus *Gymnopus* *luxurians* and laccase mediator systems for dye decolorization. *Front. Microbiol.* 12: 672620.

86 Sharma, V., Pugazhenthi, G., and Vasanth, D. (2022). Production and characterization of a novel thermostable laccase from Bacillus licheniformis VNQ and its application in synthesis of bioactive 1,4-naphthoquinones. *J. Biosci. Bioeng.* 133 (1): 8–16.

87 Lopes, P., Koschorreck, K., Nedergaard Pedersen, J. et al. (2019). Bacillus licheniformis CotA Laccase mutant: electrocatalytic reduction of O_2 from 0.6 V (SHE) at pH 8 and in seawater. *ChemElectroChem* 6 (7): 2043–2049.

88 Elsayed, A.M., Mahmoud, M., Abdel Karim, G.S. et al. (2023). Purification and biochemical characterization of two laccase isoenzymes isolated from *Trichoderma harzianum* S7113 and its application for bisphenol A degradation. *Microb. Cell Fact.* 22 (1): 1–12.

89 Agrawal, K. and Verma, P. (2020). Production optimization of yellow laccase from Stropharia sp. ITCC 8422 and enzyme-mediated depolymerization and hydrolysis of lignocellulosic biomass for biorefinery application. *Biomass Convers. Biorefin.* 1–20. https://doi.org/10.1007/s13399-020-00869-w.

90 Srinivasan, P., Selvankumar, T., Kamala-Kannan, S. et al. (2019). Production and purification of laccase by *Bacillus* sp. using millet husks and its pesticide degradation application. *3 Biotech* 9 (11): 396. https://doi.org/10.1007/s13105-019-1900-8.

91 Huy, N.D., Le, N.T.M., Chew, K.W. et al. (2021). Characterization of a recombinant laccase from *Fusarium oxysporum* HUIB02 for biochemical application on dyes removal. *Biochem. Eng. J.* 168: 107958. https://doi.org/10.1016/j.bej.2021.107958.

92 Sharma, V., Ayothiraman, S., and Dhakshinamoorthy, V. (2019). Production of highly thermo-tolerant laccase from novel thermophilic bacterium *Bacillus* sp. PC-3 and its application in functionalization of chitosan film. *J. Biosci. Bioeng.* 127 (6): 672–678. https://doi.org/10.1016/j.jbiosc.2018.11.008.

93 Pourkhanali, K., Khayati, G., Mizani, F., and Raouf, F. (2021). Isolation, identification and optimization of enhanced production of laccase from *Galactomyces geotrichum* under solid-state fermentation. *Prep. Biochem. Biotechnol.* 51 (7): 659–668. https://doi.org/10.1080/10826068.2020.1848867.

94 Umar, A. and Ahmed, S. (2022). Optimization, purification and characterization of laccase from *Ganoderma leucocontextum* along with its phylogenetic relationship. *Sci. Rep.* 12 (1): 2416. https://doi.org/10.1038/s41598-022-06111-z.

95 Si, J., Wu, Y., Ma, H.F. et al. (2021). Selection of a pH-and temperature-stable laccase from Ganoderma australe and its application for bioremediation of textile dyes. *J. Environ. Manage.* 299: 113619. https://doi.org/10.1016/j.jenvman.2021.113619.

96 Demkiv, O.M., Gayda, G.Z., Broda, D., and Gonchar, M.V. (2021). Extracellular laccase from *Monilinia fructicola*: isolation, primary characterization and application. *Cell Biol. Int.* 45 (3): 536–548. https://doi.org/10.1002/cbin.11316.

97 Coelho, G.D., Ballaminut, N., Thomaz, D.V., and Gomes Machado, K.M. (2019). Characterization of a thermostable *Deconica castanella* Laccase and application toward pentachlorophenol degradation. *Prep. Biochem. Biotechnol.* 49 (9): 908–915. https://doi.org/10.1080/10826068.2019.1636280.

98 Neelkant, K.S., Shankar, K., Jayalakshmi, S.K., and Sreeramulu, K. (2020). Purification, biochemical characterization, and facile immobilization of laccase from *Sphingobacterium* ksn-11 and its application in transformation of diclofenac. *Appl. Biochem. Biotechnol.* 192: 831–844. https://doi.org/10.1007/s12010-020-03371-1.

99 Alam, A., Manuilskiy, A., Thim, J. et al. (2012). Online surface roughness characterization of paper and paperboard using a line of light triangulation technique. *Nordic Pulp Pap. Res. J.* 27 (3): 662–670.

100 Singh, G. and Arya, S.K. (2019). Utility of laccase in pulp and paper industry: a progressive step towards the green technology. *Int. J. Biol. Macromol.* 134: 1070–1084.

101 Tanveer, A., Gupta, S., Dwivedi, S. et al. (2023). Innovations in papermaking using enzymatic intervention: an ecofriendly approach. *Cellulose* 12: 7393–7425.

102 Sánchez, O., Sierra, R., and Alméciga-Díaz, C.J. (2011). Delignification process of agro-industrial wastes an alternative to obtain fermentable carbohydrates for producing fuel. *Altern. Fuel* 7.

103 Lantto, R., Schönberg, C., Buchert, J., and Heine, E. (2004). Effects of laccase-mediator combinations on wool. *Text. Res. J.* 74 (8): 713–717.

104 Sathya, R., Arasu, M.V., Al-Dhabi, N.A., and Vijayaraghavan, P. (2023). Role of biosurfactants in enzyme production. In: *Multifunctional Microbial Biosurfactants*, 307–328. Cham: Springer Nature Switzerland.

105 Aljawish, A., Chevalot, I., Jasniewski, J. et al. (2014). Laccase-catalysed functionalisation of chitosan by ferulic acid and ethyl ferulate: evaluation of physicochemical and biofunctional properties. *Food Chem.* 161: 279–287.

106 Jaufurally, A.S., Teixeira, A.R., Hollande, L. et al. (2016). Optimization of the laccase-catalyzed synthesis of (±)-syringaresinol and study of its thermal and antiradical activities. *ChemistrySelect* 1 (16): 5165–5171.

107 Saito, K.O., Ikeda, R., Endo, K. et al. (2012). Isolation of a novel alkaline-induced laccase from *Flammulina velutipes* and its application for hair coloring. *J. Biosci. Bioeng.* 113 (5): 575–579.

108 Nagai, M., Sato, T., Watanabe, H. et al. (2002). Purification and characterization of an extracellular laccase from the edible mushroom *Lentinula edodes*, and decolorization of chemically different dyes. *Appl. Microbiol. Biotechnol.* 60: 327–335.

109 Tetsch, L., Bend, J., Janßen, M., and Hölker, U. (2005). Evidence for functional laccases in the acidophilic ascomycete *Hortaea acidophila* and isolation of laccase-specific gene fragments. *FEMS Microbiol. Lett.* 245 (1): 161–168.

110 Yupanqui, M., De La Cruz-Noriega, M., Quiñones, C. et al. (2023). Lignin-degrading bacteria in paper mill sludge. *Microorganisms* 11 (5): 1168.

111 Iqhramullah et al. (2023). Laccase immobilization using polymeric supports for wastewater treatment. Volume 224, Issue 9. Macromolecular chemistry and physics. DOI- https://doi.org/10.1002/macp.202200461.

112 Buzzo, B.B., Giuliatti, S., Pereira, P.A.M. et al. (2023). Molecular docking of Lac_CB10: highlighting the great potential for bioremediation of recalcitrant chemical compounds by one predicted bacteroidetes CopA-laccase. *Int. J. Mol. Sci.* 24 (12): 9785. https://doi.org/10.3390/ijims24129785.

113 Xuejiao, A., Yi, C., Ningjian, L. et al. (2023). Green and sustainable approach for decoloration and detoxification of azo dye by bacterial-mediated thermo-halotolerant dye-decolorizing peroxidase (DyP). *Process Biochem.* 130: 334–346. https://doi.org/10.1016/j.procbio.2023.03.037.

114 Tomar, T., Kahandawala, N., Kaur, J. et al. (2023). Bioremediation of synthetic dyes from wastewater by using microbial nanocomposites: an emerging field for water pollution management. *Biocatal. Agric. Biotechnol.* 102767. https://doi.org/10.1016/j.bcab.2023.102767.

115 Rahayu, F., Mustafa, I., Marjani, R.F. et al. (2023). Newly isolated ligninolytic bacteria and its applications for multiple dye degradation. *Water Air Soil Pollut.* 234 (6): 359. https://doi.org/10.1007/s11270-023-06377-7.

116 Le, T.N., Le, X.A., Tran, T.D. et al. (2022). Laccase-mimicking Mn–Cu hybrid nanoflowers for paper-based visual detection of phenolic neurotransmitters and rapid degradation of dyes. *J. Nanobiotechnol.* 20 (1): 1–14. https://doi.org/10.1186/s12951-022-01560-0.

117 Ali, S.S., Al-Tohamy, R., Khalil, M.A. et al. (2022). Exploring the potential of a newly constructed manganese peroxidase-producing yeast consortium for tolerating lignin degradation inhibitors while simultaneously decolorizing and detoxifying textile azo dye wastewater. *Bioresour. Technol.* 351: 126861. https://doi.org/10.1016/j.biortech.2022.126861.

118 Haq, I., Kalamdhad, A.S., and Pandey, A. (2022). Genotoxicity evaluation of paper industry wastewater prior and post-treatment with laccase producing *Pseudomonas putida* MTCC 7525. *J. Cleaner Prod.* 342: 130981. https://doi.org/10.1016/j.jclepro.2022.130981.

119 Thampraphaphon, B., Phosri, C., Pisutpaisal, N. et al. (2022). High potential decolourisation of textile dyes from wastewater by manganese peroxidase production of newly immobilised *Trametes hirsuta* PW17-41 and FTIR analysis. *Microorganisms* 10 (5): 992. https://doi.org/10.3390/microorganisms10050992.

120 Khumchai, J., Wongchai, A., On-Uma, R. et al. (2022). A viable bioremediation strategy for treating paper and pulp industry effluents and assessing the prospect of resulted bacterial biomass as single cell protein (SCP) using indigenous bacterial species. *Chemosphere* 304: 135246. https://doi.org/10.1016/j.chemosphere.2022.135246.

121 Ren, J., Li, X., Zhang, W. et al. (2022). Evaluation of application potential of dye-decolorizing peroxidase from *Bacillus amyloliquefaciens* in bioremediation of paper and pulp mill effluent. *Front. Microbiol.* 13: 1031853. https://doi.org/10.3389/fmicb.2022.10331853.

122 Kumar, A. and Chandra, R. (2021). Biodegradation and toxicity reduction of pulp paper mill wastewater by isolated laccase producing *Bacillus cereus* AKRC03. *Cleaner Eng. Technol.* 4: 100193. https://doi.org/10.1016/j.clet.2021.100193.

123 Ahsan, Z., Kalsoom, U., Bhatti, H.N. et al. (2021). Enzyme-assisted bioremediation approach for synthetic dyes and polycyclic aromatic hydrocarbons degradation. *J. Basic Microbiol.* 61 (11): 960–981. https://doi.org/10.1002/jobm.202100218.

124 Shokri, Z., Seidi, F., Karami, S. et al. (2021). Laccase immobilization onto natural polysaccharides for biosensing and biodegradation. *Carbohydr. Polym.* 262: 117963. https://doi.org/10.1016/j.carbpol.2021.117963.

125 Noreen, S., Perveen, S., Shafiq, N. et al. (2021). Laccase-loaded functionalized graphene oxide assemblies with improved biocatalytic properties and decolorization performance. *Environ. Technol. Innovation* 24: 101884. https://doi.org/10.1016/j.eti.2021.101884.

126 Hosseini, Z., Ghaneian, M.T., Ghafourzade, M., and Nodoushan, A.J. (2021). Bioremediation of cardboard recycling industry effluents using mixed fungal culture. *Pigm. Resin Technol.* 51 (1): 118–125. https://doi.org/10.1108/PRT‐05‐2020‐0047.

127 Rahi, D.K. and Parmar, A.S. (2021). Ligninolytic peroxidases: sources and applications. *J. Adv. Sci. Res.* 12 (03 Suppl 2): 69–80. https://doi.org/10.55218/JASR.s2202112310.

128 Larsson, S., Cassland, P., and Jönsson, L.J. (2001). Development of a Saccharomyces cerevisiae strain with enhanced resistance to phenolic fermentation inhibitors in lignocellulose hydrolysates by heterologous expression of laccase. *Appl. Environ. Microbiol.* 67 (3): 1163–1170.

33

Microbial ACC Deaminase: Stress Modulators in Plants

Lalita Pal[1], Vikas Dwivedi[1], Vikrant Dwivedi[2], and Diwakar M. Tripathi[3]

[1]*Agricultural Research Organization the Volcani Center, The Plant Science, ARO Volcani Institute, 68 HaMaccabim Road, Rishon LeZion 7505101, Israel*
[2]*Tangerine, Data Analysis, 3389 Steeles Avenue East Tangerine, Toronto, ON M2H0A1, Canada*
[3]*Dr. Reddy's Laboratories Ltd., Research and Development, Bachupally Qutubullapur, Medchal Malkajgiri, Telangana 500090, India*

33.1 Introduction

Several intricate physiological and environmental factors, like plant genotype, the physical and chemical properties of the soil, the accessibility of nutrients, and other elements, have an impact on the overall plant performance. Abiotic stresses are the main factor affecting global agricultural production, as approx. 50% yield loss has been reported globally for the majority of crops [1]. Abiotic variables, such as salt, drought, temperature, mechanical injury, waterlogging, organic pollutants, heavy metals, nutrients, and other xenobiotics, may have an adverse effect on crop development and production [2, 3]. Healthy soil is the key factor of the food system. Microbial enzymes are crucial for soil quality and function as they are involved in organic matter dynamics, nutrient cycling, decaying of organic matter, its petrification, and release of nutrients such as carbon, nitrogen, phosphorus, and other essential metals. Many microbial enzymes like catalase, dehydrogenase, phosphatase, phytase, cellulase, amylase, hydrolases, chitinase, helicases, and ACC-deaminase affect the recycling of nutrients and thus improve the fertility of the soil [4, 5]. The world's food supply must increase to meet the growing needs of a rapidly growing population. Various biological and nutritional deficiencies in plants could be addressed with fertilizers and chemical pesticides. By regulating hormone production, plants respond to external challenges. It boosts stress-related protein production in plants to avert the effects of stress. Modern agriculture has a significant issue from soil compaction. It makes natural sense to assume that compaction inhibits the growth of roots by preventing the root's capability from penetrating tougher soils. Due to increased operation complexity, the use of heavier equipment, and the significant degradation of approximately 65 million hectares of land worldwide caused by tillage techniques, new agricultural methods have made the soil more compact [6]. Bulkier and less porous soil limits the water and nutrient availability to the plants. The reduced soil

Microbial Enzymes: Production, Purification, and Industrial Applications, First Edition.
Edited by Dinesh Yadav, Pankaj Chowdhary, Gautam Anand, and Rajarshi Kumar Gaur.

pore space also limits the gaseous diffusion between the root and soil. Ethylene serves as an indicator controlling the growth of root in compressed soils and its production from root tissue increases in compacted soil. Ethylene concentration near the root increases due to the reduced pore space in packed soils and that affects gas diffusion from the root tissue [6].

Plants have evolved a variety of defense mechanisms throughout millions of years of development to combat negative adverse effects in response to changing environment. They alter their genotype or phenotype in some way depending on the surrounding environment during their development. The scientific literature provides numerous examples describing how plant growth-promoting bacteria (PGPB) and mycorrhizae aiding plants to grow under different environmental conditions [7, 8]. This is because certain soil microorganisms are effective at promoting plant growth.

In many plants, ethylene mediates stress response [9]. "Stress ethylene" occurs when the amount of ethylene produced exceeds the threshold. Excess ethylene adversely affects roots, shoots, and other crop reproduction [10, 11]. Since it affects the parameters, it affects the performance of the whole system. Although PGPB employs various approaches to encourage plant growth, it may be argued that one of the most important ones is utilization of the 1-aminocyclopropane-1-carboxylate (ACC) deaminase enzyme. It is significant to note that ACC is the direct precursor for ethylene production in plants. According to Ali et al. [8] and Glick [12], ethylene plays an important role during different plant growth processes like germination of seeds, differentiation of tissue, and development of primary root and lateral root. It also affects flowering time, anthocyanin production, fruit color changes and ripening, aroma of fruits, leaf aging, leaf and fruit cutting off, maintenance of interactions between plants and microbes, and mycorrhizae–plant interactions. The *AcdS* gene, which encodes the ACC deaminase enzyme, is carefully controlled, and regulated in response to environmental factors. The LRP protein and regulatory domains that are triggered by various aerobic and anaerobic environments make up the gene-regulatory components of *AcdS*. Many PGPB produce the enzyme ACC deaminase, which makes these bacterial strains extremely effective at promoting plant development under a variety of adverse circumstances. According to Singh et al. [13], ACC deaminase (EC: 3.5.99.7) is a member of the tryptophan synthase beta subunit-like pyridoxal phosphate (PLP) superfamily that is extremely common and found in archaea, bacteria, fungi, plants, and stramenopiles [14]. This chapter provides an overview of how the ACC deaminase enzyme works in many plants to counteract the harmful effects of abiotic factors on plant growth. When PGPB exhibits ACC deaminase activity, the plants have a significantly higher level of resistance to various environmental conditions, especially abiotic stresses.

33.2 Ethylene Synthesis and Response in Plants

A few biological and functional activities in plants are regulated by ethylene, the trivial and most basic gaseous plant phytohormone. Many plants' functions like the emergence of seedlings, fruit ripening or maturation, senescence, root hairs and nodules formation, epinasty, and lengthening of roots are regulated by ethylene [15, 16]. Plant ethylene regulates the geotropism of pea seedlings during etiolation, and the plant organs ripen when exposed to kerosene [17]. Many factors trigger stressed ethylene production in plants that lead to controlling the expression of genes responsible for plant senescence [12]. Ethylene biosynthesis includes methionine conversion in S-adenosyl methionine (SAM) by the enzyme SAM synthetase and this further converts to 1-aminocyclopropane 1-carboxylic acid (ACC). Then further, ACC converts into ethylene through ACC oxidase enzyme.

33.3 Biochemistry of ACC Deaminase

First ACC deaminase, a pyridoxal PO_4^{3-}-dependent enzyme was shown to transform ACC to ammonia (NH3) and α-ketobutyrate, which are then broken down by the microorganism. Firstly, ACC deaminase was purified from different microorganisms like *Pseudomonas P. chloroaphis* 6G5 and *P. putida* GR12-2 [18, 19]. ACC deaminase is 36,500 Da in size and trimeric in form in terms of protein structure. ACC deaminase, from tryptophan synthase β-superfamily having pyridoxal phosphate-binding domain is cytoplasmically localized [17, 20]. It has a mass of 100 and 112 kD with different subunits of 35–42 kD [21]. This enzyme does not have a high affinity for the substrate (1.5–6.0 mM). The pyridoxal phosphate is required as a cofactor for ACC deaminase and ACC synthase activity and is required for the activity of ACC synthase catalyzes the synthesis of ACC [17].

The ACC deaminase absorption spectra were 416 and 326 nm from *Pseudomonas* sp. at pH 6.0 and pH 9.0, respectively [22]. The K_m value of enzyme varies from 1.5 to 17.4 mM and the total efficiency (kcat/km) of ACC deaminase is around 690 M^{-1} S^{-1}. This enzyme is highly active at pH 8.0–8.5 and 30 °C. ACC deaminase activity is regulated through its substrate ACC in media if there is ACC as a nitrogen source, so it shows the highest activity [23, 24]. The soil bacteria consume ACC that has been released from plant roots or seeds, and they then hydrolyze it into ammonia and α-ketobutyrate. However, because of ACC absorption and hydrolysis, the amount of ACC becomes less outside the plant root [23]. L-Isomers of amino acids inhibit ACC deaminase activity competitively. D-Amino acids are preferable substrates for ACC deaminase. The ACC deaminase catalyzes the opening of the ACC cyclopropane ring.

33.4 Genetic Regulation and Enzymology of ACC Deaminase

ACC deaminase conceded the deamination of its precursor, namely ACC, and its activity is regulated by cofactor pyridoxal 5′-phosphate (PLP). ACC deaminase can be activated by ACC or other molecules that are similar to ACC like D-alanine, L-alanine, 2-alkyl-ACC, D-valine, 2-aminoisobutyric acid, and vinyl-ACC [25].

However, it has been discovered that the enzyme exhibits the best efficiency in the pH range of 8.5 to 9.0. It has been shown that temperature also affects ACC deaminase activity. ACC deaminase from *Pseudomonas putida* strain GR12-2 was activated at 30 °C [18]. This enzymes catalytic efficiency was roughly 690 M^{-1} S^{-1} (kcat/km) [26]. Stressed plants produce ACC, which the microbial enzyme ACC deaminase hydrolyzes to -ketobutyrate and ammonia, lowering the amount of ethylene produced by stress. The deamination of ACC through ACC deaminase enzyme is a complex process and is carried out in two ways.

1) Direct β hydrogen extraction after hydrolysis of cyclopropane ring from ACC.
2) β hydrogen extraction after nucleophilic reaction and cyclopropane ring open from Lys51

The *AcdS* gene and protein have been isolated from a variety of Gram-negative bacteria, endophytes, fungi, and rhizobia [27–30].

The ACC deaminase gene of the symbiotic bacterium *Mesorhizobium loti,* a symbiont of lotus spp. may be controlled by *NifA*, which is proven to trigger *nif* gene expressions in conjunction with the product of the *rpoN* gene [31]. The σ54 RNA polymerase interacts with the protein NifA2, which affects *AcdS* transcription and *nifA1* also affects transcription of the *AcdS* gene [32].

AcdS is highly regulated by the quantity of substrate, O_2 level, and product accumulation in bacteria [33]. It is highly produced in free-living bacteria, except it has only been found in symbiotic nodules in *M. loti* [34]. It is also known that Leucine, produced from α-ketobutyrate, inhibits the expression of the *ACC deaminase* [13]. Since the ethylene response in plants is not regulated by the ACC deaminase gene in rhizobacteria, stressed plants are not protected by it. [35].

ACC deaminase enzyme from *M. loti* MAFF303099 showed no enzyme activity [31]. ACC deaminase gene expression in *Rhizobium leguminosarum* bv. Viciae 128C53K was shown to be regulated by ACC concentration [36]. The *S. meliloti* bacterial strain controlled *Medicago sativa* nodulation efficiency as it possesses the ACC deaminase from *R. leguminosarum* bv. Viciae 128C53K [37].

33.5 Role of ACC Deaminase from PGPR in Biotic and Abiotic Stresses

Many stresses like salinity, extreme temperatures, flooding, heavy metal toxicity, water deficit, and nutrient deficiency restrict global food production. ACC deaminase producing bacteria works as PGPR and helps in reducing the ethylene concentration near roots to enhance the root growth in plants so that plants can grow in harsh conditions (Figure 33.1). Under stress condition, bacteria that produce ACC deaminase are found in the rhizosphere of wild barley (*Hordeum spontaneum*) [38]. ACC deaminase producing bacteria also support plants in phytoremediation as they are transforming toxic substances and heavy metals so that plants can grow under adverse conditions [39]. There is a positive correlation between root growth and ACC deaminase activity under cadmium accumulations.

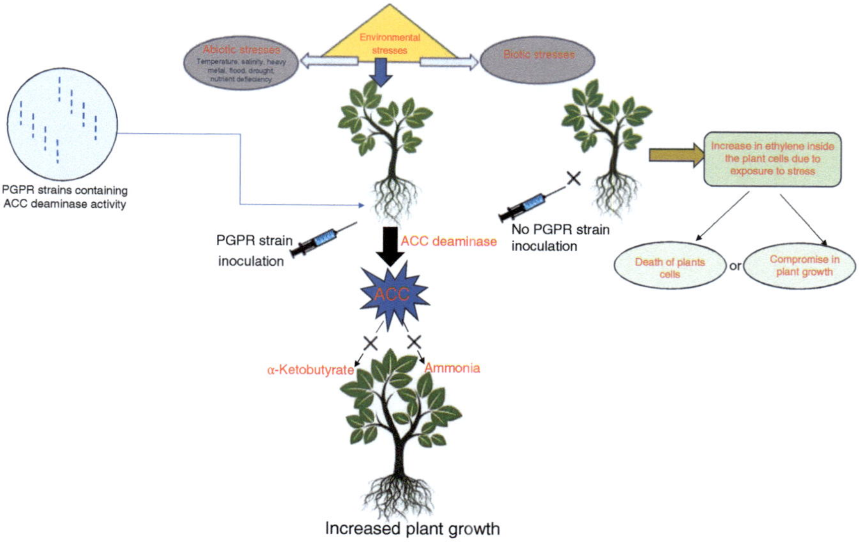

Figure 33.1 Overall effect of various abiotic and biotic and PGPR strains mitigating response in plants. Source: Adopted from [36].

Some widely known rhizosphere-associated bacterial family synthesizing ACC deaminase are *Achromobacter* [40], *Brevibacterium linens* [41], *Ensifer adhaerens* [42], and *Variovorax* sp. [43],

Rhizobium [29], *Bradyrhizobium* [44], *Bacillus* [45], *Burkholderia, Enterobacter, Serratia* [46], and *Pseudomonas* [47].

Plants are exposed to many stresses like drought, high temperature, salinity, waterlogging, excess pesticides, heavy metals, and other contaminants (Figure 33.1). Bacteria-producing ACC deaminase can protect plants from these stresses. Plants have immune responses toward different stresses. Some are physiochemical and some are phytohormone generated. Table 33.1 has summarized the previously studied microorganism associated with plant rhizosphere, which helps during stress when plant faces them. Ethylene at a lower level can ignite the other signaling molecules that regulate the expression and translation of genes [93]. The methylobacteria disseminated in the rice leaves produce the enzyme ACC deaminase, which regulates the ethylene amount [94].

33.5.1 Drought

Drought, low water condition, affects crop productivity worldwide. Under drought conditions there are several physiological and biochemical changes reported in plants [95]. Drought stress affects plant growth; thus, scientists have tried utilizing ACC deaminase-producing PGPR strains for stress tolerance. The *Pseudomonas* sp. RJ-15 and *B. subtilis* RJ-46 were used as bioinoculants in a few crops like *Vigna mungo* and *Pisum sativum* [96]. *Mucuna pruriens* was cultivated in drought by applying the *Enterobacter* HS-9 and *Bacillus* G-9 strains [69]. Many other

Table 33.1 List of the PGPR ACC deaminase and their role in different crops under various stresses.

S. no.	PGPR for ACC deaminase	Isolated from	Crop plants	Stresses	Functions	References
1	*Bacillus mycoides* PM-35	Rhizosphere soil	*Zea mays* (L.)	Salinity	Increased chlorophyll content, soluble sugar, and protein in plant	[48]
2	*Enterobacter cloacae* ZNP-4	*Ziziphus nummularia*	*Triticum aestivum* (L.)	Salinity	Increased shoot length (41%), root length (31%), and fresh plant weight (28%)	[49]
3	*Enterobacter cloacae* PM23	Rhizosphere soil	*Zea mays* (L.)	Salinity	Enhanced relative water content (RWC), proteins, phenolic content, and flavonoid content	[48]
4	*Bacillus marisflavi* CHR JH 203 and *Bacillus cereus* (BST YS1-42)	Leguminous crop	*Pisum sativum* (L.)	Salinity	Increased dry biomass, Increased carbohydrates, protein, and reducing leaf chlorophyll and flavonoids	[50]
5	*Glutamicibacter* sp. YD01	Rhizosphere of *Oryza sativa*	*Oryza sativa* (L.)	Salinity	Decreased electrolyte leakage and enhanced plant development	[51]
6	*Bacillus aryabhattai* EWR29	Wheat rhizosphere soil	*Triticum aestivum* (L.)	Salinity	Enhanced growth and reduced proline content	[52]
7	*Bacillus, Acinetobacter* and *Enterobacter*	Soil	*Medicago sativa* (L.)	Salinity	Increased fresh weight, dry biomass, height, leaf-to-stem ratio, chlorophyll, nitrogen, and phosphorus content in plants	[53]
8	*Enterobacter* sp.	Soil	*Oryza sativa* (L.)	Salinity	Improved plant yield and productivity by induced ethylene	[54]
9	*Pseudomonas* sp., *Bacillus cereus,* and *Bacillus* sp.	*Brassica napus* rhizosphere	*Festuca rubra and Brassica napus* (L.)	Salinity	Enhanced the physiological and biochemical traits in plants	[55]
10	*Bacillus cereus* LB1 and *Bacillus aerius* SB1	Rhizosphere soil	*Carthamus tinctorus*	Salinity	Promoted vegetative growth of plant	[56]
11	*Paenibacilluslentimorbus* B-30488	Rhizosphere soil	*Lycopersicon esculentum*	Salinity	Improved overall plant growth and suppressed phytopathogen's growth	[57]
12	*Dietzianatronolimnaea*	Rhizosphere soil	*Triticum aestivum* (L.)	Salinity	Improving salt tolerance ability of plant by antioxidant defensive enzymes	[58]

13	*Variovorax paradoxus* 5C-2	Soil	*Pisum sativum* (L.)	Salinity	Enhanced the plant growth by antioxidant enzymes	[59]
14	*Pseudomonas* sp. ST3	Root nodule of *Vigna unguiculata*	*Vigna unguiculata* (L.)	Salinity	Improved the RWC and photosynthetic machinery of peas	[60]
15	*Bacillus* sp., *Zhihengliuella halotolerans* and *Staphylococcus succinus*	Root nodule of *Triticum aestivum*	*Triticum estivum* (L.)	Salinity	Improved homeostasis and ion balance	[61]
16	*Pseudomonas fluorescens* YsS6	Soil	*Lycopersicum esculentum* (L.)	Salinity	Enhanced plant length (root and shoot) and plant dry biomass	[62]
17	*Pseudomonas putida* UW4	Soil	*Lycopersicum esculentum* (L.)	Salinity	Increased scavenging enzymes and proline	[63]
18	*Bacillus megaterium* (MU2)	Maize rhizosphere soil	*Triticum aestivum* (L.)	Drought	Increased germination vigor indices (SVI)	[64]
19	*Pseudomonas* sp.	Rhizosphere soil of cereal crop	*Arabidopsis thaliana* (L.)	Drought	Increased RWC, chlorophyll, malondialdehyde, glycine betaine, and stressor proline in plants	[65]
20	*Serratia marcescens* and *Pseudomonas* sp.	Rhizosphere of cereal crops	*Triticum aestivum* (L.)	Drought	Enhanced water status and osmolyte accumulation, in plant	[66]
21	*Enterobacter cloacae* 2WC2	*Withaniacoagulans* plant	*Zea mays* (L.)	Drought	Improved Morphological and biological parameters, RWC ROS in plant	[67]
22	*Bacillus velezensis* strain D_3	Rhizosphere soil of rain-fed area		Drought	Improved stomatal conductance and water-use efficiency and transpiration rate	[68]
23	*Enterobacter* HS9 and *Bacillus* G9	Soil	*Mucuna pruriens* (L.)	Drought	Improved water status and transpiration	[69]
24	*Mitsuaria* sp. and *Burkholderia*	*Arabidopsis thaliana*	*Arabidopsis thaliana* and *Zea mays* (L.)	Drought	Control levels of plant hormones and enzymes	[70]
25	*Bacillus pumilus* and *Bacillus firmus*	Rhizosphere of *Solanum tuberosum*	*Solanum tuberosum* (L.)	Drought	Enhanced ROS scavenging enzymes, proline for salt and drought stress tolerance	[71]
26	*Pseudomonas fluorescens* ACC-5	Nodule	*Pisum sativum* (L.)	Drought	Increased water status in plant	[72]

(Continued)

Table 33.1 (Continued)

S. no.	PGPR for ACC deaminase	Isolated from	Crop plants	Stresses	Functions	References
27	*Bacillus gibsonii* (PM11) and *Bacillus xiamenensis* (PM14)	Industrially polluted rhizosphere	*Linumusitatissimum* (L.)	Heavy metal	Increased fresh and dry biomass of plants	[73]
28	*Agrobacterium fabrum* and *Leclercia adecarboxylata*	Metal-contaminated rhizosphere	*Zea mays* (L.)	Heavy metal	Enhanced growth of plants by reducing metal uptake	[74]
29	*Rhizobium leguminosarum* bv. Viciae 1066S	Metal-contaminated rhizosphere	*Pisum sativum* (L.)	Heavy metal	Increased shoot biomass and nutritional mineral uptake	[75]
30	*Agrobacterium fabrum* (CdtS5) and *Stenotrophomonas maltophilia* (CdtS7)	Cd-contaminated wheat rhizosphere	*Tritium estivum* (L.)	Cd	Increased Cd tolerance and yield parameters	[76]
31	Combination of *Pseudomonas* sp., *Bacillus cereus* and *Bacillus* sp.	Rhizosphere soil	*Festuca rubra* and *Brassica napus* (L.)	Heavy metals	Sequestered metal levels in plant	[55]
32	*Pseudomonas aeruginosa*	Metal-polluted soil	*Cicer arietinum* (L.)	Heavy metals	Enhanced shoot length, nodulation, symbiotic, and seed yield	[77]
33	*Enterobacter aerogenes* MCC 3092	Rhizosphere of *Oryza sativa*	*Oryza sativa* (L.)	Cd	Reduced level of ethylene, increased chlorophyll content of plants, thus growth	[78]
34	*Enterobacter ludwigii* (HG 2) and *Klebsiella pneumonia*	*Alternanthera sessilis* and *Cyperus esculentus* rhizosphere	*Triticum aestivum* (L.)	Cr	Increased growth of seedlings.	[79]
35	*Enterobacter* sp., *Serratia* sp., and *Klebsiella* sp.	Rhizospheres of plants growing in mining waste	*Helianthus annuus* (L.)	Pb	Enhanced growth of plants	[80]
36	*Pseudomonas stutzeri* A1501	–	*Oryza sativa* (L.)	Ni	Enhanced metal tolerance	[81]
37	*Azotobacter* sp.	Metal-contaminated rhizosphere	*Zea mays* (L.)	Pb	Enhanced protein, proline, glutathione *S*-transferase and chlorophyll *a* and *b* and carotenoids, and POD and CAT enzymes	[82]

38	*Ochrobactrum* sp. and *Bacillus* spp.	Slag disposal site	*Oryza sativa* (L.)	Heavy metals	Enhanced overall growth of plant by reduced ethylene level	[83]
39	*Burkholderia* sp.	Soil	Assorted vegetables	Organic pollutant	Increased overall growth and functioning in plants	[84]
40	*Enterobacter intermedius*, *Bacillus circulans*, and *Serratia carnosus*	*Zea mays* and *per nigrum* Rhizosphere soil	*Zea mays* (L.)	Organic pollutant	Improvement of plant growth	[85]
41	*Pseudomonas aeruginosa* SLC-2 and *Serratia marcescens* BC-3	Contaminated soil	*Avena sativa* (L.)	Organic pollutant	Improvement of plant growth in petroleum-contaminated soil	[86]
42	*Pseudomonas aeruginosa* and *Serratia marcescens*	Rhizosphere of Echinochloa	*Avena Sativa* (L.)	Organic pollutant	Improved plant growth	[86]
43	*Burkholderia cepacia*	Cabbage rhizosphere	*Cicer arietinum* (L.)	Pesticide	Improved overall plant growth of chickpea	[87]
44	*Rhizobium leguminosarum*	Root nodules of pea	*Pisum sativum* (L.)	Pesticide	Increased length symbiotic features and nutrient in plant	[88]
45	*Pseudomonas putida*	*Withaniasomnifera* rhizosphere soil	*Papaver somniferum* (L.)	*Peronospora* sp. causing downy mildew disease	Enhanced stomatal behavior and rate of transpiration parameters in plant	[89]
46	*Bacillus xiamenensis* PM14	Sugarcane rhizosphere	*Saccharum officinarum* L.	*Colletotrichum falcatum* causing red rot disease	Increased production of defensive enzymes and proline in sugarcane	[90]
47	*Pseudomonas* sp. strain S3	rhizospheric soil of turmeric (*Curcuma longa*)	*Solanum lycopersicum* (L.)	*Rhizoctonia solani*	Improved osmolytes in plants, thus growth	[91]
48	*Paenibacilluslentimorbus* B-30488	rhizospheric soil of tomato	*Solanum lycopersicum* (L.)	*Scelerotiumrolfsii* causing southern blight diseases	Increased defense enzymes and enhanced plant growth	[57]
49	*Delftiatsuruhatensis* WGR–UOM– BT1	*Rauwolfia serpentina* Rhizosphere	*Solanum lycopersicum* (L.)	*Fusarium oxysporum*	Tolerance to fungal disease and improved in tomato	[92]

examples of ACC deaminase-producing strains d like *B. pumilus*, *B. firmus*, and *mitsuaria* sp. in different plant species reduced the proline level, thus causing stress tolerance [70].

33.5.2 Salinity

Crop productivity is significantly affected by salinity all over the world and around 20% of the world's cultivable land is under salinity stress [97–99]. Salinity alters many physiological processes, including homeostasis, increasing photorespiration and transpiration, and synthesis of chlorophyll in plant cells [100]. Nutrient imbalance has a negative impact on plant growth; also mineral deficits in the plant are the result of this imbalance, which prevents the proper uptake and transport of nutrients to growing shoots [98, 99, 101]. High salt concentration leads to an increase in ROS production due to oxidative rupture of cellular organelles. This results in a change in intracellular processes, including damage to the plasma membrane and negatively impacts cellular metabolism and homeostasis. The impact of the salinity later ends in enhancing the abscission of leaves and petals and speeds up organ senescence, which ultimately causes the plant to die at an early age [98, 99, 102]. Salt-tolerant and ACC deaminase-producing bacteria may flourish even in very saline environments, and their advantageous traits help plants deal with the effects of stress [103–106]. The salt stress negativity is further mitigated by these PGPR, which converts ACC to NH3 and α-ketobutyrate, which the plant uses as a source of nitrogen [107, 108].

There is an abundance of information on strains of salt-tolerant ACC deaminase-producing PGPR that can protect plants from the negative effects of salt. Halotolerant bacteria are microorganisms that can grow and live in environments that contain sodium chloride (NaCl) concentrations of up to 1–33% [109–111]. *M. sativa* (L.) plants grown in saline soil had increased plant height and biomass, more leaf-to-stem ratio, high leaf relative water content more leaf chlorophyll, and high nutrient status because of halotolerant strains of *Enterobacter, Bacillus,* and *Acinetobacter* that contained *ACC deaminase* genes [53]. The endophytic bacterium *Serratia grimesii* BXF-1 has been demonstrated to boost the nodulation and growth of common beans grown in high-saline soil [112]. Wheat (*Triticum aestivum* L.) plants grew and performed better in the soil supplemented with fertilizer and *ACC deaminase*-positive strains of *Zhihengliuella halotolerans, Bacillus* sp., and *Staphylococcus succinus* [61, 98, 99]. The PGPR strain of *Klebsiella* sp., enhanced growth of *Avena sativa* plants under salt stress and the expression profiles of the *rbcL* and *WRKY1* genes were upregulated [113].

33.5.3 Heat and Cold Stress

Low and high temperature can change many metabolic processes in plants like catalytic characteristics and performance of enzyme, membrane transport, and nutrient translocation; thus, they cause yield loss in many crops [114]. Cold stress causes yield losses by reducing germination, growth, and tiller number as they also affect photosynthesis as leaves become yellow. In grapes and tomato plants, the use of ACC deaminase-producing strain reduces the chilling effect [33, 115]. Many PGPR strains lack ACC deaminase activity, like *Sphingomonasfaeni* sp., *Pseudomonas frederiksbergensis*, and were genetically engineered with *AcdS* gene from *P. putida* and these PGPRs regulate chilling stress in *Setariaitalica* L., *Eleusine coracana* and *Solanum lycopersicum* L. [116, 117].

Heat stress downgrades many vital plant functions like seed germination, growth, and metabolism, and thus reduces crop yield throughout the world. During heat stress, PGPR-producing ACC deaminases convert ACC into α-ketobutyrate and ammonia, which reduces the adverse effect of heat in *S. lycopersicum* [118]. According to the use of *B. linens* RS16, a PGPR strain producing ACC (1-aminocyclopropane-1-carboxylate) deaminase in *Oryza sativa* reduced ethylene emission and ROS accumulation in soil and thus enhancing stress tolerance. Bensalim et al. [119] reported that the use of rhizobacterium *Burkholderia phytofirmans* strain *PsJN* in potato plants helped to grow potatoes under heat stress.

33.5.4 Other Abiotic Stresses

Several other stresses also have an impact that leads to change in different metabolic and physiological changes in plants such as flood, heavy metal stress, agrochemical stress, air pollution, nutrient deficiency, and other stress related to the organic contaminants.

During flooding stress plants feel anoxia and produce ACC that oxidizes ethylene. Ethylene causes chlorosis, necrosis, and less fruit setting in plants. There are many ethylene inhibitors like CO_2, silver nitrate, 1-methylcyclopropene, cobalt chloride, and 7-chloro-4-ethoxycarbonylmethoxy-5-methyl-2,1,3-benzothiadiazole, have been used to eliminate the ethylene effect in many plants [120]. In rice, waterlogging stress is minimized by ACC deaminase from *Streptomyces sp.* GMKU 336 as it reduces ethylene and improves chlorophyll content and root elongation [121]. In flood condition, many other strains like *P. putida* ATCC17399/pRK415, *Enterobacter cloacae* CAL2, and *E. cloacae* UW4 are used in tomato plants [122].

One of the biggest environmental and agronomic concerns currently facing the world is heavy metal-induced soil pollution such as Co, Cu, and Zn, which are utilized by plants in trace amounts, but at higher concentrations, they become toxic and negatively impact plant performance [123, 124]. As roots underneath the soil have the maximum impact due to the absorption of nutrients (including metals), stress ethylene is produced, which restricts root morphogenesis [125]. Many researchers have identified ACC deaminase-producing PGPR strains that are metal-tolerant and can be used as bioinoculants for different crops grown in heavy metal-affected soils. Many studies have demonstrated the beneficial effects of these ACC deaminase-positive PGPR strains on crops, including elevated plant performance and yield in *Brassica*, *Oryza*, and *Triticum* species against heavy metal stress. These metal-tolerating PGPR strains include *Pseudomonas* sp. to *Festuca rubra* and *Bacillus* sp., *B. cereus* [55], *Ochrobactrum* sp. and *Bacillus* spp., [83], *Enterobacter ludwigii*, and *Klebsiella pneumonia* [79].

Additionally, in legume crops, it has been proved that pesticide-tolerant and abundant PGPR can be maintained in stressed or degraded soils [126, 127]. According to reports, a PGPR strain *Burkholderia cepacia* PSBB1, which is glyphosate-tolerant isolated from the *Vicia faba* plant's contaminated rhizosphere produced a significant amount of ACC deaminase, reduced the herbicide's toxicity, and improved the overall performance of chickpea plants grown in herbicide-ameliorated soil [87].

The main factor that regulates plant tolerance to air pollutants, particularly O_3 exposure, is assumed to be the increased ethylene production during air pollution [128]. One study showed ethylene-producing gene significantly reduced O_3-induced leaf damage in tomato plants [129]. As a result, ACC deaminase-producing bacteria have drawn more focus as a stress-reduction strategy for plants exposed to air pollution.

According to Hemissi et al. [130], by converting ACC to ketobutyrate and NH3, PGPR ACC deaminase activity may, at low fertilizer application rates, lower ethylene levels in wheat under nutritional stress. The authors additionally suggest that PGPR, which includes bacteria that produce ACC deaminase, may be used in combination with fertilizers to increase nutrient uptake and plant growth.

Most plants become stressed when organic contaminants are present in the soil, which makes plants generate higher ethylene. The precise mechanisms underlying high ethylene production are still unknown. Numerous bacterial species from various genera have been discovered to digest organic pollutants like refrigerants and organic solvents [33]. ACC deaminase-producing PGPRs have consistently enhanced plant development in the presence of organic contaminants [131]. It is well recognized that petroleum, other xenobiotics made of hydrocarbons, and polycyclic aromatic hydrocarbons (PAHs) reduce crop production [132, 133]. *Burkholderia* sp., a phenol-degrading PGPR strain, was found in phenol-contaminated soil and was shown to minimize the toxic effect of phenol and enhance plant growth and biochemical activity [84]. Similarly, *Serratia marcescens* BC-3 and *P. aeruginosa* SLC-2, two PGPR strains that produce ACC deaminase and degrade petroleum, improved the development and physiological characteristics of *A. sativa* growing in contaminated soil [86]. Pyrene and phenanthrene, both dangerous PAHs, were eliminated by applying *Microbacterium* sp. strain F10a-R to polluted soil. This procedure also increased wheat growth [134].

33.6 Conclusions and Future Viewpoints

To increase food security in agricultural systems around the world while coping with agro-climatic circumstances that are continually changing, environmentally friendly management techniques are required. The past years were difficult around the world due to rise in the global warming, which ultimately affected crop health and thus yield. As the population is increasing, the world needs increased crop productivity, so there is a requirement for either stress tolerant variety or PGPRs strain-producing ACC deaminase enzymes. The current chapter focuses on how rhizobacteria that synthesize ACC deaminase interact and induce abiotic stress tolerance in plants. It is well known that a variety of stress-tolerant ACC deaminase-producing bacterial strains have an advantage compared to conventional bacterial strains and can flourish in large numbers in novel and stressful conditions to have beneficial effects on agricultural plants. Also, the chapter tries to summarize the mode of action of microbial enzyme that play a decisive role in improving agricultural soil condition with the encountered soil pollutants as the use of pesticides and chemical fertilizers become more abundant since the green revolution. Large-scale development of these advantageous PGPR strains is difficult since they must survive in severe environments, but the use of a potent PGPR strain is anticipated to offer numerous solutions to issues associated with modern agriculture. According to research, ethylene balance is essential for plants' overall development during abiotic stress and using PGPR bacteria to protect plants from such stresses may be beneficial. Therefore, keeping in mind and for the long-term goal of agriculture need, exploitation of the use of ACC deaminase synthesizing bacterial strains should be examined in abiotic stresses. It is also possible to examine rhizobacteria for the synthesis of ACC deaminase. Agriculture's long-term viability may depend on the use of bacterial strains that synthesize ACC deaminase. These strains work as biological inoculants for abiotic stress control. Furthermore, the application of this technology will be increased by revealing the key mechanistic mechanism of these PGPR strains.

Acknowledgments

We would like to express our heartfelt gratitude to Dr. Dinesh Yadav, DDU Gorakhpur University, Gorakhpur, India.

References

1 Stallworth, S., Schumaker, B., Fuller, M.G., and Tseng, T.M. (2020). Consequences and mitigation strategies of biotic and abiotic Stress in Rice (*Oryza sativa* L.). In: *Plant Stress physiology* (ed. A. Hossain). Intech Open.

2 Gull, A., Lone, A.A., and Wani, N.U.I. (2019). Biotic and abiotic stresses in plants. In: *Abiotic and Biotic Stress in Plants* (ed. A. De Oliveira). London, United Kingdom: Intech Open.

3 Gupta, K., Dey, A., and Gupta, B. (2013). Plant polyamines in abiotic stress responses. *Acta Physiol. Plant.* 35: 2015–2036.

4 Pal, L., Dwivedi, V., and Tripathi, D.M. (2023). Helicases: plant engineers in abiotic stresses. *J. Biotechnol. Crop Sci.* https://doi.org/10.5958/2582-5089.2022.00001.9.

5 Prasad, J.K. and Raghuwanshi, R. (2022). Mechanisms of multifarious soil microbial enzymes in plant growth promotion and environmental sustainability. In: *Bioprospecting of Microbial Diversity* (ed. M.P. Shah and P. Verma), 117–143. Amsterdam: Elsevier. https://doi.org/10.1016/B978-0-323-90958-7.00020-0.

6 Pandey, B.K., Huang, G., Bhosale, R. et al. (2021). Plant roots sense soil compaction through restricted ethylene diffusion. *Science* 371: 276–280. https://doi.org/10.1126/science.abf3013.

7 Glick, B.R. (2012). Plant growth-promoting bacteria: mechanisms and applications. *Scientifica* 963401: 1–15. https://doi.org/10.6064/2012/963401.

8 Ali, S., Charles, T.C., and Glick, B.R. (2017). Endophytic phytohormones and their role in plant growth promotion. In: *Functional Importance of the Plant Microbiome* (ed. S. Doty). Cham: Springer https://doi.org/10.1007/978-3-319-65897-1_6.

9 Tiwari, S., Gupta, D., Fatima, A. et al. (2020). Phytohormonal metabolic engineering for abiotic stress in plants: new avenues and future prospects. In: *Plant life under changing environment* (ed. D.K. Tripathi, V.P. Singh, and N. Ramawat), 543–576. Academic Press.

10 Klay, I., Gouia, S., Liu, M. et al. (2018). Ethylene response factors (ERF) are differentially regulated by different abiotic stress types in tomato plants. *Plant Sci.* 274: 137–145. https://doi.org/10.1016/j.plantsci.2018.05.023.

11 Mog, B., Adiga, D., and Nayak, M.G. (2018). Role of plant growth hormones in cashew: key strategy for modifying crop performance. *Int. J. Curr. Microbiol. Appl. Sci.* 7: 1470–1484. https://doi.org/10.20546/ijcmas.2018.707.174.

12 Glick, B.R. (2014). Bacteria with ACC deaminase can promote plant growth and help to feed the world. *Microbiol. Res.* 169: 30–39. https://doi.org/10.1016/j.micres.2013.09.009.

13 Singh, R.P., Shelke, G.M., Kumar, A., and Jha, P.N. (2015). Biochemistry and genetics of ACC deaminase: a weapon to "stress ethylene" produced in plants. *Front. Microbiol.* 6: 937. https://doi.org/10.3389/fmicb.2015.00937.

14 Ali, S. and Glick, B.R. (2021). The biochemistry and molecular biology of the enzyme ACC deaminase. In: *Microbes: the Foundation Stone of the Biosphere* (ed. C. Hurst), 365–390. Switzerland: Springer https://doi.org/10.1007/978-3-030-63512-1_19.

15 Sun, L.R., Zhao, Z.J., and Hao, F.S. (2019). NADPH oxidases, essential players of hormone signalings in plant development and response to stresses. *Plant Signaling Behav.* 14: 1657343. https://doi.org/10.1080/15592324.2019.1657343.

16 Zhu, T., Deng, X., Zhou, X. et al. (2016). Ethylene and hydrogen peroxide are involved in brassinosteroid-induced salt tolerance in tomato. *Sci. Rep.* 6: 35392. https://doi.org/10.1038/srep35392.

17 Glick, B.R., Todorovic, B., Czarny, J. et al. (2007). Promotion of plant growth by bacterial ACC deaminase. *Crit. Rev. Plant Sci.* 26: 227–242. https://doi.org/10.1080/07352680701572966.

18 Jacobson, C.B., Pasternak, J.J., and Glick, B.R. (1994). Partial purification and characterization of 1-aminocyclopropane-1-carboxylate deaminase from the plant growth promoting rhizobacterium *Pseudomonas putida* GR12-2. *Can. J. Microbiol.* 40: 1019–1025. https://doi.org/10.1139/m94-16.

19 Klee, H.J., Hayford, M.B., Kretzmer, K.A. et al. (1991). Control of ethylene synthesis by expression of a bacterial enzyme in transgenic tomato plants. *Plant Cell* 3: 1187–1193. https://doi.org/10.1105/tpc.3.11.1187.

20 Gamalero, E. and Glick, B.R. (2015). Bacterial modulation of plant ethylene levels. *Plant Physiol.* 169: 13–22. https://doi.org/10.1104/pp.\ignorespaces15.00284.

21 Raghuwanshi, R. and Prasad, J.K. (2018). Perspectives of rhizobacteria with ACC deaminase activity in plant growth under abiotic stress. In: *Root biology* (ed. B. Giri, R. Prasad, and A. Varma), 303–321. Cham: Springer.

22 Honma, M. (1985). Chemically reactive sulfhydryl groups of 1-aminocyclopropane-1-carboxylate deaminase. *Agric. Biol. Chem.* 49: 567–571. https://doi.org/10.1080/00021369.1985.10866774.

23 Glick, B.R., Penrose, D.M., and Li, J. (1998). A model for the lowering of plant ethylene concentrations by plant growth-promoting bacteria. *J. Theor. Biol.* 190: 63–68. https://doi.org/10.1006/jtbi.1997.0532.

24 Honma, M. (1983). Enzymatic determination of 1-aminocyclopropane-1-carboxylic acid. *Agric. Biol. Chem.* 47: 617–618.

25 Malerba, M., Crosti, P., and Bianchetti, R. (1996). 2-Aminoisobutyric acid prevents the substrate-induced inactivation of ACC-synthase without inhibiting the enzyme. *Plant Sci.* 113: 131–138. https://doi.org/10.1016/0168-9452(95)04294-6.

26 Klee, H.J., Romano, C.P., and Binns, A. (1994). The roles of phytohormones in development as studied in transgenic plants. *Crit. Rev. Plant Sci.* 13: 311–324. https://doi.org/10.1080/07352689409701918.

27 Gontia-Mishra, I., Sapre, S., Kachare, S., and Tiwari, S. (2017). Molecular diversity of 1-aminocyclopropane-1-carboxylate (ACC) deaminase producing PGPR from wheat (*Triticum aestivum* L.) rhizosphere. *Plant Soil* 414: 213–227. https://doi.org/10.1007/s11104-016-3119-3.

28 Rauf, M., Awais, M., Ud-Din, A. et al. (2021). Molecular mechanisms of the 1-aminocyclopropane-1-carboxylic acid (ACC) deaminase producing *Trichoderma asperellum* MAP1 in enhancing wheat tolerance to waterlogging stress. *Front. Plant Sci.* 11: 2213. https://doi.org/10.3389/fpls.2020.614971.

29 Saghafi, D., Ghorbanpour, M., Ajirloo, H.S., and Lajayer, B.A. (2019). Enhancement of growth and salt tolerance in *Brassica napus* L. seedlings by halotolerant *rhizobium* strains containing ACC-deaminase activity. *Plant Physiol. Rep.* 24: 225–235. https://doi.org/10.1007/s40502-019-00444-0.

30 Sofy, M.R., Aboseidah, A.A., Heneidak, S.A., and Ahmed, H.R. (2021). ACC deaminase containing endophytic bacteria ameliorate salt stress in *Pisum sativum* through reduced oxidative damage and induction of antioxidative defense systems. *Environ. Sci. Pollut. Res.* 28: 40971–40991. https://doi.org/10.1007/s11356-021-13585-3.

31 Ma, W., Guinel, F.C., and Glick, B.R. (2003). *Rhizobium leguminosarum* biovar viciae 1-aminocyclopropane-1-carboxylate deaminase promotes nodulation of pea plants. *Appl. Environ. Microbiol.* 69: 4396–4402. https://doi.org/10.1128/AEM.69.8.4396-4402.2003.

32 Nukui, N., Minamisawa, K., Ayabe, S.I., and Aoki, T. (2006). Expression of the 1-aminocyclopropane-1-carboxylic acid deaminase gene requires symbiotic nitrogen- fixing regulator gene nifA2 in *Mesorhizobium loti* MAFF303099. *Appl. Environ. Microbiol.* 72: 4964–4969. https://doi.org/10.1128/AEM.02745-05.

33 Shahid, M., Singh, U.B., Khan, M.S. et al. (2023). Bacterial ACC deaminase: Insights into enzymology, biochemistry, genetics, and potential role in amelioration of environmental stress in crop plants. *Front. Microbiol.* 14: 1132770.

34 Uchiumi, T., Ohwada, T., Itakura, M. et al. (2004). Expression islands clustered on the symbiosis island of the *Mesorhizobium loti* genome. *J. Bacteriol.* 186: 2439–2448. https://doi.org/10.1128/JB.186.8.2439-2448.2004.

35 Vargas, L.K., Volpiano, C.G., Lisboa, B.B. et al. (2017). *Potential of rhizobia as plant growth-promoting rhizobacteria*, 153–174. Springer International Publishing.

36 Chandwani, S. and Amaresan, N. (2022). Role of ACC deaminase producing bacteria for abiotic stress management and sustainable agriculture production. *Environ. Sci. Pollut. Res.* 29: 22843–22859. https://doi.org/10.1007/s11356-022-18745-7.

37 Ma, W., Charles, T.C., and Glick, B.R. (2004). Expression of an exogenous 1-aminocyclopropane-1-carboxylate deaminase gene in *Sinorhizobiummeliloti* increases its ability to nodulate alfalfa. *Appl. Environ. Microbiol.* 70: 5891–5897. https://doi.org/10.1128/AEM.70.10.5891-5897.2004.

38 Timmusk, S., Paalme, V., Pavlicek, T. et al. (2011). Bacterial distribution in the rhizosphere of wild barley under contrasting microclimates. *PLoS One* 6: e17968. https://doi.org/10.1371/journal.pone.0017968.

39 Qin, S., Zhang, Y.J., Yuan, B. et al. (2014). Isolation of ACC deaminase-producing habitat-adapted symbiotic bacteria associated with halophyte *Limonium sinense* (Girard) Kuntze and evaluating their plant growth-promoting activity under salt stress. *Plant Soil* 374: 753–766. https://doi.org/10.1007/s11104-013-1918-3.

40 Sun, L., Zhang, X., Ouyang, W. et al. (2022). Lowered cd toxicity, uptake and expression of metal transporter genes in maize plant by ACC deaminase-producing bacteria *Achromobacter* sp. *J. Hazard. Mater.* 423: 127036. https://doi.org/10.1016/j.jhazmat.2021.127036.

41 Choi, J., Roy Choudhury, A., Walitang, D.I. et al. (2022). ACC deaminase-producing *Brevibacterium linens* RS16 enhances heat-stress tolerance of rice (*Oryza sativa* L.). *Physiol. Plant.* 174: e13584. https://doi.org/10.1111/ppl.13584.

42 Katiyar, P., Dubey, R.C., and Maheshwari, D.K. (2021). ACC deaminase-producing *Ensifer adhaerens* KS23 enhances proximate nutrient of *Pisum sativum* L. cultivated in high altitude. *Arch. Microbiol.* 203: 2689–2698. https://doi.org/10.1007/s00203-021-02250-5.

43 Bessadok, K., Navarro-Torre, S., Pajuelo, E. et al. (2020). The ACC-deaminase producing bacterium *Variovorax* sp. CT7. 15 as a tool for improving *Calicotomevillosa* nodulation and growth in arid regions of Tunisia. *Microorganisms* 8: 541. https://doi.org/10.3390/microorganisms8040541.

44 Greetatorn, T., Hashimoto, S., Sarapat, S. et al. (2019). Empowering rice seedling growth by endophytic *Bradyrhizobium* sp. SUTN 9-2. *Lett. Appl. Microbiol.* 68: 258–266. https://doi.org/10.1111/lam.13114.

45 Din, B.U., Sarfraz, S., Xia, Y. et al. (2019). Mechanistic elucidation of germination potential and growth of wheat inoculated with exopolysaccharide and

ACC-deaminase producing *bacillus* strains under induced salinity stress. *Ecotoxicol. Environ. Saf.* 183: 109466. https://doi.org/10.1016/j. ecoenv.2019.109466.

46 Zafar-ul-Hye, M., Danish, S., Abbas, M. et al. (2019). ACC deaminase producing PGPR *Bacillus amyloliquefaciens* and *Agrobacterium fabrum* along with biochar improve wheat productivity under drought stress. *Agronomy* 9: 343. https://doi .org/10.3390/agronomy9070343.

47 Nascimento, F.X., Tavares, M.J., Franck, J. et al. (2019). ACC deaminase plays a major role in *Pseudomonas fluorescens* YsS6 ability to promote the nodulation of alpha-and beta proteobacteria rhizobial strains. *Arch. Microbiol.* 201: 817–822. https://doi.org/10.1007/s00203-019-01649-5.

48 Ali, B., Wang, X., Saleem, M.H. et al. (2022). PGPR-mediated salt tolerance in maize by modulating plant physiology, antioxidant defense, compatible solutes accumulation and bio-surfactant producing genes. *Plann. Theory* 11: 345. https://doi.org/10.3390/plants11030345.

49 Singh, R.P., Pandey, D.M., Jha, P.N., and Ma, Y. (2022). ACC deaminase producing rhizobacterium *Enterobacter cloacae* ZNP-4 enhance abiotic stress tolerance in wheat plant. *PLoS One* 17: e0267127. https://doi.org/10.1371/journal.pone .0267127.

50 Gupta, A., Bano, A., Rai, S. et al. (2021). ACC deaminase producing plant growth promoting rhizobacteria enhance salinity stress tolerance in *Pisum sativum*. *3 Biotech* 11: 514–517. https://doi.org/10.1007/s13205-021-03047-5.

51 Ji, J., Yuan, D., Jin, C. et al. (2020). Enhancement of growth and salt tolerance of rice seedlings (*Oryza sativa* L.) by regulating ethylene production with a novel halotolerant PGPR strain *Glutamicibacter* sp. YD01 containing ACC deaminase activity. *Acta Physiol. Plant.* 42: 42. https://doi.org/10.1007/s11738-020-3034-3.

52 Farahat, M.G., Mahmoud, M.K., Youseif, S.H. et al. (2020). Alleviation of salinity stress in wheat by ACC deaminase-producing bacillus aryabhattai EWR29 with multifarious plant growth-promoting attributes. *Plant. Arch.* 20: 417–429.

53 Daur, I., Saad, M.M., Eida, A.A. et al. (2018). Boosting alfalfa (*Medicago sativa* L.) production with rhizobacteria from various plants in Saudi Arabia. *Front. Microbiol.* 9: 477. https://doi.org/10.3389/fmicb.2018.0047.

54 Sarkar, A., Ghosh, P.K., Pramanik, K. et al. (2018). A halotolerant Enterobacter sp. displaying ACC deaminase activity promotes rice seedling growth under salt stress. *Res. Microbiol.* 169: 20–32. https://doi.org/10.1016/j.resmic.2017.08.005.

55 Grobelak, A., Kokot, P., Świątek, J. et al. (2018). Bacterial ACC deaminase activity in promoting plant growth on areas contaminated with heavy metals. *J. Ecol. Eng.* 19: 150–157. https://doi.org/10.12911/22998993/89818.

56 Hemida, K.A. and Reyad, A.M.M. (2018). Improvement salt tolerance of safflower plants by endophytic bacteria. *J. Hortic. Plant Res.* 5: 38–56. https://doi.org/10.18052/www.scipress. com/JHPR.5.38.

57 Dixit, R., Agrawal, L., Gupta, S. et al. (2016). Southern blight disease of tomato control by 1-aminocyclopropane-1-carboxylate (ACC) deaminase producing *Paenibacillus lentimorbus* B-30488. *Plant Signaling Behav.* 11: 1–36. https://doi .org/10.1080/15592324.2015.1113363.

58 Bharti, N., Pandey, S.S., and Barnawal, D. (2016). Plant growth promoting rhizobacterial *Dietzia natronolimnaea* modulates the expression of stress responsive genes providing protection of wheat from salinity stress. *Sci. Rep.* 6: 34768. https://doi.org/10.1038/srep34768.

59 Wang, C., Wang, F., Zhang, Q., and Liang, W. (2016). Individual and combined effects of tebuconazole and carbendazim on soil microbial activity. *Eur. J. Soil Bio. J.* 72: 6–13. https://doi.org/10.1016/j.ejsobi.2015.12.005.

60 Trung, N.T., Hieu, H.V., and Thuan, N.H. (2016). Screening of strong 1-aminocyclopropane-1-carboxylate deaminase producing bacteria for improving the salinity tolerance of cowpea. *J. Appl. Microbiol. Open Access* 2: 1000111. https://doi.org/10.4172/amoa.1000111.

61 Orhan, F. (2016). Alleviation of salt stress by halotolerant and halophilic plant growth-promoting bacteria in wheat (*Triticum aestivum*). *Braz. J. Microbiol.* 47: 621–627. https://doi.org/10.1016/j.bjm.2016.04.001.

62 Ali, S., Charles, T.C., and Glick, B.R. (2014). Amelioration of high salinity stress damage by plant growth-promoting bacterial endophytes that contain ACC deaminase. *Plant Physiol. Biochem.* 80: 160–167. https://doi.org/10.1016/j.plaphy.2014.04.003.

63 Yan, K., Shao, H., Shao, C. et al. (2013). Physiological adaptive mechanisms of plants grown in saline soil and implications for sustainable saline agriculture in coastal zone. *Acta Physiol. Plant.* 35: 2867–2878. https://doi.org/10.1007/s11738-013-1325-7.

64 Rashid, U., Yasmin, H., Hassan, M.N. et al. (2022). Drought-tolerant *Bacillus megaterium* isolated from semi-arid conditions induces systemic tolerance of wheat under drought conditions. *Plant Cell Rep.* 41: 549–569. https://doi.org/10.1007/s00299-020-02640-x.

65 Yasmin, H., Bano, A., Wilson, N.L. et al. (2022). Drought-tolerant *Pseudomonas* sp. showed differential expression of stress-responsive genes and induced drought tolerance in Arabidopsis thaliana. *Physiol. Plant.* 174: e13497. https://doi.org/10.1111/ppl.13497.

66 Khan, A. and Singh, A.V. (2021). Multifarious effect of ACC deaminase and EPS producing *Pseudomonas* sp. and *Serratia marcescens* to augment drought stress tolerance and nutrient status of wheat. *World J. Microbiol. Biotechnol.* 37: 198–117: https://doi.org/10.1007/s11274-021-03166-4.

67 Maqbool, S., Amna, A., Mehmood, S. et al. (2021). Interaction of acc deaminase and antioxidant enzymes to induce drought tolerance in *Enterobacter cloacae* 2wc2 inoculated maize genotypes. *Pak. J. Bot.* 53. https://doi.org/10.30848/PJB2021-3(28).

68 Nadeem, S.M., Ahmad, M., Tufail, M.A. et al. (2021). Appraising the potential of EPS-producing rhizobacteria with ACC-deaminase activity to improve growth and physiology of maize under drought stress. *Physiol. Plant.* 172: 463–476. https://doi.org/10.1111/ppl.13212.

69 Saleem, A.R., Brunetti, C., Khalid, A. et al. (2018). Drought response of *Mucuna pruriens* (L.) inoculated with ACC deaminase and IAA producing rhizobacteria. *PLoS One* 13: 1–18. https://doi.org/10.1371/journal.pone.0191218.

70 Huang, X.F., Zhou, D., Lapsansky, E.R. et al. (2017). *Mitsuaria* sp. and *Burkholderia* sp. from Arabidopsis rhizosphere enhance drought tolerance in *Arabidopsis thaliana* and maize (*Zea mays* L.). *Plant Soil* 419: 523–539. https://doi.org/10.1007/s11104-017-3360-4.

71 Gururani, M.A., Upadhyaya, C.P., Baskar, V. et al. (2013). Plant growth-promoting rhizobacteria enhance abiotic stress tolerance in *Solanum tuberosum* through inducing changes in the expression of ROS scavenging enzymes and improved photosynthetic performance. *J. Plant Growth Regul.* 32: 245–258. https://doi.org/10.1007/s00344-012-9292-6.

72 Zahir, Z.A., Munir, A., Asghar, H.N. et al. (2008). Effectiveness of rhizobacteria containing ACC deaminase for growth promotion of peas (*Pisum sativum*) under drought conditions. *J. Microbiol. Biotechnol.* 18: 958–963.

73 Zainab, N., Din, B.U., Javed, M.T. et al. (2020). Deciphering metal toxicity responses of flax (*Linum usitatissimum* L.) with exopolysaccharide and ACC-deaminase producing bacteria in industrially contaminated soils. *Plant Physiol. Biochem.* 152: 90–99. https://doi.org/10.1016/j.plaphy.2020.04.039.

74 Danish, S., Kiran, S., Fahad, S. et al. (2019). Alleviation of chromium toxicity in maize by Fe fortification and chromium tolerant ACC deaminase producing plant growth promoting rhizobacteria. *Ecotoxicol. Environ. Saf.* 185: 109706. https://doi.org/10.1016/j.ecoenv.2019.109706.

75 Belimov, A.A., Zinovkina, N.Y., Safronova, V.I. et al. (2019). Rhizobial ACC deaminase contributes to efficient symbiosis with pea (*Pisum sativum* L.) under single and combined cadmium and water deficit stress. *Environ. Exp. Bot.* 167: 103859. https://doi.org/10.1016/j.envexpbot.2019.103859.

76 Zafar-Ul-Hye, M.U., Shahjahan, A., Danish, S.U. et al. (2018). Mitigation of cadmium toxicity induced stress in wheat by ACC-deaminase containing PGPR isolated from cadmium polluted wheat rhizosphere. *Pak. J. Bot.* 50: 1727–1734.

77 Saif, S. and Khan, M.S. (2018). Assessment of toxic impact of metals on proline, antioxidant enzymes, and biological characteristics of *Pseudomonas aeruginosa* inoculated *Cicer arietinum* grown in chromium and nickel-stressed sandy clay loam soils. *Environ. Monit. Assess.* 190: 290–218. https://doi.org/10.1007/s10661-018-6652-0.

78 Pramanik, K., Mitra, S., Sarkar, A., and Maiti, T.K. (2018). Alleviation of phytotoxic effects of cadmium on rice seedlings by cadmium resistant PGPR strain Enterobacter aerogenes MCC 3092. *J. Hazard. Mater.* 351: 317–329. https://doi.org/10.1016/j.jhazmat.2018. 03.009.

79 Gontia-Mishra, I., Sapre, S., and Sharma, A. (2016). Alleviation of mercury toxicity in wheat by the interaction of mercury-tolerant plant growth-promoting rhizobacteria. *J. Plant Growth Regul.* 35: 1000–1012. https://doi.org/10.1007/s00344-016-9598-x.

80 Carlos, M.H.J., Stefani, P.V.Y., and Janette, A.M. (2016). Assessing the effects of heavy metals in ACC deaminase and IAA production on plant growth-promoting bacteria. *Microbiol. Res.* 188–189: 53–61. https://doi.org/10.1016/j.micres.2016.05.001.

81 Han, Y., Wang, R., Yang, Z. et al. (2015). 1-aminocyclopropane-1-carboxylate deaminase from pseudomonas stutzeri A1501 facilitates the growth of rice in the presence of salt or heavy metals. *J. Microbiol. Biotechnol.* 25: 1119–1128. https://doi.org/10.4014/jmb.1412.12053.

82 Hassan, W., Bano, R., Bashir, F., and David, J. (2014). Comparative effectiveness of ACC-deaminase and/or nitrogen-fixing rhizobacteria in promotion of maize (*Zea mays* L.) growth under lead pollution. *Environ. Sci. Pollut. Res.* 21: 10983–10996. https://doi.org/10.1007/s11356-014-3083-5.

83 Pandey, S., Ghosh, P.K., Ghosh, S. et al. (2013). Role of heavy metal resistant *Ochrobactrum* sp. and *bacillus* spp. strains in bioremediation of a rice cultivar and their PGPR like activities. *J. Microbiol.* 51: 11–17. https://doi.org/10.1007/s12275-013-2330-7.

84 Chen, J., Li, S., and Xu, B. (2017). Characterization of Burkholderia sp. XTB-5 for phenol degradation and plant growth promotion and its application in bioremediation of contaminated soil. *Land Degrad. Dev.* 28: 1091–1099. https://doi.org/10.1002/ldr.2646.

85 Ajuzieogu, C.A., Ibiene, A.A., and Stanley, H.O. (2015). Laboratory study on influence of plant growth promoting rhizobacteria (PGPR) on growth response and tolerance of *Zea mays* to petroleum hydrocarbon. *Afr. J. Biotechnol.* 14: 2949–2956. https://doi.org/10.5897/AJB2015.14549.

86 Liu, J.L., Xie, B.M., Shi, X.H. et al. (2015). Effects of two plant growth-promoting rhizobacteria containing 1-aminocyclopropane-1carboxylate deaminase on oat growth in petroleum-contaminated soil. *Int. J. Environ. Sci. Technol.* 12: 3887–3894. https://doi.org/10.1007/s13762-015-0798-x.

87 Shahid, M. and Khan, M.S. (2018). Glyphosate induced toxicity to chickpea plants and stress alleviation by herbicide tolerant phosphate solubilizing *Burkholderia cepacia* PSBB1 carrying multifarious plant growth promoting activities. *3 Biotech* 8: 131–117. https://doi.org/10.1007/s13205-018-1145-y.

88 Shahid, M., Shah, A.A., Basit, F. et al. (2019). *Achromobacter* sp. FB-14 harboring ACC deaminase activity augmented rice growth by upregulating the expression of stress-responsive CIPK genes under salinity stress. *Braz. J. Microbiol.* 51: 719–728. https://doi.org/10.1007/s42770-019-00199-8.

89 Barnawal, D., Pandey, S.S., Bharti, N. et al. (2017). ACC deaminase-containing plant growth-promoting rhizobacteria protect *Papaver somniferum* from downy mildew. *J. Appl. Microbiol.* 122: 1286–1298. https://doi.org/10.1111/jam.13417.

90 Xia, Y., Farooq, M.A., Javed, M.T. et al. (2020). Multi-stress tolerant PGPR Bacillusxiamenensis PM14 activating sugarcane (*Saccharum officinarum* L.) red rot disease resistance. *Plant Physiol. Biochem.* 151: 640–649. https://doi.org/10.1016/j.plaphy.2020.04.016.

91 Pandey, S. and Gupta, S. (2020). Evaluation of pseudomonas sp. for its multifarious plant growth promoting potential and its ability to alleviate biotic and abiotic stress in tomato (*Solanum lycopersicum*) plants. *Sci. Rep.* 10: 1–15. https://doi.org/10.1038/s41598-020-77850-0.

92 Prasannakumar, S.P., Gowtham, H.G., Hariprasad, P. et al. (2015). Delftiatsuruhatensis WGR–UOM–BT1, a novel rhizobacterium with PGPR properties from *Rauwolfia serpentina* (L.) Benth. Ex Kurz also suppresses fungal phytopathogens by producing a new antibiotic—AMTM. *Lett. Appl. Microbiol.* 61: 460–468. https://doi.org/10.1111/lam.12479.

93 Ek-Ramos, M.J., Gomez-Flores, R., Orozco-Flores, A.A. et al. (2019). Bioactive products from plant-endophytic gram-positive bacteria. *Front. Microbiol.* 10: 463. https://doi.org/10.3389/fmicb.2019.00463.

94 Chinnadurai, C., Balachandar, D., and Sundaram, S.P. (2009). Characterization of 1-aminocyclopropane-1-carboxylate deaminase producing methylobacteria from phyllosphere of rice and their role in ethylene regulation. *World J. Microbiol. Biotechnol.* 25: 1403–1411. https://doi.org/10.1007/s11274-009-0027-1.

95 Kaushal, M. and Wani, S.P. (2016). Plant growth-promoting rhizobacteria: drought stress alleviators to ameliorate crop production in drylands. *Ann. Microbiol.* 66: 35–42. https://doi.org/10.1007/s13213-015-1112-3.

96 Saikia, J., Sarma, R.K., Dhandia, R. et al. (2018). Alleviation of drought stress in pulse crops with ACC deaminase producing rhizobacteria isolated from acidic soil of Northeast India. *Sci. Rep.* 8: 3560. https://doi.org/10.1038/s41598-018-21921-w.

97 Kataria, S. and Verma, S.K. (2018). Salinity stress responses and adaptive mechanisms in major glycophytic crops: the story so far. In: *Salinity Responses and Tolerance in Plants*, vol. 1 (ed. V. Kumar, S. Wani, P. Suprasanna, and L.S. Tran), 1–39. Cham: Springer.

98 Singh, S., Singh, U.B., Trivdi, M. et al. (2021a). Restructuring the cellular responses: connecting microbial intervention with ecological fitness and adaptiveness to the maize (Zea mays L.) grown in saline–sodic soil. *Front. Microbiol.* 11: 568325. https://doi.org/10.3389/fmicb.2020.568325.

99 Singh, U.B., Malviya, D., Singh, S. et al. (2021b). Salt-tolerant compatible microbial inoculants modulate physio-biochemical responses enhance plant growth, Zn biofortification and yield of wheat grown in saline-sodic soil. *Int. J. Environ. Res. Public Health* 18: 9936. https://doi.org/10.3390/ijerph18189936.

100 Sahu, P.K., Singh, S., Singh, U.B. et al. (2021). Inter-genera colonization of *Ocimum tenuiflorum* endophytes in tomato and their complementary effects on Na+/K+ balance, oxidative Stress regulation, and root architecture under elevated soil salinity. *Front. Microbiol.* 12: 744733. https://doi.org/10.3389/fmicb.2021.744733.

101 Panda, A., Rangani, J., Kumari, A., and Parida, A.K. (2017). Efficient regulation of arsenic translocation to shoot tissue and modulation of phytochelatin levels and antioxidative defense system confers salinity and arsenic tolerance in the halophyte *Suaeda maritima*. *Environ. Exp. Bot.* 143: 149–171. https://doi.org/10.1016/j.envexpbot.2017.09.007.

102 Zahir, Z.A., Ghani, U., Naveed, M. et al. (2009). Comparative effectiveness of pseudomonas and Serratia sp. containing ACC deaminase for improving growth and yield of wheat (*Triticum aestivum* L.) under salt-stressed conditions. *Arch. Microbiol.* 191: 415–424. https://doi.org/10.1007/s00203-009-0466-Y.

103 Han, L., Zhang, H., Xu, Y. et al. (2021). Biological characteristics and salt-tolerant plant growth-promoting effects of an ACC deaminase-producing *Burkholderia pyrrocinia* strain isolated from the tea rhizosphere. *Arch. Microbiol.* 203: 2279–2290. https://doi.org/10.1007/s00203-021-02204-x.

104 Sagar, A., Rai, S., Ilyas, N. et al. (2022). Halotolerant rhizobacteria for salinity-stress mitigation: diversity, mechanisms and molecular approaches. *Sustainability* 14: 490. https://doi.org/10.3390/su14010490.

105 Shahid, M., Al-Khattaf, F.S., Danish, M. et al. (2022). PGPR Kosakoniaradicincitans KR-17 increases the salt tolerance of radish by regulating ion-homeostasis, photosynthetic molecules, redox potential, and stressor metabolites. *Front. Plant Sci.* 13: 2270. https://doi.org/10.3389/fpls.2022.919696.

106 Shahid, M., Ameen, F., Maheshwari, H.S. et al. (2021). Colonization of *Vigna radiata* by a halotolerant bacterium *Kosakonia sacchari* improves the ionic balance, stressor metabolites, antioxidant status and yield under NaCl stress. *Appl. Soil Ecol.* 158: 103809. https://doi.org/10.1016/j.apsoil.2020.103809.

107 Barnawal, D., Bharti, N., Maji, D. et al. (2014). ACC deaminase-containing *Arthrobacter protophormiae* induces NaCl stress tolerance through reduced ACC oxidase activity and ethylene production resulting in improved nodulation and mycorrhization in *Pisum sativum*. *J. Plant Physiol.* 171: 884–894. https://doi.org/10.1016/j.jplph.2014.03.007.

108 Siddikee, M.A., Chauhan, P.S., and Sa, T. (2012). Regulation of ethylene biosynthesis under salt stress in red pepper (*Capsicum annuum* L.) by 1-aminocyclopropane-1-carboxylic acid (ACC) deaminase-producing halotolerant bacteria. *J. Plant Growth Regul.* 31: 265–272. https://doi.org/10.1007/s00344-011-9236-6.

109 Arora, S., Singh, A.K., and Sahni, D. (2017). Bioremediation of salt-affected soils: challenges and opportunities. In: *Bioremediation of Salt Affected Soils: An Indian Perspective* (ed. S. Arora, A. Singh, and Y. Singh), 275–301. Cham: Springer.

110 Kumar, M., Etesami, H., and Kumar, V. (2019). *Saline Soil-Based Agriculture by Halotolerant Microorganisms*. Springer.

111 Singh, S., Singh, U.B., Trivedi, M. et al. (2020). Seed biopriming with salt-tolerant endophytic *Pseudomonas geniculata*-modulated biochemical responses provide ecological fitness in maize (*Zea mays* L.) grown in saline sodic soil. *Int. J. Environ. Res. Public Health* 17: 253. https://doi.org/10.3390/ijerph17010253.

112 Tavares, M.J., Nascimento, F.X., Glick, B.R., and Rossi, M.J. (2018). The expression of an exogenous ACC deaminase by the endophyte *Serratia grimesii* BXF 1 promotes the early nodulation and growth of common bean. *Lett. Appl. Microbiol.* 66: 252–259. https://doi.org/10.1111/lam.12847.

113 Sapre, S., Gontia-Mishra, I., and Tiwari, S. (2018). ACC deaminase-producing bacteria: a key player in alleviating abiotic stresses in plants. In: *Plant Growth*

Promoting Rhizobacteria for Agricultural Sustainability (ed. A. Kumar and V.S. Meena), 267–291. Singapore: Springer.

114 Wang, Q., Dodd, I.C., Belimov, A.A., and Jiang, F. (2016). Rhizosphere bacteria containing 1-aminocyclopropane-1-carboxylate deaminase increase growth and photosynthesis of pea plants under salt stress by limiting Na1 accumulation. *Funct. Plant Biol.* 43: 161–172. https://doi.org/10.1071/FP15200.

115 Subramanian, P., Kim, K., and Krishnamoorthy, R. (2016). Cold stress tolerance in psychrotolerant soil bacteria and their conferred chilling resistance in tomato (*Solanum lycopersicum* mill.) under low temperatures. *PLoS One* 11: e0161592. https://doi.org/10.1371/journal.pone.0161592.

116 Srinivasan, R., Mageswari, A., and Subramanian, P. (2017). Exogenous expression of ACC deaminase gene in psychrotolerant bacteria alleviates chilling stress and promotes plant growth in millets under chilling conditions. *Indian J. Exp. Biol.* 55: 463–468.

117 Subramanian, P., Krishnamoorthy, R., and Chanratana, M. (2015). Expression of an exogenous 1-aminocyclopropane-1-carboxylatedeaminase gene in psychrotolerant bacteria modulates ethylene metabolism and cold induced genes in tomato under chilling stress. *Plant Physiol. Biochem.* 89: 18–23. https://doi.org/10.1016/j.plaphy.2015.02.003.

118 Mukhtar, T., Rehman, S., Smith, D. et al. (2020). Mitigation of heat stress in *Solanum lycopersicum* L. by ACC-deaminase and exopolysaccharide producing *Bacillus cereus*: effects on biochemical profiling. *Sustainability* 12 (6): 2159.

119 Bensalim, S., Nowak, J., and Asiedu, S.K.A. (1998). Plant growth promoting rhizobacterium and temperature effects on performance of 18 clones of potato. *Am. J. Potato Res.* 75: 145–152.

120 Jackson, M.B. (2008). Ethylene-promoted elongation: an adaptation to submergence stress. *Ann. Bot.* 101: 229–248. https://doi.org/10.1093/aob/mcm237.

121 Jaemsaeng, R., Jantasuriyarat, C., and Thamchaipenet, A. (2018). Positive role of 1-aminocyclopropane-1-carboxylate deaminase-producing endophytic Streptomyces sp. GMKU 336 on flooding resistance of mung bean. *Agric. Nat. Res.* 52: 330–334. https://doi.org/10.1016/j.anres.2018.09.008.

122 Grichko, V.P. and Glick, B.R. (2001). Amelioration of flooding stress by ACC deaminase-containing plant growth-promoting bacteria. *Plant Physiol. Biochem.* 39: 11–17. https://doi.org/10.1016/S0981-9428(00)01212-2.

123 Ashraf, S., Ali, Q., Zahir, Z.A. et al. (2019). Phytoremediation: environmentally sustainable way for reclamation of heavy metal polluted soils. *Ecotoxicol. Environ. Saf.* 174: 714–727. https://doi.org/10.1016/j.ecoenv.2019.02.068.

124 Dixit, R., Malaviya, D., Pandiyan, K. et al. (2015). Bioremediation of heavy metals from soil and aquatic environment: an overview of principles and criteria of fundamental processes. *Sustain* 7: 2189–2212. https://doi.org/10.3390/su7022189.

125 Saif, S., Khan, M.S., Zaidi, A. et al. (2017). Metal toxicity to certain vegetables and bioremediation of metal-polluted soils. In: *Microbial Strategies for Vegetable Production* (ed. A. Zaidi and M. Khan). Cham: Springer. https://doi.org/10.1007/978-3-319-54401-4_8.

126 Rizvi, A., Zaidi, A., Khan, M.S. et al. (2017). Growth improvement and management of vegetable diseases by plant growth-promoting rhizobacteria. In: *Microbial Strategies for Vegetable Production* (ed. A. Zaidi and M. Khan). Cham: Springer. https://doi.org/10.1007/978-3-319-54401-4_5.

127 Zaidi, A., Khan, M.S., Saif, S. et al. (2017). Role of nitrogen-fixing plant growth-promoting rhizobacteria in sustainable production of vegetables: current perspective. In: *Microbial strategies for vegetable production* (ed. A. Zaidi and M. Khan), 49–79. Cham: Springer.

128 Rao, M.V. and Davis, K.R. (2001). The physiology of ozone induced cell death. *Planta* 213: 682–690. https://doi.org/10.1007/s004250100618.

129 Moeder, W., Barry, C.S., Tauriainen, A.A. et al. (2002). Ethylene synthesis regulated by biphasic induction of 1-aminocyclopropane-1-carboxylic acid synthase and 1-aminocyclopropane-1- carboxylic acid oxidase genes is required for hydrogen peroxide accumulation and cell death in ozone-exposed tomato. *Plant Physiol.* 130: 1918–1926. https://doi.org/10.1104/pp.009712.

130 Hemissi, I., Hammami, R., Hachana, A. et al. (2019). Fertilizer-dependent efficiency of *Mesorhizobium* strain for improving growth, nutrient uptake and grain yield of durum wheat (*Triticum turgidium* L.) variety. *J. New Sci.* 61: 3885–3891.

131 Xun, F., Xie, B., and Liu, S. (2015). Effect of plant growth-promoting bacteria (PGPR) and arbuscular mycorrhizal fungi (AMF) inoculation on oats in saline-alkali soil contaminated by petroleum to enhance phytoremediation. *Environ. Sci. Pollut. Res.* 22: 598–608. https://doi.org/10.1007/s11356-014-3396-4.

132 Jajoo, A. (2017). Effects of environmental pollutants polycyclic aromatic hydrocarbons (PAH) on photosynthetic processes. In: *Photosynthesis: Structures, Mechanisms, and Applications* (ed. H. Hou, M. Najafpour, G. Moore, and S. Allakhverdiev), 249–259. Cham: Springer.

133 Li, Z., Wang, W., and Zhu, L. (2019). Effects of mixed surfactants on the bioaccumulation of polycyclic aromatic hydrocarbons (PAHs) in crops and the bioremediation of contaminated farmlands. *Sci. Total Environ.* 646: 1211–1218. https://doi.org/10.1016/j.scitotenv.2018.07.349.

134 Sheng, X.F., He, L.Y., Zhou, L., and Shen, Y.Y. (2009). Characterization of microbacterium sp. F10a and its role in polycyclic aromatic hydrocarbon removal in low-temperature soil. *Can. J. Microbiol.* 55: 529–535. https://doi.org/10.1139/W09-005.

34

Ligninolytic Enzyme: Microbial Sources, Production, Purification, and Biotechnological Applications

Rohida A. Hoque, Meera Yadav, and Hardeo S. Yadav

North Eastern Regional Institute of Science and Technology, Department of Chemistry, Nirjuli, Itanagar, AP 791109, India

34.1 Introduction

All living things depend on enzymes for survival, and they can produce them. The most favored source of enzymes is microbial, which has developed a fermentation technique. We can ensure unlimited production of microbial enzymes, but there is a disadvantage of enzymes produced from microbes because a single-cell microorganism can secrete approximately 2500 enzymes, but in an industrial process or any reaction medium, it needs only one precise enzyme for conversion. The other contaminant enzymes may give some disagreeable product, so to remove those contaminants purification of the enzyme is necessary. In this chapter, we are mainly discussing the source, production, purification, and some of the industrial applications of the ligninolytic microbial enzyme [1]. The lignocellulosic compounds are very difficult to decompose; they take a lot of time to degrade naturally [2]. Lignin-degradingenzymes

produced by microorganisms, mainly white-rot fungi, act as biocatalysts and are responsible for the degradation of lignin and other lignocellulosic material [3]. Manganese peroxidase (MnP), laccase, and lignin peroxidase (LiP) are the major classes of ligninolytic enzymes. Hydrogen peroxidase is used as a cofactor for ligninolytic enzymes [4]. Laccase enzymesof fungal origin use copper for their redox capability and can oxidize various organic compounds and form water as a by-product [5]. MnP and LiP are types of glycosylated, heme group-containing enzymes, and both have isoelectric points at 3.2–4 and 4.2–4.5, respectively. However, the main distinction between LiP and MnP is that Lip only has four bonds of disulfide, and MnP has five bonds of disulfide [6–8]. These enzymes are not only able to degrade lignocellulosic material but are also used in industry and environmental applications, including pulping, dye-degradation, decolorization and detoxification of textile wastes, wastewater treatment, bioremediation of polluted soils, and biofuels [7]. In ligninolytic enzyme production, waste materials, like, rice straw, corn cobs, bagasse, banana stem, and wheat straw are used as substrates for the

Microbial Enzymes: Production, Purification, and Industrial Applications, First Edition.
Edited by Dinesh Yadav, Pankaj Chowdhary, Gautam Anand, and Rajarshi Kumar Gaur.

solid-state fermentation of microorganisms [8]. The ligninolytic enzyme plays an important role in the carbon cycle. Laccases are multinuclear enzymes that contain four coppers in the form of three groups, which are known as T1, T2, and T3. The blue color of the enzyme is responsible for the T1 copper site showing absorbance at 610 nm and T2 is colorless spectro chemically undetectable but can be detected with the help of EPR and the dinuclear T3 is diamagnetic and shows an absorbance band at 330 nm [9].

34.2 Source of Microbial Ligninolytic Enzymes

Major types of lignin degradation enzymes are heme-containing peroxidase MnP, LiP, copper ion-containing laccase, and dye-decolorizing peroxidase (DyP). Fungal peroxidases of extracellular that belong to the plant and microbial family are MnP, and LiP enzyme [10]. Laccase is found mainly in fungi and higher plants, but nowadays, it is also found in bacteria such as *Streptomyces lavendulae, Streptomyces cyaneus*, and *Marinomonas mediterranea* [11]. First laccase *Monocillium indicum* was characterized by ascomycetes, which shows activity of peroxidase enzyme [12]. Different species of *Trichoderma* are the sources of laccase enzymes [13, 14]. Production of laccase enzyme from *Pycnoporus cinnabarinus* shows ligninolytic character [14, 15]. In white-rot fungi such as *Phanerochaete chrysosporium*, *Pleurotus eryngii*, and *Trametes versicolor*, lignin peroxidase was detected [16]. The first MnP was purified from *Musa paradisiaca* (banana) stem from a plant and earlier, it was *discovered from* microbial source *P. chrysosporium,* which belongs to the white rot fungus. Various isozymes have been identified in the following organisms after LiP was found in the extracellular media of *P. chrysosporium*, a white-rot fungus: *Phlebia radiata*, *T. versicolor*, *P. chrysosporium*, and *Phanerochaete sordida*. Some sources of ligninolytic enzymes are given in Table 34.1 [1, 17–25].

34.3 Intein-mediated Affinity-fusion Purification of Ligninolytic Enzyme

The RecA protein of *Escherichia coli* is crucial for homologous recombination, recombinational DNA repair, and SOS induction. It has been overproduced and purified using various methods. This report uses a modified protein splicing element and a chitin-binding domain to facilitate one-step affinity purification without altering the native protein sequence. The purification strategy yields mutant RecA proteins for biophysical characterization without relying on intrinsic function. From this novel molecular approach, purification of manganese peroxidase isoform 1 (MnP1) from *P. chrysosporium* using an *E. coli*-expression system was performed. The strategy involved codon optimization, chemical synthesis, and purification techniques, resulting in an active enzyme [26, 27].

Table 34.1 Source of ligninolytic enzyme, with optimum pH and temperature.

Source	Enzyme	Lignocellulosebiomass	Optimum pH, temperature (°C)	References
Phanerochaetechrysosporium	MnP	Rice straw	4.5, 30	[11]
Trametes versicolor IBL-04	MnP (higher), LiP, laccase	Rice straw	4, 30	[12]
Coriolushirsutus	LiP, MnP	Rice straw	4, 25–30	[13]
Trametesvillosa CCB176	LiP, MnP	Sugarcane bagasse	5, 25–30	[14]
Pleurotus ostreatus	MnP, LiP	Banana waste	4–5, 25	[14]
Phlebia radiata Fr. 79	LiP, MnP, Laccase	Wheat straw	3–4.5, 40	[16]
Trameteshirsuta	Laccase		5–7, 25 ± 2	[17]
Trametestrogii	Laccase, MnP	Rice straw, bagasse, sawdust, cotton seed coat	3–4, room temperature	[18]
Trametes versicolor IBL-04	LiP (free and immobilized)	Corn cobs	6,60 (free), 5, 80 (immobilized)	[19]
Schizophyllum commune	LiP	Industrial waste, banana stalk	4–6, 25–45	[20]
Trametessuaveolens	Laccase and Mn-oxidizing peroxidases	Wheat straw and oak sawdust	6, 35 (laccase) 4 (MnP)	[21]
Trametes gallica	LiP, MnP, laccase	Wheat straw, banana, and apple peelings		[22]
Trametes pubescens	Laccase	Coffee husk, soybean pod husk, or cedar sawdust	2–3, 55	[23]
Pleurotus sp.	Laccase		4.5, 65	[24]

34.4 Structural View of Microbial Ligninolytic Enzyme

Major classified microbial ligninolytic enzymes are laccase (EC 1.10.3.2), MnP (EC 1.11.1.13), LiP (EC 1.11.1.14), and VP (EC 1.11.1.16). The 3D view of the substrate and the type of enzyme is determined by the EC classification of the enzyme shown in Figure 34.1a,b [7]. Oxidoreductase enzymes, which also belong to the multi-copper oxidase's (MCO's) protein superfamily enzyme this type of enzyme can oxidize substrate at the mononuclear copper center, which can catalyze one electron oxidation compound such as phenol, acryl amine, and aromatic thiol to their respective radical. Copper(Cu)-containing enzymes can act as versatile biocatalysts, and numerous oxidations of the industrial and nonindustrial compounds with by-product water depend on the active site of copper. Laccases are enzymes with three domains and 500 amino acid residues, divided into type 1(T1), type 2(T2), and type 3(T3) categories. They contain four copper molecules in their active site, contributing to water synthesis and oxygen reduction. T2 copper exhibits strong absorption under EPR, T1 Cu has a strong absorption at 600 nm, and T3 copper, a binuclear core, lacks an EPR signal and participates in compound oxidation. Laccases are unique enzymes with unique structural characteristics, such as interaction with two histidine and a water molecule, contact with oxygen atoms, and a unique axial ligand with methionine. Their redox potential varies from 300 to 800 mV, depending on the distance between copper ligands, the second sphere of amino acids in the active site, and other parameters. Additionally, ligands like monosaccharides, ions like Calcium(II), and organic compounds like glycerol are

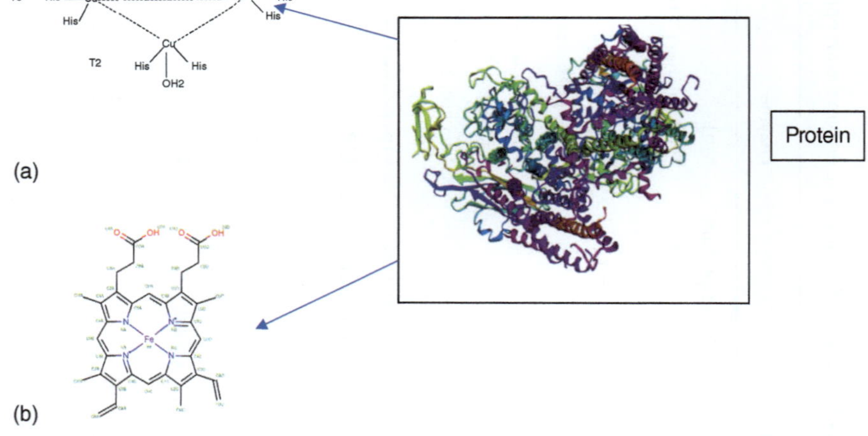

Figure 34.1 (a,b) Active site of copper and iron metal containing ligninolytic enzyme [7, 16–18]. Source: Author.

present in laccases. The mononuclear central copper (T1) is coordinated with two histidine and one cysteine residue, and The Cu atoms that surround the side chains of methionine, leucine, or isoleucine are coordinated with histidine ligands at positions T1 and T2 [7, 28]. After laccase, the two most common ligninolytic enzymes are manganese peroxidase (MnP) and lignin peroxidase (LiP).They belong to the heme-protein family since they include the prosthetic group protoporphyrin IX and have a catalytic cycle consisting of three reactions, like other heme-peroxidases. MnP, a glycoprotein having 350 amino acid residues, a molecular weight of 38–62.5 kDa, and a 43% sequence similarity to LiP, was discovered by Kuwahara in 1984. Two domains, ten major helixes, and five disulfide bridges make up the structure of MnP. One of the bridges is a part of the bonding site for manganese (Mn). One feature that sets MnP apart from other peroxidases is this site. Initially, nitrogen- and carbon-limited *P. chrysosporium* cultures were used to identify LiPs. LiP, with a low ideal pH of 3–4.5 and a high redox potential of 700–1400 mV, can catalyze the breakdown of various aromatic molecules. Lip oxidizes aromatic rings that are moderately active by substituting electrons. The catalysis of LiPs involves the production of veratryl alcohol radicals, which have higher redox potential than LiP's compounds I and II. The helicoidal secondary structure of LiPs, which are glycosylated monomers, is composed of two antiparallel beta sheets and eight main helices. Hydrogen bridges are used to form connections between the 40 residues that make up the heminic cavity and the protein. Furthermore, a His and a water molecule align with the heminic iron (Fe). This is connected to LiP's high redox potential. His, with a decreased imidazole character has a higher redox potential for the enzyme. LiP enzymes' redox potential is enhanced by an electronic deficiency in the porphyrin ring's Fe and the presence of a tryptophan residue on the enzyme's surface [29–31].

34.5 Catalytic Cycle of Ligninolytic Enzymes

34.5.1 Laccases

Electrons from reducing substrates are taken up by the T1 site laccase, which then transports them to the T2/T3 cluster, activates O_2, and reduces them to H_2O. There are two forms termed peroxide intermediate and native intermediate, present in the laccase catalyst mechanism. In the catalytic cycle of laccase, native intermediate plays, a very important role. Laccase is a slow-transformed, fully oxidized form ("resting laccase") with a low electron transfer rate on the T3 copper cluster for catalysis. Oxidation of various organic and inorganic compounds such as phenols, methoxy-substituted phenols, aminophenol, diamines, $[Mo(CN)_8]^{4-}$, $[Fe(CN)_6]^{4-}$, $[Os(CN)_6]^{4-}$, and $[W(CN)_8]^{4-}$ shown in Figure 34.2.

34.5.2 Manganese Peroxidases (MnP)

WRF produces 3 peroxidase enzymes (Lip, MnP, Laccase) and plays a key regulator of the universal catalytic cycle. Peroxidase enzyme production by Fungi starts at the

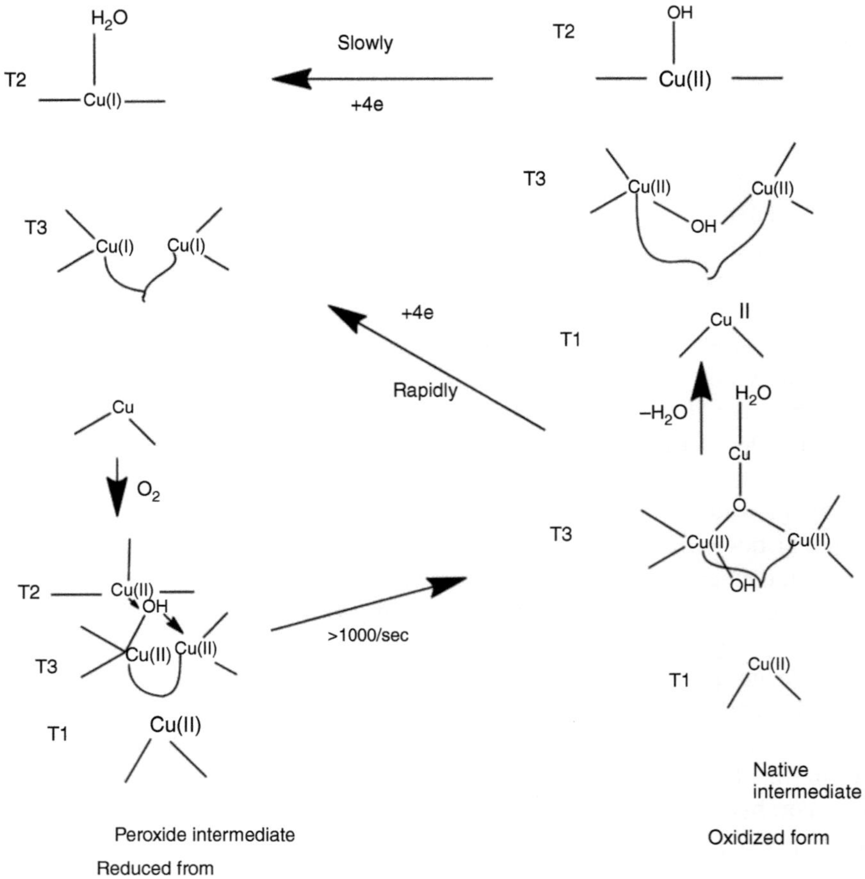

Figure 34.2 Catalytic cycle of Laccase [7, 16]. Source: Author.

time of their second metabolism. MnP belongs to oxidoreductase; it oxidizes Mn^{2+} to Mn^{3+},which can oxidize phenolic compounds to phenoxy radical. The peroxy radical may affect lignin structure and help for biodegradation of lignin [31, 32]. The mechanism of the MnP enzyme involved in the oxidation of Mn^{2+} to Mn^{3+} and chelated with organic acid and formed a chelated complex with Mn^{3+}moves freely in the enzyme active site mechanism of the catalytic cycle [33, 34]. MnP is a heme-containing compound that is similar to horseradish peroxidase [35, 36]. Step (I),H_2O_2 Oxidized the enzyme by two electrons to form MnP compound (I), which is an oxy-ferryl [Fe^{4+}=O] cation radical. Step (II) The reductant of MnP or phenolic group containing molecule, after the formation of compound (II) an oxyferryl [Fe^{4+}=O] species [RH To $R^{\cdot}$+H], oxidation of one electron to form Mn^{2+} to Mn^{3+}, where Mn(II) is very essential shown in Figure 34.3 [37]. Mn^{3+} is very reactive by chelating with organic acid produced by different fungi and can form large complexes.

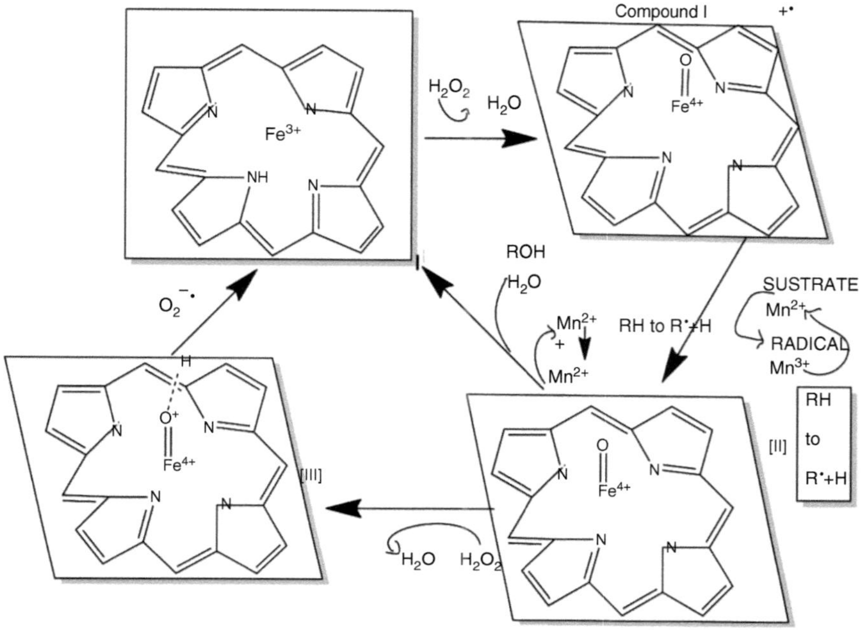

Figure 34.3 Catalytic cycle of MnP [7, 19]. Source: Author.

$$MnP + H_2O_2 \rightarrow MnP(I) + H_2O \qquad \text{(step 1)}$$

$$MnP(I) + Mn^{2+} \rightarrow MnP(II) + Mn^{3+} \qquad \text{(step 2)}$$

$$MnP(II) + Mn^{2+} \rightarrow MnP + Mn^{3+} + H_2O \qquad \text{(step 3)}$$

34.5.3 Lignin Peroxidases (LiP)

The redox potential of LiP is slightly higher than MnP enzyme [38]. LiP also belongs to the oxidoreductase family. In 1983, the first LiP enzyme was discovered from *P. chrysosporium*. it has been found in several species of basidiomycete and actinomycetes [39, 40]. Hydrogen peroxide is needed to initiate its catalytic activity; otherwise, it has a strong potential for application in a variety of industrial processes [41]. It can oxidize methoxylated aromatic rings to a cationic radical [42] as shown in Figure 34.4.

$$LiP\,(Fe^{3+})\,P + H_2O_2 \rightarrow LiP - I\,(Fe^{4+} - O)\,P^+ + H_2O \qquad \text{(step 1)}$$

$$LiP - I\,(Fe^{4+} - O)\,P^+ + R \rightarrow LiP - II\,(Fe^{4+} - O)\,P^+ + R^{\cdot} \qquad \text{(step 2)}$$

$$LiP - II\,(Fe^{4+} - O)\,P + R + 2H^+ \rightarrow LiP\,(Fe^{3+)}\,P + R^{\cdot} + H_2O \qquad \text{(step 3)}$$

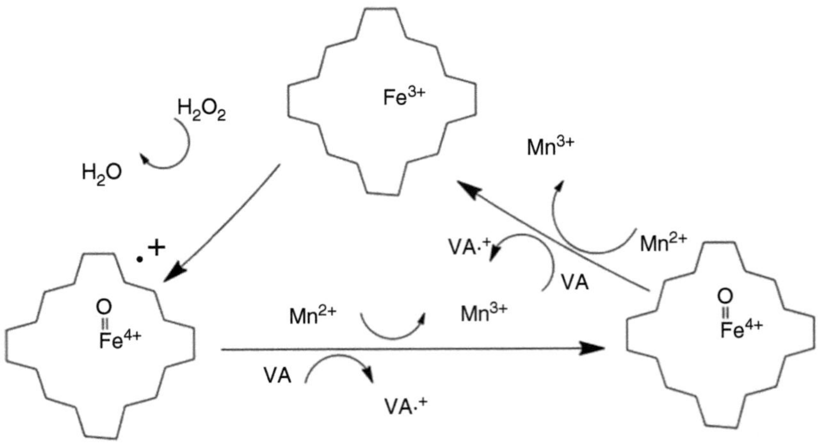

Figure 34.4 Catalytic cycle of LiP.

34.6 Industrial Application of Microbial Ligninolytic Enzymes

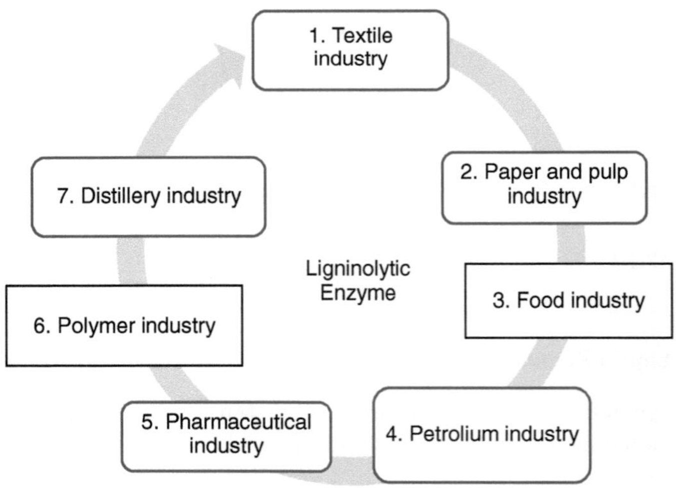

34.6.1 Textile Industry

Ligninolytic mediator enzyme shows great potential for dye bleaching in the textile industries. Recent processes to treat wastewater dye are the most effective but less economical [43]. So, ligninolytic enzyme seems an attractive way for great potential in degradation dyes of various chemical structures including different synthetic dyes also [44]. Besides the textile industry, wastewater dyes from some other industries like cosmetics, plastic, pharmaceutical, and food are also used in the ligninolytic enzyme degradation procedure, and the wastewater part of synthetic dyes is very toxic and carcinogenic [45].

34.6.2 Paper and Pulp Industry

Microbial enzymes are mostly used in the paper and pulp industry. Depletion of forest resources is increased due to satisfying the demand for paper nowadays, so to resolve this issue, recycling waste paper is gaining importance in modern society [46]. In recent studies, most microbial enzymes have been identified as having a high potential for bio-bleaching and pulp characterization properties. Besides that, the biological deinking method used by microbial enzymes is quite promising and eco-friendly as compared to the chemical deinking method. LiP has higher redox-potential, which can reduce nonphenolic lignin and MnP is a hemeprotein that can oxidize Mn^{2+} to Mn^{3+} and by chelating with Mn^{3+}it can promote to remove lignin [47]. Laccase removes lignin from the surface in the presence of low molar mass chemical; it is also found that deinking of old paper with laccase–violuric acid gave 20% and 13% extra tensile and tear strength, respectively. An improvement in wet tensile strength was found when unbleached pulp was treated with a laccase mediator system [48]. A pulp consistency of 5% with 15% laccase enzyme could reduce the lignin to the highest level [49]. In FT-IR analysis, the disappearance of C–H stretching was observed after treating the pulp with laccase enzyme, S=O vibration of sulfonyl chloride, and N–H stretching of secondary amine was also observed in FT-IR analysis after treating with laccase enzyme [48].

34.6.3 Food Industry

In the production of bread, improved flavor, texture microbial enzyme is mostly used. The strength of gluten structure is increased by adding laccase enzyme. Laccase enzyme increases the softness of bread [50]. Moreover, the food processing industry produces a large amount of wastewater all over the world, which is highly rich in the derivative of sugar so that easily utilized by microbes [51].

34.6.4 Biofuel Cell

In a recent study, there were developed zinc laccase biofuel cells in a single chamber. Membrane-less cell design was utilized and biocatalyzed by laccase was left to be freely suspended in the quasi-neutral buffer of (pH 6.5) potassium hydrogen phosphate electrolyte. The zinc-laccase biofuel cell system utilized an electron transfer mediator, controlled temperature and humidity, and oxygenated electrolytes. It was prepared with fresh, cold deionized water before running. In plastic, pesticides, and dye industry, catechol intermediate is widely used, which is toxic for organisms, can cause nervous system lesions, and is very difficult to remove from waste; the laccase biosensor can oxidize catechol to ortho quinone through zinc-oxide(ZnO) sol–gel method [52]. Due to the efficient direct electron transfer (DET) properties, MnP enzymes are enabled for the development of biosensors and biofuel cells [53].

34.6.5 Pharmaceutical, Cosmetic and Polymer Industry

Recently, it was found that for the construction of the C—N bond, the synthesis of natural products and cosmetic products with microbial enzymes is widely used.

A novel enzymatic technique based on laccase was created to simultaneously differentiate morphine and codeine in drug samples. For polymerization of acryl amine place by using MnP enzyme produced by the basidiomycete *Bjerkandera adusta* manganese-peroxidase enzyme produced by *P. chrysosporium* can degrade styrene which is an industrial polymer generally used for wrapping purposes of good during transporting [54]. Ligninolytic enzymes showed the ability to degrade azo and heterocyclic dyes, and these also can degrade 1.1.1-trichloro-2.2-bis-(4-chlorophenyl) ethane (DDT), 2.4.6-trinitrotoluene (TNT), and polycyclic aromatic hydrocarbons (PAHs) [55]. *P. chrysosporium* LiP degrades tetracycline and oxytetracycline, accelerating with increased veratryl alcohol and hydrogen peroxide concentration [56]. LiP, secreted by *B. adusta* can remove much pharmaceutical waste such as acetaminophen, naproxen, diclofenac, indomethacin, and mefenamic acid from waste material, which are very harmful to the environment and organisms [57]. Versatile peroxidase (VP) and glucose oxidase secreted by *Aspergillus niger* pair can decrease harmful by-product of pharmaceutical industry produced in low concentration like caffeine, carbamazepine, diazepam, and ciprofloxacin more over VP from *B. adusta* can oxidized different classes of medicine of pharmaceutical industry like antibiotic, anti-inflammatory, anti-depressants, tranquilizer, and endocrine disrupting chemicals. Almost 70–80% of sulfamethoxazole (antibiotic) was degraded by treatment with VP enzyme [58].

34.6.6 Petroleum Industry

The steps involved in the production are as below:

1) Pretreatment procedure for breaking down the polysaccharides to simple sugars by enzymatic hydrolysis process
2) Conversions of sugars into biofuel production through microorganisms
3) Production of ethanol from pentose and hexose sugars.

Due to the presence of huge hemicelluloses and low cost and easy availability lignocellulose biomass has great potential for bioenergy production. For biofuel production pretreatment of the lignocellulose biomass is required because the presence of lignin is a major inhibition in the utilization as a substrate of biofuel production. The main purpose of pretreatment is to enhance the convenience of lignocellulose biomass for the competent generation of reducing sugar with minimum by-products and at low doses of the enzyme. There are many procedures for pretreatment like physical, chemical, and enzymatic. Enzymatic pretreatment involving the ligninolytic enzyme produced from white-rot basidiomycetes fungus, de-lignifies lignocellulosic biomass, yielding high amount of reducing sugar after saccharification. Pretreatment, saccharification, fermentation, lipid extraction, transesterification, and purification are all steps in the manufacturing of biodiesel, with saccharification being the main process [59].

34.6.7 Pretreatment and Delignification

Pretreatment in chemical procedure can be done with alkaline alkali-metal base(potassium and sodium), carbonate of potassium, oxide of alkaline-earth metal(CaO and MgO), or acids such as sulfuric acid, phosphoric, hydrochloric, zeolites, etc. or in some biological method enzymatic treatment is given to the biomass which requires mild condition and less energy [60]. The motive for the pretreatment of lignocellulosic biomass is to reduce its size. By the hydrolysis of polysaccharides, obtaining monosaccharides is possible, which are the main source of valuable components like methanol, ethanol, furfural derivative, lactic acid, etc. The pretreatment of the degradation of lignin can be done with ozone at room temperature under atmospheric pressure without any by-product, but due to the use of ozone, this process is somewhat expensive. Besides these processes, ligninolytic enzymes (laccase, manganese peroxidase, lignin peroxidase) play a major role in the degradation of lignin; hence, they are used as an agent in the production of biofuel by eliminating the phenolic group [61]. 80–85% of the phenolic compound can removed by laccase in corn stover hydrolysate, which improves the yield of ethanol by up to 10% [62]. The formation of ethanol from lignocellulosic biomass, which can be used as a fuel, is particularly fermented-based. Moreover, organic waste with high lignocellulose content can synthesize methane by anaerobic digestion using ligninolytic enzyme and results showed that the production of bio-methane from cellulose is more than hemicelluloses. Production of biofuel from lignin cellulosic biomass by enzymatic hydrolysis is an environmentally suitable procedure. The degradation of lignin depends on the increment of the redox potential of the mediator. Transformation of biomass to ethanol without going through any pretreatment is done by fungus or group of fungus is known as integrated fungal fermentation (IFF). A white rot fungus known as *phlebia* sp. MG-60 can transform lignocellulosic biomass into ethanol in solid-state fermentation. The production of ethanol from different sources like kraft pulp, waste paper, sugarcane bagasse, rice straw, white straw, and corn cob hardwood has been evaluated by fungal strain. An integrated process using fungi coculture is an alternative to producing ethanol, achieving significant delignification and cellulose conversation. This process reduces the yield of harmful compounds like furan, pentose, and hexose, resulting in detoxification processes like filtration, anion exchange chromatography, and alkaline base of sodium precipitation. Ligninolytic enzymes are used to decrease toxic products in hydrolysate feedstock [63].

34.6.8 Detoxification

Detoxification before or after saccharification can be employed, but detoxification with enzymes before saccharification can enhance the production of C_2H_5OH. The production of ethanol can be improved by using enzyme detoxification before saccharification. Furan derivatives can be degraded by aryl-alcohol oxidase (AAO), whereas hydroxyphenyl benzothiazole mediates over 90% of phenolic compounds. Enhancing ethanol production using ligninolytic enzyme detoxification, which can also break down polyunsaturated alcohol, benzyl alcohol, m-fluorobenzyl alcohol, and p-fluorobenzyl alcohol [64].

34.6.9 Bioconversion

There are three steps in the production of biofuel from lignin cellulosic biomass

Step 1. Attainment of fermentable sugar
Step 2. Transformation of fermentable sugar into ethanol
Step 3. Isolation and purification of biofuel via distillation

The cellulose part of biomass breaks down into small sugar (monomer), which are further fermented to ethanol by cultivating different microorganisms such as *E. coli, Klebsiella, Erwinia, Lactobacillus, Bacillus* and *Clostridia, Pichiastipitis,* and *Saccharomyces cerevisiae*. The gene of *S. cerevisiae* was tried to modify for high production of biofuel. In addition to biofuel, many other organic acids like citric acid, lactic acid, acetic acid, succinic acid, and butanol can also be produced from bioconversion of cellulose and hemicelluloses. For conversion of butanol from hemicelluloses *Clostridium acetobutylicum* and *Clostridium beijerinckii*. Lactic acid production from hemicelluloses has been reported in *Lactobacillus pentosus*. Many researchers observed the production of enzymes in solid-state fermentation from different microorganisms. For the bioconversion of lignocellulosic biomass to biofuel or other bioactive compounds by enzyme action. After the pretreatment procedure conversion of lignocellulosic biomass involves hydrolysis of polysaccharides and sugar fermentation. When these two steps are done separately is known as separate hydrolysis and fermentation (SHF) and simultaneously is known as simultaneous saccharification and fermentation (SSF). In between SHF and SSF technology, SSF is more advanced as compared to SHF [65].

34.7 Conclusion

A ligninolytic enzyme is produced from most of the white-rot fungi in sufficient nitrogen medium; some examples are *G. lucidam Aspergillus sp, Trichoderma sp, Penicillium sp., P. chrysosporium, N. frowardii*. Every year, tons of waste material are formed from different industries and worldwide, almost 10^{10}tons of lignocellulosic material are formed every year, which may create many problems for the environment. Ligninolytic enzymes can degrade those waste materials and help the environment. A single-cell microorganism can secrete approximately 2,500 enzymes, but in an industrial process or any reaction medium, it needs only one precise enzyme for conversion. The other contaminant enzyme may give some disagreeable product, so to remove those contaminants, purification of the enzyme is necessary. This review explains how ligninolytic enzymes, MnP, LiP, and laccase, may all be accomplished using protein separation and purification techniques. There is no universal approach to recovery, and every enzyme needs a different purification strategy or procedure. For a combination of similar enzymes or macromolecules to yield a pure enzyme product, it may be required to combine different fractionation techniques.

Acknowledgment

For this fundamental research work, the authors are thankful to the Department of Chemistry, NERIST, Nirjuli, for giving facility to collect matter to write this chapter.

References

1 Volesky, B., Luong, J.H.T., and Aunstrup, K. (1984). Microbial enzymes: production, purification, and isolation. *Crit. Rev. Biotechnol.* 2 (2): 119–146.

2 Masalu, R. (2016). Ligninolytic enzymes of the fungus isolated from soil contaminated with cow dung. *Tanzania J. Sci.* 42 (1): 84–92.

3 Christopher, L.P., Kumar, H., and Zambare, V.P. (2014). Enzymatic biodiesel: challenges and opportunities. *Appl. Energy* 119: 497–520.

4 Chamuris, G.P., Koziol-Kotch, S., and Brouse, T.M. (2000). Screening fungi isolated from woody compost for lignin-degrading potential. *Compost Sci. Util.* 8 (1): 6–11.

5 Giardina, P., Faraco, V., Pezzella, C. et al. (2010). Laccases: a never-ending story. *Cell. Mol. Life Sci.* 67 (3): 369–385.

6 Sarkanen, S., Razal, R.A., Piccariello, T. et al. (1991). Lignin peroxidase: toward a clarification of its role in vivo. *J. Biolumin. Chemilumin.* 266 (6): 3636–3643.

7 Maciel, M.J.M. and Ribeiro, H.C.T. (2010). Industrial and biotechnological applications of ligninolytic enzymes of the basidiomycota: a review. *Electron. J. Biotechnol.* 13 (6): 14–15.

8 Asgher, M., Sharif, Y., and Bhatti, H.N. (2010). Enhanced production of ligninolytic enzymes by *Ganoderma lucidum* IBL-06 using lignocellulosic agricultural wastes. *Int. J. Chem. Reactor Eng.* 8 (1): 1–19.

9 Koroljova-Skorobogat'ko, O.V., Stepanova, E.V., Gavrilova, V.P. et al. (1998). Purification and characterization of the constitutive form of laccase from the basidiomycete *Coriolushirsutus* and effect of inducers on laccase synthesis. *Biotechnol. Appl. Biochem.* 28 (1): 47–54.

10 Abdel-Hamid, A.M., Solbiati, J.O., and Cann, I.K.O. (2013). Insights into lignin degradation and its potential industrial applications. In: *Advances in Applied Microbiology*, vol. 82, 1–28. Elsevier.

11 Shekher, R., Sehgal, S., Kamthania, M., and Kumar, A. (2011). Laccase: microbial sources, production, purification, and potential biotechnological applications. *Enzyme Res.* 2011, Article ID 217861: 1–11.

12 Thakker, G.D., Evans, C.S., and Rao, K.K. (1992). Purification and characterization of laccase from *Monocillium indicum* Saxena. *Appl. Microbiol. Biotechnol.* 37 (3): 321–323.

13 Hölker, U., Dohse, J., and Höfer, M. (2002). Extracellular laccases in ascomycetes *Trichoderma atroviride* and *Trichoderma harzianum*. *Folia Microbiol. (Praha)* 47 (4): 423–427.

14 Mary, A.V.A. and Samuel, S.J. (2016). Laccase: production and purification by pseudomonas aeruginosa. *J. Pure Appl. Microbiol.* 10 (2): 1613–1618.

15 Eggert, C., Temp, U., and Eriksson, K.-E. (1996). The ligninolytic system of the white rot fungus *Pycnoporus cinnabarinus*: purification and characterization of the laccase. *Appl. Environ. Microbiol.* 62 (4): 1151–1158.

16 Hatakka, A. (1994). Lignin-modifying enzymes from selected white-rot fungi: production and role from in lignin degradation. *FEMS Microbiol. Rev.* 13 (2–3): 125–135.

17 Yadav, P., Singh, V.K., Yadav, M., et al. (2012). Purification and characterization of Mn-peroxidase from *Musa paradisiaca* (banana) stem juice.

18 Yan, J., Chen, Y., Niu, J. et al. (2015). Laccase produced by a thermotolerant strain of *Trametes trogii* LK13. *Braz. J. Microbiol.* 46: 59–65.

19 Asgher, M., Iqbal, H.M.N., and Irshad, M. (2012). Characterization of purified and xerogel immobilized novel lignin peroxidase produced from *Trametes versicolor* IBL-04 using solid-state medium of corncobs. *BMC Biotech.* 12 (1): 1–8.

20 Muhammad, A., Muhammad, I., and Iqbal, H.M.N. (2012). Purification and characterization of LiP produced by *Schyzophyllum commune* IBL-06 using banana stalk in solid state cultures. *BioResources* 7 (3): 4012–4021.

21 Knežević, A., Milovanović, I., Stajić, M., and Vukojević, J. (2013). Trametes suaveolens as ligninolytic enzyme producer. *Zb. Matice Srp. za Prir. Nauk.* 124: 437–444.

22 Xie, J., Luo, S., Feng, L. et al. (2010). Production of *Trametes gallica* lignocellulases for wheat straw degradation. *BioResources* 5 (1): 99–107.

23 Gonzalez, J.C., Medina, S.C., Rodriguez, A. et al. (2013). Production of *Trametes pubescens* laccase under submerged and semi-solid culture conditions on agro-industrial wastes. *PLoS One* 8 (9): e73721.

24 More, S.S., Renuka, P.S., Pruthvi, K. et al. (2011). Isolation, purification, and characterization of fungal laccase from *Pleurotus* sp. *Enzyme Res.* 2011: 248735.

25 Falade, A.O., Nwodo, U.U., Iweriebor, B.C. et al. (2017). Lignin peroxidase functionalities and prospective applications. *Microbiologyopen* 6 (1): e00394.

26 Singleton, S.F., Simonette, R.A., Sharma, N.C., and Roca, A.I. (2002). Intein-mediated affinity-fusion purification of the *Escherichia coli* RecA protein. *Protein Expression Purif.* 26 (3): 476–488.

27 Pech-Canul, A.D.L.C., Carrillo-Campos, J., Ballinas-Casarrubias, M.d.L. et al. (2020). Functional expression and one-step protein purification of manganese peroxidase 1 (rMnP1) from *Phanerochaete chrysosporium* using the *E. coli*-expression system. *Int. J. Mol. Sci.* 21 (2): 416.

28 Reiss, R., Ihssen, J., Richter, M. et al. (2013). Laccase versus laccase-like multi-copper oxidase: a comparative study of similar enzymes with diverse substrate spectra. *PLoS One* 8 (6): e65633.

29 Plácido, J. and Capareda, S. (2015). Ligninolytic enzymes: a biotechnological alternative for bioethanol production. *Bioresour. Bioprocess.* 2 (1): 1–12.

30 Sundaramoorthy, M., Youngs, H.L., Gold, M.H., and Poulos, T.L. (2005). High-resolution crystal structure of manganese peroxidase: substrate and inhibitor complexes. *Biochemistry* 44 (17): 6463–6470.

31 Sundaramoorthy, M., Kishi, K., Gold, M.H., and Poulos, T.L. (1994). The crystal structure of manganese peroxidase from *Phanerochaete chrysosporium* at 2.06-A resolution. *J. Biolumin. Chemilumin.* 269 (52): 32759–32767.

32 Hofrichter, M. (2002). lignin conversion by manganese peroxidase (MnP). *Enzyme Microb. Technol.* 30 (4): 454–466.

33 Wesenberg, D., Kyriakides, I., and Agathos, S.N. (2003). White-rot fungi and their enzymes for the treatment of industrial dye effluents. *Biotechnol. Adv.* 22 (1–2): 161–187.

34 Erkurt, E.A., Erkurt, H.A., and Unyayar, A. (2010). Decolorization of azo dyes by white rot fungi. In: *Biodegradation of Azo Dyes*, 157–167. Springer.

35 Dunford, H.B. (1991). Horseradish peroxidase: structure and kinetic properties. *Perozidases Chem. Biol.* 1–23.

36 Kuwahara, M., Glenn, J.K., Morgan, M.A., and Gold, M.H. (1984). Separation and characterization of two extracelluar H_2O_2-dependent oxidases from ligninolytic cultures of *Phanerochaete chrysosporium*. *FEBS Lett.* 169 (2): 247–250.

37 Singh, S.K., Yadav, M., Yadava, S., and Yadav, K.D.S. (2011). Coal depolymerising activity and haloperoxidase activity of Mn peroxidase from *Fomes durissimus* MTCC-1173. *Bioinorg. Chem. Appl.* 2011.

38 Miettinen, K. and Mäkelä, M.M. (2002). On scalarizing functions in multiobjective optimization. *OR Spectrum* 24 (2): 193–213.

39 Martínez, Á.T., Speranza, M., Ruiz-Dueñas, F.J., et al.(2005).Biodegradation of lignocellulosics: microbial, chemical, and enzymatic aspects of the fungal attack of lignin.

40 Stephen, B., Pelling, A.L., Smith, G.J.D., and REDDY, C.A. (2005). Screening of basidiomycetes and xylariaceous fungi for lignin peroxidase and laccase gene-specific sequences. *Mycol. Res.* 109 (1): 115–124.

41 Erden, E., Ucar, M.C., Gezer, T., and Pazarlioglu, N.K. (2009). Screening for ligninolytic enzymes from autochthonous fungi and applications for decolorization of Remazole Marine Blue. *Braz. J. Microbiol.* 40: 346–353.

42 Haglund, C. (1999). Biodegradation of xenobiotic compounds by the white-rot fungus *Trametes trogii*. *Mol. Biotechnol. Program.* 30.

43 Cooper, P. (1993). Removing colour from dyehouse waste waters—a critical review of technology available. *J. Soc. Dyers Colour.* 109 (3): 97–100.

44 Blánquez, P., Casas, N., Font, X. et al. (2004). Mechanism of textile metal dye biotransformation by *Trametes versicolor*. *Water Res.* 38 (8): 2166–2172.

45 Novotný, Č., Rawal, B., Bhatt, M. et al. (2001). Capacity of *Irpex lacteus* and *Pleurotus ostreatus* for decolorization of chemically different dyes. *J. Biotechnol.* 89 (2–3): 113–122.

46 Vyas, S. and Lachke, A. (2003). Biodeinking of mixed office waste paper by alkaline active cellulases from alkalotolerant *Fusarium* sp. *Enzyme Microb. Technol.* 32 (2): 236–245.

47 Nathan, V.K. and Rani, M.E. (2020). A cleaner process of deinking waste paper pulp using *Pseudomonas mendocina* ED9 lipase supplemented enzyme cocktail. *Environ. Sci. Pollut. Res.* 27 (29): 36498–36509.

48 Xu, Q., Fu, Y., Qin, M., and Qiu, H. (2007). Surface properties of old newsprint laccasevioluric acid system deinked pulp. *Appita Technol. Innov. Manuf. Environ.* 60 (5): 372–377.

49 Nathan, V.K., Rani, M.E., Gunaseeli, R., and Kannan, N.D. (2018). Enhanced biobleaching efficacy and heavy metal remediation through enzyme mediated lab-scale paper pulp deinking process. *J. Cleaner Prod.* 203: 926–932.

50 Selinheimo, E., Kruus, K., Buchert, J. et al. (2006). Effects of laccase, xylanase and their combination on the rheological properties of wheat doughs. *J. Cereal Sci.* 43 (2): 152–159.

51 Chowdhary, P., More, N., Yadav, A., and Bharagava, R.N. (2019). Ligninolytic enzymes: an introduction and applications in the food industry. In: *Enzymes in Food Biotechnology*, 181–195. Elsevier.

52 Viswanath, B., Rajesh, B., Janardhan, A. et al. (2014). Fungal laccases and their applications in bioremediation. *Enzyme Res.* 2014.

53 Ferapontova, E.E., Shleev, S., Ruzgas, T. et al. (2005). Direct electrochemistry of proteins and enzymes. In: *Perspectives in Bioanalysis*, vol. 1, 517–598. Elsevier.

54 Lee, J.-W., Lee, S.-M., Hong, E.-J. et al. (2006). Estrogenic reduction of styrene monomer degraded by *Phanerochaete chrysosporium* KFRI 20742. *J. Microbiol.* 44 (2): 177–184.

55 Bumpus, J.A. and Aust, S.D. (1987). Biodegradation of DDT [1,1,1-trichloro-2,2-bis(4-chlorophenyl)ethane] by the white rot fungus *Phanerochaete chrysosporium*. *Appl. Environ. Microbiol.* 53 (9): 2001–2008.

56 Wen, X., Jia, Y., and Li, J. (2009). Degradation of tetracycline and oxytetracycline by crude lignin peroxidase prepared from *Phanerochaete chrysosporium*–a white rot fungus. *Chemosphere* 75 (8): 1003–1007.

57 Touahar, I.E., Haroune, L., Ba, S. et al. (2014). Characterization of combined cross-linked enzyme aggregates from laccase, versatile peroxidase and glucose oxidase, and their utilization for the elimination of pharmaceuticals. *Sci. Total Environ.* 481: 90–99.

58 Eibes, G., Debernardi, G., Feijoo, G. et al. (2011). Oxidation of pharmaceutically active compounds by a ligninolytic fungal peroxidase. *Biodegradation* 22 (3): 539–550.

59 Banerjee, S., Patti, A.F., Ranganathan, V., and Arora, A. (2019). Hemicellulose based biorefinery from pineapple peel waste: xylan extraction and its conversion into xylooligosaccharides. *Food Bioprod. Process.* 117: 38–50.

60 Kosa, M. and Ragauskas, A.J. (2012). Bioconversion of lignin model compounds with oleaginous *Rhodococci*. *Appl. Microbiol. Biotechnol.* 93 (2): 891–900.

61 Larsson, S., Cassland, P., and Jönsson, L.J. (2001). Development of a *Saccharomyces cerevisiae* strain with enhanced resistance to phenolic fermentation inhibitors in lignocellulose hydrolysates by heterologous expression of laccase. *Appl. Environ. Microbiol.* 67 (3): 1163–1170.

62 Mate, D.M. and Alcalde, M. (2017). Laccase: a multi-purpose biocatalyst at the forefront of biotechnology. *Microb. Biotechnol.* 10 (6): 1457–1467.

63 Salvachúa, D., Prieto, A., López-Abelairas, M. et al. (2011). Fungal pretreatment: an alternative in second-generation ethanol from wheat straw. *Bioresour. Technol.* 102 (16): 7500–7506.

64 Lee, S. and Shah, Y.T. (2012). *Biofuels and Bioenergy: Processes and Technologies.* CRC Press.

65 Meera, Y., Nivedita, R., Singh, Y.H., and Anindita, H. (2020). Bioconversion of lignocellulose materials using different pre-treatment strategies. *Res. J. Chem. Environ* 24: 12.

35

Bioinformatic-driven Research in Microbial Enzymes: An Overview

Kanchan Yadav[1], Varsha Rani[1], Gautam Anand[2], Umesh Yadava[3], and Dinesh Yadav[1]

[1] *Deen Dayal Upadhyaya Gorakhpur University, Department of Biotechnology, Gorakhpur, Uttar Pradesh 273009, India*
[2] *Agricultural Research Organization, Volcani Institute, Department of Plant Pathology and Weed Research, Rishon LeZion 7505101, Israel*
[3] *Deen Dayal Upadhyaya Gorakhpur University, Department of Physics, Gorakhpur, Uttar Pradesh 273009, India*

35.1 Introduction

Enzymes are powerful biocatalysts used for a variety of purposes since ancient times. Microorganisms are present everywhere in the environment and are an important source of enzymes. Many microorganisms, including bacteria, actinomycetes, fungi, and yeast, produce an abundance of robust and intriguing enzymes either extracellularly or intracellularly. They can produce enzymes within a very short span of time. The amount of intracellular microbial enzymes is effectively regulated by production pathways and degradation pathways. However, intracellular microbial enzymes have several disadvantages such as fragile nature of enzymes, which makes it difficult for them to survive in harsh environments, expensive isolation techniques, and a number of challenges in the downstream processing. Extracellular microbial enzymes are generally preferred over intracellular microbial enzymes because they have low molecular weight, high stability, are simple to analyze and assess the enzymatic activity, and minimize the cost of the purification and recovery process. Consequently, extracellular enzymes produced by microbes have ecological importance [1–4]. Microbial enzymes have numerous advantages over animal and plant enzymes. First, microbial enzymes have higher activity and stability than plant and animal enzymes. The advent of fermentation techniques enables large-scale production of purified and well-characterized enzymes particularly by selected strains. Second, Microbial enzymes are high-yielding and are easily modified and optimized as they possess a versatile biochemical composition and are susceptible to gene modification. Additionally, microbes represent an excellent source of enzymes that are discovered by contemporary techniques such as metagenome screening, genome mining, and

Microbial Enzymes: Production, Purification, and Industrial Applications, First Edition.
Edited by Dinesh Yadav, Pankaj Chowdhary, Gautam Anand, and Rajarshi Kumar Gaur.

assessing the extremophilic communities [2, 5]. Different types of enzymes from microbes have been discovered to degrade varieties of organic matter. A wide range of industrial processes have utilized them, including the production of enriched products. Additionally, they are used in clinical laboratories to analyze biological samples. These are also utilized in several industries, including pharmaceuticals, agrochemicals, animal feed and fodder, food preservatives, paper and pulp, textiles, leathers, and bioremediation since they have a hydrolyzing activity that enables them to degrade organic compounds [4, 6, 7]. At present, two hundred different types of microbial enzymes have been employed commercially from four thousand known enzymes. The use of microbial enzymes in industry has grown considerably in recent years. Various strains of bacteria, fungi, and yeasts are used to produce commercial enzymes. In the present day, the interest has also increased in the rapidly growing photosynthetic organisms, algae, as they have diverse applications in the agriculture and biofuel industries. Several approaches are used for the choice of microbes as well as relevant techniques for the production of enzymes that have novel physiological or physical characteristics and are resistant to extreme conditions such as temperature, salts, and pH used for economical purposes. Several studies have been conducted, revealing the significance and applications of biotechnologically and commercially successful microbial enzymes [8, 9]. The need for enzymes with broad-spectrum properties has increased in recent years due to the massive expansion of the biotechnology area. The use of nanotechnology for enzyme immobilization has led to major advancements in enzyme technology over the past decade. Increasing community demands for enzymes have prompted researchers to apply various approaches, including metagenomics and genome mining, to increase the database of different microorganisms and search for novel microbes and enzymes. In addition, natural enzymes are being improved with the help of recombinant DNA technology and protein engineering, which allow for a better fit into processes by redesigning the enzymes. Bioinformatics plays a key role to gain deeper knowledge about microbes and microbial enzymes. Many tools have been developed to annotate these database data in order to facilitate data mining. Therefore, with the discovery of a microorganism, one can predict a gene or protein and their structure and function, perform gene expression profiling to determine regulatory pathways, and predict metabolic pathway. Various bioinformatic tools have been developed to study protein–protein and protein–DNA interactions and molecular docking between proteins and chemicals for drug discovery, which can be utilized for formulation of new chemicals for sustainable development, as shown in Figure 35.1. Improvements in technologies and increasing computer powers, as well as access to the software containing vast state-of-the-art facilities, nowadays allow investigators to conduct and try studies on quite realistic molecules through the creation of conditions that simulate *in vivo* systems. Molecular dynamics (MD) is a complementary tool to experimental methods, by which we can make our assumptions beyond experimental limitations and theoretically observe the effect of variations in various parameters. QM/MM method is essential for understanding the molecular mechanisms of biological systems and can provide valuable insights for drug design and material science. This chapter highlights microbial enzymes,

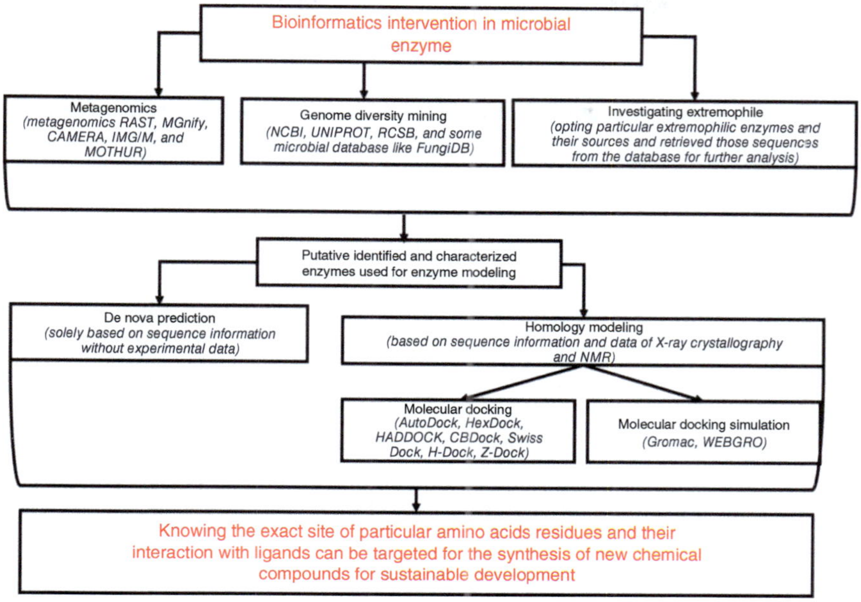

Figure 35.1 Overview of bioinformatics intervention in microbial enzyme for sustainable development.

methods for discovering novel enzymes, and bioinformatics tools for the study of enzymes.

35.2 Enzyme Mining

Microbial enzymes are found in abundance in nature. We can use immense biodiversity and discover new enzymes by using three approaches: (i) metagenomics, (ii) genome mining, and (iii) investigating extremophile diversity.

35.2.1 Metagenomics

Despite the abundance of microbes on Earth, hardly 1% can be cultured in the lab using conventional methods. Metagenomics has emerged as a substitute for traditional microbial screening techniques. It refers to the study of microbial populations and enzymes obtained directly from nature without the need for culturing. Unlike genomics, metagenomics involves the study of genomes derived from communities rather than individual organisms. As a result, metagenomics has been able to provide information on microbial diversity directly from natural sources without culturing [5, 10, 11]. Bioinformatics interventions and experimental techniques can be applied in metagenomics to reveal the biodiversity of microbes and their activities. Using the metagenomics approach, a genomic library from environmental DNA can be prepared and screened the library for the open reading frames (ORFs) potent for encoding putative novel enzymes. Structural metagenomics and functional metagenomics are the two fundamental strategies that can be implemented for exploring metagenomics in any context [12]. Structural metagenomics deals with the composition of microbial populations. The major objective of the study of community structure is to comprehend the interactions between the numerous components that contribute to the formation of a community in a certain aspect. Relationships between community members provide essential data for the study of environment and biological mechanisms. Microbial community analysis methods such as taxonomic analysis, gene prediction and annotation, and metabolic pathway prediction are covered under basic structural metagenomics approaches. Additionally, assembly and binning are also included. Functional metagenomics includes an array of basic methods, such as gene assembly, screening, and gene expression, to discover novel enzymes. These assessments can be followed by bioinformatic analysis, such as nucleotide or protein sequence mining, motif and domain prediction, structure prediction and annotation, evolutionary relationship analysis, as well as protein characterization, such as investigation of protein reaction activity and ideal pH and temperature ranges [13]. Several *in silico* tools, software, and servers are used to study microbial population, network assessment, metabolic pathway prediction, and structure and function prediction. Metagenomics RAST, MGnify, CAMERA, IMG/M, MOTHUR, etc., are examples of software used for metagenomic studies. A list of software with their description is given in Table 35.1 which are used for metagenomics studies. Various strategies are used for analyzing metadata, which includes assembly generation, binning, sequence analysis, motif and domain analysis, and phylogenetic analysis for studying the evolutionary relationship between microbes. Several microbial enzymes have been found in various habitats, including volcanic fissures, tundras, cow rumens, aquatic environments, human guts, and termite intestine, which may have the potential for use as biocatalytic enzymes. Lipase, amidase, amylase, protease, cellulase, pectinase, nitrilase, beta-glucosidase, decarboxylases, epoxy hydrolases, and many more unique enzymes are discovered using a metagenomic method from nature. A list of several enzymes that have been discovered using the metagenomic approach is shown in Table 35.2. A novel bacterial gene lac21, encoding laccase enzyme, has been reported from marine metagenomic library, which shows great potential for decolorizing azo dyes [50]. Another report of protease enzyme from organic waste, encoded by the Prt1A gene, shows its highest activity at 55 °C, making it suitable for the detergent industry [51]. Earlier studies revealed that the genes encoding cellulase enzyme were found in the microbial population of sugarcane bagasse and in the human intestine [52]. Additionally, another novel 53D1 gene producing chitinase enzyme can be exploited to manage agricultural pests [53]. Similarly, an alkaline pectate lyase enzyme isolated from an environmental soil sample has been reported to exhibit high catalytic activity at high pH and temperature range, making it suitable for bioscouring processes in the textile industry [54].

35.2.2 Extremophiles

Extremophiles are organisms that can survive in deadly or intolerably hostile environments to other terrestrial life. They can develop in environments that were once

Table 35.1 Software for metagenomics analysis.

Tools	Description	Web address	References
Metagenomics RAST	It is a free server for phylogenetic and functional analysis of metagenomes. It is also used in the study of comparative metagenomics of microbial communities	https://www.mg-rast.org/	[14]
MGnify (earlier known as EBI metagenomics)	It is a server used to submit raw nucleotide sequences for functional and taxonomic analysis. It is also utilized for analysis, visualization, and discovery of metagenomic, metatranscriptomic, amplicon, and assembly datasets	http://www.ebi.ac.uk/metagenomics/	[15]
CAMERA (Community cyberinfrastructure for Advanced Microbial Ecology Research and Analysis)	It is a database that utilize a progressive website-based analysis portal for submitting, discovering, analyzing, visualizing, and providing data about microbial communities	https://www.hsls.pitt.edu/molbio	[16]
IMG/M (Integrated Microbial Genomes with Microbiome Samples)	It contains annotated nucleotide sequences of archaea, bacteria, eukaryotes, viruses, plasmids, genome fragments (partially sequenced genomes), as well as metagenomes and metatranscriptome datasets	https://img.jgi.doe.gov/m/	[17]
Greengenes	It is a database of 16S rRNA Gene sequences	http://greengenes.lbl.gov	[18]
QIIME 2 (Quantitative Insights Into Microbial Ecology)	It is a free server for bioinformatics analysis of microbiome	https://qiime2.org/	[19]
MOTHUR	It is a free software for analyzing sequences of microbial community. It is used to predict function, heat maps, phylogenetic tree, and Venn diagrams	http://www.mothur.org	[20]
SqueezeMeta	It is a fully automatic channel for metagenomics or metatranscriptomics, covering all steps of the analysis such as assembly merging, RNA prediction and classification, ORF (CDS) prediction, homology searching against taxonomic and functional database	https://github.com/jtamames/SqueezeMeta	[21]
BBAP (BLAST-based assembly pipeline)	BBAP is an assembly pipeline designed for the de novo or reference assembly of next generation sequencing data sets. It is specifically designed for the assembly of highly polymorphic metagenomic data sets. It provides accurate and thorough assembly results with high efficiency	http://homepage.ntu.edu.tw/~youylin/BBAP.html	[22]

(Continued)

Table 35.1 (Continued)

Tools	Description	Web address	References
Genovo	It is an innovative sequence assembler that finds probable sequence reconstructions under the provided model	https://www.cs.stanford.edu/search	[23]
Kaiju	It is a program for fast and sensitive taxonomic classification of high-throughput sequencing reads from metagenomic whole genome sequencing or metatranscriptomics experiments	https://github.com/bioinformatics-centre/kaiju.git	[24]
SpaRC (SparkReadClust)	It is a software for clustering of transcriptomes and metagenomes	https://bitbucket.org/berkeleylab/jgi-sparc/src/master/	[25]
MeganServer	It is a server that allows optimized analysis of large metagenomic datasets	https://github.com/husonlab/megan-ce/tree/master/src/megan/ms	[26]
MEGAHIT	It is a sequence assembler software for assembling large and complex metagenomics datasets quickly and reasonably	https://github.com/voutcn/megahit	[27]
Meta-IDBA	It is a server for assembling sequences in metagenomic data, which includes several genomes from various species	http://www.cs.hku.hk/~alse/metaidba	[28]
CONCOCT	It is a software for binning metagenomic contigs	https://github.com/BinPro/CONCOCT	[29]
Metawatt	It is a binner program for the binning of metagenomic contigs and evaluation of the binning results. It also provides taxonomic classification of metadata	http://sourceforge.net/projects/metawatt	[30]

Table 35.2 Different microbial enzymes mined using metagenomics approach.

Enzymes	Source	References
Chitinases	Uncultured marine microorganisms	[31]
Esterase	Soil	[32]
Oxidoreductase	Enrichment cultures	[33]
Amidases	Soil and enrichment cultures	[34]
Xylanase	Antarctic seawater	[35]
Lipase	Deep-sea sediment	[36]
Decarboxylase	Soil	[37]
Phytase	*Ctenopharyngodon idellus* (grass carp)	[38]
Bleomycin resistance dioxygenase (BRPD)	Polluted agricultural soil	[39]
Beta-galactosidase	Soil	[40]
Polyketide synthase	Soil acidobacteria	[41]
Nitrilase	Soil	[42]
Lipase	Fat-contaminated soil from wastewater treatment plant	[43]
Alkaline serine protease	Forest soil	[44]
Pectinase	Soil of hot spring	[45]
Cellulase	Soil of grassland	[46]
Pectinase	Marine water	[47]
Lipase	Bovine rumen	[48]
Epoxide hydrolases	Soil	[49]

thought to be unfriendly to life, such as harmful pollutants, biological solvents, toxic metals, extremely hot areas, chilled water, salt-based solutions, acidic, and alkaline environments [5, 55]. It has been found that extremophiles exist deep within the Earth's crust, deep inside the ocean at high pressure, at extreme acidity (pH 0) and at extreme basicity (pH 12.8), even at freezing water, at 20 °C. Several studies have shown that they not only can survive under each severe environmental condition, but they are dependent on those conditions for their survival. Extremophiles are classified based on environments in which they thrive. Organisms that thrive at high temperatures are referred to as thermophiles and creatures that thrive at extremely high temperatures are hyperthermophiles. Psychrophiles are creatures that thrive at low temperature range, acidophiles are organisms that thrive in acidic condition, alkaliphiles are organisms that thrive in basic condition, barophiles are creatures that thrive under pressure, and halophiles are creatures that need NaCl to grow [56]. Extremophiles are an important source of enzymes that are extremely stable in extreme conditions. Thermophilic glutamate dehydrogenases,

Table 35.3 Extremophilic enzymes and their sources.

Extremophilic enzymes	Sources	References
Carboxylesterase	*Ferroplasma acidiphilum*	[63]
α-Glucosidase	*Ferroplasma acidiphilum*	[63]
Protease	*Geomicrobium* sp. EMB2 strain	[64]
Serine proteases	*Halobacillus* spp.	[58]
Alkaline xylanase	bacterium -OKH	[59]
Lipase	*Salinivibrio* sp. strain SA-2	[60]
α-Amylase	*Haloarcula* sp. strain S-1	[65]
Peptidase	*Pyrococcus horikoshii*	[66]
α-Amylases	*Pyrococcus woesei*	[67]
Lipases Cal-A	*Candida antarctica*	[61]
Alkaline protease	*Bacillus licheniformis* strain K7A	[68]
Serine protease	*Bacillus subtilis* K-1	[69]
Alkaline xylanase	*Caldicoprobacter algeriensis*	[70]
Xylanase	*Pyrodictium abyssi*	[71]
Transaminase	*Vulcanisaeta moutnovskia*	[72]

laccases, xylanases, nitrilases, transaminases, and lipases are used in many different industries. Thermophiles like *Geobacillus, Clostridium, Thermus, Alyciclobacillus, Anoxybacillus, Thermotoga, Methanopyrus, Pyrococcus,* and *Thermoccocus* are a few extremophiles containing enzymes that are promising for different industries [57]. The Taq polymerase enzyme, obtained from the thermophilic bacteria *Thermus aquaticus* is also an example of thermophilic enzyme that has been used in polymerase chain reaction. Additionally, psychrophilic enzymes have become increasingly useful for many industrial applications, notably because of ongoing efforts to cut back on energy use. Thus, enzymes such as Proteases, amylases, and lipases are excellent enzymes for developing detergents that reduce textile fiber depletion. The halophilic enzymes need to deal with high quantities of salts, such as NaCl or KCl. In response to these environments, these proteins acquired an abundance of acidic amino acid residues on their outer surfaces to avoid precipitation. A nonaqueous medium has been used to exploit this property. Proteases from *Chromobacter* spp. [58], xylanase from bacterium -OKH [59], Lipase from *Salinivibrio* sp. are robust at high temperature and high salt concentration, making them suitable for different industrial applications [60]. Lipase Cal-A enzyme from thermophile *Candida antarctica* is used for preparing docosahexaenoic acid in food and pharmaceutical industries [61]. Xylanases from *Trichoderma reesei* has been found to give antifirming property, thus, making them useful for beverage industries [62]. We have enlisted a few extremophilic enzymes and their microbial sources in Table 35.3.

35.2.3 Genome Mining

In recent years, genome sequencing has increased the amount of data available from sequence databases, thus providing the opportunity of finding novel natural substances such as enzymes through database mining. Genome sequencing with next-generation platforms, such as the Roche 454 GS-20, the Solexa Genome Analyzer, or the ABI-SoLiD sequencer, is set to reduce sequencing time and costs. Multiple whole genomes can be completed in less than two weeks by utilizing these platforms. So far, 30,530 genomic sequence of eukaryotes and 567,228 of prokaryotes and genome assemblies are available in the National Center for Biotechnology Information (NCBI) database (accessed on 18 July 2023 from NCBI Microbial Genomes). Genome hunting and data mining are two strategies utilized to discover novel enzymes [73, 74]. The genome-hunting approach is based on searching for ORFs in the genome of a particular microbe. Further, cloning, overexpression, and activity screening of putative enzymes are performed. An alternative approach is data mining, which uses homology-based alignment among sequences available in databases. Various *in silico* tools shown in Table 35.4 are used in genome mining to find conserved regions among homologous protein sequences that could be characterized further [5]. Genome mining relies exclusively on bioinformatics tools and computing technology. Sequence comparison of protein sequences encoding for enzymes can help in determining the pathways in which those proteins are involved. The enzymes' availability, the routes in which they function, and sequence comparisons with the genes from which they are derived can all be utilized to locate homologs and possibly the pathways in the newly studied organism. Although many enzymes exhibit similar sequences, their chemical processes may differ slightly, ultimately leading to a different pathway or very different product. Hornung et al. used genome mining to identify microbes that generate halogenases enzymes, where halogenation plays a critical role in biological activity [75]. In another study, Malik et al. applied genome mining study to the genus *Streptacidiphilus,* which reveals the presence of different secondary metabolite producing biosynthetic gene clusters and hydrolytic enzymes in the genera. A comparative analysis between 11 *Streptacidiphilus* species, selected *Streptomyces*, and *Kitasatospora* genomes was performed [76]. The genome analysis of *Paenibacillus* species *LS1* revealed xylan-active CAZyme repertoire capable of degrading xylan efficiently [77].

35.3 Computational Insight for Enzyme Modeling

Proteins may exhibit a variety of low-energy conformational states as a result of their interactions with other proteins. Protein–protein or protein–DNA interactions are possible under stable conformational states. In addition to the function of protein being influenced by exposed active sites, protein function can also be anticipated by comparing the three-dimensional structure of an unknown protein with that of a characterized protein [78, 79]. Although three-dimensional structures can be

Table 35.4 *In silico* tool used for enzyme mining and characterization.

S. No.	Bioinformatics tools	Link	Application
1.	NCBI	https://www.ncbi.nlm.nih.gov/	Data mining
2.	UNIPROT	https://www.uniprot.org/	Data mining
3.	RCSB Protein Data Bank	https://www.rcsb.org/	Data mining
4.	BLAST	https://blast.ncbi.nlm.nih.gov/Blast.cgi	Homology search
5.	MEGA	https://www.megasoftware.net/	Multiple sequence alignment and phylogenetic tree construction
6.	CLC	https://clc-sequence-viewer.software.informer.com/download/	Multiple sequence alignment
7.	Expasy Translate tool	https://web.expasy.org/translate/	Protein sequence prediction
8.	InterProscan	https://www.ebi.ac.uk/interpro/search/sequence/	Protein domain analysis
9.	Prosite	https://prosite.expasy.org/	Protein domain functional analysis
10.	HMMScan	https://www.ebi.ac.uk/Tools/hmmer/search/hmmscan	Biosequence analysis against collection of protein profile
11.	MEME Suite 5.5.2	https://meme-suite.org/meme/tools/meme	Motif search
12.	SWISS-MODEL	https://swissmodel.expasy.org/	Protein structure homology modelling server
13.	PDBSum	http://www.ebi.ac.uk/thornton-srv/databases/pdbsum/	Protein 2D structure prediction
14.	Primer3	https://primer3.ut.ee/	Primer designing
15.	Ka/Ks calculation tool	http://services.cbu.uib.no/tools/kaks	Gene duplication event prediction
16.	Expasy ProtParam server	https://web.expasy.org/protparam/	Physicochemical analysis
17.	DeepTMHMM server	https://dtu.biolib.com/DeepTMHMM	Transmembrane analysis
18.	SignalP 5.0	http://www.cbs.dtu.dk/services/SignalP/	Signal peptide prediction
19.	WoLF PSORT	https://wolfpsort.hgc.jp/	Subcellular and nuclear localization prediction
20.	STRING	https://string-db.org/	Protein–protein interaction

obtained by X-ray crystallography and nuclear magnetic resonance spectroscopy, these methods have limitations. In order to match genes, alternate mechanisms must be used. Gene sequences generally correspond closely to 3D structures, so sequence similarity is sufficient for function annotation in such cases. However, multiple sequences may correspond to the same three-dimensional structure, even if amino acid sequences do not match; therefore, the lack of matching does not exclude the presence of the same 3D structure. For verification of the function of a newly analyzed protein, it is necessary to match the 2D structure patterns of the alpha helix and beta sheet and the 3D structure [80].

The 3D structure of proteins can be modeled using two major approaches: homology modeling (*in silico*) and *ab initio* (or *de novo*) prediction. The sequence homology approach uses sequence alignment to predict the best three-dimensional structure for various components in the database, including the served portion, loop portion, and side chains, and threads them together to predict the overall three-dimensional structure of the database. Whereas, in *ab initio* structure prediction, energy minimization is used as a basis for predicting structures based solely on sequences [79]. In general words, it can be stated as, in *ab initio* method, theoretical calculations can be used to predict properties of protein-ligand complexes without any experimental data. Alternatively, *in silico* can be used to predict the properties of protein–ligand complexes through computer simulations. Modeling of protein–ligand complexes can be accomplished by using experimental data, such as X-ray crystallography or NMR spectroscopy. Generally, *in silico* studies are used to understand the interaction between enzymes with various substrates or different concentrations of a single substrate at the molecular level, to understand how genetic changes affect the enzyme's ability to detect substrates, to detect the homology of enzymes obtained from other sources and to increase production using statistical analysis [81]. By using molecular docking and MD simulations [81, 82], we can evaluate the substrate-binding efficiency.

35.3.1 Molecular Docking

This process is concerned with determining the orientation of the minimum free binding energy (BE), which determines how a ligand interacts with a target molecule [83], as well as the affinity of the ligand to form stable complexes with proteins. Most of the interactions in the docked complex are noncovalent, such as hydrophobic interactions, hydrogen bonds, ionic bonds, and van der Waals interactions. The docking phenomena can be conducted between proteins, between proteins and ligands, and between proteins and nucleotides. It consists of a number of steps, including the preparation of a three-dimensional structure of a protein, the grounding of ligands, the valuation of the BE of the protein with respect to the ligand, and the analysis of the results [84]. Molecular docking is classified into three categories: (i) induced fit docking, (ii) lock and key docking, and (iii) ensemble docking. In induced fit docking, ligands and proteins are complementary. Ligands bind flexibly at the active site of receptors in order to maximize the bonding force between them. Whereas, the lock and key docking based on 3D complementarity phenomenon, in which both of the ligand and receptor are rigid and tightly bounded. Furthermore, numerous protein structures are used in ensemble docking to dock with ligands. This approach provides insight into both the flexibility and complexity of protein conformational states [85, 86].

There are several ways to perform molecular docking, including manual docking and automated docking. In case of manual docking process, ligands and binding sites have known binding groups; they are paired with complementary groups at the binding sites and bonding distances are specified for each potential interaction. Based on the instructions provided by the operator, the program moves molecules within the binding site in order to maximize the compatibility. There is no direct stacking of groups, but rather, a preferred bonding distance between them is maintained. On the other hand, in the case of automatic docking, the software will make the decision as to how the target and ligand will be docked. A docking program must accomplish two tasks. First, it must place the ligand in different orientations within the active site. Additionally, the program must score the different binding modes in order to determine which ones are most optimal. The complexity of the system can be categorized as (i) both ligand and target as rigid bodies, (ii) targets as rigid bodies but ligands as flexible bodies, or (iii) both targets and ligands as flexible bodies (induced fit) [84].

Generating the various ligand conformations and finding the most stable position in the energy landscape is the first step in the process of protein–ligand docking. In the second step, to evaluate the binding affinity requires a good scoring function that should include all energetic components and be appropriately parameterized. To predict the potential structure of a binary complex, each docking program uses a specific search algorithm and different scoring functions are used to assign a numerical fitness value to the calculated protein–ligand structure. The aim of the docking algorithm and scoring function is to obtain a fast method that is capable of detecting novel lead compounds or reproducing the experimental structure at as high accuracy as possible [87].

It has been shown that protein-ligand docking involves the interaction of enzymes (*Fusarium oxysporum* clone GCEL-PNL 027 pectin lyase (PNL), accession no. KX021379) with ligands such as digalacturonic acid. As illustrated in Figure 35.2, which contains a binding cavity encapsulated by Gln^{93}, Leu^{164}, Asn^{165}, Pro^{166}, Tyr^{168}, Val^{169}, Trp^{170}, Gly^{171}, Gly^{172}, and Asp^{173}, these molecules are involved in interaction with ligands through various bonds [88]. Among the amino acid residues, Asp^{173} and Val^{169} interact with the ligand through Vander Waals interaction, whereas Gln^{93}, Trp^{170}, Asn^{165}, Pro^{166}, Tyr^{168}, Gly^{171}, and Gly^{172} interact with ionic bonds and Leu^{164} shares an H-bond with digalacturonic acid.

35.3.2 Molecular Dynamic Simulation

The simulation process is much more complex because the protein and ligand are physically separated, and after a few conformational movements, the ligand locates its position within the active site of the protein. Besides translations and rotations of rigid bodies, the ligand's structure is also changed internally, including rotations

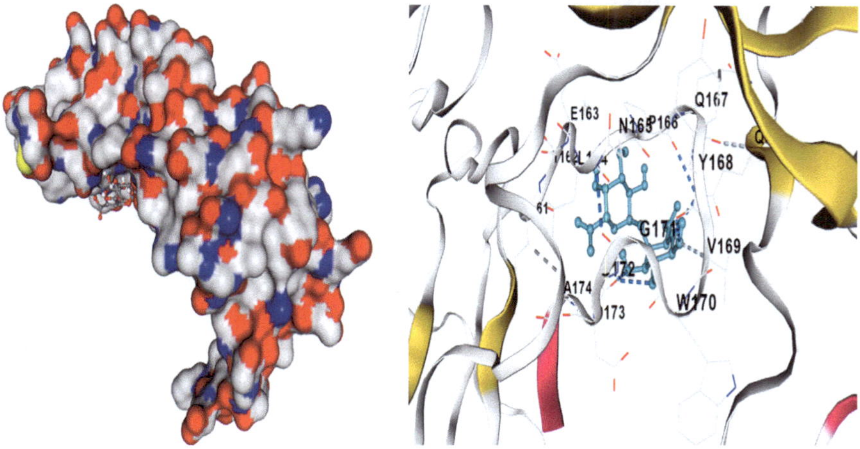

(a) (b)

Figure 35.2 Molecular docking of enzyme (PNL) and substrate (digalacturonic acid) (a) protein–ligand docked complex, (b) interaction of residues of active site with substrate molecule.

at torsion angles. Every move in the conformation space of the ligand generates a total energetic cost for the system, which is calculated at the end of each move in the conformation space of the ligand. A minimal binding free energy is usually calculated from the interaction between the ligand and receptor using various scoring functions based on force-field, empirical, knowledge, consensus, and descriptor [89]. In contrast to shape complementarity techniques, which require some inventive methods to incorporate flexibility into ligand modeling, the Simulation method is more flexible in accommodating ligand flexibility. As an additional advantage, in reality, after molecular recognition, protein and ligand interact in a similar manner. Due to the need to explore a large energy landscape, this technique is considered to have an only disadvantage in terms of time required to evaluate the optimal binding pose [84].

MD simulation is a computational technique used to study the behavior and motion of atoms and molecules over time. It allows scientists and researchers to simulate the behavior of a molecular system by numerically solving the classical equations of motion for each atom or molecule in the system. In an MD simulation, the interactions between atoms or molecules are described using a potential energy function, often derived from fundamental principles of quantum mechanics or empirical observations. The forces acting on each atom are calculated based on this potential energy function, and the positions and velocities of the atoms are updated iteratively over very small time steps using numerical integration methods (e.g. Verlet algorithm and velocity Verlet algorithm). The simulation starts with an initial configuration of atoms or molecules, often generated from experimental data or theoretical predictions. The system's evolution is then simulated by integrating the equations of motion to predict how the system's structure and dynamics change over time. MD simulations are a critical tool in computational chemistry, materials science, biophysics, and other fields, providing a powerful means to understand and predict the behavior of molecular systems at atomic and molecular scales, stability of biological complexes, etc.

35.3.3 QM/MM Method

The quantum mechanics/molecular mechanics (QM/MM) method is a computational approach used to study molecular systems that are too large or complex to be accurately described solely using either quantum mechanics (QM) or classical molecular mechanics (MM) methods. QM/MM combines the strengths of both approaches to provide a more accurate description of molecular systems. Quantum mechanics describes the behavior of atoms and molecules at the quantum level, considering wave functions, electronic structure, and the behavior of electrons. It is highly accurate but computationally intensive, making it suitable for small regions of a molecular system. QM methods are used to model the active or important regions of the system, usually involving the chemical reactions or processes of interest. Molecular mechanics is a classical approach that uses simplified potential energy functions based on empirical force fields. MM approximates molecular behavior using classical physics principles and treats atoms as interacting particles with simple mathematical potentials. MM methods are less computationally demanding than QM and are suitable for modeling the overall molecular structure and interactions in a large system.

In a QM/MM simulation, the molecular system is divided into two parts: the QM region and the MM region. QM Region of the system is treated using quantum mechanics. It typically includes the region where the chemical reaction or process of interest occurs or where electronic properties are critical for accurate modeling. The electronic structure and interactions within this region are described using a QM method. MM Region of the system is described using molecular mechanics. It involves the surrounding molecular environment where a simpler classical force field is applied to approximate molecular interactions. The QM and MM regions are coupled at the boundary, allowing information and interactions to flow between the two regions. The QM/MM approach enables accurate modeling of specific regions (e.g. reacting molecules) with quantum mechanical precision while efficiently modeling the rest of the system using molecular mechanics. This method is widely used in studying various chemical and biological processes, such as enzyme reactions, ligand binding, catalysis, and other complex molecular interactions [90].

35.4 Conclusion

The microbes provide a wealth of biocatalysts for a wide variety of industries, including domestic care, fruit juice, animal feed and fodder, technical industries, chemicals, and pharmaceuticals industries. Enzymes offer unique properties, including high specificity, quick action, and ecofriendly, that allow for more gentle reaction conditions, higher yields, and less wastage during enzyme-aided processes in industry. With the advancement of genomics, metagenomics, proteomics, and developing recombinant DNA technologies, new microbial enzymes are being discovered from nature through genomes, metagenomes, and extremophiles and are also being evolved to enhance their catalytic properties. Enzyme research is still advancing, and there is growing interest in using enzymes for commercial biocatalysis. The growing interest in biocatalysis is influenced by a variety of factors, including enzyme diverging, powerful computational approaches teamed up with directed evolution and screening techniques to enhance enzyme characteristics for better processing, and novel design and selection of enzymes catalyzing a particular preferred chemical reaction. Future research will frequently involve enzyme informatics, modified enzymes, and newly designed enzymes with their chemistry to produce more and probably new chemicals and substances from less expensive and renewable resources. This will subsequently help to establish an economy based on biology and achieve low-carbon ecological development.

Acknowledgments

The authors would sincerely like to acknowledge the Head, Department of Biotechnology, Deen Dayal Upadhyaya Gorakhpur University, Gorakhpur.

References

1 Contesini, F.J., Figueira, J.d.A., Kawaguti, H.Y. et al. (2013). Potential applications of carbohydrases immobilization in the food industry. *Int. J. Mol. Sci.* 14 (1): 1335–1369.
2 Liu, X. and Kokare, C. (2017). Microbial enzymes of use in industry. In: *Biotechnology of Microbial Enzymes: Production, Biocatalysis and Industrial Applications*, 267–298. Elsevier Inc. http://dx.doi.org/10.1016/B978-0-12-803725-6.00011-X.
3 Meghwanshi, G.K., Kaur, N., Verma, S. et al. (2020). Enzymes for pharmaceutical and therapeutic applications. *Biotechnol. Appl. Biochem.* 67 (4): 586–601.
4 Golgeri, M.D.B., Mulla, S.I., Bagewadi, Z.K. et al. (2022). A systematic review on potential microbial carbohydrases: current and future perspectives. *Crit. Rev. Food Sci. Nutr.* 64: 1–18.
5 Adrio, J.L. and Demain, A.L. (2014). Microbial enzymes: tools for biotechnological processes. *Biomolecules* 4: 117–139. http://www.mdpi.com/2218-273X/4/1/117.
6 Bagewadi, Z.K., Bhavikatti, J.S., Muddapur, U.M. et al. (2020). Statistical optimization and characterization of bacterial cellulose produced by isolated thermophilic *Bacillus licheniformis* strain ZBT2. *Carbohydr. Res.* 491 (February): 107979. https://doi.org/10.1016/j.carres.2020.107979.
7 Singh, R.S., Singh, T., and Pandey, A. (2019). Microbial enzymes—an overview. In: *Advances in Enzyme Technology*, 1e, 1–40. Elsevier B.V. http://dx.doi.org/10.1016/B978-0-444-64114-4.00001-7.

8 Khan, S., Ullah, M.W., Siddique, R. et al. (2016). Role of recombinant DNA technology to improve life. *Int. J. Genomics* 2016: 2405954.
9 Shraddha, S.R., Sehgal, S., Kamthania, M., and Kumar, A. (2011). Laccase: microbial sources, production, purification, and potential biotechnological applications. *Enzyme Res.* 2011: 217861.
10 Gilbert, J.A. and Dupont, C.L. (2011). Microbial metagenomics: beyond the genome. *Annu. Rev. Mar. Sci.* 3: 347–371.
11 Steele, H.L., Jaeger, K.E., Daniel, R., and Streit, W.R. (2008). Advances in recovery of novel biocatalysts from metagenomes. *J. Mol. Microbiol. Biotechnol.* 16 (1–2): 25–37.
12 Prayogo, F.A., Budiharjo, A., Kusumaningrum, H.P. et al. (2020). Metagenomic applications in exploration and development of novel enzymes from nature: a review. *J. Genet. Eng. Biotechnol.* 18 (1): 1–10.
13 Patel, T., Chaudhari, H.G., Prajapati, V. et al. (2022). A brief account on enzyme mining using metagenomic approach. *Front. Syst. Biol.* 2 (December): 1–10.
14 Meyer, F., Paarmann, D., D'Souza, M. et al. (2008). The metagenomics RAST server – a public resource for the automatic phylogenetic and functional analysis of metagenomes. *BMC Bioinf.* 9: 1–8.
15 Mitchell, A.L., Almeida, A., Beracochea, M. et al. (2020). MGnify: the microbiome analysis resource in 2020. *Nucleic Acids Res.* 48 (D1): D570–D578.
16 Sun, S., Chen, J., Li, W. et al. (2011). Community cyberinfrastructure for advanced microbial ecology research and analysis: the CAMERA resource. *Nucleic Acids Res.* 39 (1): 546–551.
17 Chen, I.M.A., Markowitz, V.M., Chu, K. et al. (2017). IMG/M: integrated genome and metagenome comparative data analysis system. *Nucleic Acids Res.* 45 (D1): D507–D516.
18 DeSantis, T.Z., Hugenholtz, P., Larsen, N. et al. (2006). Greengenes, a chimera-checked 16S rRNA gene database and workbench compatible with ARB. *Appl. Environ. Microbiol.* 72 (7): 5069–5072.
19 Bolyen, E., Rideout, J.R., Dillon, M.R. et al. (2019). Reproducible, interactive, scalable and extensible microbiome data science using QIIME 2. *Nat. Biotechnol.* 37 (8): 852–857.
20 Schloss, P.D., Westcott, S.L., Ryabin, T. et al. (2009). Introducing mothur: open-source, platform-independent, community-supported software for describing and comparing microbial communities. *Appl. Environ. Microbiol.* 75 (23): 7537–7541.
21 Tamames, J. and Puente-Sánchez, F. (2019). SqueezeMeta, a highly portable, fully automatic metagenomic analysis pipeline. *Front. Microbiol.* 10 (JAN): 1–10.
22 Lin, Y.Y., Hsieh, C.H., Chen, J.H. et al. (2017). De novo assembly of highly polymorphic metagenomic data using in situ generated reference sequences and a novel BLAST-based assembly pipeline. *BMC Bioinf.* 18 (1): 1–10.
23 Laserson, J., Jojic, V., and Koller, D. (2011). Genovo: de novo assembly for metagenomes. *J. Comput. Biol.* 18 (3): 429–443.
24 Menzel, P., Ng, K.L., and Krogh, A. (2016). Fast and sensitive taxonomic classification for metagenomics with Kaiju. *Nat. Commun.* 7.

25 Shi, L., Meng, X., Tseng, E. et al. (2019). SpaRC: scalable sequence clustering using Apache Spark. *Bioinformatics* 35 (5): 760–768.

26 Gautam, A., Zeng, W., and Huson, D.H. (2023). MeganServer: facilitating interactive access to metagenomic data on a server. *Bioinformatics* 39 (3): 10–12.

27 Li, D., Liu, C.M., Luo, R. et al. (2015). MEGAHIT: an ultra-fast single-node solution for large and complex metagenomics assembly via succinct de Bruijn graph. *Bioinformatics* 31 (10): 1674–1676.

28 Peng, Y., Leung, H.C.M., Yiu, S.M., and Chin, F.Y.L. (2011). Meta-IDBA: a de novo assembler for metagenomic data. *Bioinformatics* 27 (13): 94–101.

29 Alneberg, J., Bjarnason, B.S., De Bruijn, I. et al. (2014). Binning metagenomic contigs by coverage and composition. *Nat. Methods* 11 (11): 1144–1146.

30 Strous, M., Kraft, B., Bisdorf, R., and Tegetmeyer, H.E. (2012). The binning of metagenomic contigs for microbial physiology of mixed cultures. *Front. Microbiol.* 3 (DEC): 1–11.

31 Cottrell, M.T., Moore, J.A., and Kirchman, D.L. (1999). Chitinases from uncultured marine microorganisms. *Appl. Environ. Microbiol* 65 (6): 2553–2557.

32 Henne, A., Schmitz, R.A., Bömeke, M. et al. (2000). Screening of environmental DNA libraries for the presence of genes conferring lipolytic activity on *Escherichia coli*. *Appl. Environ. Microbiol.* 66 (7): 3113–3116.

33 Knietsch, A., Waschkowitz, T., Bowien, S. et al. (2003). Construction and screening of metagenomic libraries derived from enrichment cultures: generation of a gene bank for genes conferring alcohol oxidoreductase activity on *Escherichia coli*. *Appl. Environ. Microbiol.* 69 (3): 1408–1416.

34 Gabor, E.M., De Vries, E.J., and Janssen, D.B. (2004). Construction, characterization, and use of small-insert gene banks of DNA isolated from soil and enrichment cultures for the recovery of novel amidases. *Environ. Microbiol.* 6 (9): 948–958.

35 Marx, J.C., Collins, T., D'Amico, S. et al. (2007). Cold-adapted enzymes from marine antarctic microorganisms. *Mar. Biotechnol.* 9 (3): 293–304.

36 Jeon, J.H., Kim, J.T., Kim, Y.J. et al. (2009). Cloning and characterization of a new cold-active lipase from a deep-sea sediment metagenome. *Appl. Microbiol. Biotechnol.* 81 (5): 865–874.

37 Jiang, C., Shen, P., Yan, B., and Wu, B. (2009). Biochemical characterization of a metagenome-derived decarboxylase. *Enzyme Microb. Technol.* 45 (1): 58–63.

38 Huang, H., Shi, P., Wang, Y. et al. (2009). Diversity of beta-propeller phytase genes in the intestinal contents of grass carp provides insight into the release of major phosphorus from phytate in nature. *Appl. Environ. Microbiol.* 75 (6): 1508–1516.

39 Uchiyama, T. and Miyazaki, K. (2010). Substrate-induced gene expression screening: a method for high-throughput screening of metagenome libraries. In: *Methods in Molecular Biology*, 153–168. Clifton, NJ: Springer http://link.springer.com/10.1007/978-1-60761-823-2_10.

40 Wang, K., Li, G., Yu, S.Q. et al. (2010). A novel metagenome-derived β-galactosidase: gene cloning, overexpression, purification and characterization. *Appl. Microbiol. Biotechnol.* 88 (1): 155–165.

41 Parsley, L.C., Linneman, J., Goode, A.M. et al. (2011). Polyketide synthase pathways identified from a metagenomic library are derived from soil *Acidobacteria*. *FEMS Microbiol. Ecol.* 78 (1): 176–187.

42 Bayer, S., Birkemeyer, C., and Ballschmiter, M. (2011). A nitrilase from a metagenomic library acts regioselectively on aliphatic dinitriles. *Appl. Microbiol. Biotechnol.* 89 (1): 91–98.

43 Glogauer, A., Martini, V.P., Faoro, H. et al. (2011). Identification and characterization of a new true lipase isolated through metagenomic approach. *Microb. Cell Fact.* 10: 1–15.

44 Pushpam, P.L., Rajesh, T., and Gunasekaran, P. (2011). Identification and characterization of alkaline serine protease from goat skin surface metagenome. *AMB Express* 1 (1): 1–10.

45 Singh, R., Dhawan, S., Singh, K., and Kaur, J. (2012). Cloning, expression and characterization of a metagenome derived thermoactive/thermostable pectinase. *Mol. Biol. Rep.* 39 (8): 8353–8361.

46 Nacke, H., Engelhaupt, M., Brady, S. et al. (2012). Identification and characterization of novel cellulolytic and hemicellulolytic genes and enzymes derived from German grassland soil metagenomes. *Biotechnol. Lett* 34 (4): 663–675.

47 Suribabu, T.K., Govardhan, T.L., and Hemalatha, K.P.J. (2014). Strain improvement of *Brevibacillus borostelensis* R1 for optimization of α-amylase production by mutagens. *J. Microb. Biochem. Technol.* 6 (3): 123–127.

48 Privé, F., Newbold, C.J., Kaderbhai, N.N. et al. (2015). Isolation and characterization of novel lipases/esterases from a bovine rumen metagenome. *Appl. Microbiol. Biotechnol.* 99 (13): 5475–5485.

49 Stojanovski, G., Dobrijevic, D., Hailes, H.C., and Ward, J.M. (2020). Identification and catalytic properties of new epoxide hydrolases from the genomic data of soil bacteria. *Enzyme Microb. Technol.* [Internet] 139 (May): 109592. https://doi.org/10.1016/j.enzmictec.2020.109592.

50 Fang, Z.M., Li, T.L., Chang, F. et al. (2012). A new marine bacterial laccase with chloride-enhancing, alkaline-dependent activity and dye decolorization ability. *Bioresour. Technol.* 111: 36–41. http://dx.doi.org/10.1016/j.biortech.2012.01.172.

51 Devi, S.G., Fathima, A.A., Sanitha, M. et al. (2016). Expression and characterization of alkaline protease from the metagenomic library of tannery activated sludge. *J. Biosci. Bioeng.* 122 (6): 694–700. http://dx.doi.org/10.1016/j.jbiosc.2016.05.012.

52 Pessoa, T.B.A., Rezende, R.P., Marques, E.d.L.S. et al. (2017). Metagenomic alkaline protease from mangrove sediment. *J. Basic Microbiol.* 57 (11): 962–973.

53 Zhang, L., Chen, F.X., Zeng, Z. et al. (2021). Advances in metagenomics and its application in environmental microorganisms. *Front. Microbiol.* 12 (December): 1–15.

54 Wang, H., Li, X., Ma, Y., and Song, J. (2014). Characterization and high-level expression of a metagenome-derived alkaline pectate lyase in recombinant *Escherichia coli*. *Process Biochem.* 49 (1): 69–76. http://dx.doi.org/10.1016/j.procbio.2013.10.001.

55 Merino, N., Aronson, H.S., Bojanova, D.P. et al. (2019). Living at the extremes: extremophiles and the limits of life in a planetary context. *Front. Microbiol.* 10 (MAR): 780.

56 Rampelotto, P. (2013). Extremophiles and extreme environments. *Life* 3 (3): 482–485. http://www.mdpi.com/2075-1729/3/3/482.

57 Atalah, J., Cáceres-Moreno, P., Espina, G., and Blamey, J.M. (2019). Thermophiles and the applications of their enzymes as new biocatalysts. *Bioresour. Technol.* 280 (February 2019): 478–488. https://doi.org/10.1016/j.biortech.2019.02.008.

58 Enache, M. and Kamekura, M. (2010). Hydrolytic enzymes of halophilic microorganisms and their economic values. *Rom. J. Biochem.* 59 (1): 47–59.

59 Sanghvi, G., Jivrajani, M., Patel, N. et al. (2014). Purification and characterization of haloalkaline, organic solvent stable xylanase from newly isolated halophilic bacterium-OKH. *Int. Sch. Res. Not.* 2014: 1–10.

60 Amoozegar, M.A., Salehghamari, E., Khajeh, K. et al. (2008). Production of an extracellular thermohalophilic lipase from a moderately halophilic bacterium, *Salinivibrio* sp. strain SA-2. *J. Basic Microbiol.* 48 (3): 160–167.

61 Akanbi, T.O. and Barrow, C.J. (2017). *Candida antarctica* lipase A effectively concentrates DHA from fish and thraustochytrid oils. *Food Chem.* 229 (February): 509–516. http://dx.doi.org/10.1016/j.foodchem.2017.02.099.

62 Woolfson, M.M. (1997). *An Introduction to X-ray Crystallography.* Cambridge University Press https://www.cambridge.org/core/product/identifier/9780511622557/type/book.

63 Sharma, A., Kawarabayasi, Y., and Satyanarayana, T. (2012). Acidophilic bacteria and archaea: acid stable biocatalysts and their potential applications. *Extremophiles* 16 (1): 1–19.

64 Ram, K., Singh, R.K.M., Kapoor, S., and Khare, S.K. (2011). Gene identification and molecular characterization of solvent stable protease from a moderately haloalkaliphilic bacterium, *Geomicrobium* sp. EMB2. *J. Microbiol. Biotechnol.* 21 (2): 129–135.

65 Fukushima, T., Mizuki, T., Echigo, A. et al. (2005). Organic solvent tolerance of halophilic α-amylase from a Haloarchaeon, *Haloarcula* sp. strain S-1. *Extremophiles* 9 (1): 85–89.

66 Rosenbaum, E., Gabel, F., Durá, M.A. et al. (2012). Effects of hydrostatic pressure on the quaternary structure and enzymatic activity of a large peptidase complex from *Pyrococcus horikoshii. Arch. Biochem. Biophys.* 517 (2): 104–110. http://dx.doi.org/10.1016/j.abb.2011.07.017.

67 Koch, R., Spreinat, A., Lemke, K., and Antranikian, G. (1991). Purification and properties of a hyperthermoactive α-amylase from the archaeobacterium *Pyrococcus woesei. Arch. Microbiol.* 155 (6): 572–578.

68 Hadjidj, R., Badis, A., Mechri, S. et al. (2018). Purification, biochemical, and molecular characterization of novel protease from *Bacillus licheniformis* strain K7A. *Int. J. Biol. Macromol.*Elsevier B.V. 114: 1033–1048. https://doi.org/10.1016/j.ijbiomac.2018.03.167.

69 Singh, S., Gupta, P., and Bajaj, B.K. (2018). Characterization of a robust serine protease from *Bacillus subtilis* K-1. *J. Basic Microbiol.* 58 (1): 88–98.

70 Amel, B.D., Nawel, B., Khelifa, B. et al. (2016). Characterization of a purified thermostable xylanase from *Caldicoprobacter algeriensis* sp. nov. strain TH7C1T. *Carbohydr. Res.* 419: 60–68. http://dx.doi.org/10.1016/j.carres.2015.10.013.

71 Andrade, C.M.M.C., Aguiar, W.B., and Antranikian, G. (2001). Physiological aspects involved in production of xylanolytic enzymes by deep-sea hyperthermophilic archaeon *Pyrodictium abyssi. Appl. Biochem. Biotechnol.* 91–93: 655–669.

72 Stekhanova, T.N., Rakitin, A.L., Mardanov, A.V. et al. (2017). A novel highly thermostable branched-chain amino acid aminotransferase from the crenarchaeon *Vulcanisaeta moutnovskia. Enzyme Microb. Technol.* 96: 127–134. http://dx.doi.org/10.1016/j.enzmictec.2016.10.002.

73 Van Lanen, S.G. and Shen, B. (2006). Microbial genomics for the improvement of natural product discovery. *Curr. Opin. Microbiol.* 9 (3): 252–260.

74 He, X.J. (2012). Genomic data mining: an efficient way to find new and better enzymes. *Enzyme Eng.* 01 (01): 1–4.

75 Hornung, A., Bertazzo, M., Dziarnowski, A. et al. (2007). A genomic screening approach to the structure-guided identification of drug candidates from natural sources. *ChemBioChem* 8 (7): 757–766.

76 Malik, A., Kim, Y.R., and Kim, S.B. (2020). Genome mining of the genus streptacidiphilus for biosynthetic and biodegradation potential. *Genes (Basel)* 11 (10): 1–31.

77 Mukherjee, S., Lodha, T.D., and Madhuprakash, J. (2023). Comprehensive genome analysis of cellulose and xylan-active CAZymes from the genus *Paenibacillus*: special emphasis on the novel xylanolytic *Paenibacillus* sp. LS1. *Microbiol. Spectrum* 11 (3): e0502822.

78 Whisstock, J.C. and Lesk, A.M. (2003). Prediction of protein function from protein sequence and structure. *Q. Rev. Biophys.* 36 (3): 307–340.

79 Baker, D. and Sali, A. (2001). Protein structure prediction and structural genomics. *Science* 294 (5540): 93–96.

80 Bansal, A.K. (2005). Bioinformatics in microbial biotechnology – a mini review. 11 (ii): 1–11.

81 Singh, P.K., Joseph, J., Goyal, S. et al. (2016). Functional analysis of the binding model of microbial inulinases using docking and molecular dynamics simulation. *J. Mol. Model.* 22 (4): 69.

82 Singh, D., Rawat, S., Waseem, M. et al. (2016). Molecular modeling and simulation studies of recombinant laccase from *Yersinia enterocolitica* suggests significant role in the biotransformation of non-steroidal anti-inflammatory drugs. *Biochem. Biophys. Res. Commun.* 469 (2): 306–312.

83 Ferreira, L.G., Dos Santos, R.N., Oliva, G., and Andricopulo, A.D. (2015). Molecular docking and structure-based drug design strategies. *Molecules* 20 (7): 13384–13421.

84 Tripathi, A. and Misra, K. (2017). Molecular docking: a structure-based drug designing approach. *JSM Chem.* 5 (2): 1042.

85 Lorber, D.M. and Shoichet, B.K. (1998). Flexible ligand docking using conformational ensembles. *Protein Sci.* 7 (4): 938–950.

86 Huang, S.-Y. and Zou, X. (2007). Ensemble docking of multiple protein structures: considering protein structural variations in molecular docking. *Proteins* 66 (2): 399–421.

87 Yadava, U. (2018). Search algorithms and scoring methods in protein-ligand docking. *Endocrinol. Int. J.* 6: 359–367.

88 Yadav, S., Anand, G., Singh, K.V., and Yadav, D. (2021). Molecular cloning and structural insights into pectin lyase proteins from different strains of *Fusarium*. *Curr. Proteomics* 18: 326–337.

89 Kitchen, D.B., Decornez, H., Furr, J.R., and Bajorath, J. (2004). Docking and scoring in virtual screening for drug discovery: methods and applications. *Nat. Rev. Drug Discovery* 3 (11): 935–949.

90 Bhardwaj, V., Degrassi, G., and Bhardwaj, R.K. (2017). Microbial pectinases and their applications in industries: a review. *Int. Res. J. Eng. Technol.* 4 (8): 829–836.

36

Food Waste and By-products: An Opportunity to Produce Enzymes for Industrial Applications

Manoj Tripathi[1], Ajay Yadav[1], Dilip Pawar[1], Rajpal S. Jadam[1], and Rahul M. Srivastva[2]

[1] *ICAR – Central Institute of Agricultural Engineering, APPD Division, Berasia Road, NabiBagh, Bhopal, Madhya Pradesh 462038, India*
[2] *MANIT, Central Institute of Agriculture Engineering, Nabi Bagh, Berasia Road, Department of Biotechnology, Bhopal, Madhya Pradesh 462038, India*

36.1 Introduction

In recent times, food waste is a global concern due to its negative effect on the environment as well as a hurdle in meeting the requirements of food security for millions of people [1–3]. As per FAO, almost 33% of the food that is produced is wasted or lost in food chain and there is an increasing trend of food waste across the world due to rapid urbanization and an increase in population [4]. The majority of food waste accounts for the waste generated at pre-processing, during processing, and post-processing of food and includes mainly the by-products generated from the food processing industries, kitchen waste, waste from restaurants, and waste generated at retail level [5]. According to Food Waste Index developed under United Nation Environment Programme (UNEP) estimated that in 2019, the world generated nearly 961 million tonnes of food waste and out of which household waste shares 61% of the total food waste, followed by food manufacturing (26%) and retailing (13%) [6]. The disposal of food waste is creating a lot of environmental problems such as the emission of greenhouse gases and landfills are acting as breeding grounds for the disease-causing microorganisms. Globally, food waste contributes to 6% of total greenhouse gas emissions [7]. The food industry generates a lot of by-products such as peels, kernels, and seeds from fruits and vegetable processing; bones, hide, and blood from meat processing; skin, scales, and liver from fish processing; and whey and casein from dairy processing. Food waste or by-products from the food industry is a valuable source of various biomolecules such as carbohydrates, proteins, and other functional biochemical compounds having nutraceutical value [8]. These by-products have a huge potential for valorization into various value-added products such as alternative sources of food ingredients, production of biofuels such as bio-hydrogen, bioethanol, and synthesis of enzymes that have commercial usage [9, 10].

Microbial Enzymes: Production, Purification, and Industrial Applications, First Edition.
Edited by Dinesh Yadav, Pankaj Chowdhary, Gautam Anand, and Rajarshi Kumar Gaur.

Enzymes are the biocatalysts that are in huge demand due to their widespread applications ranging from pharmaceuticals and food manufacturing such as baking, brewing, and fruit juice-based industries. The enzymes world market in 2019 was valued at US$ 8636.8 million and is projected to grow at a rate of 6.5% from 2020 to 2027 [11]. Despite having huge demand, most of the enzymes available at the commercial level are expensive and researches have demonstrated that 30% of the costs of the enzymes are related to the raw material cost [12]. The food by-products being a source of carbohydrate and protein can act as an excellent raw material (nutrient media) for the growth of microorganism during fermentation and scarification process. The enhanced growth of microorganisms on food waste could be exploited for the production of enzymes from microbial sources at cheaper prices as compared to conventional raw material. Therefore, this chapter aims at providing insights into the alternative route for the production of enzymes (amylases, lignocellulolytic proteases, lipases) of industrial importance using food waste or by-products from food processing as a substrate. The chapter also highlights the fermentation techniques and recent advances in the production of enzymes from food waste.

36.2 Types of Agro-industrial Food Waste

The food processing industries generate huge amounts of plant, animal, and agricultural residue wastes and such normal food waste is a great challenge due to the nonexistence of effective waste management systems. In the food supply chain, food that is abandoned, unexploited, thrown out, and burnt from the harvest source or slaughter source is mentioned as food loss. Most of the food waste is produced during its production, harvesting, transportation, industrial processing, and consumption [13].

The different types of organic wastes are mainly derived as agricultural wastes or food processing industries waste. The agricultural waste can be principally considered as crop residues after harvesting, agro-industrial wastes, and fruit and vegetable waste [14]; however, the food industries create huge quantities of waste from cereals and pulses, fruits and vegetables, dairy, poultry, meat, egg waste, aquatic life waste, and seafood waste during their processing process (Figures 36.1 and 36.2).

36.3 Food Processing By-products from the Different Industries

The food processing by-products are the major part of total food waste and it has a genitive impact on the environment if not managed properly [15]. Utilization of these by-products into value-added products could not only help for environmental safety but will add to the nutritional profile of the products [16–18]. Pomace, seeds, stone, peel, leaves, and roots are the type of wastes generated from fruit and vegetable processing industry and they ranges from 10% to 60% of the fresh weight of produce [19]. They are rich sources of dietary fiber, bioactive compounds, and other

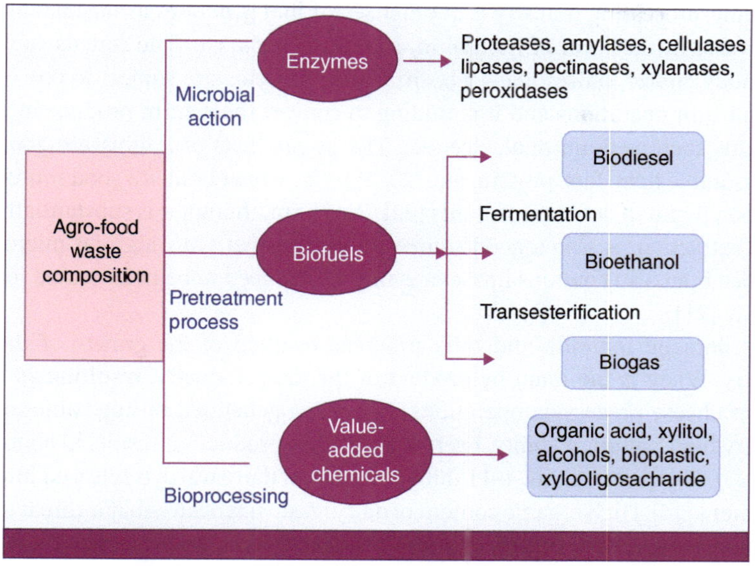

Figure 36.1 Agro-industrial food waste in the production of different bioproducts.

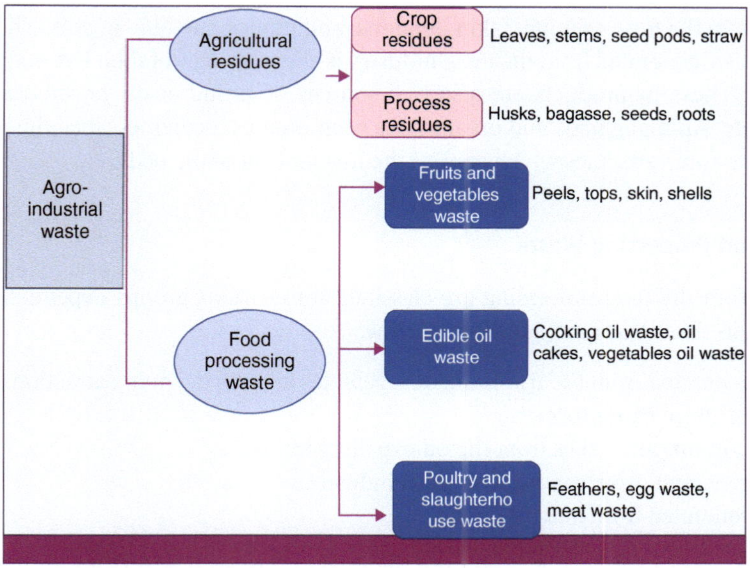

Figure 36.2 Classification of different types of agro-industrial food waste.

nutraceutical compounds. The presence of cellulose, hemicellulose, lignin, etc. such waste offers a great opportunity to recover different enzymes out of it. The canning, frozen, pulping, juice concentrate, and drying are the industrial sectors regarding fruit and vegetable processing, which generates substantial amount of waste.

Grain milling/processing industry is another sector that generates a considerable amount of waste in the form of hull, bran, grit, dust, pods, etc. The cereals such as wheat, paddy, maize, pulses like soybean, pigeon pea etc., are subject to one of the important unit operations and it is milling to convert these farm produce into different forms such as flour, dhal, rice, etc. The by-products of milling are good sources of insoluble fiber, fats, protein, etc. [20, 21]. The wheat bran is a good source of dietary fiber, β-gluten, and antioxidants [22]. Rice bran, though it is substantially used for oil extraction, is also a good source of dietary fiber with high-fat micronutrients. Rice bran also contains lipase enzyme, which need to be heat treated for better stability [21].

Increasing demand for milk and milk products resulted in the growth of the dairy industry. Whey is the main by-product of the dairy industry, resulting as a by-product of cheese processing operations. It is being generated in huge amount and has a very high pollution ability. Every kg of cheese production results in about 9 l of whey [23]. Every year, about 4–11 million tonnes of dairy waste is released into the environment [15]. High organic content of dairy waste has been a major threat to the environment. Apart from organic matter, dairy waste contains suspended solids, nitrogen, phosphorous, oil grease, and even the residues of equipment cleaning products.

Meat, poultry, and fish industries also have a significant generation of waste to the environment. The meat industry waste mainly results at slaughterhouses. This waste is in the form of bones, skin, tendons, and other nonedible organs. The volume of waste generated from the meat industry is about 66–68% of their live body weight [24]. These by-products are also rich sources of amino acids, hormones, fatty acids, etc. Animal glands and organs have been used as medicines since these glands secrete some enzymes which control the metabolism of the body.

36.3.1 Food Processing Waste

The waste from the food processing are classified into various groups depending upon its origin. The classification is listed below:

(i) Waste generated from the trimming of vegetables and during pulp extraction.
(ii) Fruit peel from fruit processing
(iii) Leftover grains and cakes from the oil-expelling industries
(iv) Waste generated from the fish and meat industries
(v) Waste generated from dairy industry

The uniqueness of waste generated from the food industries lies in that they are rich sources of carbohydrate, making them ideal for the production of enzymes. This waste possesses a high amount of other compounds, including lignin, protein, and lipids that fasten the microbial synthesis of enzymes. In addition, the dietary fibers, polyphenols present in fruit processing waste such as apple pomace act as a growth enhancer during enzyme production. In recent times, around the globe, there has been a huge demand for enzymes due to their widespread application in food and biofuel industries. At present, the enzyme industry is growing at a rapid pace and meeting the demand for enzymes using conventional substrates has posed a huge challenge of sustainability. Therefore, the exploration of the waste for the production of enzymes has become a topic of interest due to its sustainable nature and reduction in the price of enzyme production.

36.3.2 Food Industry Waste

Food waste is produced from many foods' raw materials and final products. Waste material formed by the agro-processing sector is simple to assemble, allocate, and valorize for formulate value-added products [25]. European Union has undertaken various steps, including the execution of severe laws for food waste elimination with the aim of using this waste in promoting the manufacture of several value-added products [26]. Major wastes produced are predominately lignocellulosic. In addition to cellulose, plant-based foods have a high level of pectin, inulin, xylan, mannan, glucan, starch, etc., mainly depending upon the nature of the waste product. The lignocellulosic waste material is a decent choice as a raw material for the production of lignocellulose-degrading enzymes. Many designated microorganisms produce specific enzymes for each polysaccharide component, which release sugars and are metabolized for growth, energy, and cell maintenance. Meanwhile, they are a low-cost source of carbohydrate. The lignocellulosic containing food waste is a possible media constituent for making industrially important enzymes. Numerous research has described the usage of several lignocellulosic substrates. A significant claim of the consumption of lignocellulosic waste is for the manufacture of lignocellulose-degrading enzymes viz. cellulase, hemicellulose, and laccase. Enzyme laccase finds its application in paper, textile, and petroleum industries [27]. The making of cellulase is a significant approach for cost saving in the advance of supportable ethanol manufacture.

36.4 Economic Impact of Food Waste

The waste from food processing and its valorization is an important issue in the current scenario for bioeconomy. The term bioeconomy is related to adding value to the food waste generated during food processing. In addition, bioeconomy also involves curbing food waste through legislation reducing the amount of food waste [28]. For instance, European Commission approved a circular economic package, with an aim to enrich worldwide affordability, short-term carefully supportable progress, and generate innovative occupations. Through this approach, improved reusing contributes to a positive impact on the environment and economy. The uniqueness of this approach is to promote reuse and boost the industrial association.

36.5 Challenges in Enzyme Production

For the production of enzymes through microbial fermentation require a substrate that is mostly lignocellulose. Lignocellulose is abundantly found in the cell wall of the plant and is made up of complex polysaccharides. The waste produced from the food processing units, especially fruit and vegetable processing, is rich in lignocellulose. The lignocellulose being complex in structure is resistant to breakdown into simpler sugar moieties during microbial fermentation. The resistance is attributed to the presence of lignin compound contributing crystalline nature to lignocellulose biomass [29]. The crystalline structure is always difficult to degrade by the microbes. Glucose, a simple sugar, is considered as a main source of carbon for the microbes to produce enzymes. The presence of hemicellulose also contributes to resistance in enzymatic hydrolysis due to its interference with glucose formation and uptake by the microbes [30].

36.6 Production of Enzymes from the Fermentation Process

Enzymes are the biological catalysts and involved in many biochemical reactions and show an important role in the various aspects. They are environmentally friendly and work by increasing the rate of any biochemical reactions by lowering the activation energy. The application of enzymes reduces the production cost and also the utilization of by-products for value-added product development (Table 36.1).

36.7 Fermentation Strategies and Enzyme Industries

36.7.1 Solid State Fermentation

Solid state fermentation important in higher production of numerous industrial enzymes. Majority of industrial enzymes are prepared by use of fungal origin. The microorganisms vary in both types of fermentation process [33]. Temperatures rise and can denature the enzymes that are used in production in the reactor. Aeration is a common process to take over this issue. Solid-state fermentation involves the production of more concentrated products in nominal downstream processing [34]. In one study enzyme production by using organic waste was found suitable in solid-state fermentation reported the production of different organic compounds with volatile nature (VOC) such as CH_4, N_2O, and NH_3 [35]. This method mainly boosts the growth of several fungal microorganisms on solid substrates. This method has potentials of high yield with highly concentrated products and produces less effluent, responsible for nominal downstream processing [34].

36.7.2 Submerged Fermentation

The submerged fermentation has a good technique for large-scale production of enzymes. In this method there is great provision of control pH and temperature for proper aeration and agitation within the vessel. This method requires a sterile

Table 36.1 Utility of some common enzymes in the food industries [31, 32].

S. no.	Enzyme	Food industry	Use in food industry
1.	Protease	Wine	Provide red wine stability
		Dairy	Avoid coagulation in cheese industries Flavoring
		Baking	In dough uniformity, Improve dough consistency, Gluten development, Improve organoleptic properties, Decrease mixing duration
		Meat	Meat tenderization
2.	Pectinase	Fruit	Fruit juices clarification process Peel softening of citrus fruits Improves oil extraction from citrus
		Beverages	Tea fermentation process In instant tea powders Eliminate coffee mucilaginous coat
3.	Amylase	Baking	Hydrolysis of starch Flavor enhancement Allow extra sugar in the bread Advances the taste and toasting value Increase shelf-life
		Brewing	Fermentation of alcohol
		Fruit and brewery	Fruit juices and beer Clarification
4.	β-Galactosidase	Dairy	In lactose-free milk production Prebiotics development Making ice creams, Improve milk organoleptic property
5.	Papain	Brewing	Avoids beer haze creation and helps in development of shiny bright beer
		Baking	Gluten protein breakdown helps in food production
		Meat industry	Tenderizing of meat
6.	Lipase	Fats and oils	Making of emulsifiers, Synthesis of triglycerides Trans-esterification of triglycerides for fat-making
		Milk	Improve milk flavors for usage in milk chocolates
		Cheese	Improve flavor, aging, and ripening
7.	Invertase	Sweetener	Making of invert sugar
		Confectionery	Making fructose-rich syrup Soft candies making Artificial honey making

environment for proper care within the reactor, lessening the contamination. In submerged fermentation, a homogeneous environment is created in the reactor for better control of the process. It also helps in the distribution of nutrients and oxygen to the growing microbe. This method also faces some challenges such as the presence of some compounds that induce oxidative stress and destabilize the entire operation. Several fungal strains produce many enzymes and bioactive compounds [36].

36.8 New Trends and Challenges in Enzyme Production Using By-products

Most of the plant and animal by-products contain the complex polymer like lignocellulose. Lignocellulose is one of the main components of the cell wall of various plant materials. Lignocellulose with the presence of lignin makes a complex system that is difficult to get converted during the enzyme production [29]. The crystalline nature of lignocellulose is another challenge for efficient utilization such material for enzyme production. If this crystalline nature of cellulose is not converted into an amorphous form, enzymatic hydrolysis does not occur [37].

The enzyme-producing microbes desire the presence of glucose as a source of carbon, for which the presence of cellulose is desired. However, the presence of hemicellulose therefore may be a hurdle to the conversion of cellulose, glucose concentration, and its absorption [30]. The presence of a specific substrate in the media composition assists the production of specific enzymes. The production of xylanase enzyme has been reported to be enhanced due to the presence of substrates like xylans and arabinoxylans [38]. Enzyme and substrate interaction and hydrolysis of protein components are some of the complex phenomena which play a critical role in the utilization of biomass for enzyme production.

36.9 Industrial Important Enzymes Production

Enzymes are biocatalysts that are in huge demand due to their wide range of applications in pharmaceuticals and food manufacturing such as baking, brewing, and fruit juice-based industries. The enzymes world market in 2019 was valued at US$ 8,636.8 million and projected to grow at a rate of 6.5% from 2020 to 2027 [11]. Despite having huge demand, most of the enzymes available at the commercial level are expensive and researches has demonstrated that 30% of the costs of the enzymes are related to the raw material cost [12]. The food by-products being rich sources of carbohydrate, protein can act as an excellent raw material (nutrient media) for the growth of microorganism during fermentation and scarification process. The enhanced growth of microorganisms on the food waste can be exploited for the production of enzymes from microbial sources at cheaper prices as compared to conventional raw material. Therefore, this chapter aims at providing insights into the alternative route for the production of enzymes (amylases, lignocellulolytic proteases, and lipases) of industrial importance using food waste or by-products from food processing as a substrate. The chapter also highlights the fermentation techniques and recent advances in the production of enzymes from food waste.

36.9.1 α-Amylase

α-Alpha amylases cut α-1,4 associations among glucose subunits in polysaccharides and resulting of the release of short-chain oligomers and α-limit units. α-Amylases reported as extensive applications in industrial developments for many products for food, textiles, and pharmaceuticals [39]. These are industrially formed by use of submerged fermentation process using some *Aspergillus* and *Bacillus* species [40]. Several microbial species are described to yield α-amylase enzymes that have thermos-stability, halo-tolerance, and alkali-stability. Some initial reports introduced banana waste as a significant substrate for the production of α-amylase [41]. Francis et al. [42] showed the making of α-amylase using spent brewer's grain as substrate [12]. Rajagopalan and Krishnan [43] reported very high α-amylase enzyme activity after the addition of waste-based nutrient medium (sugarcane bagasse hydrolysate) as the enzyme producer.

36.9.2 Cellulase

Cellulose molecule hydrolyzed into glucose molecules which required collective three important enzymes: endoglucanase, exoglucanase, and β-glucosidase. These are considered to initiate the hydrolysis of glycosidic bonds [44]. Cellulases are significant enzymes having greater commercial importance. Cellulases play a key role in bioethanol production. It is not only important for biofuels, but its higher application is reported in a variety of industries products [45]. An extensive number of microbial species are currently used in the production of enzymes [44].

In the case of bacteria, cellulase molecules are large and as extracellular aggregates and microbial strains are as *Bacillus circulans, Clostridium thermocellum, Proteus vulgaris, Klebsiella pneumonia, Escherichia coli*, and *Cellulomonas* sp. [46]. From the past two decades, the development of low-cost procedures for cellulase production has been the focus of researchers. Sun et al. [47] assessed the used of banana peel for cellulase production by use of *Trichoderma viride*. They also concluded that banana peel can play the role of substrates as necessary for cellulase synthesis. In another study, mango peel is used for the production of cellulase by *Trichoderma reesei* [48]. The role of apple pomace in making cellulase was also reported by Dhillon et al. [49].

36.9.3 Amyloglucosidase (AMG)

Amyloglucosidases can cleave the α-1,4 links in starch to release glucose molecules and is also known as glucoamylases. It is an exoamylase, liberating β-D-glucose from the nonreducing ends of amylose, amylopectin, and glycogen [50]. It also breaks α-1,6-glycosidic bonds at a slower rate. These enzymes show ideal activity at a pH range of 4.5–5.0 and a temperature range of 40–60 °C. It has significant applications in the food, brewing, and bakery industry [51]. *Aspergillus niger* and *Aspergillus oryzae* are common strains that are used by industry for the production of commercial AMG [52]. *Bacillus* sp., *Rhizopus* sp., and *Saccharomyces* sp. are also found to synthesize AMG [53]. Some important lignocellulose residues have been reported to act as an alternate carbon source for the production of AMG. Wheat bran can also use as a substrate for *A. niger* strain in solid-state fermentation, Pandey et al. [54] reported that yields were increased when *A. niger* growing on rice bran added with extra nitrogen sources in solid-state culture. Some other agricultural residues as banana, cassava, yam, etc., have also been effectively worked as alternate carbon sources for fungal-based production [55].

36.9.4 Xylanase

Xylanases (1,4-β-xylanxylanohydrolase) are important enzymes that hydrolyzed xylan. The xylose residue is considered as a backbone unit of polysaccharide xylan. Each subunit is associated with a β-1,4-glycosidic bond. Xylanases are formed by the use of several fungal and bacterial strains. The filamentous fungi are more efficient in the synthesis of enzymes as compared with bacteria because secretion is in very higher amounts [56]. Xylan has a very complex structure that needs various enzymes for the complete hydrolysis process as endoxylanases and β-xylosidases. *Endo*-xylanases and β-xylosidases enzymes are widely studied in this arrangement [57]. Xylanases enzymes have many applications in food, feed, and bio-refinery sectors [58]. The lignocellulosic food waste as a carbon source suitable for the production of commercial xylanases has been studied by several researchers. The study of Lowe et al. [59] reported the role of wheat straw as a good carbon source for the production of enzyme xylanase with excellent enzymatic activity (0.507 IU/ml). *A. niger* and *Aspergillus terreus* fungal strains are active for production from wheat bran reported by Gawande and Kamat [60]. Grape pomace was found as a suitable substrate for producing xylanase enzyme using *Aspergillus awamori* [61].

36.9.5 Hemicellulases

The enzyme hemicellulases work on carbohydrate β-1,4-glycosidic bonds of hemicellulose which is present in the lignocellulosic biomass. Hemicellulose is prime fraction of lignocellulose. Hemicellulases are amorphous in nature and made of complex sugar moieties. The sugar components in hemicellulose structure may vary and depend upon the plant biomass source [28]. Moreover, sugar acids are also present in the hemicellulose structure. Hemicellulases are proficient in breaking glycosidic bonds and esterified side chain groups. Some important hemicellulases that break glycosidic bonds are α-glucuronidases, α-arabinofuranosidases, α-D-galactosidases, and mannanases.

36.9.6 Lactase

Lactase is commonly known as β-D-galactohydrolase, involved in the hydrolysis of lactose into simpler units of glucose. The nonsynthesis of lactase enzyme in the human gut could lead to lactose intolerance [62]. Dairy products such as milk and yogurt are rich sources of lactose; therefore, the enzyme lactase holds a significant application in the dairy sector. The strains of *Kluyveromyces lactis*, *Kluyveromyces fragilis*, *A. niger*, and *A. oryzae* starins are being used for producing lactase at the industrial level [19]. The strain of *Candida pseudotropicalis* also demonstrated the production of lactase from whey [63]. The research from Macris (1981) found that *Fusarium moniliforme* strain produced lactase with the use of wheat bran as a substrate. The addition of agricultural by-products/waste as molasses and whey were found to increase enzyme yield [64]. A research study showed by Mustranta et al. [65] that a strain of *A. niger* produced for high yield lactase from wheat bran medium.

36.9.7 Pectinolytic Enzymes

Pectinolytic are the array of enzymes including pectinases that have the ability to hydrolyze the pectin substances present in the cell wall of plants by involving the series of reactions such as depolymerization and desertification [66]. The usage of pectinolytic enzymes in food industries includes especially for the vitamin C production, extraction and clarification of wine [67]. The researchers have found that the pectinolytic enzymes are mainly produced by solid-state fermentation using filamentous fungi and bacterial strains. The fungal strains are predominately used for synthesizing pectinolytic enzymes and are dominated by *Aspergillus* species, including *A. niger*, *A. fumigatus*, and *A. oryzae* [68, 69]. The substrate used for the synthesis of pectinolytic enzymes are the industrial by-products from fruit and vegetable processing, including pomaces of apple, citrus, peels of mango, citrus fruits such as lemon, oranges, and by-products of onion processing; cereal processing by-products including bran ad husk of wheat and rice.

Hendges et al. [70] reported the synthesis of enzyme polygalacturonase from solid-state fermentation technique by utilizing wheat bran as a substrate and using *A. niger* as a fungal strain. The study evaluated the effect of static and forced aeration condition on the cell biomass and the study revealed that a fungal cell biomass concentration of 92 and 100 mg/(g dm) was achieved with the static and forced aeration condition respectively after 96 hours. Kumar et al. [71] studied the submerged fermentation and solid state fermentation for the production of enzyme pectinases on mango peel substrate using *Aspergillus foetidus* as a fungal strain. The study concluded that the productivity of the enzyme with solid-state fermentation was higher and the enzyme obtained can be used as an alternative to commercial pectinases for the clarification of mango juice.

In another study by Diaz et al. [72] concluded that agro waste in the form of grape pomace and orange peels can be effectively utilized for the production of polygalacturonase enzyme using solid-state fermentation using *A. awamori* fungal strain. The study reported that aeration had a pounced effect on the production of enzyme and among the reactors, the tray reactor is more efficient in terms of enzyme productivity as compared to the column reactor. Poondla et al. [73] reported that orange peel and ground nut cake could be effectively used for enhancing the production of enzyme pectinase by nine folds using *Saccharomyces cerevisiae* strain using solid-state fermentation with an incubation period of 48 hours. Recent research by Amin et al. [74] reported that wheat bran can be effectively utilized as a substrate for the production of pectinolytic enzymes using solid-state fermentation technique using *Penicillium fellutanum* as a fungal strain.

36.9.8 Protease

Protease is also an important hydrolytic enzyme involved in the hydrolysis of peptide bonds (through which amino acid are joined together) by the process known as proteolysis [75]. The enzyme has industrial applications in diverse fields such as pharmaceuticals, food, and leather industries and accounts for 60% market share of total enzymes sales worldwide [12]. The enzyme can be found in plants, animals, and microbes; among all the sources, the microbial sources are mostly exploited and extensively studied for the production of proteases [76]. The fungal (*Aspergillus* sp.) and bacterial (*Bacillus* sp.) strains, including genetically modified strains, are widely used for the production of most of the proteases by using solid-state and submerged fermentation techniques [77, 78].

A study by Ramakodi et al. [79] reported the protease production from the substrate obtained from the slaughterhouse effluents and cabbage leaf waste by *Chromobacterium violaceum* bacterial strain. In the optimized conditions at pH 9, the protease production achieved was 0.1254 U/ml. Another study by Tuysuz et al. [80] concluded that potato peel, a by-product of potato processing, can be effectively utilized for the production of protease by using *Anoxybacillus rupiensis* strain. The protease activity of 26.2 U/ml was obtained after 48 hours of incubation period. Benabda et al. [81] studied the effect of relative humidity, inoculum size, and incubation period for the production of proteases from bread waste using *Rhizopus oryzae* strain via solid-state fermentation. The study revealed that the 65% relative humidity with an inoculum size of 10^5 spore/g and incubation period of 120 hours provided a conducive environment for the production of protease with an enzyme activity of 2400 U/g. Another study conducted by Hammami et al. [82] reported that wheat bran can be used as a low-cost substrate for the production of alkaline protease via *Bacillus mojavensis* bacterial strain. The obtained protease enzymes can be used for the production of protein hydrolysate from the meat by-products. Lemes et al. [83] also evaluated the by-products from the meat industry such as feather meal, residual feather meal as a substrate for the production of proteases enzyme using *Bacillus* sp. 45. The study reported that the residual feather meal achieved 89 U/ml of keratinolytic activity after 32 hours of cultivation. Afify et al. [84] reported that potato waste could be used as a substrate for the production of protease enzyme using *Saccharomyces serevisiae* via submerged fermentation. The optimized condition displayed an enzyme activity of 360 U/mg after 72 hours of incubation period at a temperature of 20 °C.

36.9.9 Lipases

Lipases is another group of industrial important enzymes that hydrolyses the fat molecules such as triacylglycerol's into various fractions of fatty acids and glycerol molecules [85, 86]. The lipase is considered to be a versatile enzyme due to its widespread application in various sectors such as manufacturing of detergent, as an active agent for pharmaceutical applications, food manufacturing, and in cosmetic industries [87]. Although lipase can be derived from plant, animal, and microbial sources, but microbial sources are most preferred for the production of lipases due to the biocompatibility, stability, and ease in genetic manipulation. The worldwide market share of microbial enzyme in 2018 was estimated at US$ 425.0 Million and will reach US$ 590.2 Million by 2023 [88]. The microbial lipases are predominately produced by bacterial strains such as *Bacillus* sp., *Pseudomonas* sp., and fungi strain, including *Aspergillus* sp. and *Penicillium* sp. via submerged and solid-state fermentation [89].

Dobrev et al. [90] investigated the production of lipase using various agro-industrial waste such as wheat bran, rice bran, and oat bran, along with sunflower cake and meal using *Rhizopus arrhizus* fungal strain. The research concluded that the maximum lipase enzyme activity of 1021.80 U/g was achieved at a moisture content of 66%. Sahoo et al. [91] reported that olive oil cakes could be used as a substrate for the production of bacterial lipase from the *Bacillus licheniformis* strain using solid-state fermentation. The study showed at optimized parameters pH (8.2), temperature (50.8 °C), and incubation period of 72 hours gave a lipase production of 62.3 IU/g. Oliveira et al. [92] evaluated the various oil cakes a by-product of vegetable oil seed industry for the production of lipase via solid-state fermentation by *Aspergillus ibericus*. The research finding reported that palm kernel and sesame oil cake seeds are excellent substrates among all the oil cakes and the lipase enzyme activity of 460 U/g was obtained using palm kernel oil cake at a moisture content of 57%. Fleuri et al. [93] demonstrated that wheat bran and soybean bran can be effectively utilized as a substrate for the production of lipase enzyme using *Aspergillus* sp. via solid-state fermentation. The research highlighted that maximum enzyme activity (13.0 U/ml) after 96 hours of cultivation period using wheat bran as a substrate. Rekha et al. [94] evaluated the various by-products of oil and cereal processing such as ground nut oil cake, coconut oil cake, wheat bran, and rice bran for the lipase production using *Candida rugosa* NCIM 3467 strain. The research finding reported that the highest enzyme activity of 57.25 U/ml was reported with groundnut oil cake after an incubation period of 05 days and 60% moisture content.

36.10 Enzyme Immobilization Strategies

The bioconversion of agro-industrial food and crop waste into value-added products mainly depends on the cost of the process, equipment, and available facility, and market price of the final products. Enzyme's role is advantageous in the valorization of plentiful produced agro-food wastes [95]. Enzymes accomplish many biochemical catalytic reactions under very mild reaction conditions, allowing the advance of many additional environmentally friendly, and sustainable biochemical processes. The operating range of enzymes is constrained nowadays. Enzymes produced from natural sources are mainly effective only in optimal conditions [96]. Enzyme stability, catalytic activity, and recovery under flexible industrial bioprocessing conditions of pH, temperature, water activity, and solvent properties are major hurdles in this industry. Hence, the advance of steady biocatalytic systems involving enzymes is key for increasing their commercial applications. In the last few years, the process of enzyme immobilization has taken significant consideration as an important bio-engineering method to boost an extensive range of enzyme catalytic characteristics, which include their activity, stability, specificity, selectivity, and acceptance of inhibitors. The total cost of the enzyme-making process can be reduced by immobilizing the industrially important enzyme support mediums. The immobilization technique is essential to create reusable, long-standing, and stable enzymes. A number of developing support resources have been newly used for the enzyme immobilization process [97]. The low-cost immobilization matrixes have numerous beneficial properties that support the development of highly efficient biocatalysts. The application of agricultural residues and food wastes as novel immobilization matrices for enzymes proposes economic answers for industrial bioprocess, in addition to solving the problems of environmental pollution and waste disposal.

36.11 Fermentation Processes and Control of Process

With the progressing fermentation technology, many studies are being conducted for enzyme production by use of diverse groups of microbial strains using agricultural waste at pilot or lab scale. These extensive studies were conducted in solid-state fermentation process for the synthesis of various enzymes. Several agricultural industry residues are found to be appropriate in terms of sustainability [98]. Newly, many investigators have familiarized the innovative term mechanical index (Imp), which is applied to characterize the physical properties of media and their supports in the execution of a high level of process control through fermentation. Moreover, Imp can also positively or negatively associate with water retention, biomass content, thermal conductivity, thermal diffusivity, and gas permeability conditions involved in the fermentation process. Hence, mechanical index can be used for the active determination of the physical properties of medium and for controlling the different parameters in solid-state fermentation process [99].

36.12 Conclusions

This chapter emphasizes the potential role of many agro-processing generated residues as a substrate for producing enzymes using microbial fermentation techniques. In addition, the application and usage of food-grade enzymes in human life in various sectors of food sectors have been well established from ancient times; therefore, these enzymes are being explored in various sectors of the food industry.

Agro-industrial wastes-based production is cost-effective as compared with industrial based fermentation substrate for enzymes. The waste from the afro-industry is beneficial not only in lowering the process economics, but also has a diminished impact on the environment during their disposal. The waste or by-products generated from the dairy and cereal sector have important potential for enzyme production in comparison to any other residues. Additionally, among the different types of fermentation as solid-state and submerged types of fermentation established for enzyme production, the majority of work has been accepted under solid-state conditions, specifically using batch fermentation. Many efficient microbial strains as sources of fermentation are required for the optimal utilization of agro-industrial wastes to attain higher yields of the enzymes. Some advanced biotechnological techniques, such as genetic engineering manipulations of microorganisms, enzyme engineering, and other bio-techniques, will be significant and useful in the production process in the near future.

References

1 Messner, R., Richards, C., and Johnson, H. (2020). The "Prevention Paradox": food waste prevention and the quandary of systemic surplus production. *Agric. Hum. Values* 37 (3): 805–817.

2 Scialabba, N. (2015). *Food Wastage Footprint & Climate Change*, 1–4. Rome, Italy: FAO.

3 Sharma, P., Gaur, V.K., Sirohi, R. et al. (2021). Sustainable processing of food waste for production of bio-based products for circular bioeconomy. *Bioresour. Technol.* 325: 124684.

4 Gustavsson, J., Cederberg, C., and Sonesson, U. (2013). *The Methodology of the FAO Study: "Global Food Losses and Food Waste—Extent, Causes and Prevention" – FAO, 2011*. The Swedish Institute for Food and Biotechnology (SIK).

5 Uçkun Kiran, E., Trzcinski, A.P., Ng, W.J., and Liu, Y. (2014). Enzyme production from food wastes using a biorefinery concept. *Waste Biomass Valorization* 5 (6): 903–917.

6 United Nation Environment Programme (UNEP) (2021). Food waste Index 2021. Nairobi. https://www.unep.org/resources/report/unep-food-waste-index-report-2021 (accessed 25 February 2022).

7 Poore, J. and Nemecek, T. (2018). Reducing food's environmental impacts through producers and consumers. *Science* 360 (6392): 987–992.

8 Yadav, A., Kumar, N., Upadhyay, A., and Pratibha Anurag, R.K. (2021). Edible packaging from fruit processing waste: a comprehensive review. *Food Rev. Int.* 39: 1–32.

9 Cecilia, J.A., García-Sancho, C., Maireles-Torres, P.J., and Luque, R. (2019). Industrial food waste valorization: a general overview. *Biorefinery* 253–277.

10 Kannah, R.Y., Merrylin, J., Devi, T.P. et al. (2020). Food waste valorization: biofuels and value added product recovery. *Bioresour. Technol. Rep.* 11: 100524.

11 Manjrekar, S., Wadekar, T., and Sumant, O. (2020). Enzymes Market Type (Protease, Carbohydrase, Lipase, Polymerase and Nuclease, and Other Types), Source (Microorganisms, Plants, and Animals), Reaction Type (Hydrolase, Oxidoreductase, Transferase, Lyase, and Other Reaction Types), and Application (Food and Beverages, Household Care, Bioenergy, Pharmaceutical and Biotechnology, Feed, and Other Applications) - Global Opportunity Analysis and Industry Forecast, 2020–2027.

12 Ravindran, R., Desmond, C., Jaiswal, S., and Jaiswal, A.K. (2018). Optimisation of organosolv pretreatment for the extraction of polyphenols from spent coffee waste and subsequent recovery of fermentable sugars. *Bioresour. Technol. Rep.* 3: 7–14.

13 Singh, A., Singhania, R.R., Soam, S. et al. (2022). Production of bioethanol from food waste: status and perspectives. *Bioresour. Technol.* 360: 127651.

14 Yaashikaa, P.R., Senthil Kumar, P., and Varjani, S. (2022). Valorization of agro-industrial wastes for biorefinery process and circular bioeconomy: a critical review. *Bioresour. Technol.* 343: 126126.

15 Karthikeyan, V., Venkatesh, K.R., and Arutchelvan, V. (2015). A correlation study on physico-chemical characteristics of dairy wastewater. *Int. J. Eng. Sci. Technol.* 7 (2): 89.

16 Dey, D., Richter, J.K., Ek, P. et al. (2021). Utilization of food processing by-products in extrusion processing: a review. *Front. Sustainable Food Syst.* 304: 603751.

17 Lai, W.T., Khong, N.M., Lim, S.S. et al. (2017). A review: modified agricultural by-products for the development and fortification of food products and nutraceuticals. *Trends Food Sci. Technol.* 59: 148–160.

18 Majerska, J., Michalska, A., and Figiel, A. (2019). A review of new directions in managing fruit and vegetable processing by-products. *Trends Food Sci. Technol.* 88: 207–219.

19 Sharma, R., Oberoi, H.S., and Dhillon, G.S. (2016). Fruit and vegetable processing waste: renewable feed stocks for enzyme production. In: *Agro-industrial Wastes as Feedstock for Enzyme Production* (eds G.S. Dhillon and S. Kaur), 23–59. Academic Press.

20 Aktas-Akyildiz, E., Masatcioglu, M.T., and Koksel, H. (2020). Effect of extrusion treatment on enzymatic hydrolysis of wheat bran. *J. Cereal Sci.* 93: 102941.

21 Wang, S., Kowalski, R.J., Kang, Y. et al. (2017). Impacts of the particle sizes and levels of inclusions of cherry pomace on the physical and structural properties of direct expanded corn starch. *Food Bioprocess Technol.* 10 (2): 394–406.

22 Fleischman, E.F., Kowalski, R.J., Morris, C.F. et al. (2016). Physical, textural, and antioxidant properties of extruded waxy wheat flour snack supplemented with several varieties of bran. *J. Food Sci.* 81: E2726–E2733.

23 Hansen, C.L. and Cheong, D.Y. (2019). Agricultural waste management in food processing. In: *Handbook of Farm, Dairy and Food Machinery Engineering* (ed. M. Kutz), 673–716. Academic Press.

24 Jayathilakan, K., Sultana, K., Radhakrishna, K., and Bawa, A.S. (2012). Utilization of byproducts and waste materials from meat, poultry and fish processing industries: a review. *J. Food Sci. Technol.* 49 (3): 278–293.

25 Pfaltzgraff, L.A., Cooper, E.C., Budarin, V., and Clark, J.H. (2013). Food waste biomass: a resource for high-value chemicals. *Green Chem.* 15: 307–314.

26 Lin, C.S.K., Pfaltzgraff, L.A., Herrero-Davila, L. et al. (2013). Food waste as a valuable resource for the production of chemicals, materials and fuels: current situation and global perspective. *Energy Environ. Sci.* 6: 426–464.

27 Couto, S.R. and Herrera, J.L.T. (2006). Industrial and biotechnological applications of laccases: a review. *Biotechnol. Adv.* 24: 500–513.

28 Ravindran, R. and Jaiswal, A.K. (2016). A comprehensive review on pre-treatment strategy for lignocellulosic food industry waste: challenges and opportunities. *Bioresour. Technol.* 199: 92–102.

29 Zeng, Y., Zhao, S., Yang, S., and Ding, S.Y. (2014). Lignin plays a negative role in the biochemical process for producing lignocellulosic biofuels. *Curr. Opin. Biotechnol.* 27: 38–45.

30 DeMartini, J.D., Pattathil, S., Miller, J.S. et al. (2013). Investigating plant cell wall components that affect biomass recalcitrance in poplar and switchgrass. *Energy Environ. Sci.* 6 (3): 898–909.

31 Panesar, P.S., Satwinder, S.M., and Harish, K.C. (2010). *Enzymes in Food Processing: Fundamentals and Potential Applications*. IK International Pvt Ltd.

32 Shraddha, S.R., Sehgal, S., Kamthania, M., and Kumar, A. (2011). Laccase: microbial sources, production, purification, and potential biotechnological applications. *Enzyme Res.* 2011: 217861. https://doi.org/10.4061/2011/217861.

33 Barrios-González, J. (2012). Solid-state fermentation: physiology of solid medium, its molecular basis and applications. *Process Biochem.* 47: 175–185.

34 Singhania, R.R., Sukumaran, R.K., Patel, A.K. et al. (2010). Advancement and comparative profiles in the production technologies using solid-state and submerged fermentation for microbial cellulases. *Enzyme Microb. Technol.* 46: 541–549.

35 Maulini-Duran, C., Abraham, J., Rodríguez-Pérez, S. et al. (2015). Gaseous emissions during the solid-state fermentation of different wastes for enzyme production at pilot scale. *Bioresour. Technol.* 179: 211–218.

36 Gibbs, J.S., Morrell, A., Valdez, T.L.S., and Hendrik, G. (2000). Regulation of alcoholic fermentation in coleoptiles of two rice cultivars differing in tolerance to anoxia. *J. Exp. Bot.* 51 (345): 785–796.

37 Bansal, P., Hall, M., Realff, M.J. et al. (2010). Multivariate statistical analysis of X-ray data from cellulose: a new method to determine degree of crystallinity and predict hydrolysis rates. *Bioresour. Technol.* 101 (12): 4461–4471.

38 Motta, F.L., Andrade, C.C.P., and Santana, M.H.A. (2013). A review of xylanase production by the fermentation of xylan: classification, characterization and applications. In: *Sustainable Degradation of Lignocellulosic Biomass-Techniques, Applications and Commercialization*, 1251–1276. IntechOpen.

39 Sahnoun, M., Kriaa, M., Elgharbi, F. et al. (2015). Aspergillus oryzae S2 alpha-amylase production under solid state fermentation: optimization of culture conditions. *Int. J. Biol. Macromol.* 75: 73–80.

40 Sundarram, A. and Murthy, T.P.K. (2014). α-Amylase production and applications: a review. *J. Appl. Environ. Microbiol.* 2: 166–175.

41 Krishna, C. and Chandrasekaran, M. (1996). Banana waste as substrate for α-amylase production by Bacillus subtilis (CBTK 106) under solid-state fermentation. *Appl. Microbiol. Biotechnol.* 46: 106–111.

42 Francis, F., Abdulhameed, S.K., Madhavan, N. et al. (2003). Use of response surface methodology for optimizing process parameters for the production of α-amylase by *Aspergillus oryzae. Biochem. Eng. J.* 15: 107–115.

43 Rajagopalan, G. and Krishnan, C. (2008). α-Amylase production from catabolite derepressed *Bacillus subtilis* KCC103 utilizing sugarcane bagasse hydrolysate. *Bioresour. Technol.* 99: 3044–3050.

44 Juturu, V. and Wu, J.C. (2014). Microbial cellulases: engineering, production and applications. *Renewable Sustainable Energy Rev.* 33: 188–203.

45 Ferreira, N.L., Margeot, A., Blanquet, S., and Berrin, J.G. (2014). Use of cellulases from *Trichoderma reesei* in the twenty-first century—part I: current industrial uses and future applications in the production of second ethanol generation. In: *Biotechnology and Biology of Trichoderma*, 245–261. Elsevier.

46 Várnai, A., Mäkelä, M.R., Djajadi, D.T. et al. (2014). Carbohydrate-binding modules of fungal cellulases. *Adv. Appl. Microbiol.* 88: 103–165.

47 Hai-Yan Sun, H., Li, J., Zhao, P., and Peng, M. (2011). Banana peel: a novel substrate for cellulase production under solid-state fermentation. *Afr. J. Biotechnol.* 10: 17887–17890.

48 Saravanan, P., Muthuvelayudham, R., and Viruthagiri, T. (2012). Application of statistical design for the production of cellulase by *Trichoderma reesei* using mango peel. *Enzyme Res.* 2012: 157643.

49 Dhillon, G.S., Kaur, S., Brar, S.K., and Verma, M. (2012). Potential of apple pomace as a solid substrate for fungal cellulase and hemicellulase bioproduction through solid-state fermentation. *Ind. Crops Prod.* 38: 6–13.

50 James, J.A. and Lee, B.H. (1997). Glucoamylases: microbial sources, industrial applications and molecular biology? A review. *J. Food Biochem.* 21: 1–52.

51 Diler, G., Chevallier, S., Pöhlmann, I. et al. (2015). Assessment of amyloglucosidase activity during production and storage of laminated pie dough. Impact on raw dough properties and sweetness after baking. *J. Cereal Sci.* 61: 63–70.

52 Singh, H. and Soni, S.K. (2001). Production of starch-gel digesting amyloglucosidase by *Aspergillus oryzae* HS-3 in solid state fermentation. *Process Biochem.* 37: 453–459.

53 Shin, H.K., Kong, J.Y., Lee, J.D., and Lee, T.H. (2000). Syntheses of hydroxybenzyl-α-glucosides by amyloglucosidase-catalyzed transglycosylation. *Biotechnol. Lett* 22: 321–325.

54 Pandey, A., Selvakumar, P., and Ashakumary, L. (1994). Glucoamylase production by *Aspergillus niger* on rice bran is improved by adding nitrogen sources. *World J. Microbiol. Biotechnol.* 10: 348–349.

55 Adeniran, H.A., Abiose, S.H., and Ogunsua, A.O. (2010). Production of fungal β-amylase and amyloglucosidase on some Nigerian agricultural residues. *Food Bioprocess Technol.* 3: 693–698.

56 Knob, A., Beitel, S.M., Fortkamp, D. et al. (2013). Production, purification, and characterization of a major *Penicillium glabrum* xylanase using brewer's spent grain as substrate. *Biomed Res. Int.* 2013: 1–8.

57 Polizeli, M.L.T.M., Rizzatti, A.C.S., Monti, R. et al. (2005). Xylanases from fungi: properties and industrial applications. *Appl. Microbiol. Biotechnol.* 67: 577–591.

58 Das, S.P., Ravindran, R., Ahmed, S. et al. (2012). Bioethanol production involving recombinant, *C. thermocellum* hydrolytic hemicellulase and fermentative microbes. *Appl. Biochem. Biotechnol.* 167: 1475–1488.

59 Lowe, S.E., Theodorou, M.K., and Trinci, A.P. (1987). Cellulases and xylanase of an anaerobic rumen fungus grown on wheat straw, wheat straw holocellulose, cellulose, and xylan. *Appl. Environ. Microbiol.* 53: 1216–1223.

60 Gawande, P. and Kamat, M. (1999). Production of *Aspergillus xylanase* by lignocellulosic waste fermentation and its application. *J. Appl. Microbiol.* 87: 511–519.

61 Botella, C., Diaz, A., de Ory, I. et al. (2007). Xylanase and pectinase production by *Aspergillus awamori* on grape pomace in solid state fermentation. *Process Biochem.* 42: 98–101.

62 Sadler, M.J. and Michèle, J. (2014). *Foods, Nutrients and Food Ingredients with Authorised EU Health Claims*, vol. 1. Amsterdam, The Netherlands: Elsevier Science, ISBN 9780857098481. 83.

63 de Bales, S.A. and Castillo, F.J. (1979). Production of lactase by *Candida pseudotropicalis* grown in whey. *Appl. Environ. Microbiol.* 37: 1201–1205.

64 Macris, B.J. and Markakis, P. (1981). Characterization of extracellular beta-D-galactosidase from *Fusarium moniliforme* grown in whey. *Appl. Environ. Microbiol.* 41: 956–958.

65 Mustranta, A., Karvonen, E., Ojamo, H., and Linko, M. (1981). Production of mold lactase. *Biotechnol. Lett* 3: 333–338.

66 Patidar, M.K., Nighojkar, A., Nighojkar, S., and Kumar, A. (2017). Purification and characterization of polygalacturonase produced by *Aspergillus niger* AN07 in solid state fermentation. *Can. J. Biotechnol.* 1 (1): 11.

67 Kohli, P., Kalia, M., and Gupta, R. (2015). Pectin methylesterases: a review. *J. Bioproc. Biotech.* 5: 1–7.

68 Mahmoodi, M., Najafpour, G.D., and Mohammadi, M. (2017). Production of pectinases for quality apple juice through fermentation of orange pomace. *J. Food Sci. Technol.* 54: 4123–4128.

69 Wong, C.W. and Tan, H.H. (2017). Production of spray-dried honey jackfruit (*Artocarpus heterophyllus*) powder from enzymatic liquefied puree. *J. Food Sci. Technol.* 54: 564–571.

70 Hendges, D.H., Montanari, Q., Malvessi, E., and Silveira, M.M.D. (2011). Production and characterization of endo-polygalacturonase from *Aspergillus niger* in solid-state fermentation in double-surface bioreactor. *Braz. Arch. Biol. Technol.* 54 (2): 253–258.

71 Kumar, Y.S., Kumar, P.V., and Reddy, O.V.S. (2012). Pectinase production from mango peel using *Aspergillus foetidus* and its application in processing of mango juice. *Food Biotechnol.* 26 (2): 107–123.

72 Diaz, A.B., Alvarado, O., de Ory, I. et al. (2013). Valorization of grape pomace and orange peels: Improved production of hydrolytic enzymes for the clarification of orange juice. *Food Bioprod. Process.* 91 (4): 580–586.

73 Poondla, V., Yannam, S.K., Gummadi, S.N. et al. (2016). Enhanced production of pectinase by *Saccharomyces cerevisiae* isolate using fruit and agro-industrial wastes: its application in fruit and fiber processing. *Biocatal. Agric. Biotechnol.* 6: 40–50.

74 Amin, F., Arooj, T., Nazli, Z.I.H. et al. (2021). Exo-polygalacturonase production from agro-waste by *Penicillium fellutanum* and insight into thermodynamic, kinetic, and fruit juice clarification. *Biomass Convers. Biorefin.* 1–11.

75 Barrett, A.J. and McDonald, J.K. (1986). Nomenclature: protease, proteinase and peptidase. *Biochem. J.* 237 (3): 935.

76 Razzaq, A., Shamsi, S., Ali, A. et al. (2019). Microbial proteases applications. *Front. Bioeng. Biotechnol.* 7: 110.

77 Chutmanop, J., Chuichulcherm, S., Chisti, Y., and Srinophakun, P. (2008). Protease production by *Aspergillus oryzae* in solid-state fermentation using agroindustrial substrates. *J. Chem. Technol. Biotechnol.* 83 (7): 1012–1018.

78 Prakasham, R.S., Rao, C.S., Rao, R.S., and Sarma, P.N. (2005). Alkaline protease production by an isolated *Bacillus circulans* under solid-state fermentation using agroindustrial waste: process parameters optimization. *Biotechnol. Progr.* 21 (5): 1380–1388.

79 Ramakodi, M.P., Santhosh, N., Pragadeesh, T. et al. (2020). Production of protease enzyme from slaughterhouse effluent: an approach to generate value-added products from waste. *Bioresour. Technol. Rep.* 12: 100552.

80 Tuysuz, E., Gonul-Baltaci, N., Omeroglu, M.A. et al. (2020). Co-production of amylase and protease by locally isolated thermophilic bacterium *Anoxybacillus rupiensis* T2 in sterile and non-sterile media using waste potato peels as substrate. *Waste Biomass Valorization* 11 (12): 6793–6802.

81 Benabda, O., M'hir, S., Kasmi, M. et al. (2019). Optimization of protease and amylase production by *Rhizopus oryzae* cultivated on bread waste using solid-state fermentation. *J. Chem.* 1–9.

82 Hammami, A., Bayoudh, A., Abdelhedi, O., and Nasri, M. (2018). Low-cost culture medium for the production of proteases by *Bacillus mojavensis* SA and their potential use for the preparation of antioxidant protein hydrolysate from meat sausage by-products. *Ann. Microbiol.* 68 (8): 473–484.

83 Lemes, A.C., Álvares, G.T., Egea, M.B. et al. (2016). Simultaneous production of proteases and antioxidant compounds from agro-industrial by-products. *Bioresour. Technol.* 222: 210–216.

84 Afify, M.M., El-Ghany, T.M.A., and Alawlaqi, M.M. (2011). Microbial utilization of potato wastes for protease production and their using as biofertilizer. *Aust. J. Basic Appl. Sci.* 5 (7): 308–315.

85 Contesini, F.J., Lopes, D.B., Macedo, G.A. et al. (2010). *Aspergillus* sp. lipase: potential biocatalyst for industrial use. *J. Mol. Catal. B: Enzym.* 67 (3–4): 163–171.

86 Pahoja, V.M. and Sethar, M.A. (2002). A review of enzymatic properties of lipase in plants, animals and microorganisms. *J. Appl. Sci.* 2 (4): 474–484.

87 Vanleeuw, E., Winderickx, S., Thevissen, K. et al. (2019). Substrate-specificity of *Candida rugosa* lipase and its industrial application. *ACS Sustainable Chem. Eng.* 7 (19): 15828–15844.

88 Chandra, P., Singh, R., and Arora, P.K. (2020). Microbial lipases and their industrial applications: a comprehensive review. *Microb. Cell Fact.* 19 (1): 1–42.

89 Szymczak, T., Cybulska, J., Podleśny, M., and Frąc, M. (2021). Various perspectives on microbial lipase production using agri-food waste and renewable products. *Agriculture* 11 (6): 540.

90 Dobrev, G., Strinska, H., Hambarliiska, A. et al. (2018). Optimization of lipase production in solid-state fermentation by *Rhizopus arrhizus* in nutrient medium containing agroindustrial wastes. *Open Biotechnol. J.* 12 (1): 189–203.

91 Sahoo, R.K., Kumar, M., Mohanty, S. et al. (2018). Statistical optimization for lipase production from solid waste of vegetable oil industry. *Prep. Biochem. Biotechnol.* 48 (4): 321–326.

92 Oliveira, F., Souza, C.E., Peclat, V.R. et al. (2017). Optimization of lipase production by *Aspergillus ibericus* from oil cakes and its application in esterification reactions. *Food Bioprod. Process.* 102: 268–277.

93 Fleuri, L.F., de Oliveira, M.C., de Lara Campos Arcuri, M. et al. (2014). Production of fungal lipases using wheat bran and soybean bran and incorporation of sugarcane bagasse as a co-substrate in solid-state fermentation. *Food Sci. Biotechnol.* 23 (4): 1199–1205.

94 Rekha, K.S.S., Lakshmi, M.V.C., Devi, V.S., and Siddartha Kumar, M. (2012). Production and optimization of lipase from *Candida rugosa* using groundnut oilcake under solid state fermentation. *Biosensors* 27: 31.

95 Bilal, M. and Iqbal, H.M.N. (2019). Sustainable bioconversion of food waste into high-value products by immobilized enzymes to meet bio-economy challenges and opportunities—a review. *Food Res. Int.* 123: 226–240.

96 Basso, A. and Serban, S. (2019). Industrial applications of immobilized enzymes—a review. *Mol. Catal.* 479: 110607.

97 Bilal, M., Zhao, Y., Rasheed, T., and Iqbal, H.M.N. (2018). Magnetic nanoparticles as versatile carriers for enzymes immobilization: a review. *Int. J. Biol. Macromol.* 120: 2530–2544.

98 Lizardi-Jiménez, M.A. and Hernández-Martínez, R. (2017). Solid state fermentation (SSF): diversity of applications to valorize waste and biomass. *3 Biotech* 7 (1): 44.

99 Zhang, Y., Wang, L., and Chen, H. (2017). Correlations of medium physical properties and process performance in solid-state fermentation. *Chem. Eng. Sci.* 165: 65–73.

Index

Microbial Enzymes: Production, Purification, and Industrial Applications, First Edition.
Edited by Dinesh Yadav, Pankaj Chowdhary, Gautam Anand, and Rajarshi Kumar Gaur.

b

g

h

q

r